MW00337960

# The Amphibians and Reptiles of the Honduran Mosquitia

# Dedication

We happily dedicate this book to the generous people of the Mosquitia, who graciously opened their homes to us and assisted us in our work in ways too numerous to mention. Without their assistance, we could not have contemplated, let alone completed, this book.

We especially dedicate this book to our two principal guides, Mario Guiffaro, of Las Delicias, Depto. Olancho, and Tomás Manzanares Ruís, of Rus Rus, Depto. Gracias a Dios, whose expertise and experience materially smoothed the way for us, as we sought to study the herpetofauna of the fascinating region of Honduras known as *La Mosquitia*.

# The Amphibians and Reptiles of the Honduran Mosquitia

James R. McCranie
Josiah H. Townsend
and
Larry David Wilson

KRIEGER PUBLISHING COMPANY
Malabar, Florida
2006

Original Edition 2006

Printed and Published by
**KRIEGER PUBLISHING COMPANY**
**KRIEGER DRIVE**
**MALABAR, FLORIDA 32950**

Copyright © 2006 by Krieger Publishing Company

All rights reserved. No part of this book may be reproduced in any form or by any means, electronic or mechanical, including information storage and retrieval systems without permission in writing from the publisher.
*No liability is assumed with respect to the use of the information contained herein.*
Printed in China.

**FROM A DECLARATION OF PRINCIPLES JOINTLY ADOPTED BY A COMMITTEE OF THE AMERICAN BAR ASSOCIATION AND A COMMITTEE OF PUBLISHERS:**
This publication is designed to provide accurate and authoritative information in regard to the subject matter covered. It is sold with the understanding that the publisher is not engaged in rendering legal, accounting, or other professional service. If legal advice or other expert assistance is required, the services of a competent professional person should be sought.

**Library of Congress Cataloging-in-Publication Data**

McCranie, James R.
The amphibians and reptiles of the Honduran Mosquitia / by James R. McCranie, Josiah H. Townsend, and Larry David Wilson
p. cm.
Includes bibliographical references and index.
ISBN 1-57524-270-2 (alk. paper)
1. Amphibians—Mosquitia (Nicaragua and Honduras). 2. Reptiles—Mosquitia (Nicaragua and Honduras). I. Townsend, Josiah H., 1978- II. Wilson, Larry David. III Title.

QL656.H8M33 2006
597.9097283—dc22

2005043500

10 9 8 7 6 5 4 3 2

# CONTENTS


Foreword by Julian C. Lee ..... vi

Preface and Acknowledgments ..... viii

Introduction ..... 1

Materials and Methods ..... 2

Description of the Honduran Mosquitia ..... 4

- Physiography ..... 4
- Climate ..... 5
- Vegetation Zones and Environments ..... 6

The Peoples and the Social History of the Honduran Mosquitia ..... 11

History of Herpetofaunal Survey Work in the Honduran Mosquitia ..... 18

The Herpetofauna ..... 20

- Keys to the Identification of the Amphibians and Reptiles of the Mosquitia of Honduras ..... 20
- Class Amphibia (Amphibians) ..... 50
- Class Reptilia (Reptiles) ..... 92

Ecological Distribution and Relationships of the Mosquitia Herpetofauna ..... 193

Biogeographic Relationships and Significance of the Mosquitia Herpetofauna ..... 210

Conservation Status of the Mosquitia Herpetofauna ..... 228

Protected Areas of the Mosquitia ..... 231

- Laguna de Caratasca Wildlife Refuge ..... 231
- Patuca National Park ..... 231
- Río Kruta Biological Reserve ..... 240
- Mocorón Multiple Use Zone ..... 241
- Río Plátano Biosphere Reserve ..... 241
- Río Warunta National Park ..... 242
- Rus Rus Biological Reserve ..... 243
- Tawahka-Asangni Biosphere Reserve ..... 244

The Future of the Mosquitia Herpetofauna ..... 246

Species of Probable Occurrence in the Honduran Mosquitia ..... 250

Glossary ..... 251

Gazetteer ..... 261

Literature Cited ..... 267

Index to Scientific Names ..... 280

# Foreword

*"I think people my age are embarrassed by too much enthusiasm and believe that too much passion about anything is naive. I want to know what it feels like to care about something passionately."*

So wrote Susan Orlean, in *The Orchid Thief*, explaining her fascination with the central character of her novel, John Laroche, a man obsessed with orchids.

To know what it feels like to care passionately, Orlean would have been well advised to associate with the authors of *The Amphibians and Reptiles of the Honduran Mosquitia*. She would have discovered that among field biologists there exists a special cadre of persons who have an abiding passion for their study organisms, and who, to paraphrase E.O. Wilson, do not practice their science in order to be successful, bu rather strive to be successful in order to practice science. James R. McCranie and Larry David Wilson are two such dedicated field biologists. With more than 68 years of experience between them working on the systematics, biogeography, and conservation of amphibians and reptiles in Honduras, their names are very nearly synonymous with Honduran herpetology, Now they are joined by talented newcomer, Josiah H. Townsend. The result of their collaboration is the present volume, an exemplary treatise dealing with the herpetofauna of a remote region in Central America.

Eastern Honduras and adjacent Nicaragua encompass one of the largest wilderness areas in Central America—the Mosquitia. The region includes savannas, mangrove swamps, rivers, lagoons, and one of earth's last great expanses of primary tropical forest. The Honduran Mosquitia is notable for its cultural, as well as its biological diversity, for five ethnic groups occupy the region: the Miskito, Tawahka, and Pech are the indigenous inhabitants of the Mosquitia, whereas the Garífuna (Garinagu), are of mixed African and Carib decent, and Ladinos, are descendants of Spanish and various indigenous groups. Hundreds of pre-Columbian archeological sites are known from the area, including the fabled Ciudad Blanca.

Until comparatively recently the Mosquitia was one of the most inaccessible areas of Honduras, and travel in the region is still largely by foot and by means of traditional dugouts called cayucos. Biological investigation in the region has lagged behind that of other more accessible areas, but that is now changing, as exemplified by The Amphibians and Reptiles of the Honduran Mosquitia. With color photographs, identification keys, and species accounts, the book serves nicely as an identification guide to the 156 species of amphibians and reptiles of the Mosquitia, and it will doubtless find an appreciative readership among the increasing number of naturalists and encotourists that now visit the region.

Yet, the book is much more than simply an identification guide. the authors characterize the environment of the Mosquitia in terms of physiography, plant associations, and climate. They provide an account of the social history of the Mosquitia, including consideration of its indigenous people, and they summarize the history of herpetological exploration in the region—essentially a synopsis of their own fieldwork in the area, which began in 1967. They provide as analysis of the ecological and biographical relationships of the herpetofauna, and they summarize the conservation status of each species. Of particular interest is a section that characterizes each of the protected areas in the Honduran Mosquitia and those proposed for protected status, in terms of their location, biological features, legal status, present conditions, and the composition of their herpertofaunas. Although guardedly optimistic, the authors warn the unrestricted human population growth in Honduras poses the greatest threat to the biota of the Mosquita. An extensive glossary of terms makes the jargon of herpetology intelligible to general readers; this is followed by a gazetteer, literature cited, and an index to scientific names.

*The Amphibians and Reptiles of the Honduran Mosquita* is an important contribution to knowledge and understanding, for, as the Chinese say, calling things by their correct name is the beginning of wisdom. Illustrated treatises such as this book inform the mind, please the eye, and thus engender an intellectual and aesthetic appreciation for the wonders of neotropical biodiversity. And by providing a summary of knowledge, this book serves as something of a benchmark, a measure of what we know—and how much there is yet to know—concerning the amphibians and reptiles of this little known sector of the lowland neotropics.

Julian C. Lee
Miami, Florida
26 April 2005

# Preface and Acknowledgments

The Mosquitia is an infamous and legendary region of Central America, the boundaries of which extend from Cabo Camarón in northeastern Honduras south throughout much of eastern Nicaragua to the area near Bluefields. English-speaking people know it as the Mosquito Coast, a name that was used as the title of a novel by Paul Theroux and a film of the same name released in 1986 that featured Harrison Ford. That the film was actually shot in Belize and not the Mosquitia itself is exemplary of the vague but widespread feeling that this is an area to be avoided. During colonial times, the Mosquitia was the only region of Central America not conquered by Spain. That resulted in providing a sanctuary for pirates and a homeland for "untamed" indigenous peoples, thus helping to develop the Mosquitia's reputation as a region apart. We have spoken to people who live elsewhere in Honduras about our work in the Mosquitia who have told us that they hear that it is a dangerous place and that it is beautiful "out there," but, of course, they have not been *there* themselves. We have found its reputation undeserved; it may be even less "dangerous" than other areas of the country. The Mosquitia, however, is certainly a region apart from the remainder of Honduras, described by Archie Carr (1953:138) as "the howling tropics of the coastal lowlands."

No scientific work is simply the work of its authors. The appearance of a book such as this one, which deals with the herpetofauna of a particular region—in this case, the Honduran Mosquitia—is preceded by several stages. All stages need to be accomplished or the book will not reach fruition, and each stage is accomplished only because of the assistance of other people.

The first stage involves fieldwork which includes the collections of specimens whose study forms the backbone of the book. The making of those collections required the issuance of scientific collecting permits from the responsible government agency. In our cases, working in Honduras, this agency was COHDEFOR (Corporación Hondureña de Desarollo Forestal, Tegucigalpa). For many years Mario R. Espinal of Comayagüela, Honduras, acted as our agent, facilitating the issuance of the necessary collecting permits. Since obtaining these permits typically takes several months, his onsite monitoring of this process was critical. At COHDEFOR, Víctor Leonel Archaga, A. Barahona, Franklin E. Castañeda, Conrado González, Leonel Marineros, Martha Lizeth Moreno, E. Muñoz, Hector Portillo, Anarda Maribel Rodríguez, and C. Romero were instrumental in supplying us collecting permits during our investigations into the herpetofauna of the Mosquitia. Wilson's wife, Elizabeth, and his colleague at Miami-Dade Community College, Nidia Romer, have assisted with the Spanish translation of permit applications (scientific investigation prospectus). Arranging for the fieldwork usually requires help from people in Honduras. In this respect, Hauke Hoops, of Tegucigalpa organized trips for us to Patuca National Park and Tawahka-Asangni Biosphere Reserve. He also put us in touch with Mario Guiffaro (see dedication page), who accompanied us as principal guide on trips to both the protected areas mentioned in the previous sentence. Franklin E. Castañeda, of Tegucigalpa and formerly with COHDEFOR, was instrumental in arranging for the first visit to the Rus Rus Biological Reserve. In addition, he introduced us to Tomás Manzanares Ruís, of Rus Rus who assisted us as principal guide on trips to the Rus Rus, Biological Reserve, Río Warunta National Park, Tawahka-Asangni Biosphere Reserve, and the Río Kruta Biological Reserve (see dedication page). Ruben Castro L., Carlos Cortés, Arnulfo Messen, and Siyyid Romero, of the COHDEFOR/PROBAP office in Puerto Lempira, were instrumental in supplying logistical support for the Río Kruta and Rus Rus areas. Several other people accompanied us on various trips to the Mosquitia and materially contributed to the enjoyment and success of these journeys. These people include Damian Almendárez, Franklin and Nereyda Castañeda, Antonio "Pato" Coello, Gerardo Flores, Steve W. Gotte, Gunther and Elke Köhler, Luís Lacuth, Froylán Llezett, Kirsten Nicholson, John Slapcinsky, and Kenneth L. Williams. Carl Franklin provided a partial list of the amphibians and reptiles known from the Mocorón region. Carlos Molinero, Osvaldo Munguia, and Adalberto Padilla of the MOPAWI (Mosquitia Pawisa Desarrollo de la Mosquitia) office in Tegucigalpa provided photocopies of several pertinent sections of unpublished reports on natural history aspects of the Mosquitia.

Funding in support of some of our herpetological fieldwork in 2003 was provided by Max A. Nickerson and F. Wayne King of the Florida Museum of Natural History, Gainesville, and also by a grant from the Reptile and Amphibian Conservation Corps (RACC).

Once the fieldwork was completed, specimens were catalogued into a major museum collection and given permanent identifying numbers. Most specimens collected during our study of the herpetofauna of the Mosquitia were deposited at the National Museum of Natural History (USNM). Steve W. Gotte was responsible for this work. A smaller amount of material was deposited in the Forschungsinstitut Naturmuseum Senckenberg (SMF), where Gunther Köhler facilitated the cataloguing, and the Florida Museum of Natural History (UF), where Townsend and his colleagues Kenneth L. Krysko, Kurt W. Larson, and Esther M. Langan carried out the cataloguing. This step is critical, inasmuch as it supplies us with the specimen numbers we can use to refer to particular specimens.

Townsend would like to thank his wife Deborah for her support, patience, and understanding during the long process of completing this book, and for being his inspiration in everything he does; and his parents, Steve and Terri, and sister, Katielynn, for always encouraging and assisting in whatever way they could. Townsend would also like to thank Max A. Nickerson for his advice and encouragement, Kenneth L. Krysko, F. Wayne King, and the staff of the UF Herpetology Division for providing a stimulating work environment that has inspired more than its share of good ideas and good times. While working on portions of this book, Townsend was supported by the Florida Museum of Natural History and later the Tropical Conservation and Development Program, University of Florida.

During a portion of the phase of this project, the third author (Wilson) was supported during a 4-month research leave at the University of Miami by funds from the National Institute of General Medical Science and the Howard Hughes Medical Institute. We are indebted to Michael S. Gaines and Robert L. Pope for providing that opportunity to Wilson. In addition, the value of the research leave was increased tremendously by the assistance and collegiality provided to Wilson by a long string of faculty and graduate students, who, among other things, helped him deal with the pressure of spending long hours in a small room in front of a computer. Wilson is especially indebted to James O'Reilly, who opened his laboratory and provided him, among a long list of kindnesses, access to the Internet. Julian C. Lee, fellow student of the Middle American herpetofauna, assisted Wilson in many ways, from providing equipment and materials to the loan of literature. Dr. O'Reilly's Postdoctoral Associate, David Bickford, and his graduate student Lisa Ganser, helped make the atmosphere in the laboratory warm and inviting. Miguel Fernandes, doctoral student of Dr. Gaines, native of Portugal, and adopted Montanan, provided friendship and discussions on a broad range of topics. Venetia Briggs, Dr. Lee's graduate student and native of Belize, provided warm smiles and happy hellos.

Information about Garinagu living in the Mosquitia, as well as some Garífuna reptile and amphibian names, were supplied by Santiago J. Ruiz of the Department of Anthropology, University of Florida. Additional information on Garífuna common names was provided by Jaime Colón, a former resident of Plaplaya, Gracias a Dios. The Honduran Garífuna names are sometimes supplemented by common names from Garinagu living in the Sarstoon-Temash region of southern Belize, based on unpublished research by Ruiz and J. Richard Stepp, the latter also of the Department of Anthropology, University of Florida.

Cathi L. Campbell and Cynthia J. Lagueux of the Wildlife Conservation Society's Nicaragua Sea Turtle Conservation Program generously shared their knowledge of marine turtle nesting and harvest in eastern Nicaragua, and provided some hard to find literature. Jocelyn Peskin, Mesoamerican and Caribbean Program Manager for the Wildlife Conservation Society, shared information she accumulated during her time as a Peace Corps volunteer at the marine turtle hatchery in Plaplaya from 1995 to 1998. Yolanda M. Leon of the University of Rhode Island kindly provided data on marine turtles tagged by her project during 1998 and 1999 and allowed us to include some of this information.

Photographs were provided by Cathi L. Campbell, Carl Franklin, John B. Iverson, Gunther Köhler, Cynthia J. Lagueux, Jocelyn Peskin, Louis Porras, and Eric N. Smith.

Finally, the printing company and its editorial personnel take over the job of turning a manuscript and its illustrations into a finished, printed work. In this regard, our work has been professionally transformed into the volume in the reader's hands by the editors at Krieger Publishing Company.

# Introduction

It is the purpose of this book to discuss the composition, distribution, natural history, biogeography, conservation status, and future well being of the herpetofauna of the Mosquitia of Honduras. A primary goal of our work has been to increase the awareness of the people of the Mosquitia, and Honduras in general, to the ecological value that amphibians and reptiles have in the maintenance of healthy, functioning, natural ecosystems. We are interested in supplementing the traditional knowledge these people have of the composition of the herpetofauna of the area in which they live, by providing a means in which they can identify these organisms to species. Once the scientific name of an animal is known, it can act as a gateway between traditional knowledge and scientific knowledge by allowing a person to link his understanding of the animal in question to the accumulated scientific understanding of that animal. Because amphibians and reptiles are not generally high on people's list of favored animals, we also have sought to decrease the level of fear these creatures engender by increasing the knowledge of what these amphibians and reptiles can and cannot do.

We also are interested in increasing the level of awareness and understanding of policymakers regarding the immense biological value of the herpetofauna of the Mosquitia and that of Honduras in general. Some policymakers live in Honduras, but others live in the United States, Europe, and other countries in Latin America. Only through the efforts of these decision makers can the natural habitats of the Mosquitia have a future.

# Materials and Methods

Most of the herpetological specimens examined in the preparation of this book have come from our own collections made since 1992 and deposited in the collection of the National Museum of Natural History (USNM), the Florida Museum of Natural History (UF), and the Forschungsinstitut und Naturmuseum Senckenberg (SMF). Specimens collected by Wilson and J.R. Meyer in 1967 in the vicinity of Tánsin, Depto. Gracias a Dios, and deposited in the Louisiana State University Museum of Science (LSUMZ) and the Los Angeles County Museum of Natural History (LACM) and additional specimens in other collections or referred to in the literature have also been used. Other museum acronyms used in this book follow those of Leviton et al. (1985). The initials CF following some Mocorón localities in the Distribution in the Mosquitia sections in the species accounts stand for pers. comm. of Carl Franklin.

Conventions in the presentation of scientific name authorship are simple, but arcane. In general, the author's name follows the scientific name, which is composed of generic (capitalized) and specific (not capitalized) portions, in turn followed by the date of first publication of the scientific name. The scientific name usually is italicized in print. As an example, the scientific name of the Boa or Waula, its authorship, and date of publication are presently rendered as *Boa constrictor* Linnaeus, 1758, signifying that this is the scientific name given to this snake by its original describer, Carolus Linnaeus, in his famous work *Systema Naturae* (see Literature Cited section), the 10th edition of which was published in 1758, and, in fact, constitutes the work from which all zoological nomenclature has its beginning. An indication of the importance of that work is given by noting that 13 of the 156 species included in this book were described by Linnaeus in 1758. When a given species has been transferred to a genus other than the one in which it was originally placed, the author's name and the date are placed in parentheses. For example, the scientific name of the Cane Toad (or Sapo Grande or Sukling), its authorship, and date of publication are given as *Bufo marinus* (Linnaeus, 1758), to indicate that the original generic name given to this species by Linnaeus (*Rana*) is different than the one in current use. Finally, when the date of publication for a scientific name is actually different from the date indicated on the work in which the name was published, the incorrect date is placed in quotation marks and the correct date in parentheses (brackets if the generic name differs). As an example, the scientific name, its authorship, and date of publication for *Leptodactylus melanonotus* is written *Leptodactylus melanonotus* (Hallowell "1860" [1861]) to signify that the work in which this species was described actually appeared in 1861, not 1860. In addition, the generic name *Leptodactylus* was not used by Hallowell in his original description.

Common or vernacular names of amphibians and reptiles in the Mosquitia generally arise from Miskito and/or Spanish, but never from English. Therefore, the assignment of English common names to these animals is meaningless. No one in the Mosquitia would recognize the animal by such a name. We have made an effort to indicate vernacular names in Spanish, Miskito, or Garífuna, but, in many cases, the names are generic ones. For example, most snakes are referred to by the generic Spanish name *culebra*, the Miskito name *piuta* or *pyuta*, or the generic Garífuna name *heve*, most lizards by the Spanish word *pichete* or the Garífuna words *henawi* or *wagagan*, and most frogs by the Miskito words *pik pik*. Other common names can be generic as well, for example, the Spanish *tamagás verde* or Garífuna *aubana* for any snake with some amount of green on its body. On the other hand, some Spanish common names are specific to a single species, for example, *Barba Amarilla* for *Bothrops asper*, often referred to simply as "*la barba*." Common names used herein were provided by native Miskito, Garífuna, and Spanish speakers from the Mosquitia. When the spelling of a common name was verified in a

Miskito-Spanish dictionary (Marx and Heath, 1992), a Garífuna-English dictionary (Cayetano, 1993), or a Garífuna-Spanish dictionary (Suazo, 2002), the spelling used herein is followed by an asterisk (*). Garífuna names followed by two asterisks (**) are names used by Garinagu in southern Belize according to unpublished research by J. Richard Stepp and Santiago J. Ruiz of the Department of Anthropology, University of Florida, and may or may not be used by Garinagu living in the Mosquitia.

The descriptions we provide are not overly technical, while still giving a means to identify a given creature to species. In instances where words may be unfamiliar to the reader, the reader is directed to the glossary at the end of the book for explanations. In the descriptions of snakes, the range-wide variation in ventrals, subcaudals, and some other scales are given in parentheses immediately following the ranges for specimens from Honduras.

The section entitled "Similar Species" provides a means to distinguish the species in question from those also known from the Mosquitia that most closely resemble it. We have used, wherever possible, the distinguishing features that are easiest to observe.

In the statement of general geographic distribution, elevational distribution is reduced to the following three categories: 1) low elevations are those found from sea level to 600 meters (m); 2) moderate elevations occur between 601 and 1500 m; and 3) intermediate elevations are those occurring between 1501 and 2700 m. Few elevations in Honduras are above 2700 m, and no amphibian or reptile found in the Mosquitia ranges at such elevations.

In the statement of distribution in Honduras, the elevational range given is that known for the species in question in Honduras, not elsewhere. Distribution in the Mosquitia is given in terms of the localities at which the species have been found.

The "Remarks" section of certain species accounts is used to identify a variety of information of potential value or interest to the reader.

In the section on biogeographic relationships, we have used Duellman's (1990) Coefficient of Biogeographic Resemblance (CBR) algorithm. The formula for this algorithm is $CBR = 2C/(N1 + N2)$, where C is the number of species in common to both formations, N1 is the number of species in the first formation, and N2 is the number of species in the second formation.

The majority of the photographs that illustrate this work were taken by McCranie, with a few by Townsend, and a few others by other photographers. In all cases, the photographer's name is indicated in the legends for these photographs. The specimens used for the photographs came from the Mosquitia, whenever possible. A few photographs of specimens from other areas of Central America were used when there was little or no distinction in general appearance from Mosquitia animals or when no photographs of Mosquitia animals were available.

The Mosquitia is located both in eastern Honduras and northeastern Nicaragua. In this book, however, when we use the term "the Mosquitia," we mean the Mosquitia of Honduras.

# Description of the Honduran Mosquitia

The following description of the Mosquitia is based both on our experience in many portions of this region of Honduras and material we have gleaned from the published literature on the area.

## Physiography

The Mosquitia (Map 1) is the largest lowland region in Honduras and, as such, constitutes one of the major physiographic features of the country (physiographic region 6 in McCranie and Wilson, 2002), the eastern portion of another (physiographic region 7 in McCranie and Wilson, 2002), and the extreme eastern portion of a third (physiographic region 8 in McCranie and Wilson, 2002). The Mosquitia also includes all of the largest ecophysiographic (Map 2) area in the country (area 21 in McCranie and Wilson, 2002), the extreme eastern portion of another (area 22 in McCranie and Wilson, 2002), and the northeastern corners of another (area 15 in McCranie and Wilson, 2002). It largely lies to the east of the complex of mountain masses comprising Nuclear Middle America and is continuous with the broad stretch of lowlands known as the Nicaraguan Depression. As defined here, the Mosquitia is that region of Honduras lying east of the westernmost boundaries of the Río Plátano Biosphere Reserve, the Tawahka-Asangni Biosphere Reserve, and the Río Patuca National Park. An arm of the Mosquitia also extends along the Río Coco, and its tributary, the Río Poteca to the vicinity of Arenales, El Paraíso. Major rivers of the Mosquitia include (from west to east) the ríos Paulaya, Plátano, Patuca, Warunta, Ibantara, Nakunta, Kruta, and Coco. Most of these rivers are identified on Map 3. Numerous tributaries of these rivers, extensive swampy areas, and numerous lagoons combine to make much of the region a truly wet environment.

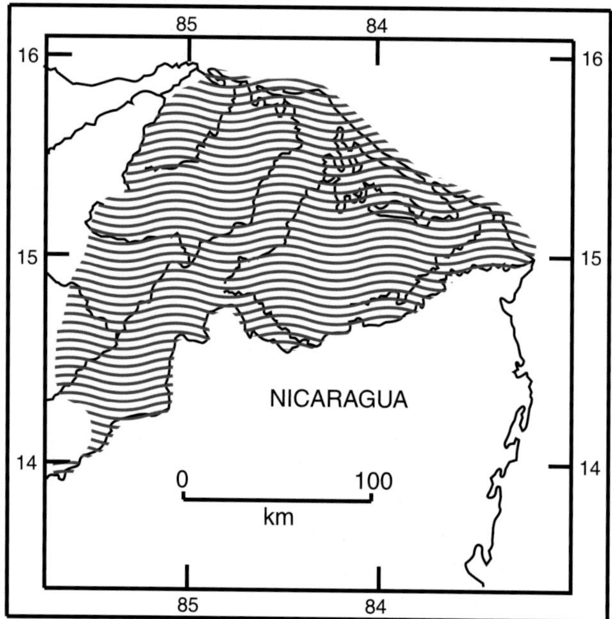


**Map 1.** Map of northeastern Honduras showing the limits of the Mosquitia.

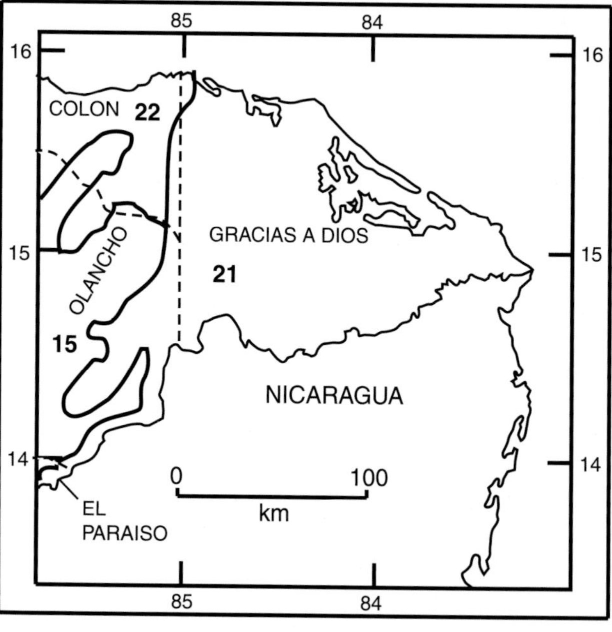


**Map 2.** Map of northeastern Honduras showing the limits of the ecophysiographic regions of the Mosquitia.

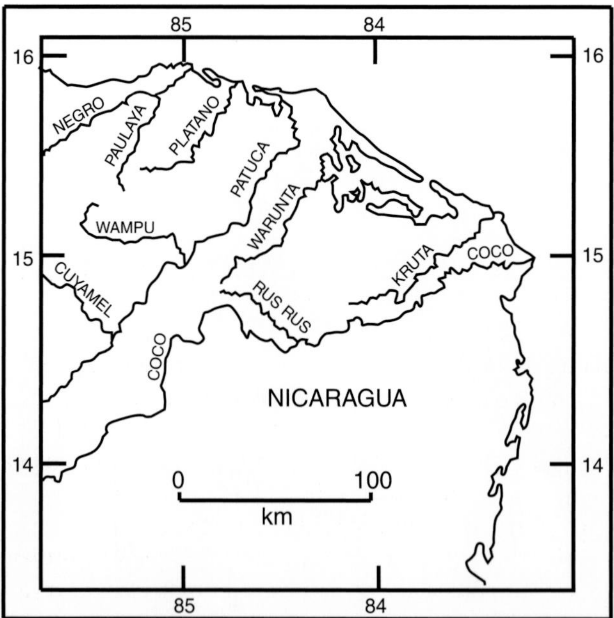


**Map 3.** Map of northeastern Honduras showing the major rivers of the Mosquitia.

## Climate

Inasmuch as the Mosquitia lies within the American tropics and is largely an Atlantic lowland region, most of the area is subject to the typical warm, humid climate found throughout such regions in the Western Hemisphere, termed the Lowland Wet climate (Wilson and Meyer, 1985). This climatic type in Honduras ". . .is restricted to the Caribbean coast, from sea level to about 600 meters. . . . Rainfall is at least 2000 mm per year and in most cases more than 2500 mm; the rainiest part of the year is that from May to December, although at least 100 m [= mm] usually fall[s] in all months of the year" (Wilson and Meyer, 1985:7). The mean annual temperature for the Lowland Wet climate is greater than 24°C (75°F). The few areas of the Mosquitia above 600 m elevation are subjected to the Intermediate Wet climate. This climatic type is characterized by annual precipitation of more than 2000 mm and mean annual temperatures between 18°C and 24°C (68°F and 75°F) (Wilson and Meyer, 1985).

Data on temperature and rainfall for lowland sites in the Mosquitia are available in Wilson and Meyer (1985) and Dodds (1994). Dodds (1994:77) noted that "Mean annual precipitation for the western coastal area of the Honduran Mosquitia is approximately 2700 mm. . ." This statement is supported by data on precipitation recorded at Ahuás, Depto. Gracias a Dios, for the years 1975 to 1985 (Dodds, 1994, Table 3.2). Ahuás is a large village alongside the Río Patuca about 37 airline km upstream from the mouth. These data indicate a mean annual precipitation over the decade of 2738.3 mm. Based on the mean monthly figures provided in this table, the rainiest month was July (422.4 mm) and the driest month was March (62.8 mm). Significant variation from the mean monthly values over the 10-year period was documented by Dodds (1994). For example, the minimum value for the rainiest month (July) was 154.5 mm and the maximum value was 799.4 mm; the difference between these two values is 644.9 mm. For the driest month (March), comparable minimum and maximum figures are 26.2 and 135.9, respectively, with a difference of 109.7 mm.

Data for precipitation are given by Wilson and Meyer (1985) for Sico, Depto. Colón, and Puerto Lempira, Depto. Gracias a Dios. Sico is a village upstream from the confluence of the Río Negro and the Río Paulaya about 29 airline km from the mouth of the Río Negro (this village lies just outside the northwestern border of the Mosquitia, as defined herein). Puerto Lempira is a town on the southwestern shore of Laguna de Caratasca. Total rainfall for Sico is 3085 mm and that for Puerto Lempira is 2805 mm. The rainiest month at Puerto Lempira is July and at Sico the rainiest month is December; the least rainy month at Puerto Lempira is March and at Sico the least rain falls in March and April.

Dodds (1994:77–78) noted that precipitation in the Mosquitia does vary, "depending primarily upon distance from the coast and geographic elevation—coastal areas receiving greater amounts of rain, while inland areas receive less; as elevation increases, precipitation begins to increase again. . . " As is typical in Honduras, Dodds (1994:78) indicated that ". . .two seasons, dry and wet, are observable; the dry season typically extends from January through May, and the wet season from June through December." This climatic pattern is illustrated by the data from Ahuás (Dodds, 1994, Table 3.2). The sum of the mean monthly precipitation figures for January through May is 597.9 mm or 21.8% of the mean annual figure given two paragraphs above. The sum for June through December is 2140.4 mm or 78.2% of the mean annual figure. The data provided by Wilson and

Meyer (1985) for Sico and Puerto Lempira demonstrate a similar pattern.

As is typical of lowland tropical climates, temperatures vary relatively little from one portion of the year to another. In lowland areas, furthermore, the temperatures are warm throughout the year. Wilson and Meyer (1985) gave the mean annual temperature at Puerto Lempira as 26.9°C (80.4°F) and illustrated in their Fig. 6 little variation about the mean throughout the year. The highest temperatures (about 28°C or 82.4°F) come in August and the lowest (about 25.5°C or 77.9°F) in January. Dodds (1994) provided temperature data for Ahuás for the years 1982–1985, which indicated a mean annual figure of 25.8°C or 78.4°F. The highest mean monthly temperature was for May (28.6°C or 83.5°F) and the lowest for March (22.9°C or 73.2°F).

Dodds (1994:82) further indicated that, "Throughout the year, average relative humidity is high on the Miskito Coast with values of 70% or more in March, and 90% or more in September." In conclusion, a typical day in the Mosquitia during the rainy season is warm and very humid; during a typical day in the dry season it is warm and only slightly less humid.

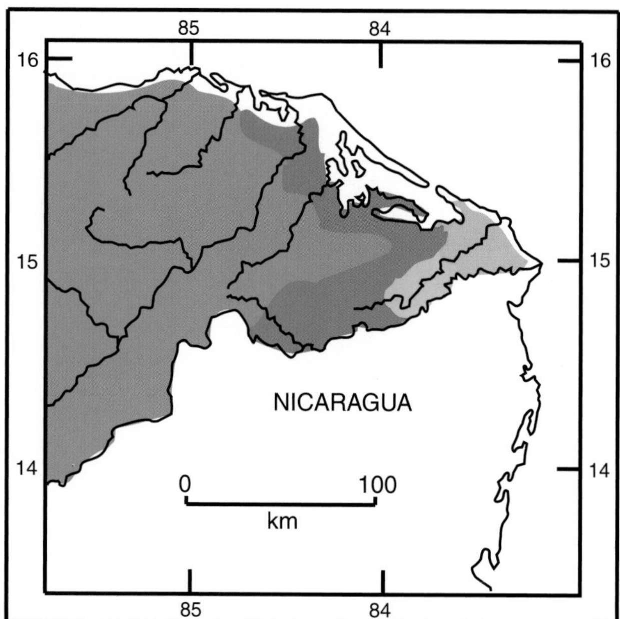


**Map 4**. Map of northeastern Honduras showing the general distribution of the vegetation zones. Green = Lowland Pine Savanna; Blue = Evergreen Broadleaf Forest; Red = Freshwater Marshes; Pink = Broadleaf Swamp Forest. Not shown are Mangrove Forest and Coastal Strand and *Cocotales* (see text for information on the distribution of these vegetation zones).

## Vegetation Zones and Environments

In the Holdridge (1967) system of forest formations, most of the Mosquitia falls within the Lowland Moist Forest formation, with smaller amounts occurring in the Premontane Wet Forest formation. This allocation masks a considerable amount of variation in vegetation zones found within this area. Accordingly, we here use a simplified system of recognizing vegetation zones (Map 4), based primarily on the type of dominant vegetation present, similar to the classification used by Stafford and Meyer ("2000" [1999]). These vegetation zones are discussed below.

**Lowland Pine Savanna** (Plates 1 and 2). Extensive areas in the interior of the Mosquitia are covered by lowland pine savanna or *sabana*. This harsh, open environment is characterized by scattered individuals of a relatively few tree species growing on a rocky, essentially soilless substrate. The dominant tree species is Caribbean Pine or *Ocote* (*Pinus caribaea*). This conifer, also known simply as *Pino* in Spanish and *Ahuás* in Miskito, occurs from Mexico to northeastern Nicaragua, as well as in the Bahamas, the Turks and Caicos Islands, and eastern Cuba (Zamora Villalobos, 2000). Also common are (vernacular names in paraenthesis are Spanish first and Miskito second) *Quercus oleoides* (*Encino* or *Usupum*), *Byrsonima crassifolia* (*Nance* or *Krabo*), *Curatella americana*

**Plate 1.** Lowland Pine Savanna at Cabeceras de Río Rus Rus, 200 m elevation. Photograph taken 26 November 2003 by McCranie.

**Plate 2.** Lowland Pine Savanna at Cabeceras de Río Rus Rus, 200 m elevation showing the fire scarred tree trunks typical of these forests. Photograph taken 25 November 2003 by McCranie.

(*Raspa Guacal* or *Yahal*), *Clethra macrophylla* (*Nance de Montaña* or *Krabo Weinka*), and various species of *Miconia*, which also grow in disturbed areas, such as abandoned crop fields or *guamiles* (Dodds, 1994; Zamora Villalobos, 2000). The floor of the forest is covered by various grasses (*Trachypogon* sp., *Paspalum* sp., *Aristida* sp., and *Leptocoryphium* sp.; Dodds, 1994) and sedges (especially *Bulbostylis paradoxa*, which Zamora Villalobos, 2000 indicated grows so thickly in areas as to be like turf grass). Scattered throughout this forest in low areas retaining water are groves of *Acoelorraphe wrightii* (*Palma Tique* or *Papta*), cane grass, and large ferns (Dodds, 1994; Zamora Villalobos, 2000; pers. observ.). Within the pine savanna are stretches of more complex savanna in which the trees grow closer together and are represented by more species of plants. Treeless swamps are also present in some areas. Pine savanna in the Mosquitia burns regularly during the dry season and people in Rus Rus indicate that the fires that sweep through this forest on essentially an annual basis are started by lightning and by cigarette butts and matches thrown to the side of the road by careless motorists (McCranie, Castañeda, and Nicholson, 2002). However, many of these fires are also deliberately set, especially those near Miskito villages (see Arguedas-Negrini, 2001). The pines are prominently fire-scarred and we have driven through extensive areas of burn in our fieldwork.

**Evergreen Broadleaf Forest** (Plates 3–7). This forest type is known as *la selva* in Spanish and is the complex, multistoried humid forest colloquially known in English as rainforest. It is characterized by the presence of several strata of tree species, with the topmost stratum extending 25 to 30 m (40 m maximum) above the forest floor, a relatively open understory of palms, tree seedlings, and ferns, and a tree burden of a large variety of epiphytic species (especially bromeliads, aroids, orchids, ferns, and mosses; Dodds, 1994; pers. observ.) and vines (Dodds, 1994; pers. observ.). This type of forest also occurs as gallery forest

**Plate 3.** Evergreen Broadleaf Forest on Cerro Wampú. Photograph taken by McCranie at 60 m elevation on 1 August 1994.

**Plate 4.** Evergreen Broadleaf Forest along Río Patuca at 100 m elevation near Caobita showing damage done by Hurricane Mitch along river. Photograph taken 12 November 1999 by McCranie. The forests along this river have subsequently suffered from the hands of man.

**Plate 5.** Evergreen Broadleaf Forest along Caño Awalwás at 70 m elevation. Photograph taken 20 May 2003 by McCranie.

**Plate 6.** Evergreen Broadleaf Forest along Río Tapalwás at Bodega de Río Tapalwás at 180 m elevation. Photograph taken 2 June 2003 by McCranie.

**Plate 7.** Evergreen Broadleaf Forest at Quebrada Machín in the southern portion of the nuclear zone of the Río Plátano Biosphere Reserve showing some of the destruction of the forests taking place in the reserve. Photograph taken at 540 m elevation on 8 August 1999 by McCranie.

along some of the rivers flowing through otherwise lowland pine savanna. Two of the forest formations of Holdridge (1967), Lowland Moist Forest and Premontane Wet Forest, are included here. A large number of tree species characterize this type of forest. At Bodega de Río Tapalwás, Tomás Manzanares gave us a list of the most common canopy tree species at this locality, including (vernacular names listed are Spanish followed by Miskito; the scientific names are those used by Zamora Villalobos, 2000):

*Brosimum allicastrum—Ojoche, Pisba Wainka*
*Brosimum guianense—Ojoche Blanco, Masica Pihni*
*Brosimum lactescens—Ojoche Amarillo, Pisba Mairin*
*Bursera simaruba—Indio Desnudo, Limsi*
*Calophyllum brasiliense—Santa María, Krasa*
*Carapa guianensis—Cedro Macho, Swa*
*Castilla elastica—Ule, Tuno*
*Cedrela odorata—Cedro Real, Yalam*
*Ceiba pentandra—Ceiba, Sisin*
*Cordia alliodora—Laurel, Sump*
*Cupania glabra—Cola de Pava, Bila Bila*
*Ficus werckleana—Chilamate, Kwa Wainka*
*Hyeronima alchorneoides—Nancitón, Kiahky Dusa*
*Luehea speciosa—Guacimo, Tuikirka*
*Manikara chicle—Níspero, Sikibul*
*Nectandra membranacea—Aguacatillo, Kuhulan*

**Plate 8.** Mangrove Forest near the confluence of the Río Kruta with Crique Canco. Photograph taken in July 2002 by Townsend.

**Plate 9.** Fresh Water marshes at Calpo at 2 m elevation. Photograph taken in July 2002 by Townsend.

*Pouteria campechiana—Zapote Calentura, Kuri Weinka*
*Spondius radlkoferi—Jobo, Pahara*
*Swietenia macrophylla—Caoba, Yulu*
*Symphonia globulifera—Cerillo, Samo*
*Tabebuia rosea—Roble, Macuelizo*
*Tetragastris panamensis—Kerosene, Saskal*
*Trichilia pallida—Cacao, Pampi*
*Virola koschnyi—Sangre, Sebo Banak*
*Vochysia ferruginea—Botarrama, Duhurang*
*Zanthoxylum ekmanii—Lagarto, Pankalkal*

Various palms are also present in the understory and lower strata, including *Astrocaryum alatum (Coquito, Kahka), Bactris gasipaes (Pejivalle, Supa),* and *Chamaedora* sp. (Dodds, 1994; Zamora Villalobos, 2000).

**Mangrove Forest** (Plate 8). Mangrove forests or *manglares* are comprised of a number of salt-tolerant trees, among which are a set of unrelated tree species whose English common name includes the word "mangrove." Mangrove forests are found on the shores of saline and brackish water bodies in the tropics and subtropics around the world. They are tidal forests, subject to the daily tidal effects, as well as seasonal influx of fresh water (Savage, 2002). In the Mosquitia, such forests are found along coastal inlets and lagoons (Dodds, 1994). The dominant trees are Red Mangrove (*Rhizophora mangle*), Black Mangrove (*Avicennia germinans*), White Mangrove (*Laguncularia racemose*), and Buttonwood (*Conocarpus erectus*).

**Freshwater Marshes** (Plate 9). At various

**Plate 10.** Coastal Strand vegetation at Cauquira. Photograph taken in June 2003 by Townsend.

**Plate 11.** Coastal Strand vegetation at Cauquira. Photograph taken in June 2003 by Townsend.

points interior to the coastal regions of the Mosquitia, one encounters freshwater marshes, which, from the viewpoint of the authors resemble the sawgrass prairies of the Florida Everglades. These marshes are dominated by various sedges and aquatic grasses, including *Paspalum pulchellum*, *Rhynchospora* spp., *Tonina fluviatilis*, and *Utricularia sublata* (Herrera-MacBryde, 2005). Dome-like thickets of the palm *Acoelorraphe wrightii* are common, and some better-drained tree-islands support *Pinus caribaea* or even some evergreen broadleaf forest species.

**Coastal Strand and Cocotales** (Plates 10 and 11). Coastal strand, as its name suggests, is the type of vegetation found along the coastline above the high tide line. *Cocotal* is a Spanish word for a coconut grove. Coconut groves can be planted by humans, but they also can result from the natural dispersal ability of the fruit of the coconut (*Cocos nucifera*). The fruit of this palm floats in water and, as such, drifts about with the currents. It can be washed ashore with the waves and germinate above the high tide line. Once the resulting palm is mature, the fruit matures, eventually falling to the ground to germinate, establishing yet more coconut palms, giving rise to a *cocotal*. The Sea Grape Tree (*Cocoloba uvifera*) dominates the understory of the coastal strand, and various palms (Arecaceae) are also common.

**Broadleaf Swamp Forest** (Plate 12). These forests predominate in low-lying areas along the Río Kruta. These forests retain water for all or most of the year, at least in depressions during the latter part of the dry season. During the rainy season, these forests become completely flooded when intact. Areas completely cleared of these forests dry out during the dry season; however, much of these cleared areas are under water during periods of heavy rainfall. We have been unable to locate any literature giving the species composition of this type of forest. However, Tomás Manzanares, who is familiar with the trees of the evergreen broadleaf forests around Rus Rus, remarked that the trees of the broadleaf swamp forest were very different from those of the tierra firme forest.

**Plate 12.** Broadleaf Swamp Forest near Krahkra at 5 m elevation. Photograph taken in June 2003 by Townsend.

In addition, there are two other environments utilized by some members of the herpetofauna of the Mosquitia. *Estuaries* are formed where rivers and streams meet the ocean and are strongly influenced by tides. The marine waters off the north coast provide food for sea turtles and the adjacent sandy beaches provide sites where these turtles lay their eggs. These environments are herein included as *marine environments*.

# The Peoples and the Social History of the Honduran Mosqitia

## Peoples of the Mosquitia

The majority of the human population of the Honduran Mosquitia is made up of indigenous peoples. This is an ethnically and culturally diverse region inhabited by four distinct indigenous groups: the Garinagu, the Miskitos, the Pech, and the Tawahka. Each of these groups has its own distinctive history, language, and cultural practices.

### Garinagu (Gariífuna)

The Garinagu (the plural form of the word Garífuna, a name more commonly associated with these people, also called Black Caribs, particularly when referring to inhabitants of Dominica and St. Vincent) are not indigenous to Central America, but are considered an Amerindian element based on their distinctive culture, language, and history. The Honduran population of Garinagu is estimated at around 200,000 (National Geographic Society, 2002). Most of this population lives along the north coast to the west of the Mosquitia, but around 9,500 Garinagu inhabit a number of small coastal villages between Cabo Camarón and the mouth of the Río Plátano in villages such as Tocamacho, Batalla, Pueblo Nuevo, and Plaplaya (S. Ruiz, unpubl. data; see Table 1).

The Garífuna culture has its roots in the Arawak-speaking Amerindians who migrated from the Orinoco River basin to the Caribbean around 1000 A.D. (González, 1997). Around 1220, a second group of Amerindians, known to Europeans as the Caribs, drove most of the Arawak men away from their Lesser Antillean islands and intermarried with the Arawak women, forming a new cultural group called the Island Caribs. After the arrival of Europeans, the territory of the Island Caribs became restricted to two islands, Dominica and St. Vincent (called Yurumai by the Garinagu). The Caribs would often raid European settlements and take prisoners, most of whom were Africans (González, 1997). In 1635, two Spanish slave ships wrecked near the tiny island of Becquia, off the coast of St. Vincent (Yuscarán, 1990). The survivors were rescued by the Island Caribs and were assimilated into their culture. The result of the integration of Island Caribs and Africans is the birth of the Garífuna culture. The Garinagu were relocated to Honduras by the British in 1797, settling in Trujillo after a brief stay on Roatán. Within 30 years, they had dispersed along the Caribbean coast and were well known from Belize to the Río Patuca (Roberts, 1827), with a small number of Garinagu eventually setting up communities as far south as the Pearl Lagoon, Nicaragua (González, 1997).

**Table 1.** Demographics of Amerindian populations in the Mosquitia. Population numbers based on National Geographic Society (2002), except for Garífuna (S. Ruiz, unpubl. data). Protected area abbreviations are as follows: LCWR=Laguna de Caratasca Wildlife Refuge; PNP=Patuca National Park; RKBR=Río Kruta Biological Reserve; MMUZ=Mocorón Multiple Use Zone; RPBR=Río Plátano Biosphere Reserve; RRBR=Rus Rus Biological Reserve; TABR=Tawahka-Asangni Biosphere Reserve.

| Group | Mosquitia Population | Number of Settlements | Protected Areas Inhabited |
|---|---|---|---|
| Garífuna | 9,500 | 8 | RPBR |
| Miskito | 64,000 | 141 | LCWR, RKBR, MMUZ, RPBR,RRBR, TABR |
| Pech | 2,900 | 11 | RPBR |
| Tawahka | 1,353 | 7 | PNP, TABR |

The Garífuna language has a primarily Arawak vocabulary, with "male" words derived from Carib and words that have entered the Garífuna lexicon since the 1500s derived from English, Spanish, and the African languages Bantu, Swahili, and Yoruba (Yuscarán, 1990). In 2001, UNESCO proclaimed the Garífuna language, music, and dance to be one of the Nineteen Masterpieces of the Oral and Intangible Heritage of Humanity, illustrating the need to promote native language education and cultural awareness among future generations of Garinagu (López, 2001). Most Garinagu in the Mosquitia practice subsistence agriculture based around the staples cassava, plantains, and coconuts, plus a large amount of food provided by the sea. Garinagu are well known as skilled boatmen at sea, and the primary activity for men in Garífuna villages is fishing.

### Miskitos

The Miskitos are the most populous and widespread ethnic group in the Mosquitia. The current Honduran Miskito population is estimated to be over 64,000 (National Geographic Society, 2002; see Table 1), spread among approximately 141 settlements (Dodds, 1998) that are primarily positioned along the Caribbean coast and in the watershed of the Río Coco. Offen (1999) stated that one-quarter of the entire Miskito population (over 185,000 in Nicaragua and Honduras [National Geographic Society, 2002]) live along the banks of the Río Coco (called the Wangkí by Miskitos). In Nicaragua, these people use the name Miskitu, but traditionally the name Miskito has been used in Honduras (De Vries, 2000). The Miskito language is part of the Misumalpa language family (Dodds, 1998). The Misumalpa family has similarities to the Chibcha language family (L. Campbell, 1979), which is spoken by indigenous peoples in parts of Costa Rica, Panama, Colombia, and Ecuador. There is some dispute as to the implications of this relationship, whether the Miskito are descendants of migrants who settled the Mosquitia from more southern areas or instead they are the ancestral group to the southern Chibcha speakers having settled in the Mosquitia as the remainder of their people continued to move south (Smutko, 1988).

In contrast to most other native ethnic groups in the Western Hemisphere, the Miskito have grown in numbers and expanded their territory in the time since European contact (Conzemius, 1932; Dodds, 1994). While it is often postulated in historical literature that the Miskito are a post-contact group, formed as a result of coastal Amerindians being influenced by and integrating with Africans and Europeans (Conzemius, 1932; Helms, 1969), linguistic studies, as well as genetic analysis, support that the Miskitos were an established ethnic group prior to European contact (Azofeifa et al., 1998; Matson and Swanson, 1963; Matson et al., 1963; Moreira, 1986). That said, the Miskitos did take in and assimilate former African slaves who shipwrecked near the mouth of the Río Kruta after fleeing the failed colony at Providence Island in the year 1641, and also intermingled with some settlements of English, Dutch, Spanish, and French who resided along the coast (Offen, 1999).

Since interactions with Europeans began in the 1500s, the Miskitos have utilized the resources of the Mosquitia to trade for manufactured goods and perceived economic benefit. Miskitos living near the coast harvested Hawksbill Turtles (*Eretmochelys imbricata*) from the northern banks of the Miskito Cays and supplied the European market for their shell into the 1900s (Offen, 1999). They also hunted Green Turtles (*Chelonia mydas*) for their meat, a practice that is now illegal in Honduras, but which continues among Miskitos living in neighboring Nicaragua. Mahogany (*Swietenia macrophylla*) has always been a popular trade resource, since privateers first realized the high quality of the wood for boat and ship building in the 1500s (Offen, 1999). During various time periods leading up through the 20$^{th}$ century, pine (*Pinus caribaea*), rubber (*Castilla elastica*), gum (*Sapota zapodilla*), coconut (*Cocos nucifera*), and banana (*Musa* spp.) have all been commercially exported from the Mosquitia, with little benefit (other than employment as laborers) to the Miskitos (Dodds, 1994). This is also the case with the lobster industry in the Mosquitia, as Miskitos are employed to work as lobster divers in unsafe conditions, often to end up crippled or killed by decompression sickness (Dodds, 1998).

Miskitos residing on or near the coast live off abundant fish and freshwater turtle populations (*Chelydra serpentina*, *Kinosternon leucostomum*, *K. scorpioides*, and *Trachemys venusta*) and subsistence farming along the margins of rivers, as most of the surrounding lands are inhospitable swamp forest and freshwater marshes. Miskitos living in the interior typically live in the pine savannas near rivers and have access to well-drained broadleaf forest. They make use of the alluvial soils of the rivers for farming and the remaining gallery forest and connecting broadleaf forest for hunting. Frequently utilized game animals include White-tailed Deer or *Sula* (*Odocoileus virginianus*), White-lipped Peccary or *Wari*), Tepezcuintle (*Agouti paca*), Armadillo or *Tahira* (*Dasypus novemcinctus*), Great Curassow (*Crax rubra*), Crested Guan (*Penelope purpurascens*), Great Tinamou (*Tinamus major*), the river turtles *Rhinoclemmys funerea* and *Trachemys venusta*, and various species of fish.

### Pech

Also called the Paya or Pesch, the Pech currently inhabit the valleys of eastern and northern Depto. Olancho, as well as parts of the middle course of the Río Plátano in Depto. Gracias a Dios. Today, there are about 2900 Pech (National Geographic Society, 2002; see Table 1), living primarily in the vicinities of 11 communities (Samson, 1993), including Dulce Nombre de Culmí, San Esteban, and El Carbón in Olancho and Las Marías in Gracias a Dios. The origin of the Pech language is unclear, and it has been classified by various scholars as Chibcha-affiliated or possibly independent (Dodds, 1994). The Pech possibly had the largest and most politically complex culture in the Pre-Columbian Mosquitia, but today little is known about the history of their society.

When Columbus came to the Mosquitia during his fourth voyage to the Western Hemisphere, the people he first encountered along the coast of northeastern Honduras were probably ancestors of the modern Pech (Offen, 1999). The Pech inhabited at least the drainages of the ríos Aguán, Tinto, Paulaya, and Plátano (Offen, 1999), and their territory at one time may have reached as far south as the Río Coco and inland as far as the Olancho and Jamastrán valleys (F. Johnson, 1948). After European contact, the Pech population rapidly diminished due to the sudden appearance of Eastern Hemisphere diseases and the antagonistic relationship between the Pech and the quickly expanding Miskito population (Offen, 1999). Today, the Pech inhabit a greatly reduced territory that is fragmented into small areas separated from each other by the ever-increasing population of *ladinos*. Despite ongoing efforts by the Pech to secure protection for their lands, their territory continues to shrink and be colonized by outsiders, threatening the very survival of their language and culture (Kolankiewicz, 1989).

### Tawahka

Also referred to in the literature as Sumu or Sumo, the Tawahka primarily reside in and around seven villages along the banks of the Río Patuca in the vicinity of its confluence with the Río Wampú (Herlihy and Leake, 1989), and today have a population around 1353 (National Geographic Society, 2002; see Table 1). The Tawahka are closely related to the Panamahka of north-central Nicaragua and both speak dialects of the Mayangna language, which is derived from the same language as Miskito (Offen, 1999). Miskito and Mayangna, both in the Misumalpa language family, have diverged as languages for over 4200 years (Moreira, 1986). Malkin (1956) summarized Panamahka herpetological knowledge, based on work done in the town Musuwás on the Río Waspuk, a Nicaraguan tributary of the Río Coco.

Almost nothing is known about the precontact Tawahka. In the late 1600s, it is estimated they inhabited a territory covering some 9300 km, which stretched from the area they inhabit today to the southwest along the course of the Río Patuca to its confluence with the Río Poteca, with the Montañas de Patuca to the west and the Río Coco to the east (Davidson and Cruz, 1995). Once Spanish missions began to appear at the western edge of Tawahka territory, the Tawahka abandoned the contact zone and relocated to the cultural heart of their territory, the area of the confluence of the ríos Patuca and Wampú (Davidson and Cruz, 1995).

Historically, the Tawahka utilized swidden agricultural practices, deforesting small plots to grow crops for a few years at a time, and then allowing the plots to go fallow and eventually return to forest as the farmers move to a new plot. They typically relied on hunting to provide most of their protein, supplemented by chicken or other small livestock. More recently, the Tawahka have begun to rely more on trade with outside communities, selling small amounts of rice and other crops, and providing labor to ranchers, loggers, and nongovernmental organizations (Godoy et al., 1997). They have also begun to recognize the economical benefits of owning and raising cattle, a reality that will almost certainly lead to increased deforestation in the future (Godoy et al., 1996).

The territory of the Tawahka has been threatened in recent years by encroachment from the crowded areas of western Honduras. In the early 1980s, there was a proposal to construct a road through the heart of Tawahka territory to provide the Honduran military access to the eastern Honduras–Nicaragua border (Anonymous, 1983). Beginning in 1991, an effort was undertaken by various parties to secure legal designation and protection for the Tawahka's territory (Herlihy, 1993). In the late 1990s, there was a push by U.S. energy companies to build a hydroelectric dam on the Río Patuca just upriver from the Tawahka settlements (Johnston-Dodds and Dodds, 1999). The creation of Patuca National Park in 1999 effectively ended this initiative. Finally, in October of 1999 the Honduran Congress declared the Tawahka's indigenous lands to be protected as the Tawahka-Asangni Biosphere Reserve (Zepeda, 1999).

During work in the Tawahka-Asangni Biosphere from 2001–2003, we observed a marked increase in deforestation along the edges of the reserve, particularly along the Río Coco. Recent plans to relocate a large number of *ladinos* to pristine areas of the Río Coco versant of Patuca National Park would prove devastating not only to the forests of that park, but also to the forests of the Tawahka-Asangni Biosphere and to the Tawahka homeland.

## Social History of the Mosquitia

The Mosquitia has an interesting and complex history and has consistently garnered the attention of world powers for over 500 years. The pre-Columbian history of the Mosquitia is not well understood, with archaeological exploration of the region still in its early stages.

Eastern Honduras was first occupied approximately 3000 years ago, when the earliest Macro-Chibchan-speaking people (early ancestors to the Pech, Miskitos, and Tawahkas) began to migrate north from lower Central America (Begley, 1999; Hasemann, 1991). Remains of a village found near the Río Talgua in northeastern Olancho date to 980 B.C. and represent a well organized and densely settled population that traded with the Mayans to the west and buried their dead in cave ossuaries (Brady et al., 1995). Around the same time period, Macro-Chibchan people inhabited the lower Aguán valley in Colón to the west of the Mosquitia and were also burying their dead in caves (Joyce and Brady, 2001). From around 250 to 600 A.D., a number of large archaeological sites were constructed in eastern Honduras, providing evidence of a widespread and complex society in northeastern Olancho, as well as along the Río Patuca near its confluence with the Río Wampú (Begley, 1999).

From 600 A.D. until the arrival of Europeans, an influential, but poorly understood society flourished in the lower Aguán valley, as well as the Tinto, Paulaya, and Plátano valleys, demonstrating ties with both lower Central American cultures and Mesoamerican (Maya and Lenca) cultures (Schortman and Urban, 2001). The pottery of these people was very similar to types found in Costa Rica and displays little Mayan influence; however, other evidence (such as the utilization of maize and presence of jade) demonstrates active trade with the Mayans (Stone, 1948). This little-known culture appears to have commercially cultivated cacao in the vicinity of city complexes, such as Río Claro, near the mouth of the Río Aguán, and the impressive Las Crucitas, located near the confluence of the ríos Wampú and Aner in eastern Olancho (Schortman and Urban, 2001). This civilization appears to have been near its peak culturally and territorially at the time of first contact with Europeans, declining rapidly thereafter. Some scholars postulate that the inhabitants of this area were actually Nahua (a language group from the Valley of Mexico) colonies rather than descendants of the Macro-Chibchans (Lara Pinto, 1991; Lara Pinto and Hasemann, 1988). While evidence for a Nahuan influence in eastern Honduras is abundant, the nature of the influence is not clear (for a review of Nahua presence in eastern Honduras, see Begley, 1999).

Around the year 1500, just before the first Europeans arrived, early Miskito-speaking people resided in 10 to 15 villages along the margins of coastal lagoons and pine savannas near the Caratasca Lagoon and the ríos Coco and Kruta (Offen, 1999). It would be these early Miskitos who would come into contact with the Europeans and Africans that would come to form an important part of their modern cultural identity.

European people first set eyes on the Honduran Mosquitia in 1502, when Christopher Columbus skirted the Caribbean coastline during his fourth voyage to the Western Hemisphere. The first European impression of the Mosquitia was not a good one, as Columbus and his men were victims of such foul weather and rough conditions along the Honduran coast that they christened the cape that marked a departure from this region "Gracias a Dios" (Tompson, 2001). Shortly after this time, the Spanish began efforts to colonize Jamaica, an act that would later impact the inhabitants of the Mosquitia. Claiming Middle America as its territory, Spain in 1537 declared the Río Coco to be the point of demarcation between two administrative territories: Guatemala (present day Guatemala, El Salvador, and Honduras) and Veragua (present day Nicaragua, Costa Rica, and Panama; Dodd, 1994). However, it would be over 70 years before any recorded efforts were made by the Spanish to establish themselves in the Mosquitia, and it may be accurately stated that the Spanish never succeeded in occupying the Mosquitia.

As was the case in other areas they were trying to conquer, the Spanish attempted to use religious conversion as a means to "tame" the indigenous peoples of the Mosquitia. While they met with some successes, these missions were often attacked and destroyed by Miskito, Tawahka, or Pech raiding parties. Rather than simply defending their territory from intruders, these groups (particularly the Miskitos) actively sought out and attacked Spanish settlements to the west of their territories (Offen, 1999). When these encounters are considered along with the hot, wet climate and legendarily abundant insects of the Mosquitia, it is not that surprising that the 17th century Spanish colonizers viewed the area "as a singularly unhealthy region" (Tompson, 2001:21) and, instead, chose to focus their occupation efforts on the cooler mountain climate and deep water ports of western Honduras. This left the vast lowlands and shallow coastal waters of the Mosquitia to develop without the Spanish influence that is so apparent throughout the rest of Middle America. While the Spanish were concerned with exerting political control over their territories, often by using religious conversion as a tool, their rival power England had begun to view the Mosquitia as fertile grounds to gain a foothold in Middle America and undermine Spanish authority there.

Unlike the rest of Spanish-controlled Central America, the colonial history of the Mosquitia centered around interaction with the English, characterized by the establishment of the Miskito Empire (see Floyd, 1967, and Naylor, 1989, for detailed accountings of British exploits in the Mosquitia). By the early 17th century, English settlers and pirates had begun to establish small colonies along the Mosquitia coast, living and working alongside the Miskitos. A colony of Puritans established on Providence Island began trading with the coastal people at Cabo Gracias a Dios in 1633 and led the way in establishing trade and good relations between the English and Miskitos (Offen, 1999). English and Dutch privateers took advantage of the lack of Spanish control in the waters of the Mosquitia and also established commerce with the Amerindians living along the coast. The English encouraged the Miskitos to launch attacks on Spanish settlements throughout central Honduras and Nicaragua, beginning in the 1650s and continuing on until the 1740s. The presence of English traders increased throughout the late 17th century, and, in 1699, William Pitt founded the settlement of Black River near the present day town of Palacios (Floyd, 1967). Black River served as the most important outpost and political seat for the English in the Mosquitia, and was the point from which much of the Honduran part of the Miskito Kingdom was overseen. Having recognized the first Miskito King, Jeremy I, in 1687 (Olien, 1983), the English began to confer titles upon Miskitos and delineated jurisdictions for them to govern. In Honduras, a general was appointed to oversee the region from the Río Plátano to the Río Kruta, with the King ruling over the heart of the Miskito culture, the vicinity of the Río Coco from the Río Kruta south into Nicaragua and upriver as far as the watershed of the Río Rus Rus (Offen, 1999). By allowing the Miskitos to maintain self-rule in their territory, the English created a situation that was favorable to their continued presence and economic activities in the Mosquitia, despite the claim of sovereignty over the region by the Spanish.

With the support of the English, the Miskitos became the dominant ethnic group in the Mosquitia, and gradually the Pech were forced up their river valleys into the mountainous western Mosquitia. Pech communities were raided for supplies and to take slaves, which the Miskito then used as labor or sold to the English (Offen, 1999). The relationship between the Miskitos and the Tawahka was much less difficult, and Miskitos actively traded manufactured goods from the coast for food supplies harvested by the Tawahka (Offen, 1999).

The inhabitants of the Mosquitia were regarded

as dangerous enemies by the Spanish and, in 1720, and again in 1723, Spanish flotillas were dispatched to attack and conquer the Miskitos, only to be routed by Miskito fleets (Tompson, 2001). By 1739, the Spanish Crown had realized the extent of English involvement in the Mosquitia and considered the security of the coast the foremost problem facing the Spanish empire (Floyd, 1967). The 1763 Treaty of Paris recognized Spanish sovereignty over Central America and stipulated that the English remove their military outposts there, but allowed for English settlers living in the Mosquitia to remain (Dodds, 1994). A convention between the English and Spanish in 1786 called for British settlers to leave the Mosquitia, and within a year, most residents of Black River had evacuated (Naylor, 1989).

From the 1760s to the 1790s, the British undertook a campaign to increase their control of the Caribbean island of St. Vincent, an island inhabited by the Garinagu. In 1795, the British launched a full-scale invasion of St. Vincent and by 1796 had effectively defeated the Garinagu, taking approximately 4644 prisoners whom they sent to live in what can be described as inhumane conditions on the nearby island of Balliceau (González, 1997). In 1797, the 2000 or so surviving Garinagu were relocated to Roatán by the English and quickly took up friendly relations with the Spanish in Trujillo, leading a large part of the Garífuna population to relocate to the mainland (González, 1997). Within 30 years, the Garinagu had established settlements as far west as Belize, and along the Mosquitia coast as far east as the Río Patuca (Roberts, 1827).

Central America declared its independence from Spain on 15 September 1821, and in 1838, both Honduras and Nicaragua declared themselves sovereign republics (Dodds, 1994). The Mosquitia, an essentially autonomous region inhabited by Amerindians who had previously had an antagonistic relationship with the Spanish, became a major obstacle to the development of Honduras as a unified state with internationally recognized borders (see Tompson, 2001, for a detailed review of the role of the Mosquitia in the formation of Honduras and Nicaragua). In fact, for over 120 years that the eastern border between Honduras and Nicaragua was disputed by the two countries (Dodds, 1994).

In 1859 and 1860, Britain signed treaties with Honduras and Nicaragua, ending its territorial claims in the Mosquitia and setting up a Miskito reservation (Naylor, 1989). In 1894, Nicaragua abolished the reservation and ended the rule of the Chief Robert Henry Clarence, the last Miskito King (Olien, 1983). Despite these acts, a sort of de facto autonomy would persist in the Miskito areas until the Sandinista revolution in 1979.

In the early 1900s, a number of industries tried their luck at exploiting the resources of the Mosquitia, but none of these efforts bore any long-term success. The harvest of *Pinus caribaea* for wood removed many millions of board feet by the 1950s (Parsons, 1955), but had almost completely stopped by the late 1900s. Banana exports were an economic mainstay of the Mosquitia from around 1900 to the 1950s, but large banana plantations were not viable in the long term, due to poor soil quality in the Mosquitia (Parsons, 1955). At various times during the 1900s, the extraction and export of rubber and gum was undertaken, but met with limited success due to inconsistent demand. In the latter part of the 20th century, the export of lobster and seafood from the Mosquitia was a booming business, leaving current shellfish stocks off the coast depleted and many Miskito lobster divers dead or disabled due to decompression sickness (Dodds, 1998).

Between 1926 and 1933, the United States militarily intervened in a civil war in Nicaragua, and in 1928 sent troops to the Río Coco in an attempt to establish a Caribbean access to the Nuevo Segovia region of Nicaragua (Brooks, 1989). The U.S. Marines were able to establish friendly and helpful relations with the Miskitos, but were unable to control the river and withdrew from the area in 1931 (Brooks, 1989). This would not be the last time the United States attempted to use the cultural separation between Hispanic Central America and the Mosquitia for military and political advantage.

In 1960, a border was finally delineated between Honduras and Nicaragua in the Mosquitia, with the World Court declaring the Río Coco to be that border, forcing many Miskitos living on the northern bank of the river to move to the southern bank (Dodds, 1994). This decision effectively cut the Miskito culture in half and made their most culturally significant river the dividing line. In the same year, the Honduran military established a base on the Laguna de Caratasca that would later become Puerto Lempira, the present-day capital of the department of Gracias a Dios (Dodds, 1994).

For centuries, the Miskito and Mayangna-speaking peoples living along the Río Coco practiced migratory agricultural practices, utilizing different soils and habitats on both sides of the Río Coco for farming and hunting (Ortega, 1991). The river is both the major route for trade and transportation and the cultural heart of the Miskito people. The traditional way of life for the inhabitants of the Río Coco was drastically altered by the 1979 Sandinista revolution in Nicaragua. By 1981, the Sandinistas were attempting to incorporate the Miskitos' land into a massive agrarian reform project, and the Miskitos were resisting. In 1981, the Sandinistas killed as many as 50 Miskitos in Leimus and killed a Miskito political leader while trying to arrest him, leading to an outbreak of hostilities (G. Russel, 1984). Soon after, the Sandinistas began forced relocations of the Miskito and Panamahka that lived near the Honduran border. Many people fled to Honduras as refugees, settling in refugee camps near the Río Nakunta and the towns of Mocorón, and Rus Rus (Ortega, 1991). The remnants of one such camp, near the confluence of the ríos Rus Rus and Tapalwás, are still apparent today. The Tapalwás camp was used by Nicaraguan Panamahka refugees and was close to a Contra military base, which led to forced conscription of young Panamahka men by the Miskito guerrillas (Manuel, 1987). Other Panamahka refugees fled to stay among the Tawahka, traveling from the Río Coco to the Río Patuca by way of ancient footpaths marked with petroglyphs. Many Miskitos joined the United States-backed Contra guerrilla groups, which were based in the forests and mountains of the Mosquitia and conducted cross-border raids into Nicaragua. After 6 years of fighting, the Nicaraguan government declared an autonomous zone for the Miskitos in the northeastern part of the country (Dodds, 1994). Refugee repatriation began the same year, reaching a high point in 1989 with the return of over 8000 displaced Miskitos and Panamahkas (Ortega, 1991). Today, with Miskito autonomy on the southern shore of the Río Coco, the region enjoys relative stability, and Miskitos are once again able to utilize their "golden river."

During the last week of October 1998, Hurricane Mitch dropped huge amounts of rain over much of Honduras, resulting in massive floods as the Mosquitia's long river drainages struggled to cope with the vast quantity of water that had been dumped on the mountainous areas of the country (De Vries, 2000; Jukofsky, 1999). One of the most heavily impacted parts of the Mosquitia was the area of the Río Patuca, which swelled to over nine times its normal size due to extensive deforestation in the river's rather expansive headwaters (De Vries, 2000; Jukofsky, 1999). All residents of the river were impacted, entire villages were wiped out, and the once heavily vegetated banks of the river were scoured as high as 15 m above the normal water level. Along the Patuca, 711 homes were destroyed, another 1500 were flooded, hundreds of livestock were killed, and 95% of crops were lost before harvest, with a majority of farmers losing everything (De Vries, 2000). Food shortages soon followed, and relief was slow to come. The economic impact on the people was devastating, and the infrastructure of these remote towns has slowly been rebuilt.

Miskito residents of Tikiraya, a community along the Río Kruta, recalled that after Mitch the floodwaters were to the level of the roofs of the single story buildings, and remained that way for over a week. This puts the flood level at around 20 m above the level of the river during our visit in 2003.

Communities along the Río Coco were also hard hit by Hurricane Mitch, but benefited from an international relief and reconstruction program called Hijos del Río (Conaway, 2001). Unfortunately for residents of the Honduran Mosquitia, the Hijos del Río program was undertaken with the Nicaraguan government and was only of benefit to communities on the Nicaraguan side of the Río Coco.

# History of Herpetofaunal Survey Work in the Honduran Mosquitia

Although the odd specimen of amphibian or reptile made its way into collections previously, the first serious herpetofaunal survey work took place in 1967, when John R. (Jack) Meyer and Wilson spent the period of 4–10 July at the village of Tánsin on the northern shore of Laguna de Tánsin (i.e., the southern shore of Isla de Tánsin, an island narrowly separated from the terrain to the south of the lagoon by navigable channels) and collected in its vicinity. During this period, Meyer and Wilson collected a total of 111 specimens of 31 species of amphibians and reptiles.

In 1977, the Honduran biologist Gustavo A. Cruz Díaz initiated herpetofaunal survey work in the watershed of the Río Plátano. His early work led to his thesis entitled "Herpetofauna del Río Plátano," completed in 1978. In this thesis, Cruz reported 40 species, based on a collection of 88 specimens (Cruz, 1978). Cruz has continued to work in what is now the Río Plátano Biosphere Reserve until the present.

O'Shea (1986a) led the herpetological part of an "Operation Raleigh" expedition that surveyed the Río Paulaya and Laguna Bacalar regions in the northwestern portion of the Mosquitia during April to June 1985.

In 1992, McCranie spent 25 August to 9 September collecting between La Llorona and the Río Wampú and then downriver along the Río Wampú to its confluence with the Río Patuca. He also spent 3 days in the vicinity of the Tawahka village of Yapuwás along the Río Patuca and 1 night was spent collecting at Casamacoa along the Río Patuca. All collecting localities are in Depto. Olancho, except for a short stretch of the lowermost portion of the Río Wampú, which is in Depto. Gracias a Dios. Collected were 254 specimens representing 44 species, including 4 anurans (*Hyalinobatrachium pulveratum, Agalychnis saltator, Anotheca spinosa,* and *Craugastor fitzingeri*), 1 lizard (*Norops lionotus*), and 1 snake (the highly venomous coral snake *Micrurus alleni*) new for the country (McCranie, 1993). In addition, an undescribed species of anole (*Norops wampuensis*; see McCranie and Köhler, 2001) was discovered.

In 1994, from 25 July to 4 August, McCranie and Wilson (in the company of Gerardo Flores) collected along the Ríos Patuca and Wampú. The trip began on the river near the town of Nueva Palestina, Olancho. McCranie and Wilson traveled downriver to the mouth of the Río Wampú, thence upriver on the Río Wampú to Quebrada Siksatara. The mouth of this stream is located a few kilometers upriver from the juncture of the Río Wampú and the Río Patuca. Collections were made from Caño El Cajón to Quebrada Siksatara. A total of 36 specimens of 23 species were collected, including a new species of centrolenid frog (*Hyalinobatrachium cardiacalyptum*; see McCranie and Wilson, 1997b) and a new species of polychrotid lizard (*Norops wampuensis*; see McCranie and Köhler, 2001).

From 28 July to 31 July 1997, McCranie and Wilson collected at the locality of Quebrada Las Marías, Depto. Olancho, in the buffer zone of the Río Plátano Biosphere Reserve. A total of 76 specimens of 22 species were found, including 2 new species of *Craugastor* (*C. epochthidius* and *C. pechorum*; see McCranie and Wilson, 1997a, 1999).

In 1998, McCranie and Wilson, accompanied by Kenneth L. Williams, returned to Quebrada Las Marías from 31 July to 5 August. At this locality, 76 specimens of 31 species were collected, including a species of snake (*Sibon longifrenis*; see McCranie et al., 2001) new to the herpetofauna of Honduras.

During the period of 26 July to 8 August, 1999, the three authors and Steve W. Gotte worked within and around the southern end of the nuclear zone of the Río Plátano Biosphere Reserve in the town of Nueva Esperanza, Depto. Olancho (in the buffer zone), and at the locality of Quebrada Machín, Depto. Colón (within the nuclear zone). At the former locality, we collected 15 specimens of 11 species and at the latter 217 specimens of 44 species, including 2 species of snakes (*Ninia maculata* and *Urotheca guentheri*; see McCranie et al., 2001) new to the herpetofauna of Honduras.

From 2 to 12 November 1999, McCranie (with Kirsten Nicholson, Elke Köhler, and Gunther Köhler) worked along the Río Cuyamel between Matamoros and the confluence of the Río Cuyamel with the Río Patuca. Work was also done along the Río Patuca between Caobita and Quebrada El Guásimo. Collected were 185 specimens representing 46 species. Results of this survey work were published in Köhler et al. (2000) and Nicholson et al. (2000).

In the year 2000, the three authors (in the company of Kirsten Nicholson) spent the period from 24 July to 10 August on the Río Patuca and several of its tributaries. We began the trip on the Río Cuyamel, then traveled downriver from the point it joins the Río Patuca. On the Río Patuca, we traveled as far downriver as the Río Sutawala and as far upriver as Quebrada El Guásimo. We also made short trips up the ríos Sutawala and Kosmako. We collected 154 specimens of 43 species, including a glass frog (*Cochranella spinosa*) new to the amphibian fauna of Honduras (reported in McCranie and Wilson, 2002).

From 23 July to 9 August 2001, the three authors worked along the Río Coco from Boca Español, Depto. El Paraíso, to Awasbila, Depto. Gracias a Dios, collecting 301 specimens of 54 species, including the first specimens of the frog *Scinax boulengeri* known from the country (reported in the Appendix in McCranie and Wilson, 2002). Most of this time was spent in the Tawahka-Asangni Biosphere Reserve and the environs of the town of Awasbila. Later in the same year, McCranie and Kirsten Nicholson spent the period of 8 to 17 October in the vicinity of Rus Rus and at Bodega de Río Tapalwás, Depto. Gracias a Dios, surveying the proposed Rus Rus Biological Reserve. They documented the presence of 69 species in this proposed reserve (McCranie, Castañeda, and Nicholson, 2002), including two frogs (*Eleutherodactylus cerasinus* and *E. diastema*) not previously reported from Honduras (see McCranie and Wilson, 2003, and McCranie, Nicholson, and Castañeda, 2002, respectively).

In 2002, from 9 July to 6 August, the three authors and Steve W. Gotte made a trip to three protected areas, the Río Kruta Biological Refuge, the Rus Rus Biological Reserve, and the Tawahka-Asangni Biosphere Reserve, all in Depto. Gracias a Dios. The collections from the Río Kruta Biological Reserve and environs came at localities from the Crique Canco, which connects Laguna Sirpi with the Río Kruta, upriver on the Río Kruta to a locality called Kasunta. We also collected in the vicinity of the village of Rus Rus and at Bodega de Río Tapalwás in the Rus Rus Biological Reserve. Finally, we worked in the vicinity of Awasbila and at Caño Awalwás in the Tawahka-Asangni Biosphere Reserve. In all, we collected 534 specimens of 82 species, including 2 species of snakes (*Dendrophidion vinitor* and *Pliocercus euryzonus*) new to the herpetofauna of Honduras (Wilson et al., 2003).

In the year 2003, from 13 May to 16 June, the three authors traveled to the same three protected areas as in the previous year. The collections from the Río Kruta Biological Reserve were made at Swabila and Tikiraya. In the Rus Rus Biological Reserve, we collected again at Bodega de Río Tapalwás and in the area around Rus Rus. In the Tawahka-Asangni Biosphere Reserve, we collected once more at Caño Awalwás. In total, we collected 407 specimens of 82 species, including 1 hylid frog (*Hyla miliaria*) and 3 colubrid snakes (*Enuliophis sclateri, Sibon annulatus*, and *Urotheca decipiens*) new to the herpetofauna of Honduras (McCranie et al., 2003a, b).

Also in 2003, from 4 to 27 November, McCranie traveled to the Rus Rus Biological Reserve and the proposed Río Warunta National Park. In the former, McCranie collected in the areas around Bodega de Río Tapalwás, the village of Rus Rus, and in the headwaters of the Río Rus Rus. In the latter, McCranie collected at three campsites in the upper portion of the Río Warunta and its tributaries. These latter collections represent the first herpetological specimens from that proposed national park. A total of 56 species representing 138 specimens were collected in the two proposed reserves, including the first Honduran specimen of *Rhadinaea decorata* (McCranie, 2004a).

In 2004, from 11–30 May, McCranie collected at the same previous localities in the headwaters of the Río Warunta and in the vicinity of the village of Rus Rus. A total of 77 species representing 120 specimens were collected, including the first country record for *Anomalepis mexicanus* (McCranie, 2004b) and an undescribed species of *Sibon* (McCranie, 2006).

# The Herpetofauna

The herpetofauna of the Mosquitia comprises 156 species, including 1 caecilian (of 2 species recorded for Honduras, or 50.0%), 3 salamanders (of 26 species recorded for Honduras, or 11.5%), 44 anurans (of 93 species or 47.3%), 2 crocodilians (of 2 species or 100.0%), 12 turtles (of 14 species or 85.7%), 31 lizards (of 88 species or 35.2%), and 63 snakes (of 122 species or 51.6%) (Table 2). The total number (156) makes up 45.0% of the 347 species of amphibians and reptiles known from Honduras or its coastal waters, including the Islas del Cisne (McCranie, unpubl. data). Thus, almost half of the entire Honduran herpetofauna is known from the Mosquitia.

Ninety-one genera of amphibians and reptiles are known to occur in the Mosquitia of the 137 (66.4%) known to occupy the country as a whole, including 1 genus of caecilian (of 2 genera known from Honduras or 50.0%), 2 genera of salamanders (of 5 genera or 40.0%), 15 genera of anurans (of 23 genera or 65.2%), 2 genera of crocodilians (of 2 genera or 100.0%), 8 genera of turtles (of 10 genera or 80.0%), 18 genera of lizards (of 29 genera or 62.1%), and 45 genera of snakes (of 66 genera or 68.2%). Therefore, about two-thirds of the genera recorded for the country occur in the Mosquitia.

Thirty families of amphibians and reptiles are recorded from the Mosquitia of the 38 (78.9%) known from the entire country, including 1 family of caecilians (of 1 family known from Honduras or 100.0%), 1 family of salamanders (of 1 family or 100.0%), 5 families of anurans (of 7 or 71.4%), 2 families of crocodilians (of 2 or 100.0%), 6 families of turtles (of 6 or 100.0%), 9 families of lizards (of 12 or 75.0%), and 6 families of snakes (of 9 or 66.7%). Thus, more than three-quarters of the families known from the country are recorded for the Mosquitia.

In summary, it is clear from these figures that the herpetofauna of the Mosquitia comprises a highly significant portion of the entire Honduran herpetofauna at all taxonomic levels. This situation has important implications for the conservation of the amphibians and reptiles of Honduras, as will be discussed below.

## Keys to the Identification of the Amphibians and Reptiles of the Mosquitia of Honduras

It should be understood that keys to identification have their strengths and their limitations. The principal strength is that keys provide a relatively rapid means of providing a tentative identification of a particular species in hand. It will only identify species of amphibians and reptiles that are known

**Table 2.** Composition of the herpetofauna of the Mosquitia of Honduras.

| Group | Families | Genera | Species |
|---|---|---|---|
| Caecilians | 1 | 1 | 1 |
| Salamanders | 1 | 2 | 3 |
| Anurans | 5 | 15 | 44 |
| Crocodilians | 2 | 2 | 2 |
| Turtles | 6 | 8 | 12 |
| Lizards | 9 | 18 | 31 |
| Snakes | 6 | 45 | 63 |
| Totals | 30 | 91 | 156 |

to occur in the Mosquitia, plus a few species that are strongly expected to occur there (these latter species indicated by an asterisk; also see Species of Probable Occurrence in the Honduran Mosquitia). Thus, it will not identify amphibians and reptiles that have either not been found, or are strongly expected to occur in the Mosquitia. It also needs to be understood that an identification key constitutes only an initial step in the effort to place the correct scientific name on a given specimen. The next step in identification is to proceed to the description section of the species account for the species one thinks is in hand. If that description, which is obviously more detailed, fits, then it is a good bet that the animal has been correctly identified. A final check can be made by examining the photograph provided, but it should be understood that the photographs included here are only of single specimens that happened to be collected and photographed. All organismic species possess genetic variability, which fact is easily ascertained by simply looking at other humans around oneself or examining the variation in a litter of puppies or kittens. Thus, it is not expected that the animal in hand exactly resembles the photograph in this book. For example, *Xenodon rabdocephalus* is a mimic of the highly venomous *Bothrops asper*, but the mimic has at least two pattern forms, one of shades of gray and the other of shades of rust red. Nonetheless, given these provisos, after having gone through these three steps, one can be reasonably assured of a correct identification. If other reference books covering the amphibians and reptiles of Central America are available, then some steps of the above-described process can be pursued further. The bottom line is that the key that follows will allow only a part of the identification process to be completed.

## Key to the Classes Amphibia and Reptilia

1 A. No epidermal scales present; skin with numerous mucus and/or poison glands, generally moist to the touch ........ Class Amphibia

B. Epidermal scales present on at least a portion of the body; skin free of mucus and poison glands, generally dry to the touch ........ Class Reptilia

## Key to the Orders of Amphibia of the Mosquitia

1 A. No limbs present; eyes covered with skin or bone; body encircled by annuli (Fig. 1) ........ Gymnophiona (caecilians)

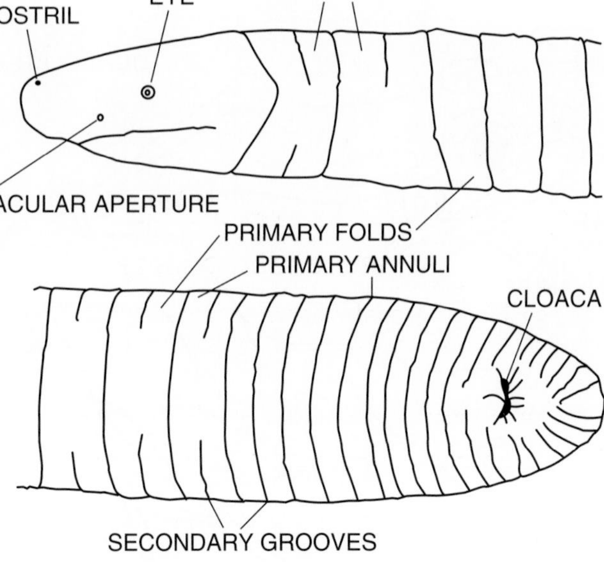


**Figure 1.** An adult caecilian (top: a lateral view of head and anterior portion of body; bottom: a ventral view of posterior portion of body) showing general features. Modified from Fig. 1 in McCranie and Wilson (2002).

B. Four limbs present; eyes well developed, not covered with skin or bone, with moveable eyelids; body not encircled by annuli ........................................ 2

2 A. Hind limbs with three segments, subequal in size to forelimbs; costal grooves present; tail present in adults (Fig. 2) ........................................ Caudata (salamanders)

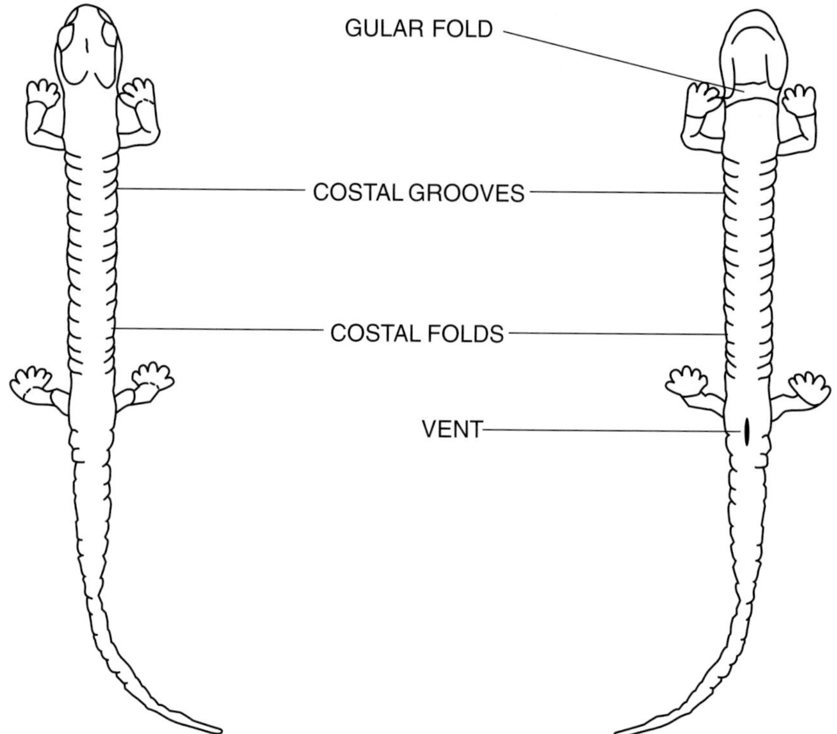


**Figure 2.** An adult salamander (dorsal view left; ventral view right) showing general features. Modified from Fig. 2 in McCranie and Wilson (2002).

B. Hind limbs with four segments, larger than forelimbs; costal grooves absent; tail absent in adults (Fig. 3) ........................................ Anura (frogs and toads)

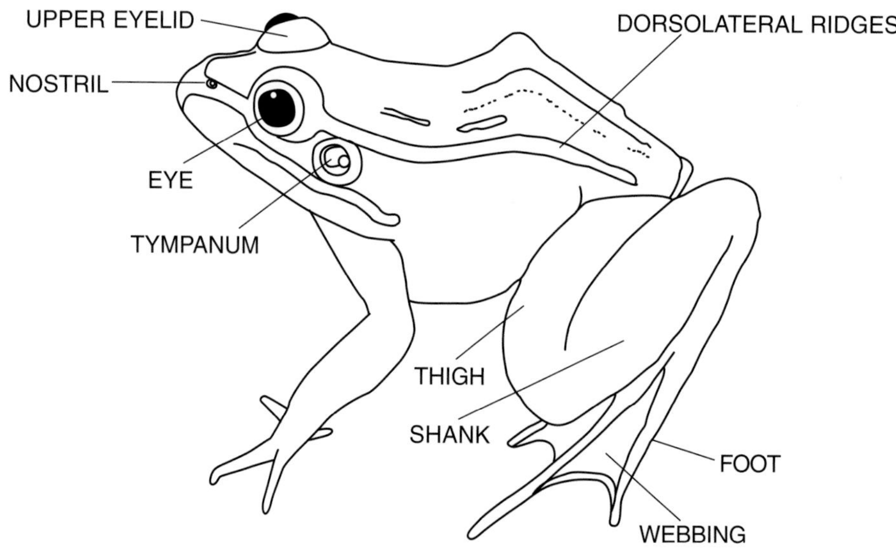


**Figure 3.** An adult frog showing general features. Modified from Fig. 3 in McCranie and Wilson (2002).

## Key to the Species of Salamanders of the Mosquitia

1 A. Costal grooves 19 or 20 ........ *Oedipina cyclocauda*
B. Costal grooves 13 ........ 2
2 A. Dorsum pale brown to yellowish brown, with narrow darker brown longitudinal stripes; ventral surfaces of head and trunk with dark brown streaking ........ *Bolitoglossa striatula*
B. Dorsum of body with broad, pale middorsal longitudinal stripe that is usually broken into three longitudinal stripes, or a suggestion thereof by invasion of dark lateral coloration onto dorsal surface, occasionally invasion of darker color so complete only paired pale dorsolateral stripes remain ........ *Bolitoglossa mexicana*

## Key to the Species of Frogs and Toads of the Mosquitia

1 A. Conspicuous inner tarsal tubercle present near mid-tarsus (Fig. 4) ........ *Physalaemus pustulosus**

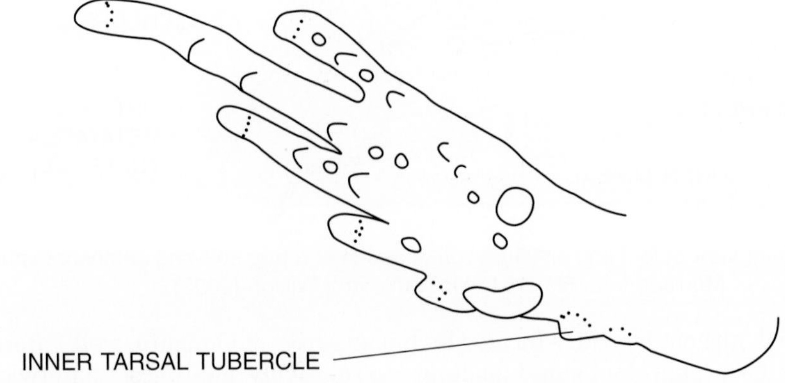


**Figure 4**. Anuran metatarsal segment showing distinct inner tarsal tubercle. Drawing by R. Nutt.

B. Conspicuous inner tarsal tubercle absent ........ 2
2 A. Conspicuous enlarged parotoid gland present posterior to each eye (Fig. 5) ........ 3

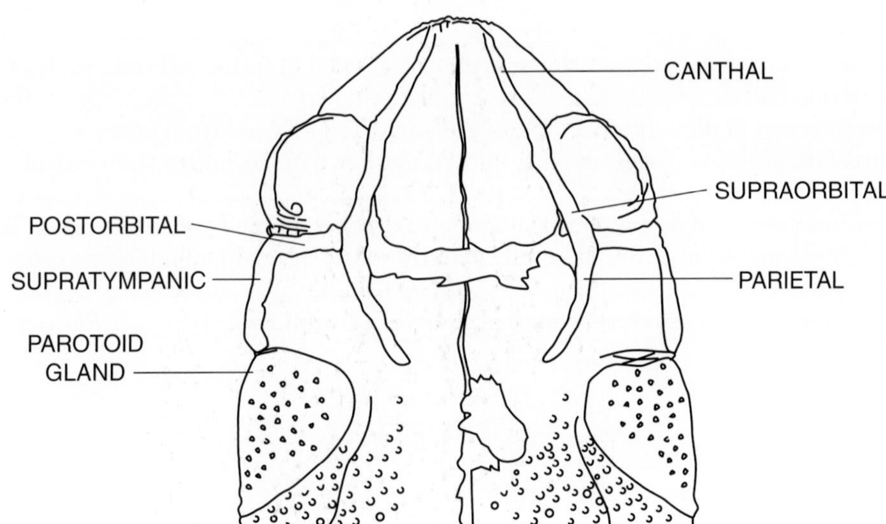


**Figure 5.** Doral view of *Bufo* sp. showing enlarged parotoid gland and cranial crests. Modified from Fig. 6 in McCranie and Wilson (2002).

B. No enlarged parotoid gland ........ 6

**3** A. Well developed inner tarsal fold present (Fig. 6); parotoid gland very large to huge, several times area of upper eyelid .......... 4

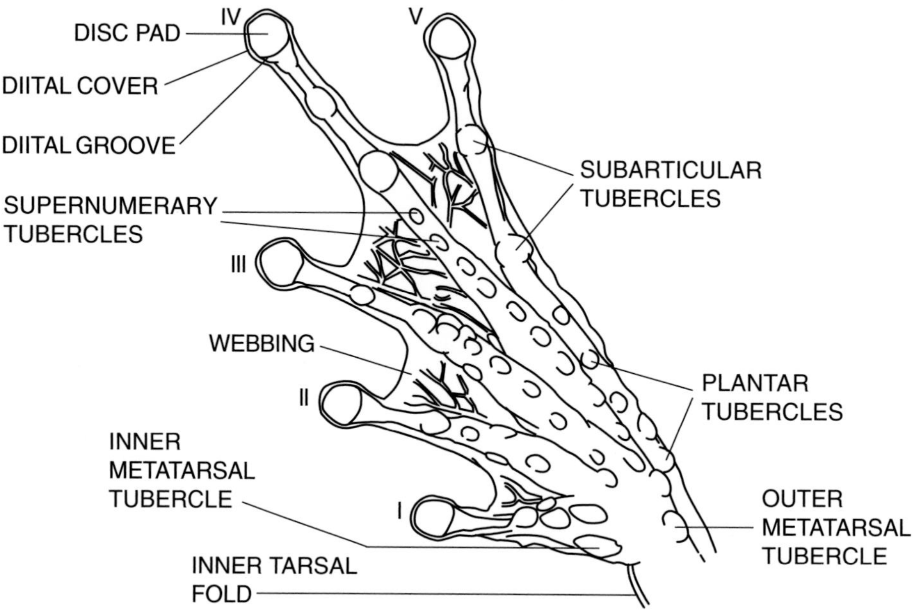


**Figure 6.** Plantar view of foot and distal portion of tarsus of a frog showing pertinent features. Modified from Fig. 10 in McCranie and Wilson (2002).

B. No inner tarsal fold, although a ridge formed by linear series of elongate, well differentiated tubercles can be present; parotoid gland moderate to relatively small, less than twice area of upper eyelid .......... 5

**4** A. Prominent cranial crests present (Fig. 5); numerous supernumerary tubercles present on fingers and toes (Fig. 6); no black band extending posteriorly from snout onto side of head and body; size in adults very large to huge, males to at least 145 mm SVL, females to more than 200 mm SVL .......... *Bufo marinus*

B. Cranial crests absent; no supernumerary tubercles on fingers and toes; broad black band on each side of head extending to posterior margin of parotoid gland; size large, males to 62 mm SVL, females to 80 mm SVL .......... *Bufo haematiticus*

**5** A. Definite linear series of dorsolateral tubercles clearly demarcated from other tubercles present; parotoid glands usually subtriangular, usually larger than size of upper eyelid .......... *Bufo valliceps*

B. No definite linear series of dorsolateral tubercles distinguishable from other tubercles on dorsal and lateral surfaces; parotoid glands usually round or ovoid, about same size as, or larger than, upper eyelid .......... *Bufo coccifer*

**6** A. Four digits on foot; paired enlarged digging tubercles present (Fig. 7) .......... *Rhinophrynus dorsalis**

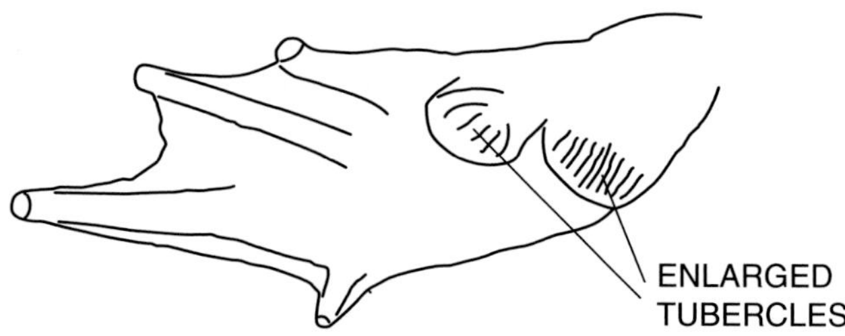


**Figure 7.** Plantar view of foot of *Rhinophrynus dorsalis* showing enlarged digging tubercles. Drawing by McCranie.

B. Five digits on foot; enlarged digging tubercles absent on foot ........ 7

7 A. No digital groove completely around tips of fingers and toes ........ 8

B. A small digital groove around tips of toes and at least Fingers III–IV, groove separating upper surface (disc cover) from subterminal disc pad (Fig. 6) ........ 14

8 A. Toes with extensive webbing; tongue deeply notched posteriorly (Fig. 8) ........ 9

**Figure 8.** Notched tongue of *Rana*. Modified from Fig. 42 in Powell et al. (1998).

B. Toes with basal webbing or webbing absent; tongue not or only slightly notched posteriorly ........ 12

9 A. Outer metatarsal tubercle present (Fig. 6); well-defined toe discs with marginal grooves laterally; posterior of thigh with large pale spots or vertical bars; size moderately large, males ≤52 mm SVL ........ *Rana warszewitschii*

B. Outer metatarsal tubercle absent; no lateral grooves along margins of toe tips; posterior of thigh with pale mottling or small spots; size large, adult males ≤49 mm SVL ........ 10

10 A. Skin of dorsum smooth to weakly granular, except skin can be denticulate on lower back and hind limbs; toe tips not expanded (Fig. 9); distinct dark dorsal spots usually present ........ *Rana brownorum*

B. Skin of dorsum usually denticulate; toe tips slightly expanded (Fig. 10); dark dorsal spots, if present, usually indistinct ........ 11

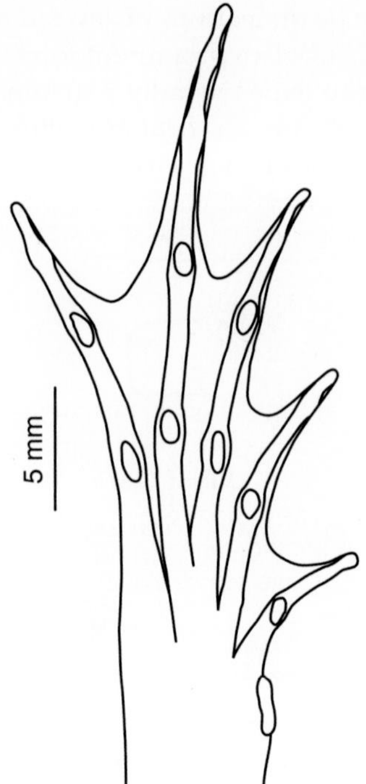


**Figure 9.** Foot of *Rana brownorum* showing unexpanded toe tips. Drawing by Uta Imhoff and provided by Gunther Köhler.

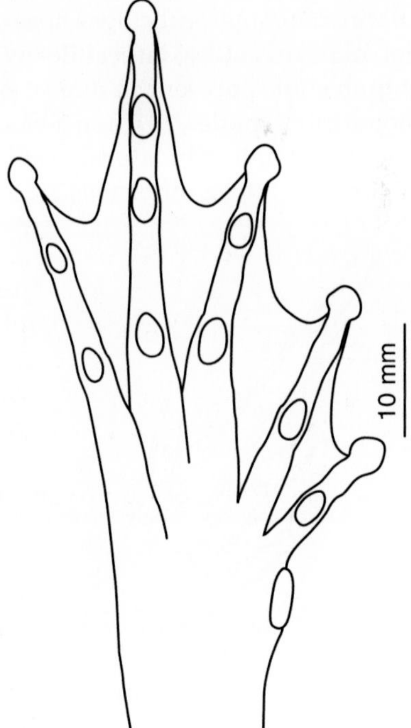


**Figure 10.** Foot of *Rana vaillanti* showing expanded toe tips. Drawing by Uta Imhoff and provided by Gunther Köhler.

**11** A. Tympanum large, tympanum length/eye length >0.700; distinct dark face mask usually absent; pale supralabial stripe usually absent (stripe, if present, posterior to eye) .................... *Rana vaillanti*

B. Tympanum moderately large, tympanum length/eye length <0.700; distinct dark face mask usually present; distinct pale supralabial stripe usually present ............................................. *Rana maculata*

**12** A. Moderately distinct to distinct pale longitudinal stripe on posterior surface of thigh; lateral fleshy fringes absent on toes; keratinized thumb spines absent in males; size small, ≤44 mm SVL ........................................................................................ *Leptodactylus fragilis*

B. Posterior surface of thigh mottled, spotted, or uniform, without distinct pale longitudinal stripe; lateral fleshy fringes present or absent on toes; one or two keratinized thumb spines present in males (Fig. 11); size variable ........................................................................................................ **13**

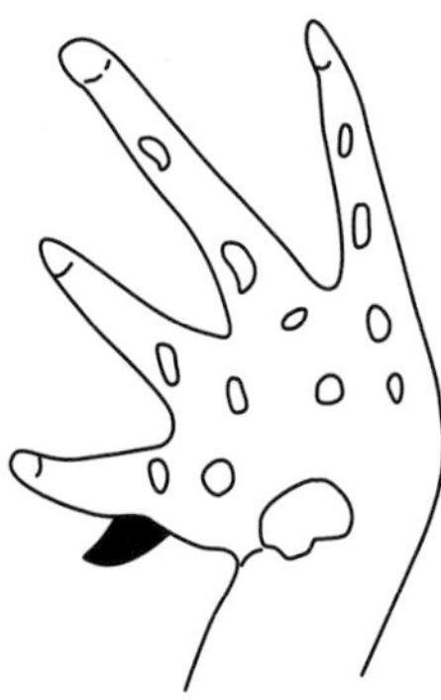

**Figure 11.** Keratinized thumb spine in a leptodactylid. Drawing by McCranie.

**13** A. Distinct dorsolateral ridges extending from eye to sacrum; lateral fleshy fringes absent on toes; a single, prominent, keratinized thumb spine present in males; size very large to huge, adults >100 mm SVL ................................................................................ *Leptodactylus pentadactylus*

B. Distinct dorsolateral ridges absent, although rarely there can be indications of several tuberculate dorsolateral ridges; lateral fleshy fringes present on toes (Fig. 12); two prominent keratinized thumb spines present in males; size relatively small, Honduran males usually ≤40 mm SVL, Honduran females ≤43 mm SVL ............................................................... *Leptodactylus melanonotus*

**14** A. Snout protruding in lateral profile (Fig. 13); webbing between Toes I–II greatly reduced relative to webbing between other toes ................................................................................................................ **15**

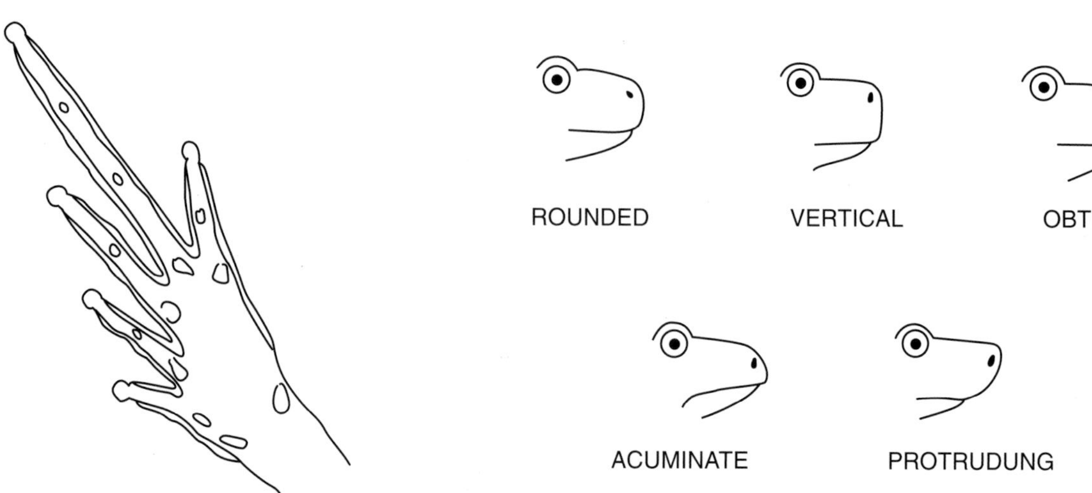


**Figure 12.** *Leptodactylus* foot with well-developed lateral fleshy toe fringes. Drawing by McCranie.

**Figure 13.** Snout lateral profile standards. Modified from Fig. 80 in Heyer et al. (1990).

B. Snout rounded, vertical, obtuse, or only slightly protruding (with rounded upper edge) in lateral profile (Fig. 13); webbing (if present) between Toes I–II not greatly reduced relative to that between other toes ........ **16**

**15** A. Posterior surface of thigh with dark bars alternating with pale areas (bright yellow in life); males to 49 mm SVL, females to 53 mm SVL ........ *Scinax boulengeri*

B. Posterior surface of thigh usually uniformly brown, lacking distinct dark bars; males to 29 mm SVL, females to 32 mm SVL ........ *Scinax staufferi*

**16** A. Bony occipital and canthal spines present (Fig. 14) ........ *Anotheca spinosa*

**Figure 14.** Head of *Anotheca* showing occipital and canthal spines. Redrawn from Duellman (2001).

B. Bony occipital and canthal spines absent ........ **17**

**17** A. No finger webbing ........ **18**

B. Finger webbing present, at least basally, between outer fingers ........ **27**

**18** A. Toe V longer than Toe III ........ **19**

B. Toe V shorter than Toe III ........ **21**

**19** A. Heels with distinct pointed to pustular tubercle (Fig. 15) ........ *Eleutherodactylus cerasinus*

B. Heels smooth to rugose, lacking a distinct tubercle (Fig. 15) ........ **20**

**20** A. Most disc covers palmate (Fig. 16) ........ *Eleutherodactylus diastema*

B. Disc covers rounded (Fig. 16) ........ *Eleutherodactylus ridens*

**21** A. Paired cranial crests present in frontoparietal region ........ *Craugastor megacephalus*

B. Cranial crests absent ........ **22**

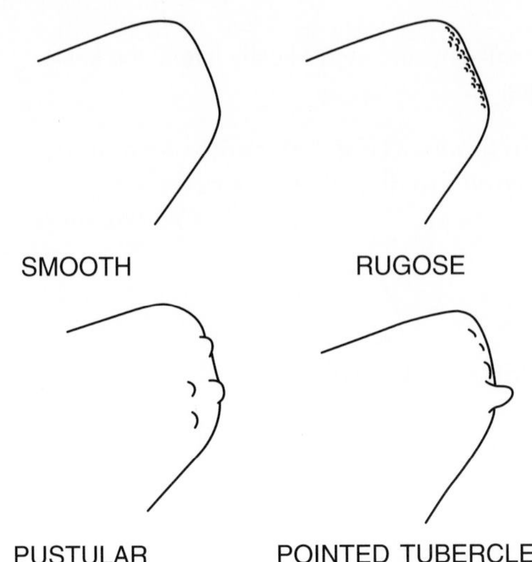


**Figure 15.** Anuran heel ornamentation. Modified from Fig. 6 in Savage (1987).

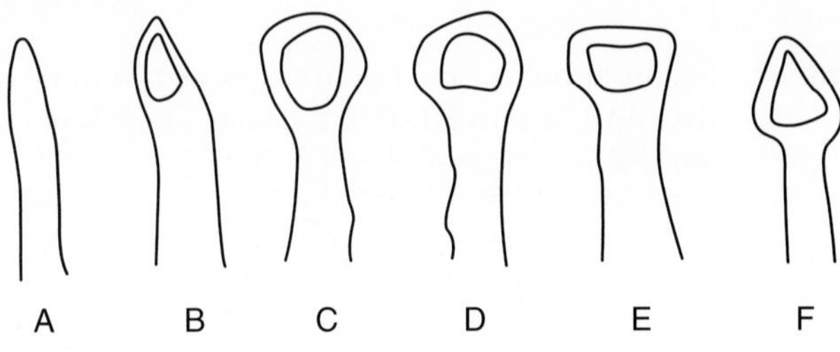


**Figure 16.** Terminology for anuran finger and toe disc covers and pads. A = not expanded, no digital groove; B = not expanded, but slightly swollen, digital groove present; C–F = expanded, digital groove present; C = rounded or ovoid; D = broadened; E = truncate; F = palmate. Drawings by McCranie.

22 A. Finger and toe discs not expanded, although discs and disc covers on outer fingers and toes can be somewhat swollen (Fig. 16); supernumerary tubercles (Fig. 6) well developed on fingers and toes ........ *Craugastor lauraster*
B. Finger and toe discs narrowly to broadly expanded (Fig. 16); supernumerary tubercles (Fig. 6) absent on fingers and toes ........ **23**

23 A. Tympanum indistinct to absent ........ *Craugastor epochthidius*
B. Tympanum prominent ........ **24**

24 A. Dark eye mask extending from snout through eye and above tympanum to level of axilla or beyond; snout slightly protruding (Fig. 13) with a rounded upper edge in lateral profile ........ **25**
B. Dark eye mask, as described above, absent; snout rounded in lateral profile (Fig. 13) ........ **26**

25 A. Discs on Fingers III–IV markedly larger than those on Fingers I–II; nonfleshy lateral keels present on unwebbed portion of toes (Fig. 17); dark seat patch mark absent ........ *Craugastor noblei*
B. Discs on fingers subequal, or nearly so; fleshy lateral keels present on unwebbed portions of toes (Fig. 17); dark seat patch mark present ........ *Craugastor mimus*

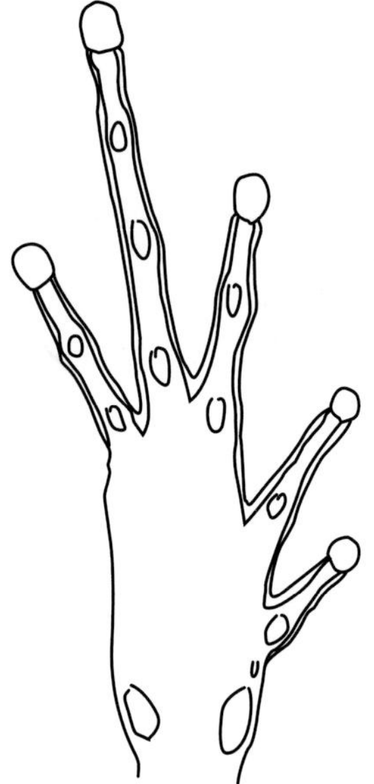

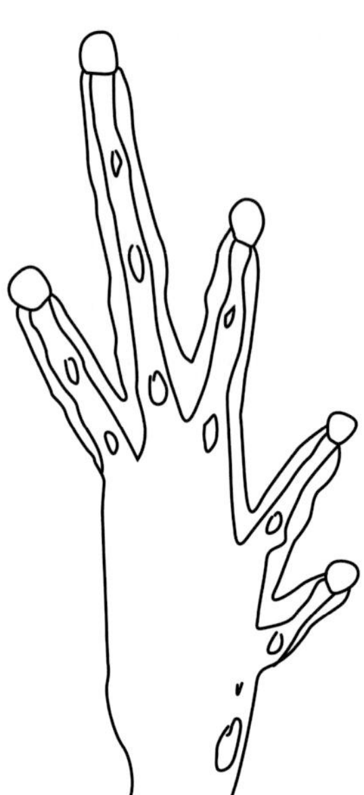

**Figure 17.** Plantar view of foot of *Craugastor* showing (left) nonfleshy and (right) fleshy lateral toe keels. Drawings by McCranie.

26 A. Snout subelliptical in dorsal aspect in males, subovoid in females (Fig. 18); canthus angular; disc on Fingers III–IV ≥2.5 times width of digit just proximal to disc; disc covers on toes somewhat truncated ........ *Craugastor fitzingeri*

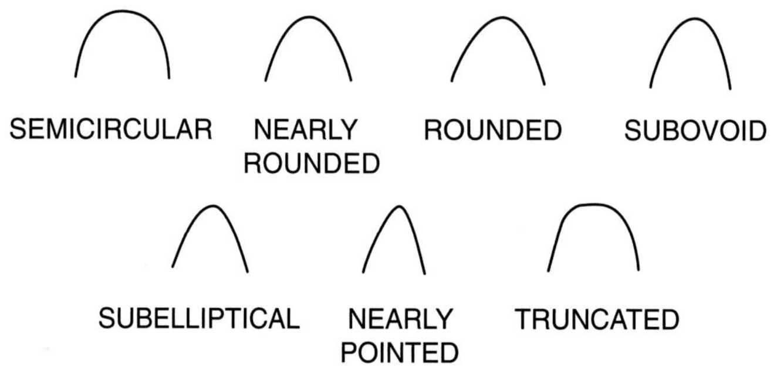


**Figure 18.** Anuran snout dorsal outline standards. Modified from Fig. 79 in Heyer et al. (1990).

B. Snout nearly rounded in dorsal aspect in both sexes; canthus rounded; disc on Fingers III–IV ≤2.3 times width of digit just proximal to disc; disc covers on toes rounded ........ *Craugastor pechorum*

27 A. Pupil of eye vertically elliptical in preservative or in bright light in life (Fig. 19) ........ **28**

B. Pupil of eye horizontally elliptical in preservative or rounded in bright light in life (Fig. 19) ........ **30**

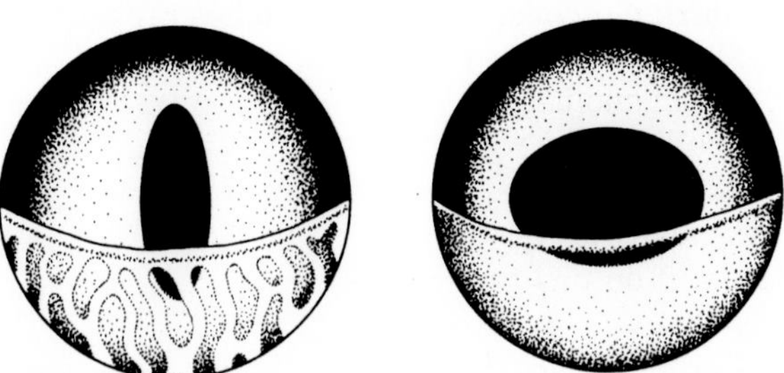

**Figure 19.** Anuran pupil shape and palpebral membrane pattern; (left) vertically elliptical pupil and reticulated palpebral membrane; (right) horizontally elliptical pupil and unpatterned palpebral membrane. Copied from Duellman (2001) with permission from The Society for the Study of Amphibians and Reptiles.

28 A. Flanks uniformly purple in life and in preservative ........ *Agalychnis saltator*

B. Flanks barred or striped ........ **29**

29 A. Flanks with several pale vertical stripes or bars on purple ground color; no calcar; palpebral membrane reticulated (Fig. 19); iris red in life ........ *Agalychnis callidryas*

B. Flanks with black vertical stripes or bars on a yellow ground color; calcar present (Fig. 20); palpebral membrane unpigmented (Fig. 19); iris yellow to gray in life ........ *Agalychnis calcarifer*

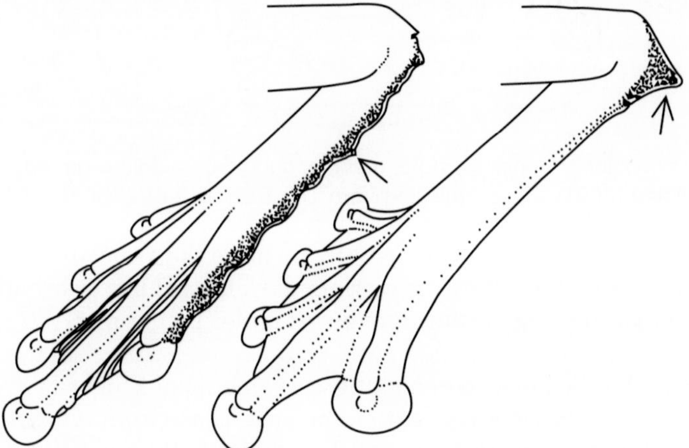

**Figure 20.** Anuran scalloped dermal fringes (left) and calcar (right). Copied from Duellman (2001) with permission from The Society for the Study of Amphibians and Reptiles.

30 A. Dense zone of dermal glandular tissue, indicated by thickened skin in at least occipital and frontal regions; males with paired, lateral vocal sacs located posterior to angle of jaws ........ *Phrynohyas venulosa*

B. No dense zone of dermal glandular tissue in occipital and frontal regions; male vocal sac subgular, single, or paired ........ **31**

31 A. Scalloped dermal fringes (Fig. 20) present on posterior surfaces of forearms and tarsi; osteoderms present in skin on top of head giving appearance of head co-ossified with underlying skull; size large, adult males to 110 mm SVL, females to 86 mm ........ *Hyla miliaria*

B. Scalloped dermal fringes absent on posterior surfaces of forearms and tarsi; osteoderms absent on top of head; size variable ........ **32**

**32** A. Males with paired subgular vocal sacs (Fig. 21); adult female size moderate to large (48–90 mm SVL); adult male size moderate to large (34–76 mm SVL); dorsum commonly marked with dark blotches ........ **33**

B. Males with single, median, subgular vocal sac (Fig. 21); female size moderate to small (≤47 mm SVL); male size moderate to very small (≤45 mm SVL); dorsum not marked with dark blotches, or if dark blotches present, size small (≤29 mm SVL in males, ≤37 mm SVL in females) ........ **35**

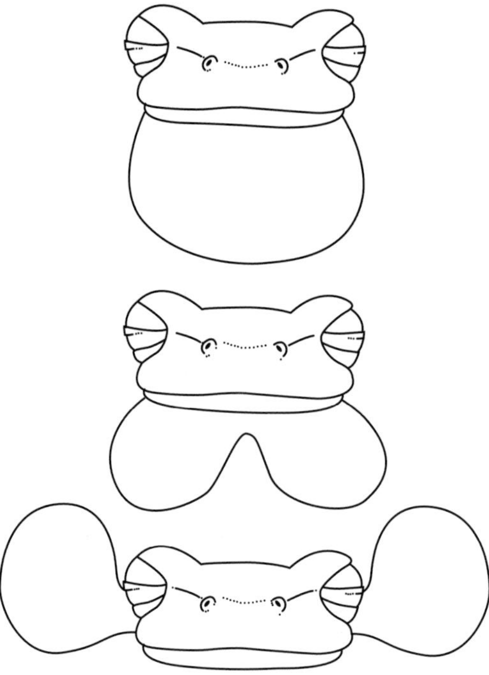

**Figure 21.** Male vocal sac conditions. Upper = single, median, subgular; middle = paired, subgular; bottom = paired, lateral. Copied from Duellman (2001) with permission from The Society for the Study of Amphibians and Reptiles.

**33** A. Web between Fingers III–IV substantial, usually no more than one and one quarter segments of Finger IV free of webbing; no distinct dark lateral bar or broad stripe extending posteriorly from tympanum; size moderately large, males to 45 mm SVL, females to 64 mm SVL ........ *Smilisca sordida*

B. Web between Fingers III–IV moderate, about two segments of Finger IV free of webbing; distinct dark lateral bar or broad stripe extending posteriorly from tympanum to level of axilla or slightly beyond; size large, males to 76 mm SVL, females to 90 mm SVL ........ **34**

**34** A. Contrasting dark vertical bars usually present on upper lip; a row of low, prominent tubercles usually present along posterior ventrolateral edge of forearm; flanks mottled or reticulated with cream and brown, especially in groin region; no dark tarsal stripe; larger size, males to 76 mm SVL, females to 90 mm SVL ........ *Smilisca baudinii*

B. Pale labial stripe present, stripe most prominent below and posterior to eye; row of prominent tubercles absent along posterior ventrolateral edge of forearm, although a few tubercles can be present in some specimens; flanks cream with dark brown venation, including groin region; thin, dark stripe present from heel along tarsal segment to foot; smaller size, males to 65 mm SVL, females to 78 mm SVL ........ *Smilisca phaeota*

**35** A. Belly usually not transparent in life or translucent in preservative or, if so, disc covers on fingers and toes rounded and disc pads on fingers and toes broadened to ovoid (Fig. 16) ........ **36**

B. Belly transparent in life, translucent in preservative, so that at least some internal organs, or their linings are visible; disc covers and pads of fingers and toes truncate (Fig. 16) ........ **40**

**36** A. Axillary membrane (Fig. 22) abbreviated, not extending more than one-half distance towards elbow; males with pointed keratinous spines on prepollex (Fig. 23) and usually with prominent ventrolateral glands ........ *Ptychohyla hypomykter*

B. Axillary membrane (Fig. 22) broad, attaching to upper arm near elbow, or at least extending to over one-half distance towards elbow ........ **37**

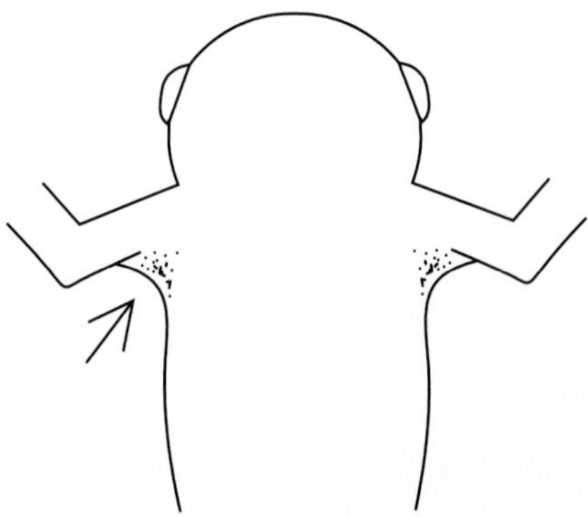

**Figure 22.** Anuran axillary membrane. Copied from Duellman (2001) with permission from The Society for the Study of Amphibians and Reptiles.

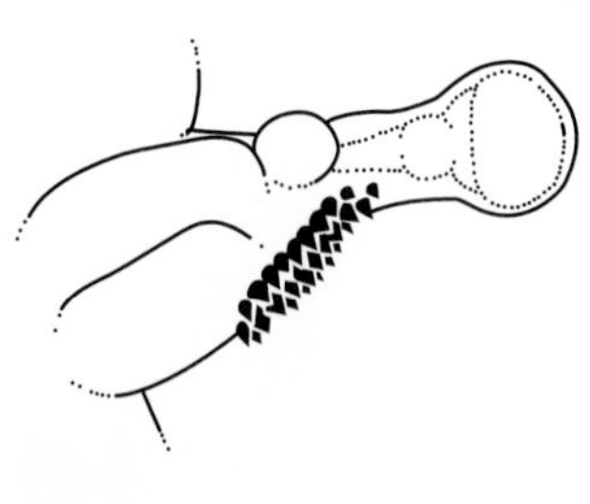

**Figure 23.** Ventral view of a hylid prepollex and Finger I showing prepollical spines. Copied from Duellman (2001) with permission from The Society for the Study of Amphibians and Reptiles.

**37** A. Size moderate, males to 45 mm SVL, females to 47 mm SVL; dorsolateral stripe absent; dorsal pattern uniform or patterned with dark flecks, scattered small dark spots, or dark mottling ........ *Hyla loquax*

B. Size small, males <30 mm SVL, females <38 mm SVL; dark and/or pale dorsolateral stripes usually extending posteriorly from tympanum, or, if dorsolateral stripes absent, dorsum usually with distinct dark markings ........ **38**

**38** A. Vomerine teeth absent; size very small (to 23 mm SVL) ........ *Hyla picta*

B. Vomerine teeth present (Fig. 24); size small (males reach 27–29 mm SVL, females 31–37 mm SVL) ........ **39**

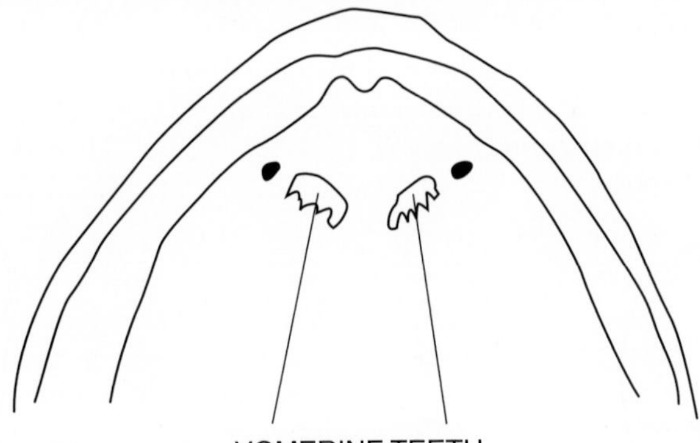


**Figure 24.** The inside of an anuran mouth showing location of vomerine teeth. Drawing by McCranie.

**39** A. Dorsal pattern consisting of irregular dark dashes forming X-shaped mark, fragmented crossbars, fragmented lines, or reticulated pattern, or occasionally dorsum with only scattered flecks; males to 27 mm SVL, females to 31 mm SVL ........ *Hyla microcephala*

B. Dorsal pattern consisting of dark hourglass-shaped mark, dark blotches, or dark spots; males to 29 mm SVL, females to 37 mm SVL ........ *Hyla ebraccata*

**40** A. Parietal peritoneum colorless; dorsum white to pale yellow in preservative, without purple spots and/or purple upper eyelids ........ **41**

**Figure 25.** Venter of *Centrolene prosoblepon* showing white parietal peritoneum. Photograph by McCranie.

B. Parietal peritoneum white anterior to about midpoint of belly or to level slightly posterior to midpoint of belly (Fig. 25) .......... **43**

**41** A. Webbing between Fingers II–III basal .......... *Hyalinobatrachium fleischmanni*

B. Webbing between Fingers II–III nearly as extensive as that between Fingers III–IV .......... **42**

**42** A. Vomerine teeth present; snout strongly obtuse in lateral profile; tympanum distinct or indistinct; parietal pericardium white .......... *Hyalinobatrachium pulveratum*

B. Vomerine teeth absent; snout bluntly rounded in lateral profile; tympanum very indistinct; parietal pericardium colorless .......... *Hyalinobatrachium cardiacalyptum*

**43** A. Humeral spine present (Fig. 26) in males and in some females .......... *Centrolene prosoblepon*

B. Humeral spines absent .......... **44**

**44** A. Prepollex with free, spiny distal end (Fig. 27); dorsum lacking distinct spots .......... *Cochranella spinosa*

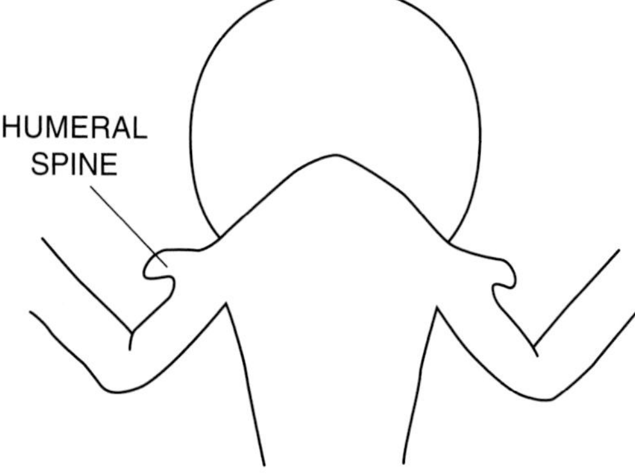


**Figure 26.** Ventral view of *Centrolene prosoblepon* showing male humeral spine. Modified from Fig. 26 in McCranie and Wilson (2002).

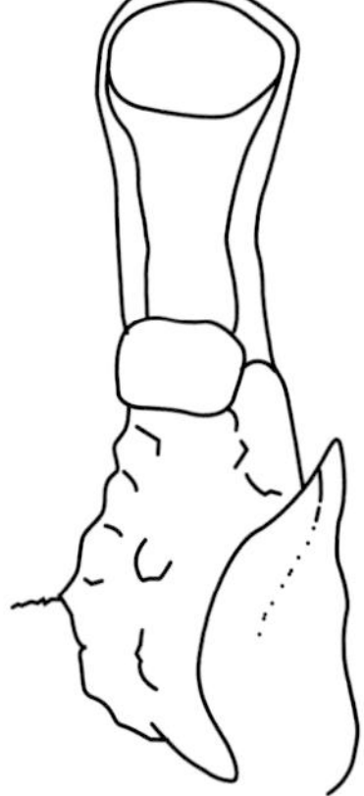

**Figure 27.** Spiny distal end to prepollex in *Cochranella spinosa*. Redrawn from Flores (1985).

B. Prepollex lacking free, spiny distal end; dorsum usually with distinct spots ..... **45**

**45** A. Dorsum marked with numerous pale spots; dorsal ground color lavender to gray in preservative; snout bluntly rounded in lateral profile ..... *Cochranella albomaculata*

B. Dorsum lacking pale spots, usually marked with purple spots; dorsal ground color pale yellow with purple upper eyelids in preservative; snout obtuse in lateral profile ..... *Cochranella granulosa*

## Key to the Orders of Reptiles of the Mosquitia

1 A. Body encased in a shell, which encloses girdles; no teeth present, jaws enclosed in a horny sheath ..... Testudines (turtles)

B. Body not encased in a shell; teeth present on jaws ..... 2

2 A. Cloacal opening longitudinal; secondary palate present; teeth socketed ..... Crocodylia (crocodilians)

B. Cloacal opening transverse; secondary palate absent; teeth not socketed ..... Squamata (lizards and snakes)

## Key to the Species of Crocodilians of the Mosquitia

1 A. Fourth mandibular tooth fitting into a pit in the upper jaw and not visible when mouth is closed; .... ventral scales without apical pits ..... *Caiman crocodilus*

B. Fourth mandibular tooth fitting into a notch in upper jaw and visible when mouth is closed; ventral scales with one apical pit per scale ..... *Crocodylus acutus*

## Key to the Species of Turtles of the Mosquitia

1 A. Forelimbs paddle-like; marine ..... 2

B. Forelimbs not paddle-like; nonmarine ..... 5

2 A. Carapace and plastron covered by soft skin over a layer of connective tissue (Fig. 28) ..... *Dermochelys coriacea*

B. Carapace and plastron covered by hard scutes (Fig. 29) ..... 3

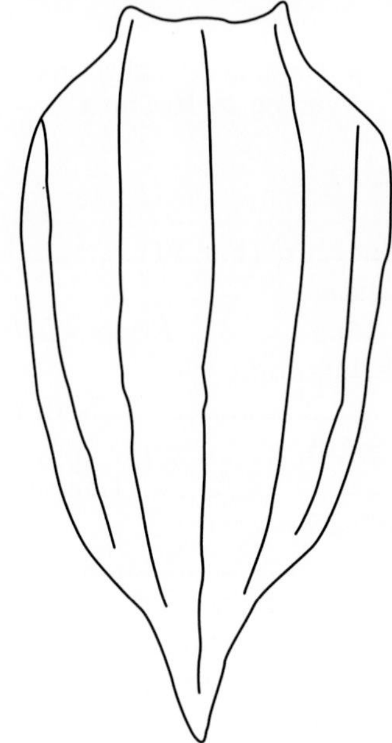

**Figure 28.** *Dermochelys* carapace. Drawing by McCranie.

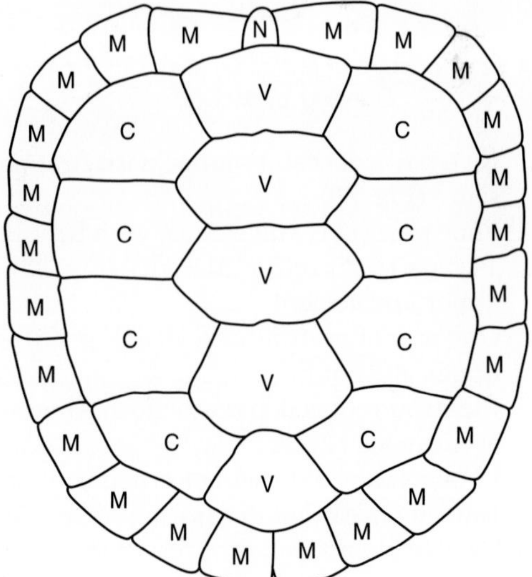


**Figure 29.** *Trachemys venusta* carapace with scutes labeled. C = costals; M = marginals; N = nuchal; V = vertebrals. Drawing by Philipp Groß and provided by Gunther Köhler.

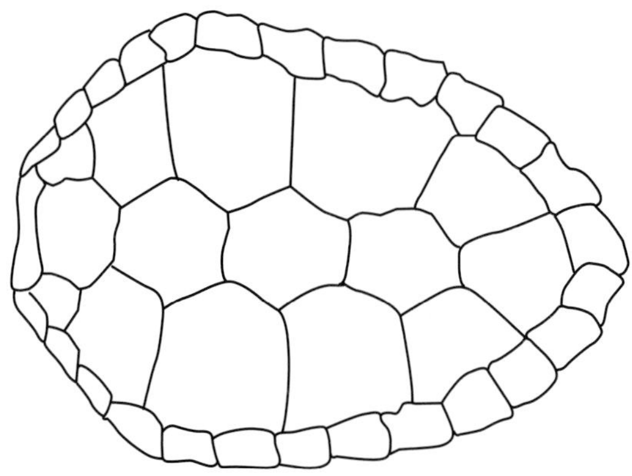

**Figure 30.** Carapace of *Caretta* showing five pairs of costal scutes with first pair in contact with nuchal scute. Drawing by McCranie.

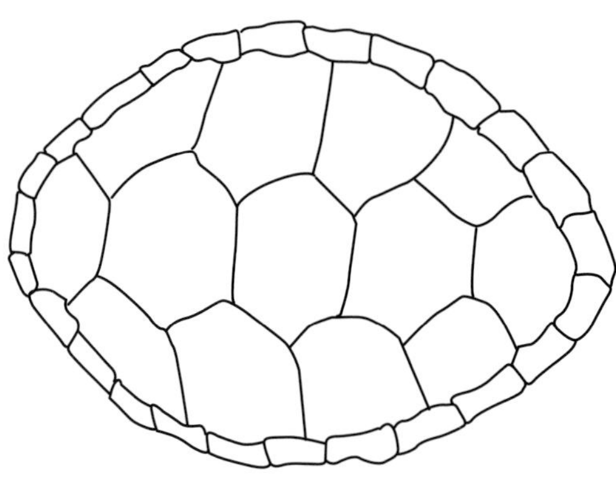

**Figure 31.** Carapace of *Chelonia* showing four pairs of costal scutes with first pair separated from nuchal scute. Drawing by McCranie.

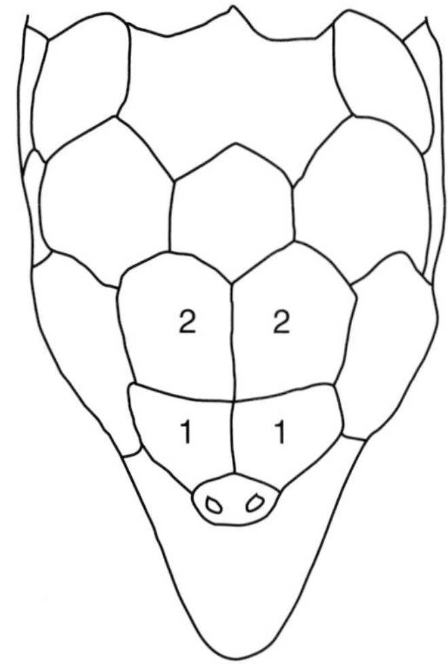


**Figure 32.** Two pairs of prefrontal scales in *Eretmochelys*. Drawing by McCranie.

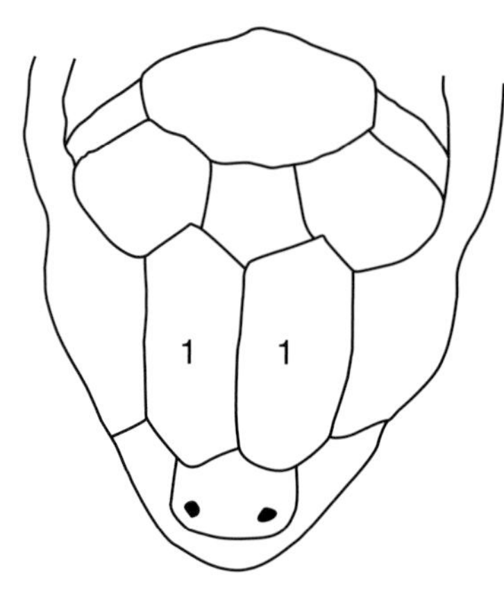


**Figure 33.** One pair of prefrontal scales in *Chelonia*. Drawing by McCranie.

**3** A. Five pairs of costal scutes, with first pair in contact with nuchal scute (Fig. 30) ........ *Caretta caretta*

B. Four pairs of costal scutes, with first pair separated from nuchal scute (Fig. 31) ........ **4**

**4** A. Two pairs of prefrontal scales (Fig. 32); carapacial scutes imbricate; upper jaw hooked ........ *Eretmochelys imbricata*

B. One pair of prefrontal scales (Fig. 33); carapacial scutes nonoverlapping; upper jaw not hooked ........ *Chelonia mydas*

**5** A. Plastron reduced and cruciform (Fig. 34); tail more than half length of carapace ........ *Chelydra serpentina*

B. Plastron not reduced nor cruciform; tail less than half length of carapace ........ **6**

**6** A. Eleven plastral plates present (Fig. 35) ........ **7**

B. Twelve plastral plates present (Fig. 36) ........ **8**

**7** A. Intergular scute broader on dorsal surface of plastron than on ventral surface; opposable patches of spines on posterior thigh and calf in adult males; carapace never with more than a median keel; head uniformly pale, with small pale spots or blotches on a dark ground color, or with a distinct broad temporal pale stripe (pale areas some shade of yellow in life) ........ *Kinosternon leucostomum*

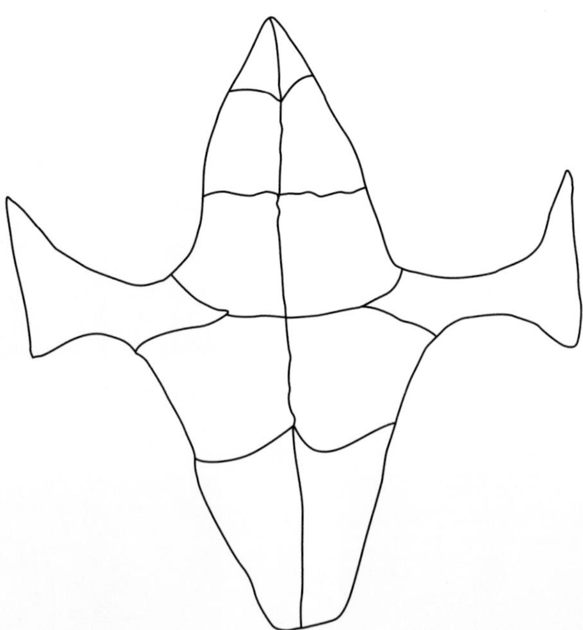

**Figure 34.** Cruciform plastron of *Chelydra serpentina*. Drawing by McCranie.

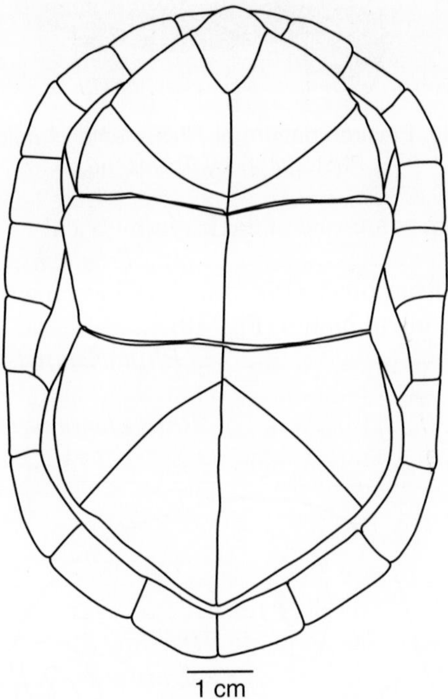



**Figure 35.** Plastron of *Kinosternon leucostomum* showing 11 plastral scutes. Drawing by Philipp Groß and provided by Gunther Köhler.

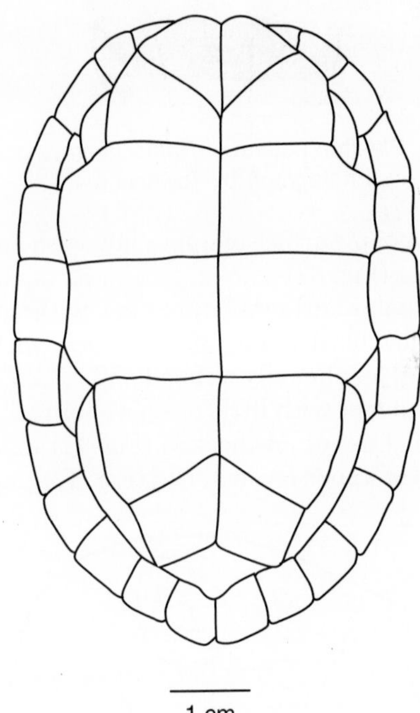



**Figure 36.** Plastron of *Trachemys venusta* showing 12 plastral scutes. Drawing by Philipp Groß and provided by Gunther Köhler.

B. Intergular scute no broader on dorsal surface of plastron than on ventral surface; no opposable patches of spines on thigh and calf in adult males; two or three keels on carapace in adults, usually indicated only posteriorly; head mottled with dark and pale markings (pale markings some shade of red or orange in life) ....................................... *Kinosternon scorpioides*

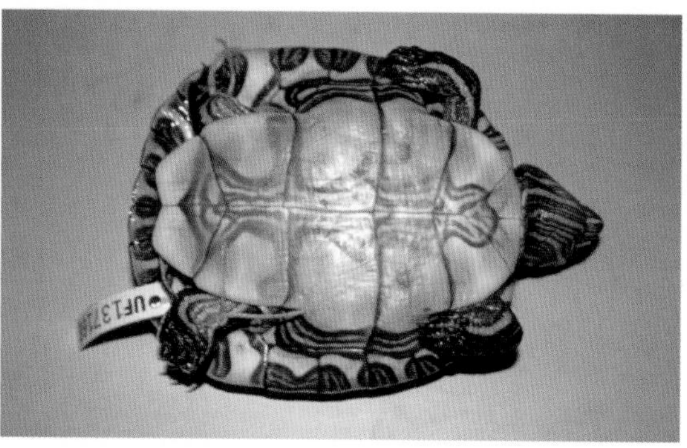

**Figure 37.** Plastron pattern of *Trachemys venusta*. Photograph by Townsend.

**Figure 38.** Plastron pattern of *Rhinoclemmys funerea*. Photograph by Townsend.

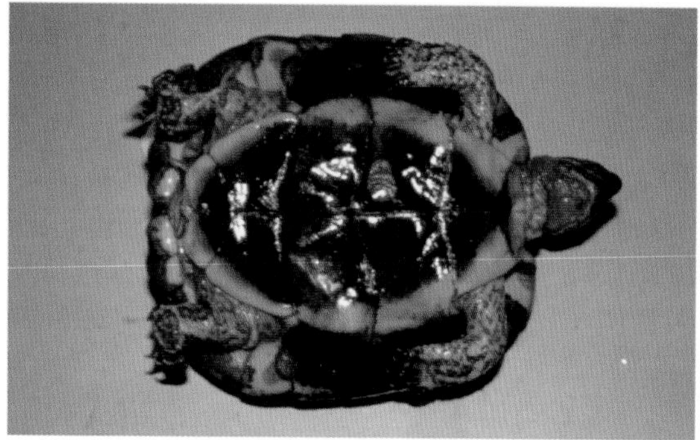

**Figure 39.** Plastron pattern of *Rhinoclemmys annulata*. Photograph by Townsend.

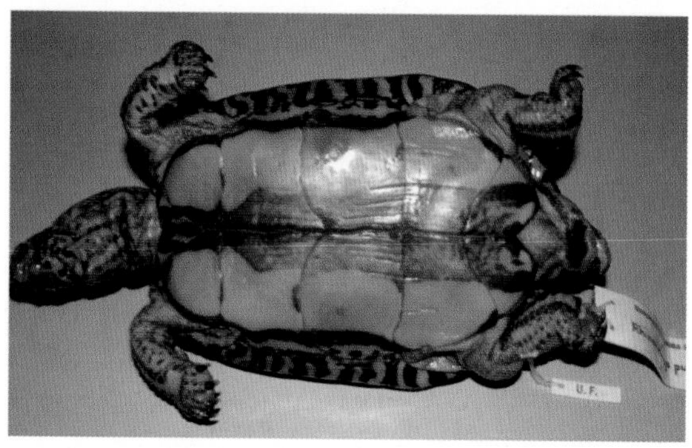

**Figure 40.** Plastron pattern of *Rhinoclemmys pulcherrima*. Photograph by Townsend.

8 A. Alveolar surface of upper jaw with a ridge; plastron figure composed of dark symmetrical lines (Fig. 37) .......... *Trachemys venusta*

B. Alveolar surface of upper jaw without a ridge; plastron either black (Fig. 38), dark brown with a yellow border (Fig. 39), or yellow with a brown to black central blotch (Fig. 40) .......... **9**

9 A. Hind feet heavily webbed .......... *Rhinoclemmys funerea*

B. Hind feet with little or no webbing .......... **10**

10 A. Tip of upper jaw hooked (Fig. 41) .......... *Rhinoclemmys annulata*

B. Tip of upper jaw notched (Fig. 42) .......... **11**

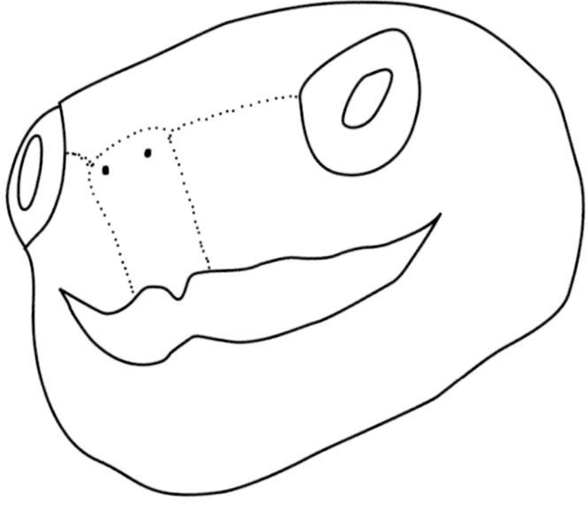

**Figure 41.** Hooked upper jaw in *Rhinoclemmys*. Drawing by McCranie.

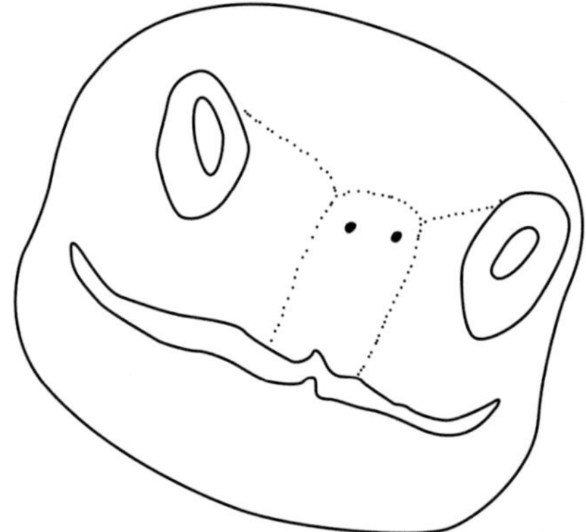

**Figure 42.** Notched upper jaw in *Rhinoclemmys*. Drawing by McCranie.

**11** A. Head pattern of a single pair of supratemporal stripes posterior to eye; bridge usually yellow without extensive dark coloration ................................ *Rhinoclemmys areolata*
B. Head pattern of two or three red stripes, crossing tip of snout, and a prefrontal arrow produced where medial sagittal stripe meets two supratemporal stripes on dorsal tip of snout; bridge with extensive dark coloration ................................ *Rhinoclemmys pulcherrima*

## Key to the Species of Lizards of the Mosquitia

**1** A. No moveable eyelids ................................ **2**
B. Moveable eyelids present ................................ **7**
**2** A. Dorsal surface of head with enlarged, platelike scales (Fig. 43) ................................ **3**
B. Dorsal surface of head covered with granular scales ................................ **4**
**3** A. Scales of venter large, squarish, juxtaposed, and platelike; five digits present on forelimbs ................................ *Lepidophyma flavimaculatum*
B. Scales of venter large, smooth, imbricate, and cycloid; four digits present on forelimbs ................................ *Gymnophthalmus speciosus*
**4** A. Several lamellae (or at least terminal lamellae) beneath toes expanded and double ................................ **5**
B. Lamellae beneath toes not expanded or, if expanded, they are single ................................ **6**
**5** A. More than 12 divided subdigital lamellae on Digit IV of hands and feet, distalmost ones widely separated by skin (Fig. 44) ................................ *Thecadactylus rapicauda*
B. Less than 12 divided subdigital lamellae on Digit IV of hands and feet, distalmost ones not separated by skin (Fig. 44) ................................ *Hemidactylus frenatus*
**6** A. Claws displaced laterally by distinctly expanded terminal subdigital scale (Fig. 44); claws retractable ................................ *Sphaerodactylus millepunctatus*
B. Claws not displaced laterally, terminal subdigital scales about same size as others (Fig. 44); claws nonretractable ................................ *Gonatodes albogularis*

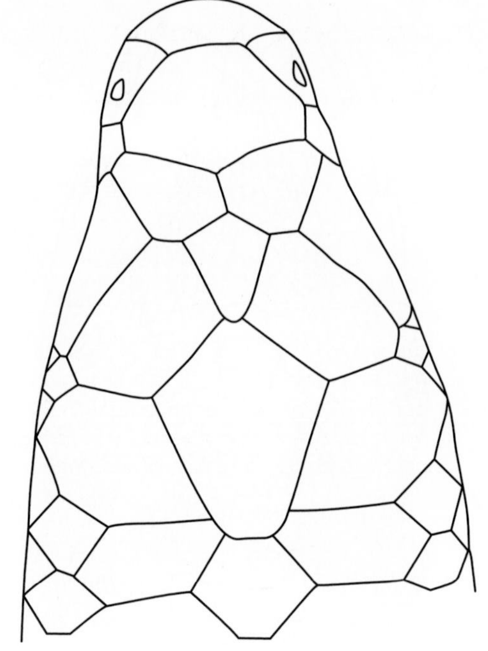


**Figure 43.** Dorsal surface of head of *Gymnophthalmus speciosus* showing enlarged plates. Drawing by Uta Imhoff and provided by Gunther Köhler.

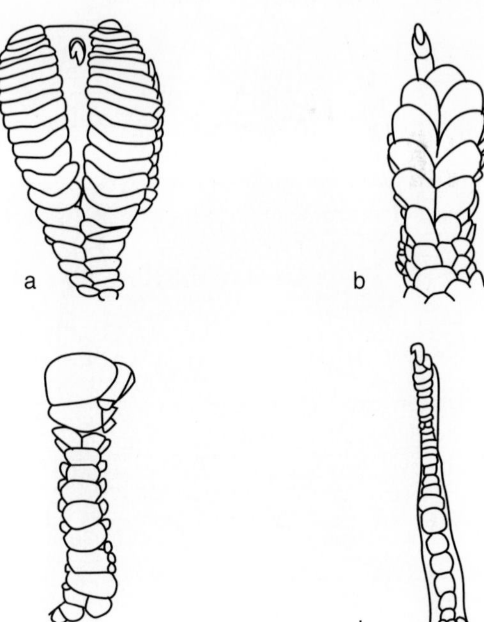


**Figure 44.** Toe structure of *Thecadactylus* (a), *Hemidactylus* (b), *Sphaerodactylus* (c), and *Gonatodes* (d). Copied from Fig. 105 in Köhler (2003) with permission of author/artist.

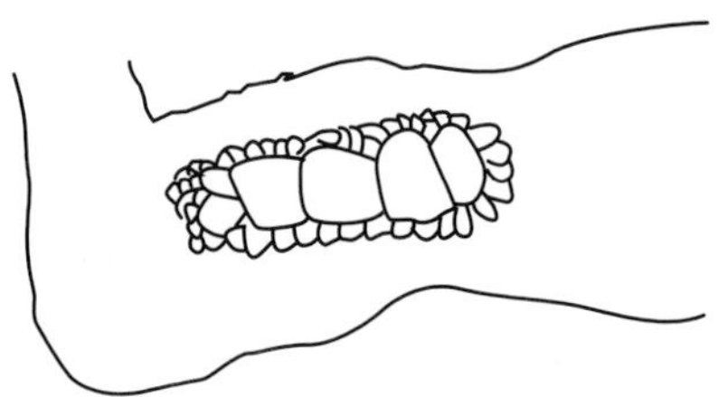
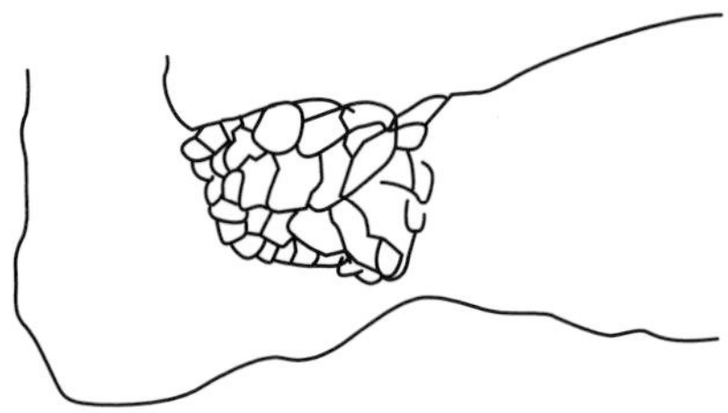

**Figure 45.** Enlarged upper arm scale rows in *Ameiva* (left) and *Cnemidophorus* (right). Drawing by McCranie.

**7** A. Venter covered with squarish, juxtaposed, large platelike scales .......... **8**
B. Venter covered with cycloid, rounded, pointed, granular, or tuberculate scales, either smooth or keeled .......... **11**

**8** A. Dorsolateral surface of upper arm with a single row of enlarged scales (Fig. 45); one row of enlarged mesoptychial scales (Fig. 46) .......... **9**
B. Dorsolateral surface of upper arm with two or three rows of enlarged scales (Fig. 45); two to four rows of enlarged mesoptychial scales (Fig. 46) .......... **10**

**9** A. Midgular scales much enlarged; pale vertebral stripe present in all but largest adults .......... *Ameiva festiva*
B. Midgular scales moderately enlarged; pale vertebral stripe always absent in juveniles and adults .......... *Ameiva undulata*

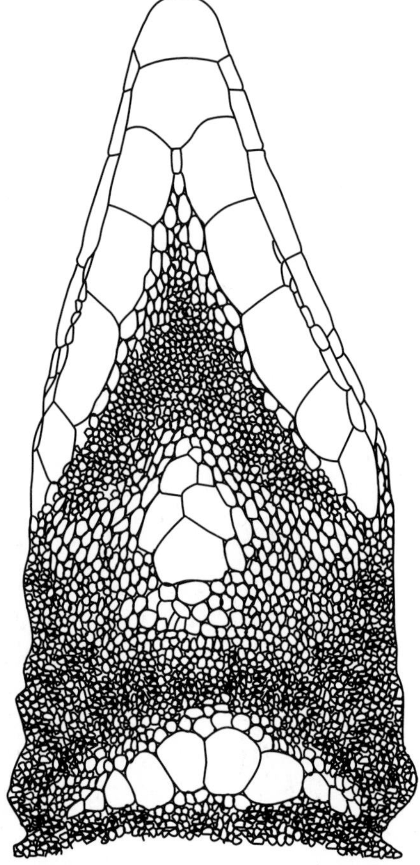
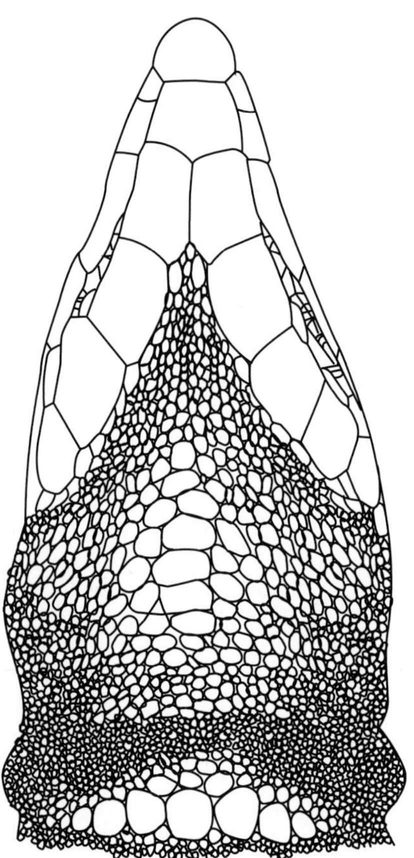

**Figure 46.** Midgular and mesoptychial scales in *Ameiva festiva* (left) and *A. undulata* (right). Copied from Fig. 379 in Köhler (2003) with permission of author/artist.

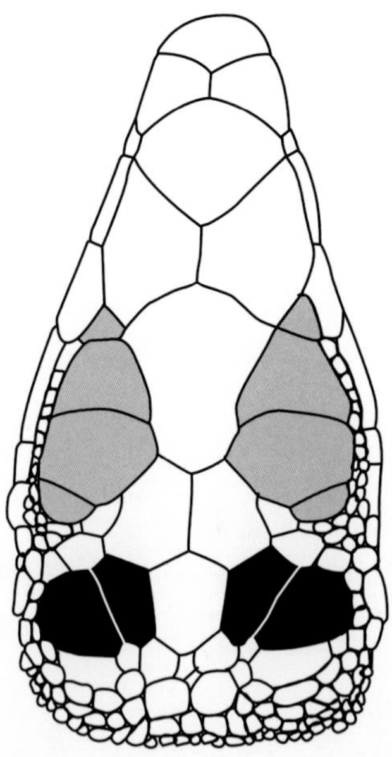

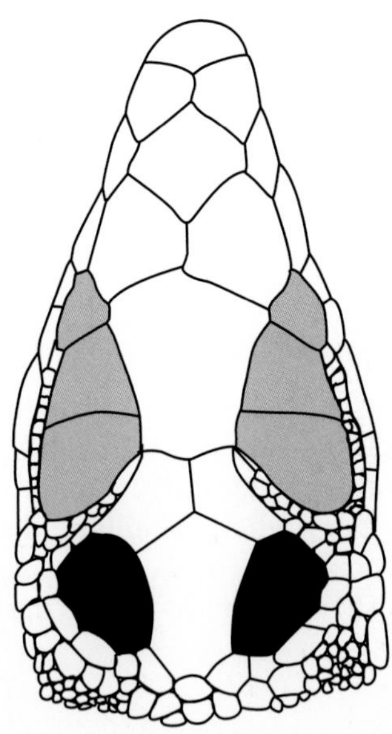

**Figure 47.** Parietal scales (black), interparietal, and supraocular scales (gray) in *Cnemidophorus lemniscatus* (left) and *Aspidoscelis deppii* (right) Copied from Fig. 386 in Köhler (2003) with permission of author/artist.

**10** A. One interparietal and four parietal scales present (Fig. 47); four supraoculars (Fig. 47) ........ *Cnemidophorus lemniscatus*
B. One interparietal and two parietal scales present (Fig. 47); three supraoculars (Fig. 47) ........ *Aspidoscelis deppii*

**11** A. Body covered by uniform large cycloid scales ........ **12**
B. Body not covered by uniform large cycloid scales ........ **13**

**12** A. Paired supranasal (internasal) scales absent; a single frontoparietal scale present (Fig. 48) ........ *Sphenomorphus cherriei*
B. Paired supranasal (internasal) scales present (Fig. 48); two frontoparietal scales present (Fig. 48) ........ *Mabuya unimarginata*

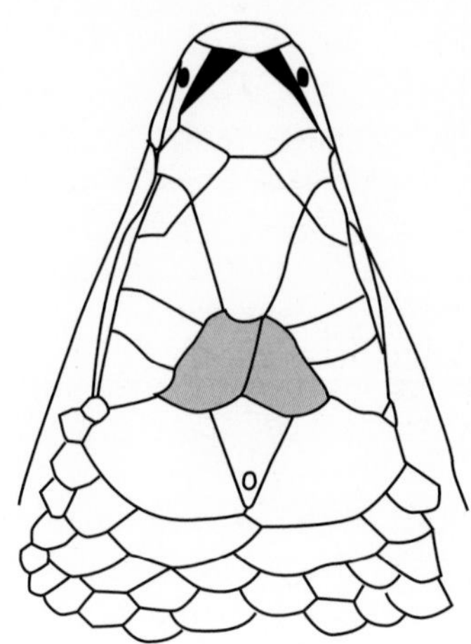

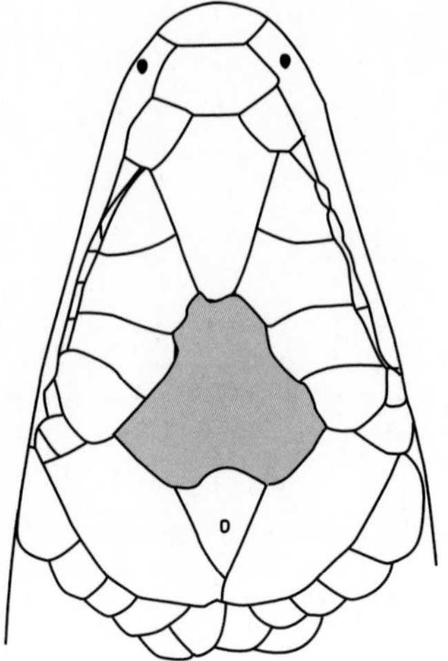

**Figure 48.** Dorsal head scales of skinks showing supranasal scales (black) and paired frontoparietal scales (gray) in *Mabuya unimarginata* (left) and supranasals absent and single frontoparietal scale in *Sphenomorphus cherriei* (right). Copied from Fig. 355 in Köhler (2003) with permission of author/artist.

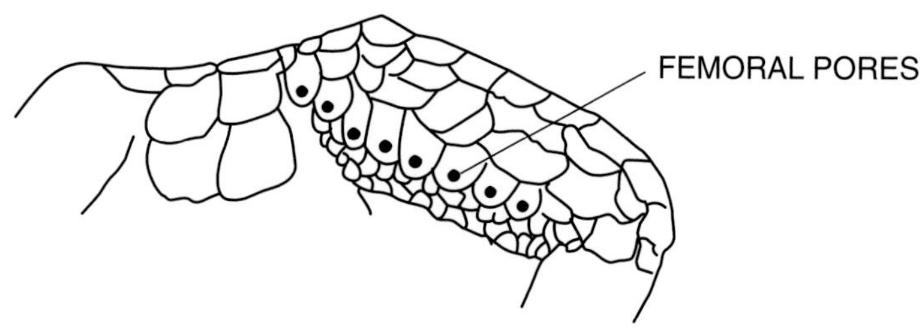


**Figure 49.** Underside of a hind limb of a lizard showing femoral pores. Drawing by McCranie.

**13** A. Femoral pores present (Fig. 49) .................... **14**
B. Femoral pores absent .................... **18**

**14** A. Tail bearing whorls of enlarged spiny scales, separated by a row or rows of interwhorls (Fig. 50) .................... *Ctenosaura similis*
B. Tail with scales more-or-less uniform in size, not in conspicuous whorls .................... **15**

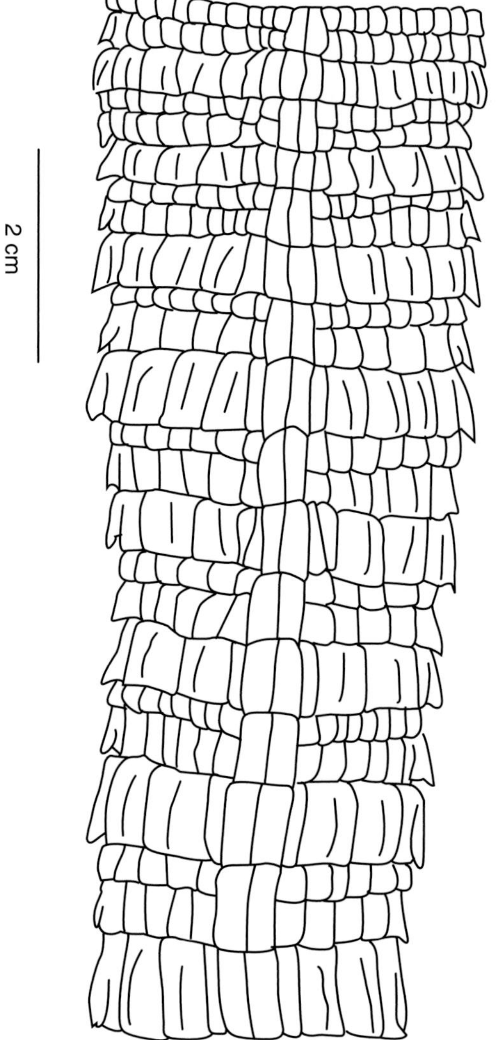


**Figure 50.** Enlarged whorls of spiny scales on *Ctenosaura similis* tail. Drawing by Philipp Groß and provided by Gunther Köhler.

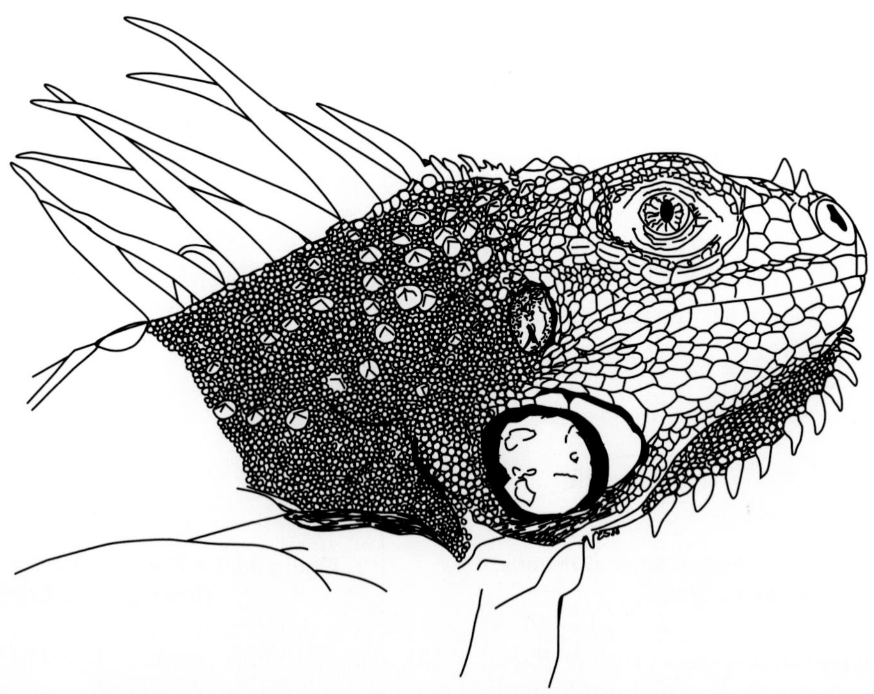

**Figure 51.** Side of head of *Iguana iguana* showing enlarged circular head scale below tympanum. Drawing by Elke Köhler and provided by Gunther Köhler.

**15** A. Enlarged circular scale present on side of head below tympanum (Fig. 51) ........ *Iguana iguana*
B. Enlarged circular scale absent on side of head below tympanum ........ **16**

**16** A. Toe IV about same length as or only slightly longer than Toe III ........ *Polychrus gutturosus*
B. Toe IV much longer than Toe III ........ **17**

**17** A. Postfemoral dermal pocket present (Fig. 52); dorsal ground color some shade of brown, usually with paler brown dorsolateral stripes ........ *Sceloporus variabilis*
B. No postfemoral dermal pocket; dorsal ground color some shade of green in life, without pale dorsolateral stripes ........ *Sceloporus malachiticus*

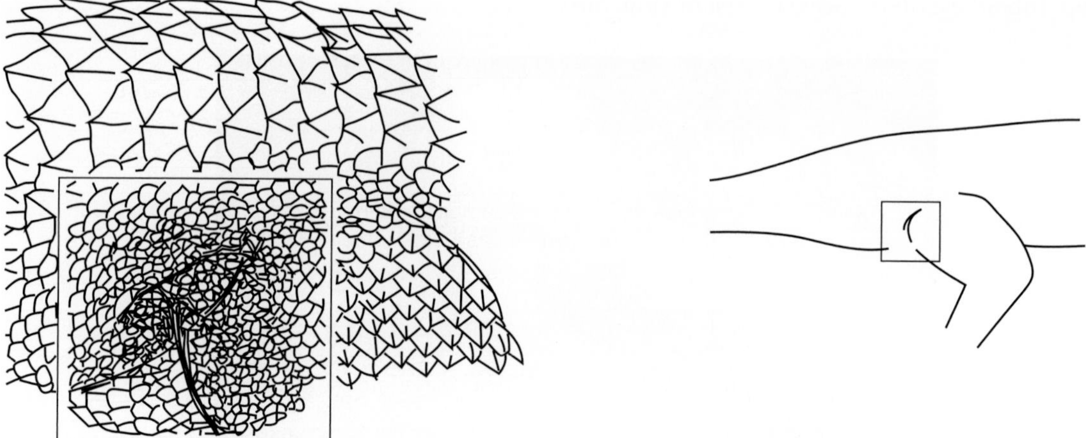

**Figure 52.** Postfemoral dermal pocket in *Sceloporus variabilis*. Copied from Fig. 347 in Köhler (2003) with permission of author/artist (as modified from H. Smith, 1939).

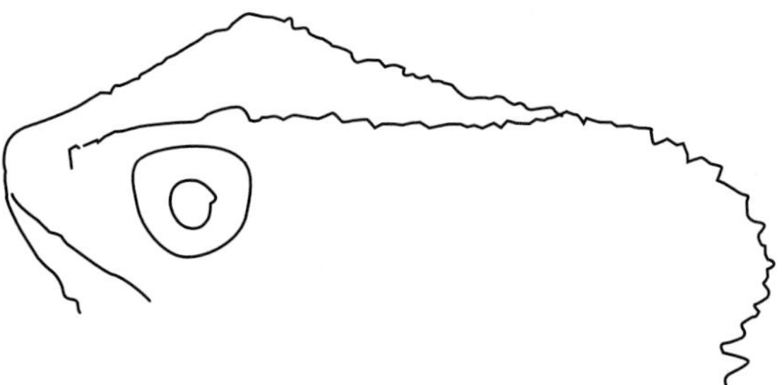

**Figure 53.** Cephalic crest in *Corytophanes cristatus*. Drawing by McCranie.

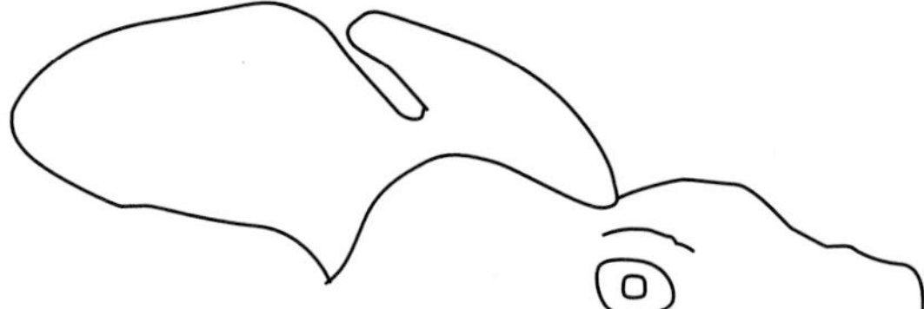

**Figure 54.** Cephalic crest in *Basiliscus plumifrons*. Drawing by McCranie.

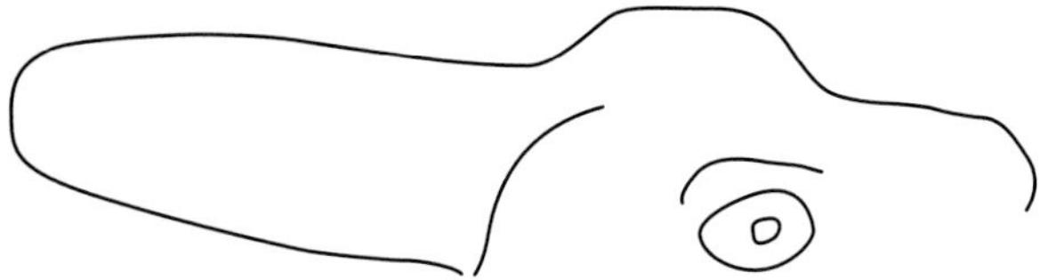

**Figure 55.** Cephalic crest in *Basiliscus vittatus*. Drawing by McCranie.

**18** A. Distinctive parietal crests present (Figs. 53–55), although these crests reduced to knobs in subadults of one genus; subdigital lamellae narrow, keeled or knobbed throughout ........ **19**

B. Parietal crests absent; subdigital lamellae of medial portions of digits expanded, smooth ........ **21**

**19** A. Cephalic crest formed by raised parietal ridges that unite posteriorly (Fig. 53); cephalic crests equally developed in both sexes; lateral flap of scales absent on outer edges of hind toes ........ *Corytophanes cristatus*

B. Cephalic crest formed by laterally compressed flap of skin lacking raised parietal ridges, cephalic crests reduced to knobs on posterior portion of head in subadults; cephalic crests much better developed in adult males than in adult females; lateral flap of scales present on outer edge of outer three hind toes ........ **20**

**20** A. Ventral scales smooth; dorsal color some shade of green in life; no yellowish or cream postorbital stripe present; adult cephalic crest bilobed (Fig. 54) ........ *Basiliscus plumifrons*

B. Ventral scales keeled; dorsal color some shade of brown in life; distinct yellowish or cream postorbital stripe extending onto dorsolateral portion of body, becoming indistinct posteriorly; adult cephalic crest single lobed (Fig. 55) ........ *Basiliscus vittatus*

**21** A. Deep, tubelike axillary pocket present (Fig. 56) ........ **22**

**Figure 56.** Axillary pocket in *Norops tropidonotus*. Photograph by Townsend.

| | | | |
|---|---|---|---|
| | B. | Tubelike axillary pocket absent | **24** |
| **22** | A. | Scales anterior to ear opening small, equal in size to scales posterior to ear opening; male dewlap reddish orange to red with yellow outer margin | *Norops quaggulus* |
| | B. | Scales anterior to ear opening much larger than scales posterior to ear opening | **23** |
| **23** | A. | Male dewlap orange-red without central dark streak; adult males 40–50 mm SVL, adult females 42–51 mm SVL | *Norops wampuensis* |
| | B. | Male dewlap orange-red with large burnt orange or brilliant red central streak; adult males 50–60 mm SVL, adult females 45–55 mm SVL | *Norops tropidonotus* |
| **24** | A. | Ventral scales smooth or slightly conical | **25** |
| | B. | Ventral scales distinctly keeled | **26** |
| **25** | A. | Hind limbs long, when adpressed against body, fourth toe reaches between eye and snout; throat lining not pigmented; male dewlap white with orangish yellow basal spot, dewlap absent in females; adult males to 43 mm SVL, adult females to 45 mm | *Norops limifrons* |
| | B. | Hind limbs very short, when adpressed against body, fourth toe reaches to shoulder; throat lining black; dewlap red to purple, well developed in both sexes; adult males to 79 mm SVL, adult females to 63 mm | *Norops pentaprion* |
| **26** | A. | Dorsal scales flattened, smooth to weakly keeled, usually juxtaposed to one another | **27** |
| | B. | Dorsal scales keeled, not flattened nor juxtaposed to one another | **28** |
| **27** | A. | Lateral scales slightly smaller than middorsals; head extremely short and deep; no pale lateral stripe; size large, females to 96 mm SVL, males to 90 mm; male dewlap small, not extending past level of axilla; male dewlap cinnamon, buff yellow, greenish yellow, or greenish white in life | *Norops capito* |
| | B. | Lateral scales much smaller than middorsals; head normal; pale lateral stripe extending from posterior border of eye to groin region; size moderate, females to 68 mm SVL, males to 85 mm; male dewlap large, extending past level of axilla; male dewlap orangish yellow in life | *Norops lionotus* |
| **28** | A. | Dorsal and lateral scales raised, tuberculate; lining of throat black; dorsum bright green in active adults; adults to 105 mm SVL; male dewlap white basally, mostly powder blue centrally, and with yellowish orange or reddish orange outer portion | *Norops biporcatus* |
| | B. | Dorsal scales not tuberculate, lateral scales small, usually granular; lining of throat flesh colored; dorsum brown to gray in life; adults 47 to 79 mm maximum SVL | **29** |
| **29** | A. | Conspicuous dark brown lines radiating outward from eye and conspicuous dark brown interorbital bar present; adults of both sexes reach 79 mm SVL; male dewlap pinkish orange to reddish orange in life | *Norops lemurinus* |
| | B. | No conspicuous dark brown lines radiating outward from eye, nor conspicuous dark brown interorbital bar; adults less than 53 mm SVL; male dewlap not pinkish orange to reddish orange in life | **30** |
| **30** | A. | Subocular scales separated from supralabials by one scale row (occasionally one subocular in contact with one supralabial); 0–2 middorsal scale rows slightly enlarged; male dewlap large, extending posteriorly well past axillae onto belly; male dewlap chocolate brown to purplish brown with darker brown basal spot | *Norops dariense* |
| | B. | Subocular scales in broad contact with supralabials; 6–8 middorsal scale rows slightly enlarged; male dewlap moderately large, extending posteriorly only slightly past axillae; male dewlap yellowish orange with blue or purple central spot | *Norops sericeus* |

## Key to the Species of Snakes of the Mosquitia

| | | | |
|---|---|---|---|
| 1 | A. | All scales around the body of approximately equal size; eyes vestigial, located beneath an ocular scale | **2** |
| | B. | Ventral scales distinctly larger than dorsal scales; eye covered by a transparent brille | **3** |

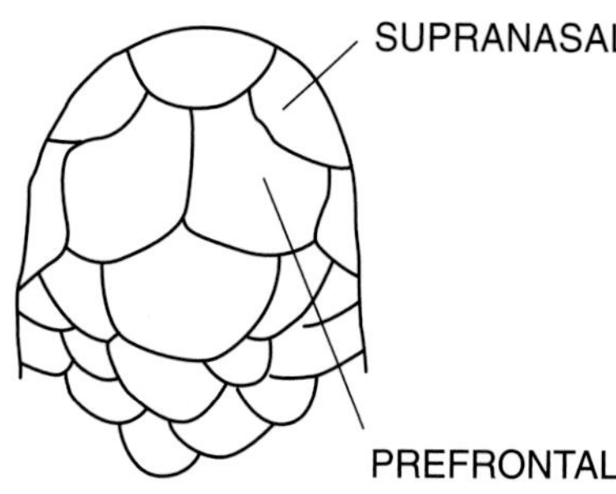


**Figure 57.** Dorsal surface of head of *Anomalepis mexicanus* showing prefrontal and supranasal scales. From Fig. 406 in Köhler (2003) with permission of author/artist.

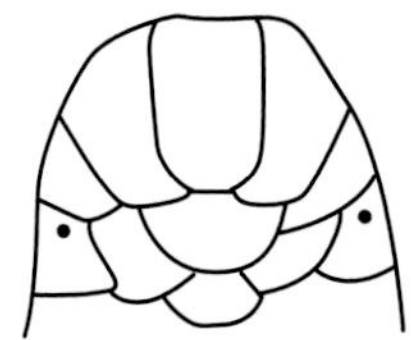

**Figure 58.** Dorsal surface of head of *Typhlops costaricensis* showing prefrontal-supranasal (see Fig. 57) fusion. Copied from Fig. 413 in Köhler (2003) with permission of author/artist.

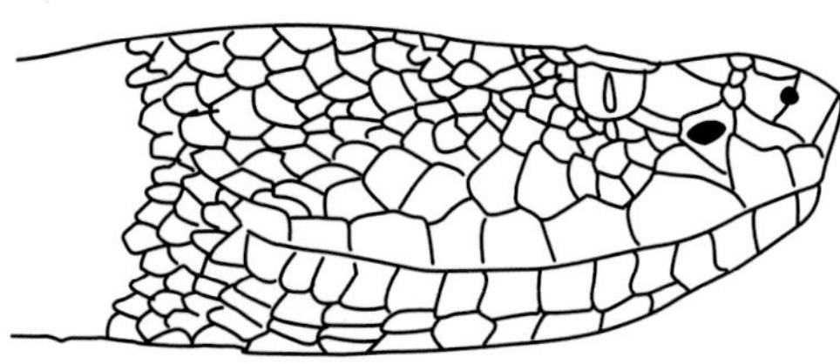

**Figure 59.** Lateral view of a head of a pitviper showing loreal pit located between eye and nostril opening. Drawing by McCranie.

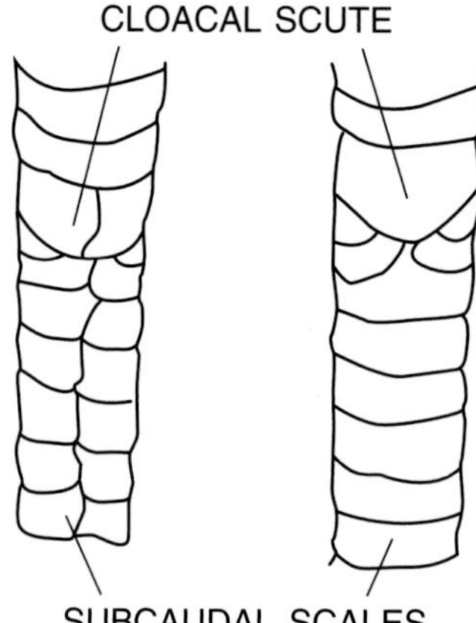


**Figure 60.** Divided cloacal scute and subcaudal scales (left) and entire cloacal scute and subcaudal scales (right). Drawings by McCranie.

2 A. Prefrontal and supranasal scales present (Fig. 57); body scales in 22 to 24 rows .......... *Anomalepis mexicanus*
B. Prefrontal and supranasal scales fused (Fig. 58); body scales in 20 rows .......... *Typhlops costaricensis*

3 A. A loreal pit present between eye and nostril (Fig. 59); a pair of erectile fangs located in front of mouth .......... 4
B. No loreal pit present between eye and nostril; if fangs present, either in anterior or posterior portion of mouth, nonerectile (fixed) .......... 7

4 A. Subcaudals mostly paired (Fig. 60) .......... *Bothrops asper*
B. Subcaudals mostly single (Fig. 60) .......... 5

5 A. Tail prehensile; small, spinelike supraciliary scales present between eye and supraoculars .......... *Bothriechis schlegelii*
B. Tail nonprehensile; spinelike supraciliary scales absent .......... 6

6 A. Tip of snout with a dorsal extension, giving snout a pointed appearance (Fig. 61); one canthal scale on each side; ventrals fewer than 150 .......... *Porthidium nasutum*
B. Tip of snout not strongly upturned (Fig. 62); two canthal scales on each side; ventrals more than 150 .......... *Porthidium ophryomegas*

7 A. A pair of nonerectile (fixed) fangs located in front of mouth; ringed body pattern present; two scales present between eye and nostril .......... 8
B. No pair of nonerectile (fixed) fangs located in front of mouth, although one or two pairs can be located in back of mouth on posterior portion of maxilla; body pattern variable, if body pattern ringed, usually three scales present between eye and nostril .......... 10

8 A. Black head cap not extending posterior to anterior edges of supraoculars and frontal; ventral scales more than 235 in males, more than 255 in females .......... *Micrurus multifasciatus**

**Figure 61.** Head of *Porthidium nasutum* showing dorsal extension on tip of snout. Copied from Fig. 721 in Köhler (2003) with permission of author.

**Figure 62.** Head of *Porthidium ophryomegas* showing snout not strongly upturned. Copied from Fig. 722 in Köhler (2003) with permission of author.

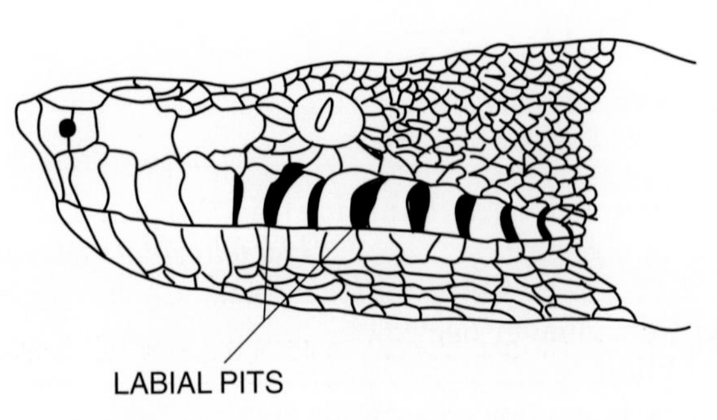


**Figure 63.** Lateral view of head of a *Corallus* showing labial pits. Drawing by McCranie.

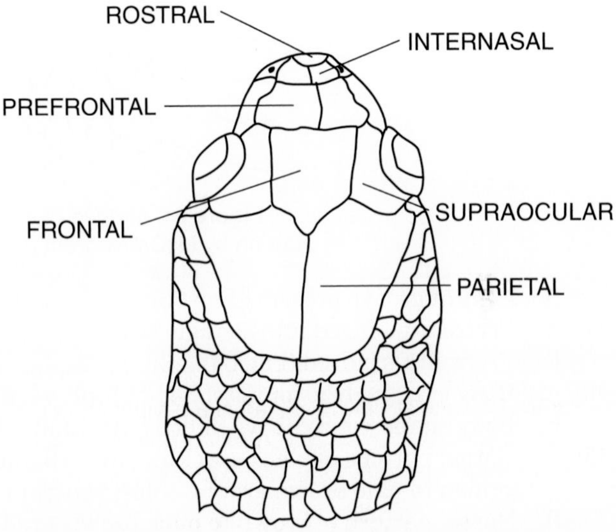

**Figure 64.** Dorsal surface of the head of a colubrid snake with pertinent scales identified. Drawing by McCranie.

B. Black head cap extending posteriorly to include at least a substantial part of supraoculars and frontal; ventral scales less than 230 in males, less than 245 in females ........ **9**

**9** A. Black head cap extending posteriorly along interparietal suture ........ *Micrurus alleni*

B. Black head cap not extending posteriorly along interparietal suture ........ *Micrurus nigrocinctus*

**10** A. Ventral scales not extending entire width of venter ........ **11**

B. Ventral scales extending entire width of venter ........ **13**

**11** A. Dorsal scales keeled ........ *Nothopsis rugosus* (part)

B. Dorsal scales smooth ........ **12**

**12** A. Well developed labial pits present (Fig. 63); 11–15 supralabials ........ *Corallus annulatus*

B. No labial pits present; 17–25 supralabials ........ *Boa constrictor*

**13** A. Numerous small, irregular scales present on top of head ........ *Nothopsis rugosus* (part)

B. Large scales present on top of head (Fig. 64) ........ **14**

**14** A. Dorsal scales in even number of rows ........ **15**

B. Dorsal scales in odd number of rows (Fig. 65) ........ **16**

**15** A. Dorsal scales in 10 rows (rarely 8) at midbody; cloacal scute divided (Fig. 60) ........ *Chironius grandisquamis*

B. Dorsal scales in 14 to 18 rows at midbody; cloacal scute entire (Fig. 60) ........ *Spilotes pullatus*

**16** A. Mental groove absent; anterior chinshield single, nearly rectangular ........ *Dipsas bicolor*

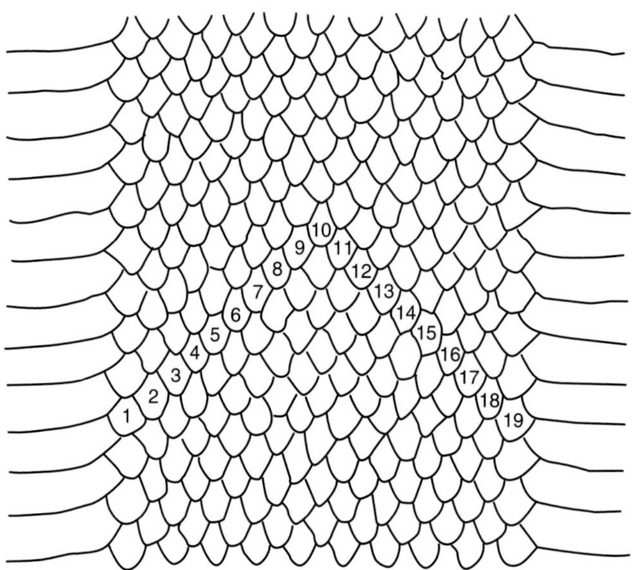


**Figure 65.** Method of counting snake dorsal scale rows.
Drawing by McCranie from a template provided by Jay M. Savage.

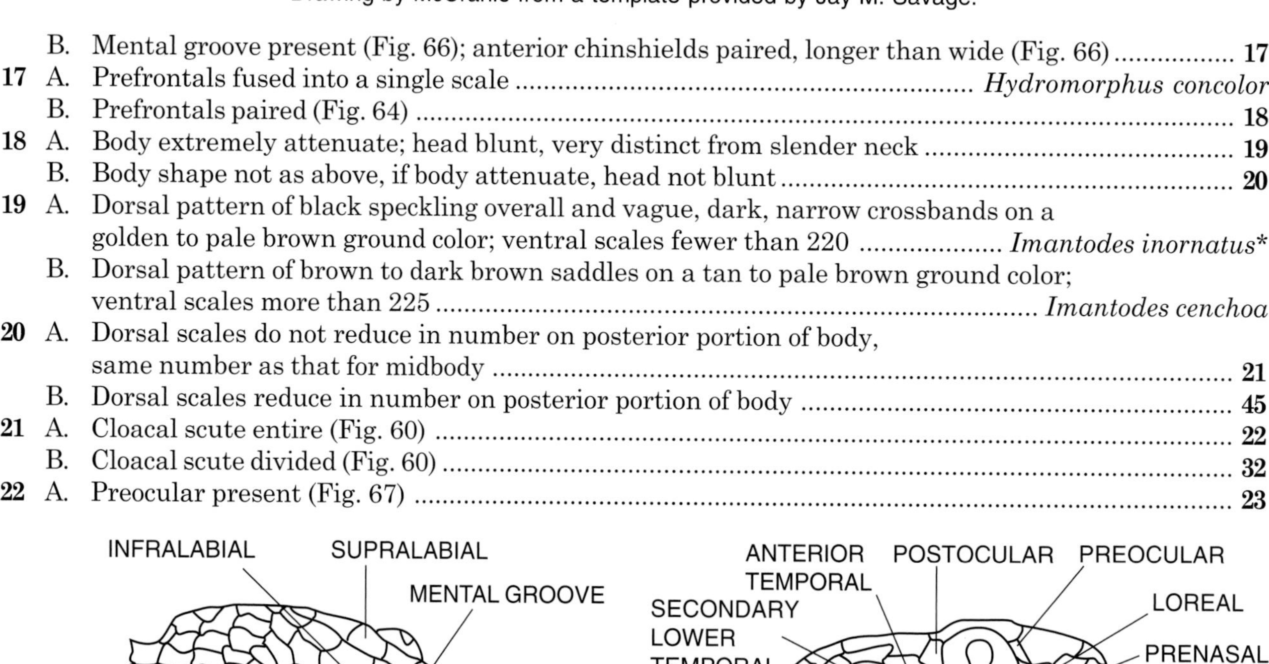

B. Mental groove present (Fig. 66); anterior chinshields paired, longer than wide (Fig. 66) ................ **17**

**17** A. Prefrontals fused into a single scale ................................ *Hydromorphus concolor*

B. Prefrontals paired (Fig. 64) ................................ **18**

**18** A. Body extremely attenuate; head blunt, very distinct from slender neck ................................ **19**

B. Body shape not as above, if body attenuate, head not blunt ................................ **20**

**19** A. Dorsal pattern of black speckling overall and vague, dark, narrow crossbands on a golden to pale brown ground color; ventral scales fewer than 220 .................... *Imantodes inornatus**

B. Dorsal pattern of brown to dark brown saddles on a tan to pale brown ground color; ventral scales more than 225 ................................ *Imantodes cenchoa*

**20** A. Dorsal scales do not reduce in number on posterior portion of body, same number as that for midbody ................................ **21**

B. Dorsal scales reduce in number on posterior portion of body ................................ **45**

**21** A. Cloacal scute entire (Fig. 60) ................................ **22**

B. Cloacal scute divided (Fig. 60) ................................ **32**

**22** A. Preocular present (Fig. 67) ................................ **23**

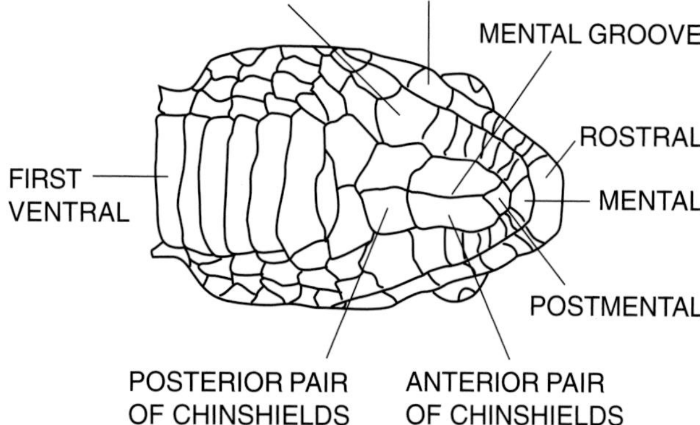


**Figure 66.** Ventral surface of the head of a colubrid snake with pertinent scales identified. Drawing by McCranie.

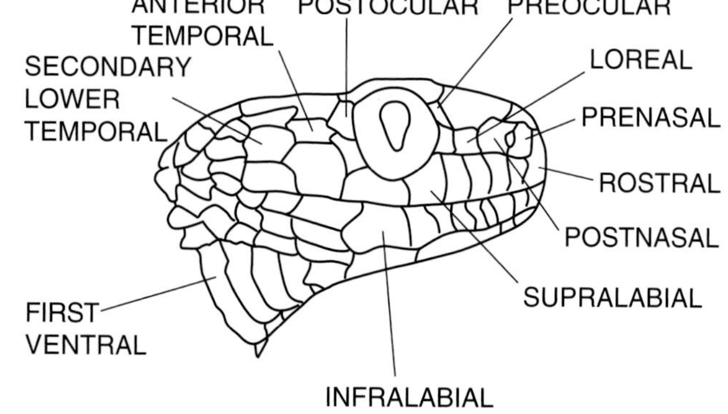


**Figure 67.** Lateral surface of the head of a colubrid snake with pertinent scales identified. Drawing by McCranie.

B. Preocular absent ........ 26

**23** A. First pair of infralabials in contact with one another behind mental ........ 24

B. First pair of infralabials not in contact with one another behind mental (Fig. 66) ........ 25

**24** A. Dorsal body scales weakly keeled, in 17–17–17 rows; pattern of bicolor rings ........ *Tropidodipsas sartorii*

B. Dorsal body scales smooth, in 15–15–15 rows; pattern of dark dorsal bands ........ *Sibon nebulatus* (part)

**25** A. Enlarged penultimate supralabial bordering eye; venter mostly pale, with dark longitudinal mottling and stippling ........ *Sibon longifrenis* (part)

B. Enlarged penultimate supralabial not bordering eye (Fig. 67); components of dorsal bands or rings continue well onto or across venter ........ *Sibon annulatus* (part)

**26** A. Dorsal scales strongly keeled length of body ........ 27

B. Dorsal scales smooth length of body, lightly keeled, or keeled only directly above cloaca ........ 28

**27** A. Venter pale with a pattern of black markings; dorsum brown to gray with a series of black crossbars; a distinct pale nuchal band absent ........ *Ninia maculata*

B. Venter immaculate or lacking distinct black markings; dorsum red; yellow nuchal band present ........ *Ninia sebae*

**28** A. Ventrals 135 or fewer ........ *Geophis hoffmanni*

B. Ventrals 150 or more ........ 29

**29** A. First pair of infralabials in contact with one another behind mental ........ *Sibon nebulatus* (part)

B. First pair of infralabials not in contact with one another behind mental (Fig. 66) ........ 30

**30** A. Enlarged penultimate supralabial bordering eye; venter mostly pale, with dark longitudinal mottling and stippling ........ *Sibon longifrenis* (part)

B. Enlarged penultimate supralabial not bordering eye (Fig. 67); components of dorsal bands or rings continue well onto or across venter ........ 31

**31** A. Usually a pair of postmentals, postmentals sometimes partially fused or reduced to a single tiny scale; dorsal components of bands or rings darker than dorsal components of interspaces ........ *Sibon annulatus* (part)

B. A single large postmental present (Fig. 66); dorsal components of bands or rings paler than dorsal components of interspaces ........ *Sibon* sp.

**32** A. Dorsal scales in 15 rows at midbody ........ 33

B. Dorsal scales in 17 or more rows at midbody ........ 39

**33** A. Preocular absent; loreal bordering eye ........ 34

B. Preocular present (Fig. 67); loreal present or absent ........ 35

**34** A. Dorsum with lineate pattern; pale nuchal collar absent; subcaudals 50 or fewer ........ *Adelphicos quadrivirgatum*

B. Dorsum unicolor; white headband present; subcaudals 96 or more ........ *Enuliophis sclateri*

**35** A. Preocular and loreal present (Fig. 67) ........ 36

B. Loreal absent; prefrontal in contact with supralabials or not ........ 38

**36** A. Dorsum green in life; keels of median three rows black ........ *Drymobius melanotropis* (part)

B. Body with ringed (i.e., black components cross venter) pattern throughout or with banded (i.e., black components do not cross venter) pattern, at least anteriorly ........ 37

**37** A. Distinct dorsal pattern of red, black, and yellow rings extending length of body; ventrals more than 170 ........ *Erythrolamprus mimus*

B. Red, black, and yellow or gray bands usually present only on anterior portion of body, remainder of body usually brown with longitudinal rows of small darker spots; ventrals fewer than 170 ........ *Scaphiodontophis annulatus* (part)

**38** A. Ventrals fewer than 120; subcaudals fewer than 57; pale middorsal and lateral stripes absent ........ *Tantillita lintoni*

B. Ventrals more than 140; subcaudals more than 60; pale middorsal and lateral stripes present ........ *Tantilla taeniata*

**39** A. Dorsal pattern lineate throughout length of body ........ 40

B. Dorsal pattern not lineate throughout length of body ........ 42

40 A. Tail gradually tapering throughout its length ........ *Rhadinaea decorata*
B. Tail disproportionately thick for most of its length ........ **41**
41 A Pale parietal spot present on each side of head; pale nuchal spot present on each side, above, or joined with, upper pale lateral stripe; venter orange or yellow in life ........ *Urotheca guentheri*
B. Pale parietal and nuchal spots absent; venter white in life ........ *Urotheca decipiens*
42 A. Dorsum cream to grayish tan with 10–21 dark brown to black body bands extending laterally to ventrals ........ *Leptodeira nigrofasciata* (part)
B. Dorsum not as above ........ **43**
43 A. Red, black, and yellow or gray bands usually present only on anterior portion of body, remainder of body usually brown with longitudinal rows of small darker spots; 9–10 supralabials ........ *Scaphiodontophis annulatus* (part)
B. Dorsal pattern of red, black, and yellow or red and black rings extending length of body; 8 supralabials ........ **44**
44 A. Subcaudal scales 119 in Mosquitia specimen; black body rings much longer than red rings ........ *Pliocercus euryzonus*
B. Subcaudal scales 115 or fewer; black body rings shorter than, or equal in length to, red rings ........ *Pliocercus elapoides*
45 A. Cloacal scute entire (Fig. 60) ........ **46**
B. Cloacal scute divided (Fig. 60) ........ **57**
46 A. Dorsal scale rows 15 or 17 at midbody ........ **47**
B. Dorsal scale rows 19 or more at midbody ........ **51**
47 A. Dorsal scale rows 15 at midbody ........ **48**
B. Dorsal scale rows 17 at midbody ........ **49**
48 A. Dorsal scale rows 13 at cloaca; head narrow and pointed ........ *Oxybelis brevirostris*
B. Dorsal scale rows 11 at cloaca; head shape normal ........ *Leptophis depressirostris* (part)*
49 A. Dorsal scales smooth; a diagonal black mark present on neck ........ *Drymarchon melanurus*
B. Dorsal scales keeled; never a diagonal black mark on neck ........ **50**
50 A. Subcaudal scales fewer than 130; dorsum of adults with dark-edged pale crossbands more than one scale row long on neck, crossbands becoming indistinct posteriorly ........ *Dendrophidion vinitor*
B. Subcaudal scales more than 130; head rust brown with pale upper lip, well differentiated from green to brown anterior body coloration; dorsal surface of tail usually pale tan or reddish brown ........ *Dendrophidion nuchale* (part)*
51 A. Dorsal scales keeled, at least posteriorly on body ........ **52**
B. Dorsal scales smooth throughout body ........ **54**
52 A. Ventral scales fewer than 182; dorsal pattern lineate ........ *Thamnophis proximus*
B. Ventral scales more than 181; dorsal pattern not lineate ........ **53**
53 A. Nasal divided (Fig. 67); loreals 2 or more; pupil vertically elliptical; dorsum blotched with a dark chevron or lyre-shaped mark on posterior portion of head ........ *Trimorphodon biscutatus* (part)*
B. Nasal single; loreal single (Fig. 67); pupil circular; dorsum not as above ........ *Pseustes poecilonotus*
54 A. Dorsum with red and black or red, black, and yellow bands or rings extending length of body ........ **55**
B. Dorsal coloration not as above ........ **56**
55 A. Dorsum of body banded; venter immaculate, without pattern; subcaudals 79 or more ........ *Oxyrhopus petola*
B. Dorsum of body ringed (rings extending completely across venter); subcaudals 63 or fewer ........ *Lampropeltis triangulum*
56 A. Dorsum with a series of blotches; ventrals fewer than 155 ........ *Xenodon rabdocephalus*
B. Dorsal pattern of dark head cap, pale nuchal band, and red body color (in juveniles) or uniformly bluish black (in adults); ventrals more than 190 ........ *Clelia clelia*
57 A. Dorsal scale rows 15 to 17 at midbody ........ **58**
B. Dorsal scale rows 19 or more at midbody ........ **70**
58 A. Dorsal scale rows 15 at midbody ........ **59**

B. Dorsal scale rows 17 at midbody .......... **62**
**59** A. Loreal (Fig. 67) normally present .......... **60**
B. Loreal normally absent .......... **61**
**60** A. Dorsum with lateral stripe on rows 2 through 4, 5, or 6 .......... *Leptophis mexicanus*
B. Dorsum green in life, without lateral stripe .......... *Leptophis depressirostris* (part)*
**61** A. Adult color pattern consisting of broad, greenish blue dorsolateral stripe anteriorly on rows 3 to 4 or 3 to 5; adult total length less than 855 mm .......... *Leptophis nebulosus*
B. Adult color pattern not as above; almost always uniformly green dorsally, except keels of paravertebral rows black; adult total length in excess of 1000 mm .......... *Leptophis ahaetulla*
**62** A. Loreal absent; head narrow and pointed .......... **63**
B. Loreal present (Fig. 67); head shape normal .......... **64**
**63** A. Supralabials usually 10; dorsum green in life; venter with two longitudinal white or pale yellow stripes near lateral edges .......... *Oxybelis fulgidus*
B. Supralabials usually 8 or 9; dorsum pale brown to gray; no longitudinal pale stripes near lateral edges of venter .......... *Oxybelis aeneus*
**64** A. Dorsal scales keeled .......... **65**
B. Dorsal scales smooth .......... **68**
**65** A. Adult dorsal pattern uniformly green in life, except keels of median three dorsal scale rows black .......... *Drymobius melanotropis* (part)
B. Adult dorsal pattern not uniformly green in life .......... **66**
**66** A. Adult dorsal pattern of green or yellow spots on otherwise dark scales .......... *Drymobius margaritiferus*
B. Dorsum brown, without green or yellow spots .......... **67**
**67** A. Head rust brown with pale upper lip, well differentiated from gray or brown anterior body coloration; dorsal surface of tail usually pale tan or reddish brown; dorsocaudal scale row reduction from 8 to 6 scales around tail occurs between subcaudal scales 28 to 71 .......... *Dendrophidion nuchale* (part)*
B. Head pale to dark brown, same color as anterior portion of body; color of dorsal surface of tail not as above; dorsocaudal scale row reduction from 8 to 6 scales around tail occurs between subcaudal scales 7 to 24 .......... *Dendrophidion percarinatum*
**68** A. Some portion of anterior body with red, black, and yellow or gray bands .......... *Scaphiodontophis annulatus* (part)
B. Pattern not as above .......... **69**
**69** A. Dorsal scales in 19–17–13 rows; a single supralabial borders eye .......... *Masticophis mentovarius*
B. Dorsal scales in 17–17–15 rows; two supralabials border eye .......... *Mastigodryas melanolomus*
**70** A. Pattern of red, black, and yellow rings; naris very large .......... *Rhinobothryum bovallii*
B. Dorsal pattern not as above; naris normal in size .......... **71**
**71** A. Dorsal pattern of stripes extending some portion of length of body and/or head .......... **72**
B. Dorsal pattern not as above, consisting of spots, blotches, or uniform .......... **75**
**72** A. Two anterior temporal scales; ventrals 149 or more .......... *Conophis lineatus*
B. One anterior temporal scale (Fig. 67); ventrals 146 or fewer .......... **73**
**73** A. Dorsal scale rows 19 at midbody .......... *Coniophanes imperialis*
B. Dorsal scale rows usually 21 (rarely 23) at midbody .......... **74**
**74** A. Venter immaculate, with numerous small black dots, or with one pair of small spots per ventral scale .......... *Coniophanes fissidens*
B. Venter with a double row (one pair per ventral scale) of regular dark spots .......... *Coniophanes bipunctatus*
**75** A. Dorsal scales keeled, at least posteriorly .......... **76**
B. Dorsal scales smooth throughout body .......... **77**
**76** A. Naris in a dorsolateral position; ventral scales fewer than 155; apical pits absent .......... *Tretanorhinus nigroluteus*

B. Naris laterally placed; ventral scales more than 210; apical pits paired ........ *Trimorphodon biscutatus* (part)*

**77** A. Pattern of 21 or fewer bands, which extend to venter ........ *Leptodeira nigrofasciata* (part)

B. Pattern of 22 or more blotches, which do not extend to venter ........ **78**

**78** A. Ventrals 186 or more in Honduran specimens ........ *Leptodeira septentrionalis*

B. Ventrals fewer than 186 in Honduran specimens ........ *Leptodeira annulata*

## Class Amphibia (Amphibians)

### Order Gymnophiona (Caecilians)

The caecilian fauna of Honduras consists of two species (McCranie and Wilson, 2002), only one of which is known from the Mosquitia. Caecilians are legless, wormlike burrowing or aquatic amphibians, whose bodies are wreathed in serial folds or annuli delimited by grooves or furrows. Upon casual examination, these amphibians might be mistaken for large earthworms, although, upon closer examination, it is obvious that caecilians have a jawed mouth, evidence of an eye, although it is covered with skin or skin and bone, and lack the clitellum or swollen region about a third of the distance from the anterior end of the body typical of earthworms. Both the higher level and specific level taxonomy of the caecilians remain unsettled.

**Plate 13.** *Gymnopis multiplicata*. Photograph by McCranie.

#### Family Caeciliidae

The relationships within the family Caeciliidae are poorly understood (Pough et al., 2003), and the family is not monophyletic. Caecilians lack a tail, the mouth is recessed beneath the snout, and most species are apparently burrowers (Pough et al., 2003). The family occurs in the Western Hemisphere from southern Veracruz and Jalisco, Mexico, to central Peru and eastern Brazil east of the Andes and to western Ecuador west of the Andes. They also occur in the Eastern Hemisphere in equatorial eastern and western Africa, islands in the Gulf of Guinea, the Seychelles Archipelago, India, and Bangladesh. There are 26 genera containing 109 species in this family (Frost, 2004). Two genera comprising two species are known to occur in Honduras, with one species occurring in the Mosquitia.

*Gymnopis multiplicata* **W. Peters, 1874**
**Common name(s):** Culebra de Dos Cabezas (Spanish)
**Description (Plate 13):** This caecilian is an elongate, limbless amphibian whose body is encircled by a series of folds separated by annular grooves extending from behind the head to the posterior end of the body. The head is the same diameter as the body, but is distinguishable from the posterior end by the presence of a distinct mouth supported by jaws that possess teeth. The snout projects well beyond the mouth. The eye is covered by both bone and skin and, thus is distinguishable only as a small, pale spot in about the center of the lateral portion of the head. The nostril is situated just posterior to the anterior end of the head. A sensory tentacle located within a tentacular aperture is also present and is located between the nostril and the eye. The tentacular aperture is located much closer to the place the eye socket would be than to the nostril and just below the lower level of the nostril. Color in life is dark gray dorsally with medium gray annular grooves, and a pale gray venter. Total length in this species reaches 480 mm (Savage, 2002).
**Similar species:** *Gymnopis multiplicata* is the only species of caecilian known from the Mosquitia. It cannot be confused with any other amphibian in the region.
**General geographic distribution:** *Gymnopis multiplicata* occurs at low and moderate elevations from southeastern Guatemala to western Panama

on the Atlantic versant and from northwestern Costa Rica to western Panama on the Pacific versant.
**Distribution in Honduras:** This caecilian is known from widely scattered low elevation localities (about 30 to about 400 m) from northwestern Honduras (east of the Sula Plain) to eastern and south-central Honduras.
**Distribution in the Mosquitia:** El Paraíso—Arenales (LACM). Gracias a Dios—Caño Awalwás (UF, USNM); near Awasbila (USNM); Rus Rus (USNM); Bodega de Río Tapalwás (UF, USNM); Cerro Wahatingni (UF). Olancho—Quebrada El Guásimo (USNM); confluence of Quebrada Siksatara and Río Wampú (USNM).
**Natural history comments:** *Gymnopis multiplicata* is a fossorial and semi-fossorial amphibian that occurs in primary evergreen broadleaf forest in the Mosquitia. Most Mosquitia specimens we collected were under or in rotten logs. Another was beneath leaf litter in a tree buttress.
**Remarks:** McCranie and Wilson (2002) reported a total of only seven specimens of this caecilian from the entirety of Honduras. However, we collected an additional 15 specimens during four recent trips to primary forest localities in the Río Coco drainage system.

## Order Urodela (Salamanders)

Of the 26 species of salamanders known to occur in Honduras (McCranie and Wilson, 2002; McCranie et al., 2005), only three have been recorded from the Mosquitia. The apparent lack of salamander diversity in the Mosquitia is consistent with the pattern displayed in other parts of northern Mesoamerica, with the majority of species being found between 1000–2800 m elevation and lowland areas having relatively few species (Wake et al., 1992). Salamanders are tailed amphibians with two pairs of limbs of subequal size. Those salamanders found in the Mosquitia (and throughout Honduras) have direct development, hatching out of the egg as a miniature of the adult (although they can be a different color); thus, they have no larval stage.

### Family Plethodontidae

The salamanders of the family Plethodontidae are all lungless and possess a nasolabial groove, which assists in chemoreception (Pough et al., 2003). The members of this family occur from southern British Columbia, Canada, southward to northern Baja California, Mexico, in western North America and from Quebec, Canada, southward throughout much of the eastern United States; also from northwestern and northeastern Mexico southward through central and southern Mexico, Central America, and northern South America to northern Bolivia and eastern Brazil. Several additional isolated populations occur in the United States between the eastern and western portions of the range. Members of this family also occur in central Mediterranean Europe and in southwestern Korea. Twenty-seven genera containing 364 species were included in this family by Frost (2004), but new species are being described on a regular basis. Five genera comprising 26 species are known to occur in Honduras. Two genera with three species are found in the Mosquitia.

*Bolitoglossa mexicana* **A.M.C. Duméril, Bibron, and Duméril, 1854c**
**Common name(s):** Salamandra (Spanish); Akak* (Miskito)
**Description (Plate 14):** This is a large salamander (to 64 mm SVL in males and 82 mm SVL in females) with 13 costal grooves (McCranie and Wilson, 2002). The snout is broadly rounded to truncate in dorsal aspect and rounded to broadly rounded in lateral profile, and the eyes are slightly protuberant. Males have 3 to 7 premaxillary teeth, 35 to 47 maxillary teeth, and 20 to 25 vomerine teeth; females have 0 to 6 premaxillary teeth, 35 to 49 maxillary teeth, and 20 to 37 vomerine teeth (McCranie and Wilson, 2002). There is no sublingual fold. Females are larger and have more

**Plate 14.** *Bolitoglossa mexicana*. Photograph by McCranie.

robust bodies than males. The tail is moderately long, about 81 to 109% of the SVL, somewhat rectangular in crosssection anteriorly, becoming ovoid distally, and slightly constricted basally. Limbs are slender and moderately long (adpressed limb interval 1.5 to 4.0 costal folds) and the toes lack subdigital pads. Feet are extensively webbed with those toe tips protruding from the webbing acutely rounded to pointed. Dorsal surfaces are usually dark brown with a pale brown to reddish brown to red middorsal stripe and paired yellowish cream to brownish cream dorsolateral stripes. Ventral and subcaudal surfaces are a slightly paler shade of the dorsal ground color.

**Similar species:** *Bolitoglossa striatula* has a pale brown to yellowish brown dorsum with usually incomplete, thin dorsolateral brown stripes beginning just posterior to the head and continuing onto the tail. *Oedipina cyclocauda* has 19 or 20 costal grooves, a sublingual fold, and uniformly black dorsal surfaces.

**General geographic distribution:** *Bolitoglossa mexicana* occurs at low and moderate elevations on the Atlantic versant from southern Veracruz, Mexico, to northeastern Honduras.

**Distribution in Honduras:** This salamander is widely distributed at low and moderate elevations (about sea level to 1400 m) across most of the country, with the exception of the southwestern and extreme southern portions.

**Distribution in the Mosquitia:** Colón—Quebrada Limoncito (BMNH); Quebrada Machín (USNM). Gracias a Dios—Mocorón (CF); Río Sutawala (USNM); Crique Wahatingni (USNM); Warunta Tingni Kiamp (USNM). Olancho—confluence of Ríos Aner and Wampú (USNM); Quebrada de Las Marías (MVZ, SMF, USNM); confluence of Ríos Yanguay and Wampú (USNM).

**Natural history comments:** *Bolitoglossa mexicana* has been found active at night on leaves of understory plants in primary evergreen broadleaf forest in the Mosquitia. All Mosquitia specimens were taken on wet vegetation following or during heavy rains.

**Remarks:** The species *Bolitoglossa mexicana* in Honduras is a composite of two distinct mitochondrial DNA lineages that cannot be distinguished based on any morphological or color pattern characteristics (García-París et al., 2000, 2002; McCranie and Wilson, 2002). The known easternmost extent of the range of this species is in the Mosquitia at the Mocorón locality.

*Bolitoglossa striatula* **(Noble, 1918)**

**Common name(s):** Salamandra (Spanish); Akak* (Miskito)

**Description (Plate 15):** This is a moderate sized salamander (to 59 mm SVL in males and 66 mm SVL in females) with 13 costal grooves (McCranie and Wilson, 2002). The snout is truncate in dorsal aspect and broadly rounded in lateral profile, and the eyes are slightly protuberant. Males have about 4 premaxillary teeth, 30 to 34 maxillary teeth, and 22 to 28 vomerine teeth; females have about 4 to 5 premaxillary teeth, 30 to 38 maxillary teeth, and 34 to 37 vomerine teeth (McCranie and Wilson, 2002). A sublingual fold is absent. Females have larger and more robust bodies than do males. The tail is moderately long (usually being about equal in length to the SVL), nearly round in crosssection, and slightly constricted basally. Limbs are slender and moderately long (adpressed limb interval 3.5 to 5.0 costal folds), and the toes lack subdigital pads. Feet are extensively webbed with those toe tips protruding from the webbing acutely rounded. Dorsal surfaces are pale brown to yellowish brown, with darker brown longitudinal streaks beginning just posterior to the head and continuing onto the tail. Ventral and subcaudal surfaces are yellowish brown with brown streaks and peppering.

**Similar species:** *Bolitoglossa mexicana* has a dorsum marked with a broad, pale middorsal longitudinal stripe that is usually broken into three longitudinal stripes (or a suggestion thereof) by invasion of dark coloration, occasionally the invasion of dark pigment is so complete that only paired pale dorsolateral stripes remain. *Oedipina cyclocauda* has 19 or 20 costal grooves, a sublingual fold, and uniformly black dorsal surfaces.

**General geographic distribution:** *Bolitoglossa striatula* occurs at low and moderate elevations of

**Plate 15.** *Bolitoglossa striatula.* Photograph by McCranie.

the Atlantic versant from eastern Honduras to eastern Costa Rica and on the Pacific versant from northwestern to south-central Costa Rica.
**Distribution in Honduras:** This salamander is known only from low elevation localities (about 20 to 190 m) in the Mosquitia.
**Distribution in the Mosquitia:** Gracias a Dios—Caño Awalwás (UF, USNM); Awasbila (USNM); Kropunta (MCZ); Rus Rus (USNM); Bodega de Río Tapalwás (USNM); trail to Bodega de Río Tapalwás (UF); Warunta Tingni Kiamp (USNM). Olancho—Quebrada El Guásimo (SMF, USNM); Río Kosmako (USNM); Quebrada El Mono (USNM).
**Natural history comments:** *Bolitoglossa striatula* has been found active at night on leaves of understory plants in primary to lightly disturbed evergreen broadleaf forest (including gallery forest through pine savanna). The species is most common on nights when the vegetation is wet following rains. It can also be occasionally found sleeping during the day in exposed areas on wet leaves or tree trunks or under leaf litter. A newly hatched individual was seen on a wet leaf about 0.5 m above the ground in November.

### *Oedipina cyclocauda* Taylor, 1952

**Common name(s):** None
**Description (Plate 16):** This is a moderately sized salamander (to 50 mm SVL in males and 56 mm in females) with 19 or 20 costal grooves (McCranie and Wilson, 2002). The snout is broadly rounded to rounded in dorsal aspect and rounded in lateral profile, and the eyes are not protuberant. Males have about 1 or 2 premaxillary teeth, 26 to 45 maxillary teeth, and 10 to 21 vomerine teeth, whereas females have about 2 to 3 premaxillary teeth, 38 to 53 maxillary teeth, and 16 to 27 vomerine teeth (McCranie and Wilson, 2002). A sublingual fold is present. The body is elongate and slender, and the tail is long (about 1.5 to 2.0 times the SVL) and nearly rectangular in crosssection, and barely constricted basally. Limbs are slender and short (adpressed limb interval 11 to 13 costal folds), and there are weakly developed subdigital pads present on the toe tips. Toes I and II, as well as Toes III and IV, are fused on the forelimbs, and Toes I and II and Toes IV and V are fused on the hind limbs. Dorsal surfaces are uniformly black and the ventral and subcaudal surfaces are slightly paler.

**Plate 16.** *Oedipina cyclocauda.* Photograph by McCranie.

**Similar species:** *Bolitoglossa mexicana* and *B. striatula* have 13 costal grooves and lack a sublingual fold and uniformly dark dorsal surfaces.
**General geographic distribution:** *Oedipina cyclocauda* occurs at low, moderate, and intermediate elevations on the Atlantic versant from north-central Honduras to central Panama (see Remarks).
**Distribution in Honduras:** This salamander is known from the northern portion of the country (about sea level to 1780 m elevation) from west-central Yoro to southern Gracias a Dios.
**Distribution in the Mosquitia:** Colón—near Cañon del Chilmeca (formerly in UNAH, now lost); Quebrada Limoncito (BMNH); Quebrada Machín (USNM). Gracias a Dios—Kaska Tingni (USNM); Cabeceras de Río Rus Rus (USNM); Urus Tingni Kiamp (USNM); between Urus Tingni Kiamp and Warunta Tingni Kiamp (USNM); Warunta Tingni Kiamp (USNM). Olancho—confluence of Ríos Sausa and Wampú (USNM); confluence of Quebrada Siksatara with Río Wampú (USNM); confluence of Ríos Yanguay and Wampú (USNM).
**Natural history comments:** *Oedipina cyclocauda* is a semi-fossorial (under and within rotten logs and leaf litter) species that occurs in primary evergreen broadleaf forests in the Mosquitia.
**Remarks:** *Oedipina cyclocauda*, as currently recognized, ranges from north-central Honduras to Panama. However, salamanders from the lowlands of north-central and eastern Honduras may be sufficiently distinct from Costa Rican *Oedipina cyclocauda* to represent an undescribed species (McCranie and Wilson, 2002).

## Order Anura (Frogs and Toads)

Ninety-three species of anurans are known from Honduras (McCranie and Wilson, 2002, see also the addendum on p. 610; McCranie, Nicholson, and

Castañeda, 2002; McCranie et al., 2003a; McCranie, unpubl. data), of which 44 are recorded from the Mosquitia. Anurans have four limbs, with the hind limbs larger than the forelimbs, a specialization for a jumping or saltational mode of locomotion. As adults, anurans lack a tail. Many anurans have a larval stage in the life cycle, which stage is known as a tadpole. Some species (all those of the genera *Craugastor* and *Eleutherodactylus* in the Mosquitia), however, have direct development. As a consequence, they hatch from eggs as miniatures of the adults.

## Family Bufonidae

The members of this family, the classic "toads," possess a Bidder's organ in male tadpoles and male adults (except in adults of a few species) and lack teeth (Pough et al., 2003). Members of this family are the only anurans known from the Mosquitia that have parotoid glands. This toad family is cosmopolitan in temperate and tropical regions, except for the Australo-Papuan (where *Bufo marinus* has been introduced), Madagascan, African Saharan, and Oceania (where *B. marinus* has also been introduced) regions. Thirty-five genera containing 463 species were included in this family by Frost (2004). Two genera comprising eight species occur in Honduras, with four species placed in a single genus known from the Mosquitia.

### *Bufo coccifer* Cope, 1866

**Common name(s):** Sapo (Spanish); Sukling* (Miskito)
**Description (Plate 17):** This large toad (males to 69 mm SVL, females to 99 mm; McCranie and Wilson, 2002, although Mosquitia populations are smaller with males known to reach 55 mm SVL and females 65 mm) has well-developed cranial crests and round to ovoid parotoid glands. Parotoid glands are about the same size as, or larger than, the size of the upper eyelids and do not extend posterior to the level of the axilla. There is no row of distinctly enlarged dorsolateral tubercles; all dorsolateral tubercles are more or less similar in size to one another. An inner tarsal fold is absent and there are numerous, distinct supernumerary tubercles present. Finger webbing is absent and the toes are moderately webbed (modal webbing formula **I** 1—2 **II** 1—3 **III** 2—3 1/2 **IV** 3 1/2—2 **V**). Dorsal and ventral surfaces are strongly tuberculate with many tubercles spiculate. Dorsal ground color is dark brown to black. A pale middorsal line extends from the tip of the snout to the vent. A pale interocular bar that is bordered anteriorly and posteriorly by dark pigment is present. Parotoid glands are yellowish brown to grayish brown.

**Plate 17.** *Bufo coccifer*. Photograph by McCranie.

**Similar species:** *Bufo haematiticus* has strongly elongated parotoid glands that extend posteriorly to well beyond the level of the axilla, an inner tarsal fold, and a broad dark brown band laterally on the head and lacks cranial crests, supernumerary tubercles, and a pale interorbital bar. *Bufo marinus* has huge parotoid glands that extend posteriorly well onto the body, an inner tarsal fold, and a very large to huge size. *Bufo valliceps* has subtriangular parotoid glands and a row of distinctly enlarged, pointed dorsolateral tubercles.
**General geographic distribution:** *Bufo coccifer* occurs at low, moderate, and intermediate elevations on the Pacific versant from southeastern Oaxaca, Mexico, to central Costa Rica. It is also found on the Atlantic versant in eastern Honduras and in several interior valleys and surrounding mountains in Honduras.
**Distribution in Honduras:** This species is widely distributed in about the southern two-thirds of Honduras from western Ocotepeque to east-central Olancho and eastern El Paraíso. An apparently isolated population is also known from the pine savannas of Gracias a Dios. It is known from about sea level to 2070 m elevation.
**Distribution in the Mosquitia:** El Paraíso—2.0 km E of Arenales (USNM). Gracias a Dios—Mavita (USNM); Mocorón (UNAH); Rus Rus (UF; USNM).
**Natural history comments:** *Bufo coccifer* is known primarily from pine savanna in the Mosquitia; a single specimen taken near Arenales,

El Paraíso, probably represents a recent dispersal into that highly disturbed area formerly cloaked in evergreen broadleaf forest. It breeds around temporary and permanent ponds and inundated areas during the rainy season. This terrestrial species is active at night and solitary individuals can be found hopping on roads or in grassy areas, even in villages. One specimen was regurgitated by a snake (*Thamnophis proximus*).
**Remarks:** The populations of *Bufo coccifer* in Gracias a Dios are isolated from the nearest populations to the west and southwest in Honduras by an extensive area of evergreen broadleaf forest. This distributional pattern is shared with several other amphibians and reptiles that usually occur in subhumid habitats elsewhere in Honduras and in Central America.

*Bufo haematiticus* **Cope, 1862b**
**Common name(s):** Sapo (Spanish); Sukling* (Miskito)
**Description (Plate 18):** This large toad (males to 62 mm SVL, females to 80 mm; Savage, 2002) lacks cranial crests. Parotoid glands are strongly elongated, are much larger than the size of the upper eyelid, and extend posteriorly to well beyond the level of the axilla. There is no row of enlarged dorsolateral tubercles and supernumerary tubercles are also absent. An inner tarsal fold is present. Finger webbing is absent and the toes are moderately webbed (modal webbing formula **I** $2^-$—2 2/3 **II** 1 1/2—$3^+$ **III** $2^+$—3 2/3 **IV** $4^-$—$2^+$ **V**). Dorsal surfaces are smooth with numerous tiny to small tubercles present. The belly is smooth to weakly areolate. Dorsal ground color is dark brown with a slightly paler brown middorsal line extending from the top of the head to near the vent. A broad, lateral dark brown band extends from the tip of the snout onto the body.

**Plate 18.** *Bufo haematiticus*. Photograph by McCranie.

**Similar species:** *Bufo coccifer* has round or ovoid parotoid glands that do not extend past the level of the axilla, well-developed cranial crests, distinct supernumerary tubercles, and a pale interorbital bar and lacks an inner tarsal fold and a broad dark brown lateral head band. *Bufo marinus* has cranial crests, distinct supernumerary tubercles, and a very large to huge size and lacks a broad dark brown lateral headband. *Bufo valliceps* has well-developed cranial crests, subtriangular parotoid glands that do not extend past the level of the axilla, a row of distinctly enlarged dorsolateral tubercles, and distinct supernumerary tubercles and lacks a broad dark brown lateral headband.
**General geographic distribution:** *Bufo haematiticus* occurs at low and moderate elevations on the Atlantic versant from eastern Honduras to Colombia, and from northwestern Costa Rica to Ecuador on the Pacific versant.
**Distribution in Honduras:** This species is known from low elevations (40 to 540 m) in about the eastern one-third of the country.
**Distribution in the Mosquitia:** Colón—Cañon del Chilmeca (formerly in UNAH, now lost); Empalme Río Chilmeca (formerly in UNAH, now lost); Río Cuyamel (BMNH); Río Guaraska (BMNH); Quebrada Machín (USNM); Río Mata de Guineo (formerly in UNAH, now lost); Río Tulito (BMNH). Gracias a Dios—Río Klanea (UNAH); Mocorón (CF); Sin Sin Warra (formerly in UNAH, now lost); Bodega de Río Tapalwás (UF; USNM); Urus Tingni Kiamp (USNM); Crique Wahatingni (USNM); Warunta Tingni Kiamp (USNM). Olancho—Quebrada El Guásimo (SMF); Río Kosmako (USNM); Matamoros (USNM); Quebrada El Mono (SMF); Qururia (USNM); confluence of Quebrada Siksatara with Río Wampú (USNM).
**Natural history comments:** *Bufo haematiticus* occurs in primary or lightly disturbed evergreen broadleaf forest in the Mosquitia. Nothing is known about the breeding habits of this species in the Mosquitia, except that recent metamorphs have been found active during the day along rivers and streams in July and November. Adults and subadults of this terrestrial species are active at night and during the day following heavy rains and can be found near watercourses and in the forest well away from surface water. One adult was found

beneath loose bark on the underside of a log suspended over a small stream.

*Bufo marinus* **(Linnaeus, 1758)**
**Common name(s):** Sapo Grande, Sapo de Servicio (Spanish); Sukling* (Miskito); Huwa (Garífuna)
**Description (Plate 19):** This huge toad (Honduran males to 144 mm SVL, Honduran females to at least 177 mm with a few reported over 200 mm in South America) has cranial crests and huge parotoid glands that extend well onto the body. There is no row of enlarged dorsolateral tubercles. An inner tarsal fold is present and the supernumerary tubercles are distinct. Finger webbing is absent and the toes are moderately webbed (modal webbing formula **I** 1—2$^+$ **II** 1—3$^-$ **III** 2—3 1/2 **IV** 3 1/2—2 **V**). Dorsal surfaces have numerous tubercles with dark brown to black keratinized tips. Dorsal ground color varies from pale olive green to dark brown. Adults lack a pale middorsal stripe or conspicuous interorbital bar (juveniles and subadults can have a pale middorsal stripe).
**Similar species:** Adults of *Bufo marinus* cannot be confused with any other Mosquitia anuran. Juveniles and subadults of *B. marinus* differ from all other Mosquitia toads, except *B. haematiticus*, in having an inner tarsal fold. *Bufo haematiticus* lacks cranial crests, which are present in all but the smallest juvenile *B. marinus*.
**General geographic distribution:** *Bufo marinus* occurs at low, moderate, and intermediate elevations from extreme southern Texas, U.S.A., to Peru and central Brazil on the Atlantic versant and from Sinaloa, Mexico, to southern Ecuador on the Pacific versant. The species also occurs naturally on the Caribbean islands of Trinidad and Tobago and is widely introduced elsewhere in the world.
**Distribution in Honduras:** This toad is extensively distributed at low and moderate elevations (sea level to 1435 m) on the Honduran mainland and has recently been introduced on Isla de Guanaja, Islas de la Bahía.
**Distribution in the Mosquitia:** Colón—Empalme Río Chilmeca (formerly in UNAH, now lost); Quebrada Machín (USNM); Cañon Subterráneo del Río Plátano (formerly in UNAH, now lost). El Paraíso—2.0 km E of Arenales (USNM); Boca Español (USNM). Gracias a Dios—Ahuás (LACM); Caño Awalwás (UF); Awasbila (USNM); Caño Awawás (USNM); Baltiltuk (formerly in UNAH, now lost); Barra Patuca (USNM); Barra Río Plátano (formerly in UNAH, now lost); Canco (UF); Cauquira (UF); Kaska Tingni (USNM); Krahkra (USNM); Krausirpe (LSUMZ); Mocorón (CF); Prumnitara (UF); Rus Rus (USNM); Swabila (UF); Tánsin (LACM); Tikiraya (UF); Warunta Tingni Kiamp (UF); confluence of Quebrada Waskista with Río Wampú (USNM). Olancho—Quebrada El Guásimo (USNM); Matamoros (USNM); Quebrada El Mono (USNM); confluence of Ríos Sausa and Wampú (USNM); Villa Linda (USNM); confluence of Ríos Yanguay and Wampú (USNM); Yapuwás (USNM).
**Natural history comments:** *Bufo marinus* occurs in primary to highly disturbed evergreen broadleaf forest, pine savanna, broadleaf swamp forest, coastal strand, and freshwater marshes in the Mosquitia. The species is primarily a human commensal that is most common in highly disturbed habitats in the vicinity of villages. Adults of this terrestrial species are active at night, whereas juveniles and subadults can be active during the day and at night. *Bufo marinus* breeds along rivers, as well as in temporary and permanent ponds.

**Plate 19.** *Bufo marinus*. Photograph by McCranie.

*Bufo valliceps* **Wiegmann, 1833**
**Common name(s):** Sapo (Spanish); Sukling* (Miskito); Huwa (Garífuna)
**Description (Plate 20):** This large toad (males to 70 mm SVL, females to 95 mm; McCranie and Wilson, 2002) has well-developed cranial crests (see Remarks) and subtriangular parotoid glands. Parotoid glands are larger than, or about equal to, the size of the upper eyelids and extend posteriorly to about the level of the axilla. There is a distinct row of enlarged, pointed tubercles present

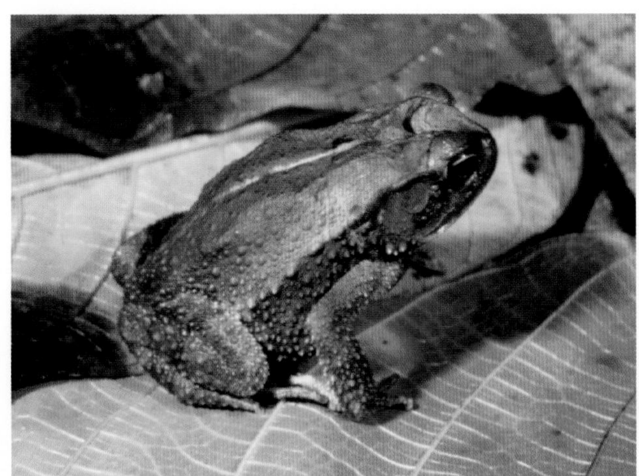

**Plate 20.** *Bufo valliceps*. Photograph by McCranie.

dorsolaterally on the body. An inner tarsal fold is absent and there are numerous and distinct supernumerary tubercles present. Finger webbing is absent and the toes are moderately webbed (modal webbing formula **I** 1—2 **II** 1—3 **III** 2—3 1/2 **IV** 3 1/2—2 **V**). Dorsal ground color is usually some shade of brown with a few darker colored spots present on the back. An incomplete middorsal line is usually present from the scapular region to near the vent. A dark brown interocular bar or a distinct series of spots is usually present.

**Similar species:** *Bufo coccifer* has round or ovoid parotoid glands and lacks a row of distinctly enlarged, pointed dorsolateral tubercles. *Bufo haematiticus* lacks cranial crests, a row of distinctly enlarged dorsolateral tubercles, and supernumerary tubercles and has an inner tarsal fold and a broad dark brown lateral headband. *Bufo marinus* is a very large to huge toad that has a well-developed inner tarsal fold (even in juveniles) and a huge parotoid gland that extends posteriorly well onto the body. *Bufo marinus* also lacks a row of distinctly enlarged dorsolateral tubercles.

**General geographic distribution:** *Bufo valliceps* occurs at low, moderate, and intermediate elevations from Veracruz, Mexico, to extreme northern Costa Rica on the Atlantic versant (including Isla del Maíz Grande, Nicaragua). It also occurs on the Pacific versant from the Isthmus of Tehuantepec, Mexico, to southwestern El Salvador and in the mountains to the east of Tegucigalpa, Francisco Morazán, Honduras.

**Distribution in Honduras:** This species is widely distributed at low and moderate elevations and occasionally intermediate elevations throughout the country, with the exception of the southwestern and much of the southern portions. It is known from about sea level to 1610 m elevation.

**Distribution in the Mosquitia:** Colón—Amarillo (BMNH); Empalme Río Chilmeca (formerly in UNAH, now lost); Río Guaraska (BMNH); Quebrada Machín (USNM); Río Paulaya (BMNH); Cañon Subterráneo del Río Plátano (formerly in UNAH, now lost); Río Tulito (BMNH). El Paraíso—2.0 km E of Arenales (USNM); Arenales (LACM); Boca Español (USNM). Gracias a Dios—Caño Awalwás (UF; USNM); Awasbila (USNM); Caño Awawás (USNM); Barra Patuca (USNM); Canco (UF); Dursuna (USNM); Karasangkan (USNM); Kaska Tingni (USNM); Krahkra (USNM); Mocorón (UNAH); about 30 km S of Mocorón (UTA); Palacios (BMNH); Loma Pinto Quiath (USNM); Raudal Pomokir (formerly in UNAH, now lost); Rus Rus (USNM); Sin Sin Warra (formerly in UNAH, now lost); Río Sutawala (USNM); Swabila (UF); Tánsin (LACM); Bodega de Río Tapalwás (UF; USNM); Tikiraya (UF); Urus Tingni Kiamp (USNM); Crique Wahatingni (UF); Walpunpansilpi (formerly in UNAH, now lost); Wampusirpe (LACM; LSUMZ); Warunta Tingni Kiamp (USNM). Olancho—Raudal La Caldera (SMF); Caobita (USNM); Casamacoa (USNM); Quebrada El Guásimo (SMF); Río Kosmako (USNM); Quebrada Kuilma Tingni (USNM); La Llorona (USNM); between La Llorona and Villa Linda (USNM); Las Marías (USNM); Quebrada de Las Marías (USNM); Matamoros (USNM); Quebrada El Mono (SMF); Nueva Esperanza (USNM); confluence of Ríos Pao and Wampú (USNM); Qururia (USNM); confluence of Ríos Sausa and Wampú (USNM); confluence of Quebrada Siksatara with Río Wampú (USNM); confluence of Ríos Yanguay and Wampú (USNM); Yapuwás (USNM).

**Natural history comments:** In the Mosquitia, *Bufo valliceps* is primarily an inhabitant of broadleaf forests (both evergreen and swamp forests), but occasionally can be found in transition areas between broadleaf and pine forests, as well as occasionally in pine forest stands that have not been burned recently (e.g., at Dursuna). Tadpoles were found in side pools of rivers and a small stream through primary evergreen broadleaf forest in the Mosquitia during May. Recent metamorphs were on rocks or the ground near watercourses at the same time. Members of this species also form breeding aggregations around inundated areas in disturbed forest after heavy rain in the Mosquitia, as indicated by one calling aggregation seen in water-filled puddles in a road through disturbed gallery forest in May. In primary evergreen broadleaf forests of the Mosquitia, adults and subadults of this terrestrial species are active both during the day and at night. In disturbed areas, it is primarily active at night.

**Remarks:** Adult females, and to a lesser extent, adult males of *Bufo valliceps* from deep within primary evergreen broadleaf forest usually have cranial crests that are strongly elevated compared to populations of the species from disturbed areas. The significance of this variation in cranial crest development is unknown.

**Plate 21.** *Centrolene prosoblepon.* Photograph by McCranie.

## Family Centrolenidae

Centrolenid frogs are characterized by the presence of a dilated medial process on the third metacarpal (Pough et al., 2003). Members of this family in the Mosquitia are distinguished by the combination of having the belly transparent in life and translucent in preservative so that at least some of the internal organs or their linings are visible, the disc covers on the fingers and toes truncate, finger webbing present, toe webbing moderately developed, and the snout either bluntly rounded to rounded, nearly vertical to vertical, or obtuse in lateral profile. This family of arboreal frogs occurs from central Guerrero and central Veracruz, Mexico, to south-central Bolivia and extreme northern Brazil. Centrolenids also occur in southeastern Brazil and adjacent Argentina and southeastern Paraguay. Three genera containing 137 species are currently recognized in the family (Frost, 2004). Eight species included in all three genera are known to occur in Honduras. Three genera are found in the Mosquitia, as well as seven species.

*Centrolene prosoblepon* **(Boettger, 1892)**

**Common name(s):** Ranita Cristal (Spanish)

**Description (Plate 21):** This small frog (males to 28 mm SVL, females to 31 mm; Savage, 2002) has well-developed humeral spines in males and in occasional females. Fore- and hind limbs have expanded disc pads with truncated distal ends and truncated disc covers. Webbing between Fingers II–III is basal, that between Fingers III–IV is moderately developed (modal webbing formula **III** 2—$2^-$ **IV**). Webbing is absent between Fingers I–II. Webbing is moderately developed between all toes (modal webbing formula **I** 1—$2^+$ **II** 1—$2^+$ **III** 1—$2^+$ **IV** $2^+$—1 **V**). The snout is bluntly rounded to vertical in lateral profile. Vomerine teeth are present and prepollical spines are absent. Dorsal surfaces are green in life and lavender in preservative. Darker colored small or tiny spots can be present or absent. The parietal peritoneum is white anterior to the level slightly posterior to the midpoint of the belly. The visceral peritoneum is colorless. Bones are green in life.

**Similar species:** All other Mosquitia centrolenids lack humeral spines. Since female *Centrolene prosoblepon* can lack humeral spines, this species also differs from the other Mosquitia centrolenids in the following characters. All species of *Hyalinobatrachium* have a colorless parietal peritoneum and a white visceral peritoneum. *Cochranella albomaculata* has distinct yellow dorsal spots in life and cream to white dorsal spots in preservative. *Cochranella granulosa* has distinct purple dorsal spots in life and preservative, a white visceral peritoneum, and a pale yellow dorsal ground color in preservative. *Cochranella spinosa* has a prepollical spine.

**General geographic distribution:** *Centrolene prosoblepon* occurs at low, moderate, and intermediate elevations from eastern Honduras to northwestern Colombia on the Atlantic versant and from northwestern Costa Rica to west-central Ecuador on the Pacific versant. It is also found on the Atlantic versant of the Cordillera Central and middle portion of the valley of the Río Magdalena in Colombia.

**Distribution in Honduras:** This frog is known from low and moderate elevations (80 to 1100 m) in the eastern half of Olancho, southeastern Colón, and western Gracias a Dios.
**Distribution in the Mosquitia:** Colón—Quebrada Machín (USNM). Gracias a Dios— Caño Awalwás (USNM); Baltiltuk (UNAH); Urus Tingni Kiamp (USNM); confluence of Quebrada Waskista with Río Wampú (USNM). Olancho—Quebrada de Las Marías (USNM).
**Natural history comments:** *Centrolene prosoblepon* breeds along streams and small rivers flowing through primary or lightly disturbed evergreen broadleaf forest in the Mosquitia. Males call from vegetation (both upper and lower surfaces) overhanging streams and small rivers or from high up in trees near these watercourses. Females lay eggs on vegetation overhanging the water and the larvae drop into the water upon hatching. This species is most active on nights following heavy rains.
**Remarks:** *Centrolene prosoblepon* was placed in the genus *Centrolenella* by Savage (2002). Savage (2002) restricted the genus *Centrolene* to "three small-eyed species . . . from Colombia and Ecuador" (p. 358). We are not convinced of the merits of Savage's arrangement and do not follow it here.

*Cochranella albomaculata* **(Taylor, 1949)**
**Common name(s):** Ranita Cristal (Spanish)
**Description (Plate 22):** This small frog (males to 29 mm SVL, females to 32 mm; Savage, 2002) has expanded disc pads with truncated distal ends and truncated disc covers. Webbing between Fingers II–IV is moderately developed (modal webbing formula **II** $2^{-}$—$3^{+}$ **III** 2—1 1/3 **IV**), that between Fingers I–II is basal. Webbing is moderately developed between all toes (modal webbing formula **I** 3/4—2 **II** 3/4—2 **III** 3/4—2 1/4 **IV** 2—3/4 **V**). The snout is bluntly rounded in lateral profile. Vomerine teeth are present, whereas prepollical and humeral spines are absent. Dorsal surfaces are green in life and lavender to gray in preservative. Distinct yellow (in life) or cream to white (in preservative) dorsal spots are present. The parietal peritoneum is white anterior to about the midpoint of the belly and the visceral peritoneum is colorless. Bones are green in life.

**Plate 22.** *Cochranella albomaculata*. Photograph by McCranie.

**Similar species:** *Centrolene prosoblepon* has humeral spines in the males and in some females and lacks distinct pale dorsal spots. *Cochranella granulosa* has purple dorsal spots, a white visceral peritoneum, and a pale yellow dorsal ground color in preservative. *Cochranella spinosa* has a prepollical spine and lacks distinct pale dorsal spots. All Mosquitia species of *Hyalinobatrachium* have a colorless parietal peritoneum and a white visceral peritoneum.
**General geographic distribution:** *Cochranella albomaculata* occurs at low and moderate elevations from northwestern Costa Rica to central Panama on the Pacific versant and on the Atlantic versant from north-central Honduras to northwestern Colombia.
**Distribution in Honduras:** This species is known from scattered localities in northern and eastern Olancho and eastern Colón. It has been collected from 100 to 1200 m elevation.
**Distribution in the Mosquitia:** Colón—Quebrada Machín (USNM); 4 km ESE of Tulito (BMNH). Olancho—Caobita (SMF; USNM); Quebrada El Guásimo (USNM); Quebrada de Las Marías (USNM).
**Natural history comments:** *Cochranella albomaculata* breeds along streams flowing through primary and lightly disturbed evergreen broadleaf forest in the Mosquitia. Males call from low vegetation (both upper and lower surfaces) overhanging streams. Females lay eggs on vegetation overhanging the water and the larvae drop into the water upon hatching. This species is most active on nights following heavy rains. The distribution of this species in the Mosquitia is very spotty. *Cochranella albomaculata* can be very common along some streams, but is apparently absent from numerous other streams with seemingly similar conditions.

*Cochranella granulosa* **(Taylor, 1949)**
**Common name(s):** Ranita Cristal (Spanish)
**Description (Plate 23):** This small frog (males to 29 mm SVL, females to 32 mm; Savage, 2002) has expanded disc pads with truncated distal ends and truncated disc covers. Webbing between Fingers II–III is basal, that between Fingers III–IV is moderately developed (modal webbing formula **III** $2^{-}$—3/4 **IV**). Webbing is absent between Fingers I–II. The webbing is moderately developed between all toes (modal webbing formula **I** 3/4—$2^{-}$ **II** 3/4—1 2/3 **III** 3/4—2 **IV** 2—1 **V**). The snout is obtuse in lateral profile. Vomerine teeth are present, whereas prepollical and humeral spines are absent. Dorsal surfaces are yellowish green (in life) or pale yellow (in preservative) with distinct turquoise blue (in life) or purple (in preservative) spots. The parietal peritoneum is white anterior to about the midpoint of the belly and the visceral peritoneum is white. Bones are pale green in life.
**Similar species:** *Cochranella granulosa* differs from all other Mosquitia centrolenids in having prominent purple dorsal spots in life and in preservative. The only other Mosquitia centrolenid with an obtuse snout in lateral profile is *Hyalinobatrachium pulveratum*. That species has a colorless parietal peritoneum and small white dorsal spots.
**General geographic distribution:** *Cochranella granulosa* occurs at low and moderate elevations from eastern Honduras to central Panama on the Atlantic versant and from northwestern Costa Rica to western Panama on the Pacific versant.
**Distribution in Honduras:** This species is known only from the Mosquitia at elevations from 60 to 680 m.
**Distribution in the Mosquitia:** Gracias a Dios—Kaska Tingni (USNM); Rus Rus (UF; USNM); Urus Tingni Kiamp (USNM); Crique Wahatingni (UF; USNM); Warunta Tingni Kiamp (USNM). Olancho—Quebrada de Las Marías (USNM); Matamoros (SMF).
**Natural history comments:** *Cochranella granulosa* breeds along streams flowing through primary to lightly disturbed evergreen broadleaf forest (including gallery forest through pine savanna) in the Mosquitia. Males call from the upper surfaces of vegetation overhanging streams or from high up in trees near streams. Thus, they are difficult to locate, even though they can be quite common, as noted from the number of calling males. Females lay eggs on vegetation overhanging the water and the larvae drop into the water upon hatching. This species is most active on nights following heavy rains.

*Cochranella spinosa* **(Taylor, 1949)**
**Common name(s):** Ranita Cristal (Spanish)
**Description (Plate 24):** This small frog (males to 20 mm SVL, females to 23 mm; Savage, 2002) has a free distal end to the prepollex that forms a prepollical spine in both sexes. Fore- and hind limbs have expanded disc pads with truncated distal ends and truncated disc covers. Webbing between Fingers II–III is basal, that between Fingers III–IV is moderately developed (modal webbing formula **III** $2^{-}$—$2^{-}$ **IV**). Webbing is absent between Fingers I–II. Webbing is moderately developed between all toes (modal webbing formula **I** 1—2 **II** $1^{-}$—2 **III** $1^{-}$—2 **IV** 2—$1^{-}$ **V**). The snout is nearly vertical in lateral profile. Vomerine teeth are not evident in the Mosquitia specimens. Humeral spines are absent.

**Plate 23.** *Cochranella granulosa*. Photograph by McCranie.

**Plate 24.** *Cochranella spinosa*. Photograph by McCranie.

Dorsal surfaces are green in life and lavender in preservative. The parietal peritoneum is white anterior to about the midpoint of the belly and the visceral peritoneum is colorless. Bones are green in life.
**Similar species:** *Cochranella spinosa* differs from all other Mosquitia centrolenids in having a free distal end to the prepollex that forms a prepollical spine.
**General geographic distribution:** *Cochranella spinosa* occurs at low elevations from southeastern Costa Rica to northwestern Ecuador on the Pacific versant and on the Atlantic versant in eastern Honduras and from northern Costa Rica to at least central Panama.
**Distribution in Honduras:** This species is known only in the Mosquitia from 100 to 190 m elevation.
**Distribution in the Mosquitia:** Gracias a Dios—Awasbila (USNM); Bodega de Río Tapalwás (USNM). Olancho—Quebrada El Guásimo (USNM); Río Kosmako (USNM); near Quebrada El Mono (USNM).
**Natural history comments:** *Cochranella spinosa* breeds along streams flowing through primary to lightly disturbed evergreen broadleaf forest in the Mosquitia. Males call from the upper surfaces of vegetation overhanging or near streams. The call of this species is not as loud as that of other sympatric centrolenids, thus the species can be easily overlooked. Females lay eggs on vegetation overhanging the water and the larvae drop into the water upon hatching. This species breeds at night following heavy afternoon or early nighttime rains.

**Plate 25.** *Hyalinobatrachium cardiacalyptum.* Photograph by McCranie.

**Plate 26.** *Hyalinobatrachium cardiacalyptum* ventral surface showing visible heart. Photograph by Townsend.

*Hyalinobatrachium cardiacalyptum* **McCranie and Wilson, 1997b**
**Common name(s):** Ranita Cristal (Spanish)
**Description (Plates 25 and 26):** This small frog (males and females to 26 mm SVL; McCranie and Wilson, 2002) has moderately developed webbing between Fingers II–III and III–IV (modal webbing formula **II** 1—3⁻ **III** 1 3/4–1 1/2 **IV**). Webbing between Fingers I–II is basal. Webbing is moderately developed between all toes (modal webbing formula **I** 3/4—1 3/4 **II** 3/4—2⁻ **III** 3/4—2 **IV** 2—3/4 **V**). Fore- and hind limbs have expanded disc pads with truncated distal ends and truncated disc covers. The snout is bluntly rounded to vertical in lateral profile. Vomerine teeth and humeral and prepollical spines are absent. Dorsal surfaces are green to yellow-green in life and pale yellow in preservative. Small yellow dorsal spots are present in life. The parietal peritoneum is colorless and the visceral peritoneum is white. The parietal pericardium is colorless, thus the red heart is clearly visible through the transparent ventral skin. Bones are white in life.
**Similar species:** *Hyalinobatrachium cardiacalyptum* is the only centrolenid in the Mosquitia in which the parietal pericardium is colorless. Also, the moderately developed webbing between Fingers II–III occurs in only one other Mosquitia centrolenid, *H. pulveratum*. *Hyalinobatrachium pulveratum* has an obtuse snout in lateral profile, vomerine teeth, and pale green bones in life.
**General geographic distribution:** *Hyalinobatrachium cardiacalyptum* occurs at low and moderate elevations on the Atlantic versant in northeastern Honduras.

**Distribution in Honduras:** This species is known only in the Mosquitia from 60 to 700 m elevation.
**Distribution in the Mosquitia:** Colón—Cañon Subterráneo del Río Plátano (formerly in UNAH, now lost). Gracias a Dios—Awasbila (USNM); Mocorón (CF); Crique Wahatingni (UF; USNM); Warunta Tingni Kiamp (USNM). Olancho—Caño El Cajón (USNM); Caobita (SMF; USNM); Quebrada El Guásimo (SMF; USNM); Matamoros (SMF; USNM); Quebrada de Las Marías (USNM).
**Natural history comments:** *Hyalinobatrachium cardiacalyptum* breeds along streams in primary to lightly disturbed evergreen broadleaf forest in the Mosquitia. Males call from both the upper and lower surfaces of leaves overhanging or along streams and from high up in trees near these watercourses. Females lay eggs on vegetation overhanging streams and the larvae drop into the water upon hatching. Males of this species commonly attend egg clutches at night, but leave them unattended during the day. The species is most active on nights following heavy rains.
**Remarks:** As presently known, *Hyalinobatrachium cardiacalyptum* is endemic to the Honduran Mosquitia. However, as the species is common along several tributary streams of the Río Coco, it is likely to occur on the Nicaraguan side of the Río Coco as well.

*Hyalinobatrachium fleischmanni* **(Boettger, 1893)**
**Common name(s):** Ranita Cristal (Spanish)
**Description (Plate 27):** This small frog (males to 28 mm SVL, females to 32 mm; Savage, 2002) has basal webbing between Fingers II–III. Webbing is absent between Fingers I–II and moderately developed between Fingers III–IV (modal webbing formula **III** $2^{-}$—$2^{-}$ **IV**). Webbing is moderately developed between all toes (modal webbing formula **I** 3/4—2 **II** 1—2 **III** 3/4—2 **IV** 2—1 **V**). Fore- and hind limbs have expanded disc pads with truncated distal ends and truncated disc covers. The snout is rounded to bluntly rounded in lateral profile. Vomerine teeth and humeral and prepollical spines are absent. Dorsal surfaces are green to yellow green in life and yellowish white in preservative. Small yellow dorsal spots are present in life. The parietal peritoneum is colorless and the visceral peritoneum is white. The parietal pericardium is white. Bones are white in life.

**Plate 27.** *Hyalinobatrachium fleischmanni.* Photograph by McCranie.

**Similar species:** Members of the centrolenid genera *Centrolene* and *Cochranella* have a white parietal peritoneum and all Mosquitia members of these two genera, save for *Cochranella granulosa*, have lavender dorsal surfaces in preservative. *Cochranella granulosa* has prominent purple dorsal spots in life and in preservative and an obtuse snout in lateral profile. *Hyalinobatrachium cardiacalyptum* and *H. pulveratum* have moderately developed webbing between Fingers II–III. In addition, *H. cardiacalyptum* has a colorless parietal pericardium and *H. pulveratum* has vomerine teeth, an obtuse snout in lateral profile, and pale green bones in life.
**General geographic distribution:** *Hyalinobatrachium fleischmanni* occurs at low, moderate, and intermediate elevations from central Veracruz, Mexico, to Colombia on the Atlantic versant and from central Guerrero, Mexico, to western Colombia on the Pacific versant.
**Distribution in Honduras:** This species is widely distributed at low and moderate elevations and occasionally intermediate elevations in the northern half of the country. Specimens are also known from two widely separated localities in the southern half of Honduras. It is known from about sea level to 1550 m elevation.
**Distribution in the Mosquitia:** Gracias a Dios—Mocorón (CF); Río Plátano (UNAH); Rus Rus (USNM). Olancho—confluence of Ríos Sausa and Wampú (USNM).
**Natural history comments:** *Hyalinobatrachium fleischmanni* is an uncommon frog in the Mosquitia that seems to be replaced by *H. cardiacalyptum* at most sites (we have never taken the two species along the same stream). *Hyalinobatrachium fleischmanni* has been found in the Mosquitia along streams in primary and lightly disturbed evergreen broadleaf forest (including gallery forest through

pine savanna). Males call from the upper surfaces of leaves overhanging streams. Females lay eggs on vegetation overhanging streams and the larvae drop into the water upon hatching. Males of this species commonly attend egg clutches at night, but leave them unattended during the day. The species is most active on nights following heavy rains.

*Hyalinobatrachium pulveratum* **(W. Peters, 1873)**
**Common name(s):** Ranita Cristal (Spanish)
**Description (Plate 28):** This small frog (males to 29 mm SVL, females to 33 mm; Savage, 2002) has moderately developed webbing between Fingers II–IV (modal webbing formula **II** 1—3$^{-}$ **III** 1 3/4—1 **IV**). Webbing between Fingers I–II is basal. Webbing is moderately developed between all toes (modal webbing formula **I** 1—2$^{-}$ **II** 3/4—2$^{-}$ **III** 3/4—2$^{-}$ **IV** 2—3/4 **V**). Fore- and hind limbs have expanded disc pads with truncated distal ends and truncated disc covers. The snout is obtuse in lateral profile and vomerine teeth are present. Humeral and prepollical spines are absent. Dorsal surfaces are green in life and yellowish white with numerous tiny lavender flecks in preservative (giving an appearance of having lavender surfaces upon casual observation). Distinct small white dorsal spots are present. The parietal peritoneum is colorless and the visceral peritoneum is white. The parietal pericardium is white. Bones are pale green in life.
**Similar species:** The moderately developed webbing between Fingers II–III in *Hyalinobatrachium pulveratum* occurs in only one other Mosquitia centrolenid, *H. cardiacalyptum*. *Hyalinobatrachium cardiacalyptum* has a bluntly rounded to vertical snout in lateral profile, a colorless parietal pericardium so that the red heart is visible through the transparent ventral skin, white bones in life, and lacks vomerine teeth.

**Plate 28.** *Hyalinobatrachium pulveratum.* Photograph by McCranie.

**General geographic distribution:** *Hyalinobatrachium pulveratum* occurs at low and moderate elevations from north-central Honduras to the Valle de Cauca, Colombia, on the Atlantic versant and from southeastern Costa Rica to southeastern Panama on the Pacific versant.
**Distribution in Honduras:** This frog is known from a few localities in northwestern and eastern Olancho, southeastern Colón, and southern Gracias a Dios. Known from 100 to 950 m elevation.
**Distribution in the Mosquitia:** Colón—Quebrada Machín (USNM). Gracias a Dios—Rus Rus (UF); Bodega de Río Tapalwás (UF); trail to Bodega de Río Tapalwás (UF). Olancho—Quebrada de Las Marías (USNM); Matamoros (USNM); confluence of Ríos Sausa and Wampú (USNM).
**Natural history comments:** *Hyalinobatrachium pulveratum* breeds along streams in primary to lightly disturbed evergreen broadleaf forest in the Mosquitia. Males call from both the upper and lower surfaces of leaves overhanging streams. Females lay eggs on vegetation overhanging streams and the larvae drop into the water upon hatching. The species is most active on nights following heavy rains.

## Family Hylidae

Hylid frogs have claw-shaped terminal phalanges and most species are arboreal and have well-developed finger and toe discs (Pough et al., 2003). This family is probably not monophyletic (Duellman, 2003). Members of this family in the Mosquitia are distinguished by the combination of having the belly usually not transparent in life or translucent in preservative, the disc covers on the fingers and toes usually rounded (somewhat truncated in one genus; if the disc covers are somewhat truncated, then the snout is protruding in lateral profile), finger webbing present, and the toe webbing moderate to extensive. The members of this family range from the southwestern part of the Northwest Territories of Canada on the west and central Quebec, Canada, on the east to east-central Argentina. They also occur in the West Indies, the Australo-Papuan Region, and discontinuously in temperate Eurasia (including extreme northern Africa and the Japanese Archipelago). One species also occurs on the

Azores, Madeira, and Canary Islands in the Atlantic Ocean. Forty-one genera containing 865 species were included in this family by Frost (2004). Ten genera with 33 species are known to occur in Honduras. Seven genera comprising 16 species are recorded from the Mosquitia.

*Agalychnis calcarifer* **Boulenger, 1902**
**Common name(s):** None
**Description (Plate 29):** This large frog (males to 81 mm SVL, females to 87 mm; Duellman, 2001) has vertically elliptical pupils and a prominent calcar on the heel. Fingers and toes are extensively webbed (modal webbing formula **I** 1—2 **II** 3/4—$2^-$ **III** 3/4—3/4 **IV** and **I** 3/4—$1^-$ **II** 3/4—1 **III** 3/4—$2^-$ **IV** $2^-$—3/4 *V*, respectively) and have very large disc pads with rounded disc covers. Dorsal surfaces are smooth to weakly granular. The dorsum of the head and body are green and the flanks are yellow with black vertical stripes or bars. Dorsal and ventral surfaces of the fingers and toes are orange, except for the outer edges of the outer most digit (Finger IV and Toe V), which are green. The dorsal surfaces of the upper arms and the thighs are yellow to orange; black transverse and cross stripes can also be present on the thighs. The iris is yellow on the upper half and pale gray on the lower half. The palpebral membrane is unpigmented.
**Similar species:** The only other Mosquitia hylids with vertical pupils are *Agalychnis callidryas* and *A. saltator*. Both of these species lack a heel calcar and have a red iris and a reticulated palpebral membrane. In addition, *A. callidryas* has purple flanks with yellow vertical stripes and usually a yellow longitudinal stripe separating the dorsal and flank colorations. Also, *A. saltator* has unbarred or unstriped purple flanks.
**General geographic distribution:** *Agalychnis calcarifer* occurs at low and moderate elevations from eastern Honduras to central Panama and northern Colombia on the Atlantic versant and from eastern Panama to northwestern Ecuador on the Pacific versant.
**Distribution in Honduras:** This species is known only in the Mosquitia from 30 to 190 m elevation.
**Distribution in the Mosquitia:** Gracias a Dios—near Baltiltuk (UNAH); Bodega de Río Tapalwás (UF; USNM); Urus Tingni Kiamp (USNM). Olancho—Quebrada El Guásimo (SMF; USNM).
**Natural history comments:** *Agalychnis calcarifer* occurs in primary evergreen broadleaf forest in the Mosquitia. Three adults were collected between about 2000 and 2250 h about 1 to 2 m above the ground on fronds of palms. Another was collected in early afternoon after it jumped from a tall tree (G.A. Cruz, pers. comm.). The species is unusual among Central American hylids in that it deposits its eggs above small pools formed in cavities or depressions of large fallen trees. A series of tadpoles and one egg clutch of this species were found in such a situation in the Mosquitia (McCranie and Wilson, 2002).

**Plate 29.** *Agalychnis calcarifer.* Photograph by McCranie.

*Agalychnis callidryas* **(Cope, 1862d)**
**Common name(s):** None
**Description (Plate 30):** This moderately large frog (males to 59 mm SVL [Duellman, 2001], females to 77 mm [McCranie and Wilson, 2002]) has vertically elliptical pupils, but lacks a calcar on the heel. Fingers and toes are moderately webbed (modal webbing formula **I** 2—2 **II** $2^-$—$3^-$ **III** 2—2 **IV** and **I** 2—2 **II** $2^-$—$3^-$ **III** $1^+$—2 1/2 **IV** 2—$1^+$ **V**, respectively) and have very large disc pads with rounded disc covers. Dorsal surfaces are smooth to weakly granular. The dorsum of the head and body are green and the flanks are purple with yellow vertical stripes. A yellowish-white longitudinal stripe separating the dorsal and flank colorations usually occurs in specimens from the Mosquitia (see Remarks). Dorsal and ventral surfaces of the fingers and toes are orange or yellowish orange, except for the outer edges of the outermost digit (Finger IV and Toe V), which are green. The upper arms and the posterior and anterior surfaces of the thighs are purple. The iris is red and the palpebral membrane is reticulated.
**Similar species:** The only other Mosquitia hylids

**Plate 30.** *Agalychnis callidryas.* Photograph by McCranie.

with vertical pupils are *Agalychnis calcarifer* and *A. saltator. Agalychnis calcarifer* has a heel calcar, yellow flanks with black vertical stripes or bars, a yellow to gray iris, and an unpigmented palpebral membrane. *Agalychnis saltator* has purple flanks that lack pale stripes (see Remarks).
**General geographic distribution:** *Agalychnis callidryas* occurs at low and moderate elevations from central Veracruz and northern Oaxaca, Mexico, to northern Colombia on the Atlantic versant and from southwestern Nicaragua to eastern Panama on the Pacific versant.
**Distribution in Honduras:** This frog is widely distributed in the northern and eastern halves of the country from about sea level to 1200 m elevation.
**Distribution in the Mosquitia:** Colón—Quebrada Machín (USNM). El Paraíso—2.2 km E of Arenales (USNM). Gracias a Dios—Caño Awalwás (USNM); Caño Awawás (USNM); Baltiltuk (UNAH); Laguna Baraya (ROM); Barra Patuca (UNAH); Brus Laguna (UNAH); Crique Ibantara (UF; USNM); Kalila Plapan Tingni (UNAH); Karasangkan (USNM); Kaska Tingni (USNM); Kasunta (USNM); Krahkra (USNM); Limaraya (UNAH); Mocorón (UNAH); Rus Rus (UF; USNM); Swabila (UF); Bodega de Río Tapalwás (UF; USNM); Wampusirpe (LSUMZ); Warunta Tingni Kiamp (USNM); confluence of Quebrada Waskista with Río Wampú (USNM); Crique Yulpruan (USNM). Olancho—Kauroahuika (SMF; USNM); Quebrada de Las Marías (USNM); Matamoros (USNM); confluence of Ríos Sausa and Wampú (USNM); confluence of Quebrada Siksatara with Río Wampú (USNM); confluence of Ríos Yanguay and Wampú (USNM).
**Natural history comments:** *Agalychnis callidryas* occurs in primary to highly disturbed evergreen broadleaf forest and broadleaf swamp forest in the Mosquitia. The species is able to survive in areas in which the entire original vegetation has been removed. The reason for its ability to survive in denuded areas is likely its ability to adapt to breeding in a wide array of habitats. The "usual" mode of reproduction for *A. callidryas* is to deposit eggs on vegetation overhanging temporary and permanent ponds (Duellman, 2001). McCranie and Wilson (2002) and McCranie, Wilson, and Townsend (2003) discussed several "unusual" breeding sites for this species, both in primary forest and in completely denuded areas. The species is active at night and appears to have an extended reproductive season. *Agalychnis callidryas* can also be an explosive breeder. On the nights of 27–28 July 2001, we encountered several hundred amplecting pairs on emergent vegetation growing from a temporary pond following heavy rains during each of these two days. Numerous pairs still in amplexus were sleeping on this vegetation during the daylight hours of 28 July.
**Remarks:** Occasional specimens of *Agalychnis callidryas* can have the flank pattern strongly reduced to two or three poorly defined pale vertical stripes (i.e., USNM specimens from Kasunta, Gracias a Dios; also see McCranie and Wilson, 2002).

*Agalychnis saltator* **Taylor, 1955**
**Common name(s):** None
**Description (Plate 31):** This moderately large frog (males to 54 mm SVL, females to 66 mm; Savage, 2002) has vertically elliptical pupils, but lacks a calcar on the heel. Fingers and toes are moderately webbed (modal webbing formula **I** $2^{+}$—$3^{-}$ **II** $2^{-}$—$3^{-}$ **III** 2—2 **IV** and **I** 2—2 **II** $2^{-}$—3 **III** 1 1/2—$3^{-}$ **IV** $3^{-}$—1 1/2 **V**, respectively) and have very large disc pads with rounded disc covers. Dorsal surfaces are smooth to weakly granular. The dorsum of the head and body is green (see Remarks) and the flanks are purple without pale vertical stripes. Dorsal and ventral surfaces of the fingers and toes are orange or yellowish orange, except for the outer edges of the outermost digit (Finger IV and Toe V), which are green. The upper arms and the posterior and anterior surfaces of the thighs are purple. The iris is red and the palpebral membrane is reticulated.

**Plate 31.** *Agalychnis saltator*. Photograph by Townsend.

**Similar species:** The only other Mosquitia hylids with vertical pupils are *Agalychnis calcarifer* and *A. callidryas*. *Agalychnis calcarifer* has a heel calcar, yellow flanks with black vertical stripes or bars, a yellow to gray iris, and an unpigmented palpebral membrane. *Agalychnis callidryas* has yellow vertical stripes on the flanks and usually a yellowish-white longitudinal stripe separating the dorsal and flank colorations.
**General geographic distribution:** *Agalychnis saltator* occurs at low and moderate elevations on the Atlantic versant from northeastern Honduras to eastern Costa Rica.
**Distribution in Honduras:** This species is known only in the Mosquitia from 20 to 95 m elevation.
**Distribution in the Mosquitia:** Gracias a Dios—Baltiltuk (UNAH); Kaska Tingni (SMF; USNM); Krahkra (USNM). Olancho—confluence of Quebrada Siksatara with Río Wampú (USNM).
**Natural history comments:** *Agalychnis saltator* occurs in primary and second growth broadleaf forest (both evergreen and swamp forest) in the Mosquitia. The species is an explosive breeder following heavy rains. On the nights of 27–28 July 2001, we found a breeding aggregation of several hundred *A. saltator* on emergent vegetation growing in a temporary pond following heavy rains during each of these two days (several hundred *A. callidryas* were also present at these times on the same vegetation). Numerous pairs of *A. saltator* still in amplexus were sleeping on this vegetation during the daylight hours of 28 July.
**Remarks:** Duellman (2001) and Savage (2002) stated that the dorsal surfaces of *Agalychnis saltator* are reddish brown at night. All Honduran *A. saltator* we have seen were some shade of green at night.

*Anotheca spinosa* **(Steindachner, 1864)**
**Common name(s):** None
**Description (Plate 32):** This large frog (males to 69 mm SVL, females to 80 mm; Savage, 2002) has strong bony occipital and canthal spines present. The pupil is horizontally elliptical. The skin of the head is co-ossified with the skull. Webbing is absent between Fingers I–II, and only basal between Fingers II–III–IV. Toe webbing is moderate (modal webbing formula **I** $2^{+}$—$3^{-}$ **II** 1 2/3—3 **III** 2—3 **IV** $3^{-}$—1 3/4 **V**). Fingers and toes have large disc pads with rounded disc covers. Dorsal surfaces of the head and body are dark brown with black, white-outlined blotches present on the back. Flanks of the body also have similarly colored blotches. The dorsal, anterior, and posterior surfaces of the fore- and hind limbs are dark brown with black, white-outlined crossbars.
**Similar species:** *Anotheca spinosa* is the only Honduran frog with bony occipital and canthal spines.
**General geographic distribution:** *Anotheca spinosa* occurs at low, moderate, and intermediate elevations from central Veracruz, Mexico, to western Panama on the Atlantic versant (not known from Guatemala, Belize, or Nicaragua) and from southeastern Costa Rica to west-central Panama on the Pacific versant.
**Distribution in Honduras:** This species is known only in the Mosquitia from 95 to 190 m elevation (see Remarks).
**Distribution in the Mosquitia:** Gracias a Dios—Bodega de Río Tapalwás (UF; USNM). Olancho—confluence of Quebrada Siksatara with Río Wampú (USNM).

**Plate 32.** *Anotheca spinosa*. Photograph by Townsend.

**Natural history comments:** *Anotheca spinosa* occurs in primary evergreen broadleaf forest in the Mosquitia. Two Mosquitia specimens (both males) were sitting on a tree branch and a vine about 2 m above the ground in July and September, respectively. Both were collected at night after heavy rains. Another male was collected while calling from a water-filled tree hole. The hole measured 49 x 53 mm in circumference with a depth of 102 mm. The tree (*Virola koschnyi*; Sangre, Sebo Banak) measured 593 mm in circumference at chest height and the entrance to the hole was 217 cm above the ground. In other parts of its range, *A. spinosa* is known to breed in water-filled tree holes, bromeliads, or open internodes of bamboo (Duellman, 2001; Savage, 2002).
**Remarks:** The Mosquitia records are the lowest elevations recorded for *Anotheca spinosa*. The species is known from 500 to 1800 m elevation in Mexico (see McCranie, 1993) and from 350 to 1330 m elevation in Costa Rica and Panama (Savage, 2002). The elevation of 2068 m given by Duellman (2001) and Savage (2002) is in error for 1068 m (see J. Johnson et al., "1976" [1977]).

*Hyla ebraccata* **Cope, 1874**
**Common name(s):** None
**Description (Plate 33):** This small frog (males to 29 mm SVL, females to 37 mm; Duellman, 2001) has a well-developed axillary membrane. The pupil is horizontally elliptical. The snout is rounded to vertical in lateral profile. Fingers and toes are extensively webbed (modal webbing formula **I** 2—2 1/3 **II** 3/4—$2^+$ **III** $2^+$—$2^-$ **IV** and **I** 1—1 1/2 **II** 3/4—$2^-$ **III** 3/4—2 **IV** $2^+$—3/4 **V**, respectively) and have large disc pads with rounded disc covers. Vomerine teeth are present. Males have a single, median, subgular vocal sac. The dorsal pattern consists of a dark brown hourglass-shaped mark or dark brown blotches and a yellow to white band present from across the snout, across the upper eyelids, and onto the dorsolateral portion of the body. The lower back usually has a yellow to white blotch. The side of the head is dark brown with a yellow to white subocular spot or expanded lip stripe.

**Plate 33.** *Hyla ebraccata*. Photograph by McCranie.

**Similar species:** *Hyla loquax* is a larger frog (males to 45 mm SVL, females to 43 mm) that lacks dorsolateral pale stripes and large dorsal blotches. *Hyla microcephala* has moderate finger webbing (basal between I–II, remaining modal webbing formula **II** $1^+$—2 1/2 **III** 2 1/3—$2^+$ **IV**), a thin dorsolateral brown stripe usually present that is bordered above by a thin white stripe, and a dorsal pattern usually consisting of irregular brown dashes forming a X-shaped mark, fragmented crossbars, fragmented lines, or a reticulated pattern. *Hyla picta* is a smaller frog (to 23 mm SVL), has moderate finger webbing (basal between I–II, remaining modal webbing formula **II** 2—3 **III** 2 1/2—2 **IV**), and lacks vomerine teeth and large dorsal blotches.
**General geographic distribution:** *Hyla ebraccata* occurs at low and moderate elevations from central Veracruz and northern Oaxaca, Mexico, to eastern Panama on the Atlantic versant and from northwestern Costa Rica to the Chocó of Colombia on the Pacific versant. It is also found on the Atlantic versant in the valley of the Río Magdalena in Colombia.
**Distribution in Honduras:** This species is known only in the Mosquitia from near sea level to 660 m elevation.
**Distribution in the Mosquitia:** Gracias a Dios—Caño Awawás (USNM); Laguna Baraya (ROM); Kalila Plapan Tingni (USNM); Karasangkan (UF); Kaska Tingni (SMF; USNM); Kasunta (USNM); Krahkra (USNM); Mocorón (CF); Rus Rus (USNM); Swabila (UF); Bodega de Río Tapalwás (UF); Crique Yulpruan (USNM). Olancho—Kauroahuika (USNM); Quebrada de Las Marías (USNM).
**Natural history comments:** *Hyla ebraccata* occurs in primary, moderately disturbed, and second growth evergreen broadleaf forest (including gallery forest through pine savanna) and in lightly disturbed to denuded broadleaf swamp forest in the Mosquitia. The species breeds around temporary

and permanent ponds and inundated areas during the rainy season. Breeding activity appears to peak after heavy rains. Males call from low vegetation above the water. *Hyla ebraccata* is the only Mosquitia species of *Hyla* to lay its eggs on vegetation above the water. This species is active at night, although one large chorus of males continued calling until about 1000 h on the day of 28 July 2001.

*Hyla loquax* **Gaige and Stuart, 1934**
**Common name(s):** None
**Description (Plate 34):** This moderate-sized frog (males to 45 mm SVL, females to 47 mm; Savage, 2002) has an extensive axillary membrane. The pupil is horizontally elliptical. The snout is rounded in lateral profile. Fingers and toes are extensively webbed (modal webbing formula **I** 2—$2^{+}$ **II** 1—$2^{-}$ **III** $2^{-}$—$1^{+}$ **IV** and **I** 3/4—1 **II** 3/4—$1^{+}$ **III** 3/4—$1^{-}$ **IV** $1^{+}$—3/4 **V**, respectively) and have large disc pads with rounded disc covers. Vomerine teeth are present. Males have a single, median, subgular vocal sac. Dorsal color is pale gray-tan to yellowish brown with tiny brown flecks, scattered small brown spots, or brown mottling. Dorsolateral stripes are absent. The anterior and posterior surfaces of the thighs and the webbing of the hands and feet are orange. The side of the head is similar in color to that of the dorsum.
**Similar species:** *Hyla ebraccata* is a smaller frog (males to 29 mm SVL, females to 37 mm) that has a pale dorsolateral band and usually large dorsal blotches. *Hyla microcephala* is a smaller frog (males to 27 mm SVL, females to 31 mm) that usually has a thin dorsolateral brown stripe that is

**Plate 34.** *Hyla loquax*. Photograph by McCranie.

bordered above by a thin white stripe and has moderate finger webbing (basal between Fingers I–II, remaining modal webbing formula **II** $1^{+}$—2 1/2 **III** 2 1/3—$2^{+}$ **IV**). *Hyla picta* is a smaller frog (to 23 mm SVL) that has a pale dorsolateral stripe and moderate finger webbing (basal between Fingers I–II, remaining modal webbing formula **II** 2—3 **III** 2 1/2—2 **IV**) and lacks vomerine teeth.
**General geographic distribution:** *Hyla loquax* occurs at low and moderate elevations on the Atlantic versant from southern Veracruz and eastern Oaxaca, Mexico, to east-central Costa Rica and on Islas del Maíz, Nicaragua. It is also found at moderate and intermediate elevations on the Pacific versant of south-central Honduras.
**Distribution in Honduras:** This frog is widely distributed in the northern half of the country. The species is also known from Cerro Uyuca and the Tegucigalpa region, Francisco Morazán, in south-central Honduras. It is known from about sea level to 1585 m elevation.
**Distribution in the Mosquitia:** Gracias a Dios—Caño Awawás (USNM); Barra Patuca (UNAH); Kalila Plapan Tingni (USNM); Kaska Tingni (SMF; USNM); Kasunta (USNM); Krahkra (USNM); Swabila (UF); Tikiraya (UF).
**Natural history comments:** *Hyla loquax* occurs in lightly disturbed to denuded evergreen broadleaf forests and in disturbed broadleaf swamp forest in the Mosquitia. We have never found this species in the primary broadleaf forests of the Mosquitia. The species breeds in flooded fields and temporary and permanent ponds in the Mosquitia. *Hyla loquax* has an extended reproductive season, lasting about the duration of the rainy season, but it can also be an explosive breeder. We encountered a breeding aggregation of several hundred *H. loquax* on the nights of 27–28 July 2001, following heavy rains (also see *Agalychnis callidryas* and *A. saltator* accounts). Although the species is active at night, males from the large breeding aggregation continued to call until about 1000 h on the day of 28 July 2001. Males call from low vegetation above the water or from in the water.

*Hyla microcephala* **Cope, "1885" (1886)**
**Common name(s):** None
**Description (Plate 35):** This small frog (males to 27 mm SVL [McCranie and Wilson, 2002], females to 31 mm [Duellman, 2001]) has a well-developed axillary membrane. The pupil is horizontally elliptical. The snout is rounded in lateral profile.

**Plate 35.** *Hyla microcephala.* Photograph by McCranie.

Fingers are moderately webbed (basal between Fingers I–II, remaining modal webbing formula **II** $1^{+}$—2 1/2 **III** 2 1/3—$2^{+}$ **IV**) and the toes are extensively webbed (modal webbing formula **I** $1^{-}$—$2^{-}$ **II** 3/4—2 **III** 3/4—2 **IV** 2—3/4 **V**). Moderately expanded disc pads with rounded disc covers are present on the fingers and toes. Vomerine teeth are present. Males have a single, median, subgular vocal sac. Dorsal coloration is pale brown with a dorsal pattern usually consisting of irregular brown dashes forming an X-shaped mark, fragmented crossbars, fragmented lines, or a reticulated pattern. A thin brown dorsolateral stripe is usually present, with the brown stripe bordered above by a thin white stripe. There is no pale subocular spot.

**Similar species:** *Hyla ebraccata* has extensive finger webbing (modal webbing formula **I** 2—2 1/3 **II** 3/4—$2^{+}$ **III** $2^{+}$—$2^{-}$ **IV**), large dorsal blotches, and a distinct pale dorsolateral band. *Hyla loquax* is a larger frog (males to 45 mm SVL, females to 47 mm) that has extensively webbed fingers (modal webbing formula **I** 2—$2^{+}$ **II** 1—$2^{-}$ **III** $2^{-}$—$1^{+}$ **IV**) and lacks pale dorsolateral stripes. *Hyla picta* is a smaller frog (to 23 mm SVL) that lacks vomerine teeth. *Scinax staufferi* is often confused with *H. microcephala*. However, *S. staufferi* is most easily distinguished from *H. microcephala* by having a protruding snout.

**General geographic distribution:** *Hyla microcephala* occurs at low and moderate elevations on the Atlantic versant from central Veracruz and northern Oaxaca, Mexico, to southern Nicaragua and northwestern Costa Rica and additionally on the Atlantic versant from central Panama to southeastern Brazil. It is also found on the Pacific versant from south-central Honduras to eastern Panama. The species also occurs on the Caribbean Islands of Trinidad and Tobago and the Bay Islands of Honduras.

**Distribution in Honduras:** This frog is widely distributed (including Islas de Guanaja, Roatán, and Utila), except for the southwestern and extreme southern portions of the country. It is known from about sea level to 1000 m elevation.

**Distribution in the Mosquitia:** El Paraíso—1.5 km E of Arenales (USNM). Gracias a Dios—Awasbila (USNM); Caño Awawás (USNM); Baltiltuk (UNAH); Barra Patuca (UNAH); Belén (UNAH); Brus Laguna (UNAH); Kalila Plapan Tingni (USNM); Karasangkan (USNM); Kaska Tingni (SMF; USNM); Kasunta (USNM); Krahkra (USNM); Limaraya (UNAH); Mavita (USNM); Mocorón (UNAH); Rus Rus (UF; USNM); Swabila (UF); Bodega de Río Tapalwás (UF); Tikiraya (UF). Olancho—confluence of Ríos Aner and Wampú (USNM); Casamacoa (USNM); Kauroahuika (USNM); Quebrada Kuilma Tingni (USNM); Quebrada de Las Marías (USNM); Matamoros (USNM); Yapuwás (USNM).

**Natural history comments:** *Hyla microcephala* is known from primary to denuded evergreen broadleaf forests, lightly disturbed to denuded broadleaf swamp forest, coastal strand, and pine savanna in the Mosquitia. The species breeds in inundated areas and temporary and permanent ponds and swamps and sometimes forms large breeding aggregations. Males call at night from grasses and other low vegetation growing in and around the water. The species has an extended reproductive season lasting for much of the rainy season. *Hyla microcephala* can be common in the vicinity of villages.

### *Hyla miliaria* (Cope, "1885" [1886])

**Common name(s):** None

**Description (Plate 36):** This large frog (males to 110 mm SVL, females to 86 mm; Duellman, 2001) lacks an axillary membrane. The pupil is horizontally elliptical. The snout is vertical in lateral profile. The skin on top of the head contains osteoderms, giving the appearance that the head is co-ossified with the underlying skull. Fingers and toes are extensively webbed (modal webbing formula **I** $2^{-}$—$2^{-}$ **II** 1/2—$1^{-}$ **III** 1—3/4 **IV** and **I** 3/4—1 **II** 3/4—1 **III** 3/4—3/4 **IV** 1—$1^{-}$ **V**, respectively) and have large disc pads with rounded disc covers. Scalloped dermal fringes are present along the

**Plate 36.** *Hyla miliaria.* Photograph by McCranie.

posterior edges of the forearms and tarsi. The prepollex is distinctly enlarged, projecting and curved backwards distally. Vomerine teeth are present. Males have a single, median, subgular vocal sac, but the sac is apparently not distensible. Dorsal color is olive-green with dark grayish brown mottling. Flanks are cream with olive-brown blotches. The anterior and posterior surfaces of the thighs are pale pinkish tan with dark brown blotches. The scalloped dermal fringes on the arms and legs are olive-cream. Webbing of the hands and feet is dark brown.

**Similar species:** *Hyla miliaria* is a very large treefrog (males to 110 mm and females to 86 mm, according to Duellman, 2001), the largest in the Mosquitia, with huge, extensively webbed hands and feet, scalloped dermal fringes along the outer limb margins, and a prominent, projecting prepollex that is recurved distally, and is unlikely to be confused with any other Mosquitian anuran. Nonetheless, the three species of *Smilisca* and *Phrynohyas venulosa* are moderate to large treefrogs and, conceivably, might be mistaken for this frog. Males of the *Smilisca* species have paired external subgular vocal sacs; both sexes usually have a blotched dorsal pattern. *Phrynohyas venulosa* has a highly glandular, pustulose skin and generally a dorsal pattern consisting of a large dorsal dark blotch; males have paired lateral external vocal sacs.

**General geographic distribution:** *Hyla miliaria* occurs at low and moderate elevations on the Atlantic versant from eastern Honduras to eastern Costa Rica and on the Pacific versant from southern Costa Rica to central Panama.

**Distribution in Honduras:** This frog is known from two nearby localities (150 and 190 m elevation) in the eastern portion of the Mosquitia.

**Distribution in the Mosquitia:** Gracias a Dios—Bodega de Río Tapalwás (UF); Urus Tingni Kiamp (USNM).

**Natural history comments:** *Hyla miliaria* occurs in primary evergreen broadleaf forests in the Mosquitia. Two calling males were traced to water-containing tree holes in late May and early June 2003. One was collected on the same night it was calling and the other was collected the day after it was heard calling (see McCranie et al., 2003a). Another calling male was traced to a water-containing tree hole in early May 2004, and was collected at that time. Another male was calling from high up in a huge tree on the nights of 12–13 and 18 May 2004. The calls of all were similar to that described by McCranie et al. (2003a). The species apparently breeds in water-containing tree holes.

**Remarks:** This spectacular frog was recently reported from Honduras by McCranie et al. (2003a).

*Hyla picta* **(Günther, 1901)**

**Common name(s):** None

**Description (Plate 37):** This small frog (males to 22 mm SVL, females to 23 mm; McCranie and Wilson, 2002) has a well-developed axillary membrane. The pupil is horizontally elliptical. The snout is rounded in lateral profile. Fingers are moderately webbed (basal between Fingers I–II, remaining modal webbing formula **II** 2—3 **III** 2 1/2—2 **IV**) and the toes are extensively webbed (modal webbing formula **I** 1 1/3—2 **II** 3/4—$2^+$ **III** 3/4—2 **IV** 2—3/4 **V**). Moderately expanded disc pads

**Plate 37.** *Hyla picta.* Photograph by McCranie.

with rounded disc covers are present on the fingers and toes. Vomerine teeth are absent. Males have a single, median, subgular vocal sac. Dorsal surfaces are some shade of brown, usually with dark blue-green spots and a dusting of rust-red punctuations. These rust-red punctuations are visible under a microscope as reddish-brown flecking in preserved specimens. A pale dorsolateral stripe is present, the stripe can be more distinct anterior to the eye (the pale dorsolateral stripe can disappear in specimens preserved for many years).
**Similar species:** *Hyla picta* is the only hylid in the Mosquitia that lacks vomerine teeth. It is also the smallest hylid in the area.
**General geographic distribution:** *Hyla picta* occurs at low, moderate, and intermediate elevations on the Atlantic versant from eastern San Luis Potosí, Mexico, to northeastern Honduras.
**Distribution in Honduras:** This frog is found at low and moderate elevations (about sea level to 770 m) across the northern portion of the country.
**Distribution in the Mosquitia:** Gracias a Dios—Barra Patuca (UNAH).
**Natural history comments:** *Hyla picta* is known only from one highly disturbed locality in the Mosquitia that is apparently in coastal strand. In other parts of Honduras, males are known to call from low emergent vegetation around the periphery of temporary ponds or from water hyacinths floating in a permanent lake on nights following heavy rains. The soft call of this species is usually not well audible in a mixed chorus consisting of several other species of hylids. Thus, this small frog can oftentimes be overlooked at these breeding sites.

*Phrynohyas venulosa* **(Laurenti, 1768)**
**Common name(s):** None
**Description (Plate 38):** This large frog (males to 101 mm SVL, females to 114 mm; Duellman, 2001; although Honduran specimens are smaller with males known to reach 83 mm SVL and females to 87 mm) has dense glandular skin in the occipital and frontal regions. The pupil is horizontally elliptical. The snout is rounded to nearly vertical in lateral profile. Fingers are moderately webbed (basal between Fingers I–II, remaining modal webbing formula **II** 1 1/2—2 1/2 **III** 2$^+$—2 **IV**) and the toes are extensively webbed (modal webbing formula **I** 1$^+$—2 **II** 3/4—2 **III** 3/4—2 **IV** 2$^-$—3/4 **V**). Fingers and toes have large disc pads with rounded disc covers. Males have paired lateral vocal sacs

**Plate 38.** *Phrynohyas venulosa.* Photograph by McCranie.

that are located posterior to the angles of the jaws. Vocal sacs are grayish brown to dark gray in breeding males. Dorsal surfaces are olive-green, pale gray, or some shade of brown, with or without a large darker brown blotch.
**Similar species:** *Phrynohyas venulosa* is the only hylid in the Mosquitia with dense glandular skin in the occipital and frontal regions and males with paired lateral vocal sacs located posterior to the angles of the jaws.
**General geographic distribution:** *Phrynohyas venulosa* is found at low, moderate, and intermediate elevations from central Tamaulipas, Mexico, to Nicaragua and northwestern Costa Rica on the Atlantic versant and from southern Sinaloa, Mexico, to eastern Panama on the Pacific versant. It is also widespread in South America east of the Andes to northern Argentina and is also known from Ecuador on the Pacific versant and on the Caribbean Islands of Trinidad and Tobago.
**Distribution in Honduras:** This species is widely distributed at low and moderate elevations and occasionally at intermediate elevations in the country. It is known from about sea level to 1610 m elevation.
**Distribution in the Mosquitia:** Gracias a Dios—Barra Patuca (UNAH); Cauquira (UF); Karasangkan (USNM); Kasunta (USNM); Krahkra (USNM); Krausirpe (LSUMZ); Mocorón (CF); Rus Rus (USNM); Tánsin (LSUMZ).
**Natural history comments:** *Phrynohyas venulosa* occurs in highly disturbed broadleaf forest (both evergreen and swamp forests), coastal strand, and pine savanna in the Mosquitia. The species breeds in temporary ponds and areas that are

inundated by heavy rains. *Phrynohyas venulosa* is an explosive breeder following unusually heavy rains. Males form large choruses that can be heard from long distances. The choruses sometimes begin in late afternoon two or three hours before nightfall. Males call while floating on the water surface or while sitting in shallow water, usually in association with dense growths of grasses and low vegetation.

*Ptychohyla hypomykter* **McCranie and Wilson, 1993**

**Common name(s):** None

**Description (Plate 39):** This is a moderate-sized frog (males to 36 mm SVL, females to 44 mm; McCranie and Wilson, 2002) in which the males have pointed keratinized spines on the prepollex and usually prominent ventrolateral glands. An abbreviated axillary membrane is present (not extending more than one-half the distance towards the elbow). The pupil is horizontally elliptical and the snout is vertical with a rounded upper end in lateral profile. Fingers are moderately webbed (basal between Fingers I–II, remaining modal webbing formula **II** 2—2 3/4 **III** $2^{+}$—2 **IV**) and the toes are extensively webbed (modal webbing formula **I** $1^{+}$—2 **II** $1^{-}$—2 **III** 1—2 **IV** 2—1 **V**). Fingers and toes have large disc pads with rounded disc covers. Males have a single, median, subgular vocal sac. Dorsal surfaces are some shade of gray or brown, with or without darker mottling or small, scattered blotches.

**Similar species:** *Ptychohyla hypomykter* is the only hylid in the Mosquitia in which the males have pointed keratinized prepollical spines and usually prominent ventrolateral glands. Since female *P. hypomykter* lack these sexually dimorphic characters, the species also can be distinguished from other Mosquitia hylids by the following characters. All species of *Agalychnis* have vertical pupils. *Anotheca spinosa* has occipital and canthal spines. All small to moderate sized Mosquitia species of *Hyla* have a well-developed axillary membrane (extending more than one-half of distance towards elbow) and most are smaller species. *Phrynohyas venulosa* has dense glandular skin in the occipital and frontal regions. Both species of *Scinax* have protruding snouts in lateral profile. *Smilisca baudinii* and *S. phaeota* have a dark brown postorbital bar or broad stripe that extends dorsolaterally at least to the level of the axilla. *Smilisca sordida* has more finger and toe webbing (modal webbing formula **II** 1—2 1/3 **III** $2^{-}$—1 **IV** and **I** 3/4—$1^{-}$ **II** 3/4—1 **III** 3/4—1 **IV** 1—3/4 **V**, respectively).

**General geographic distribution:** *Ptychohyla hypomykter* occurs at low, moderate and intermediate elevations on the Atlantic versant from west-central Guatemala to north-central Nicaragua, exclusive of the Cordillera Nombre de Dios of north-central Honduras. It is also found on the Pacific versant in southwestern to south-central Honduras.

**Distribution in Honduras:** This species is widely distributed at moderate and intermediate elevations (620 to 2070 m) in the mountainous regions.

**Distribution in the Mosquitia:** Olancho—Nueva Esperanza (USNM).

**Natural history comments:** *Ptychohyla hypomykter* is a montane species that only marginally occurs in the Mosquitia (known from only one specimen in the Mosquitia) and what follows is based on our experience outside the Mosquitia. The species breeds in mountain streams, with adults normally found on low vegetation near these streams. The species probably breeds throughout the year. Males have been collected while calling from January to November and females with large ovarian eggs were collected in February and April and from July to November. Many tadpoles of this species collected since 1997 have deformed mouthparts.

**Plate 39.** *Ptychohyla hypomykter*. Photograph by McCranie.

*Scinax boulengeri* **(Cope, 1887)**

**Common name(s):** None

**Description (Plate 40):** This moderate-sized frog

**Plate 40.** *Scinax boulengeri.* Photograph by Townsend.

(males to 49 mm SVL, females to 53 mm; Duellman, 2001) has a protruding snout in lateral profile. The pupil is horizontally elliptical. Webbing is absent between Fingers I–II and basal between Fingers II–III–IV. Webbing between Toes I–II is greatly reduced relative to that of the other toes, which are extensively webbed (modal webbing formula **I** 2—2 1/2 **II** 1—2 **III** 1—2 **IV** $2^{+}$—$1^{-}$ **V**). Fingers and toes have large disc pads with somewhat truncated disc covers. Vomerine teeth are present. Males have a single, median, subgular vocal sac. The dorsal and lateral surfaces of the head have numerous distinct tubercles, including along the edge of the upper and lower lips; these tubercles are more pronounced in males. Dorsal surfaces are mottled greenish olive, olive green, and yellow. The groin is yellowish green with black spots or mottling. The anterior and posterior surfaces of the thighs are yellow with black bars. Posterior surfaces of the shanks are also yellow with black bars.

**Similar species:** *Scinax boulengeri* is the only Mosquitia hylid with bold black bars on the otherwise yellow anterior and posterior surfaces of the thighs and the posterior surface of the shanks. The protruding snout in lateral profile and the strongly reduced webbing between Toes I–II only occurs in one other Mosquitia hylid, *S. staufferi. Scinax staufferi* is a smaller frog (males to 29 mm SVL, females to 32 mm) and, in addition to lacking black bars on the hind limbs, it also lacks distinct tubercles on the head.

**General geographic distribution:** *Scinax boulengeri* occurs at low and moderate elevations from eastern Honduras to north-central Colombia on the Atlantic versant and from northwestern Costa Rica to northwestern Ecuador on the Pacific versant.

**Distribution in Honduras:** This frog is known only in the Mosquitia from 5 to 60 m elevation.

**Distribution in the Mosquitia:** Gracias a Dios—Caño Awawás (USNM); Kalila Plapan Tingni (SMF; USNM); Krahkra (USNM); Mocorón (CF); Rus Rus (USNM); Swabila (UF); Tikiraya (UF).

**Natural history comments:** *Scinax boulengeri* occurs in primary to highly disturbed evergreen broadleaf forest (included denuded gallery forest through pine savanna) and in lightly disturbed to denuded broadleaf swamp forest in the Mosquitia. Males were collected while calling at night in June, July, August, and October following heavy rains. Breeding sites were thorn palm swamps, a flooded rice field carved from a palm swamp, a grassy inundated area carved from gallery forest, a grass-filled and palm-encircled pond, and swampy areas in remnant broadleaf swamp forest. Males call from trunks or limbs of shrubs or small trees. A single female was taken from vegetation along a stream in primary evergreen broadleaf forest during the day.

*Scinax staufferi* **(Cope, 1865)**

**Common name(s):** None

**Description (Plate 41):** This small frog (males to 29 mm SVL, females to 32 mm; Duellman, 2001) has a protruding snout in lateral profile. The pupil is horizontally elliptical. Webbing is absent between Fingers I–II and basal between Fingers II–III–IV.

**Plate 41.** *Scinax staufferi.* Photograph by McCranie.

Webbing between Toes I–II is greatly reduced relative to that of the other toes, which are extensively webbed (modal webbing formula **I** 2—2 3/4 **II** 1—$3^-$ **III** $1^+$—$3^-$ **IV** 2 1/2—1 **V**). Fingers and toes have large disc pads with somewhat truncated disc covers. Vomerine teeth are present. Males have a single, median, subgular vocal sac. Dorsal and lateral surfaces of the head lack distinct tubercles, although small tubercles can be present. Dorsal surfaces are some shade of brown, usually with darker brown broken longitudinal lines or stripes. The groin and anterior and posterior surfaces of the thighs are some shade of brown. Dorsal surfaces of the thighs are brown with darker brown crossbars.

**Similar species:** *Scinax staufferi* and *S. boulengeri* are the only Mosquitia hylids with protruding snouts and greatly reduced webbing between Toes I–II. *Scinax boulengeri* is a larger frog (males to 49 mm SVL, females to 53 mm) that has bold black bars on the otherwise yellow anterior and posterior surfaces of the thighs and the posterior surface of the shanks. *Scinax boulengeri* also has distinct tubercles on the dorsal and lateral surfaces of the head. *Hyla microcephala* is often confused with *S. staufferi*. However, *H. microcephala* is most easily distinguished from *S. staufferi* by having a short snout that is rounded in lateral profile.

**General geographic distribution:** *Scinax staufferi* is found at low, moderate, and intermediate elevations from southern Tamaulipas, Mexico, to extreme northern Costa Rica on the Atlantic versant (including the Islas de la Bahía, Honduras, and Isla del Maíz Grande, Nicaragua) and from Guerrero, Mexico, to northwestern Costa Rica on the Pacific versant.

**Distribution in Honduras:** This species is widely distributed at low and moderate elevations and rarely at intermediate elevations. It also occurs on Islas de Guanaja and Utila, Islas de la Bahía, and is known from about sea level to 1530 m elevation.

**Distribution in the Mosquitia:** Colón—Río Paulaya (BMNH). Gracias a Dios—Caño Awawás (USNM); Laguna Bacalar (BMNH); Barra Patuca (UNAH); Belén (UNAH); Brus Laguna (UNAH); near Calpo (UF); Cauquira (UF); Laguna de Ébano (FMNH; MCZ); Kalila Plapan Tingni (USNM); Kaska Tingni (SMF; USNM); Krahkra (USNM); Limaraya (UNAH); Mocorón (UNAH); Rus Rus (UF; USNM); Swabila (UF); Tánsin (LSUMZ); Tikiraya (UF).

**Natural history comments:** *Scinax staufferi* occurs in lightly disturbed to denuded broadleaf forest (both evergreen and swamp forest), pine savanna, freshwater marshes, and coastal strand in the Mosquitia. We have never found this species in the primary broadleaf forests of the Mosquitia. It breeds in temporary ponds and inundated areas during the rainy season. *Scinax staufferi* has an extended reproductive season. Males call at night from grasses and other low emergent vegetation growing in the water. It was also heard calling from the tops of coconut palms at Cauquira during periods of light rain in early June near the end of the dry season. This species can be common in the vicinity of villages.

*Smilisca baudinii* **(A.M.C. Duméril and Bibron, 1841)**

**Common name(s):** None

**Description (Plate 42):** This moderately large frog (males to 76 mm SVL, females to 90 mm; Duellman, 2001) has paired subgular vocal sacs in the males. The pupil is horizontally elliptical. The snout is rounded in lateral profile. Fingers are moderately webbed (basal between Fingers I–II, remaining modal webbing formula **II** 1 2/3—2 2/3 **III** 2 1/3—2 **IV**) and the toes are extensively webbed (modal webbing formula **I** 1—2 **II** 3/4—$2^+$ **III** 1—2 **IV** 2—3/4 **V**). Fingers and toes have large disc pads with rounded disc covers. A row of low, distinct tubercles is usually present along the posterior ventrolateral edge of the forearm. Dorsal surfaces vary from some shade of brown to green. A brown interorbital bar and brown dorsal body blotches are usually present. A distinct dark brown

**Plate 42.** *Smilisca baudinii.* Photograph by McCranie.

to black postorbital bar or broad stripe extends above the tympanum and then downward onto the dorsolateral portion of the body to at least the level of the axilla. Contrasting dark brown vertical lip bars are present. Flanks are mottled with brown and white. A brown outer tarsal stripe is absent.
**Similar species:** *Smilisca baudinii*, and its congenerics *S. phaeota* and *S. sordida*, are the only Mosquitia hylids with paired subgular vocal sacs in males. *Smilisca phaeota* has a narrow pale labial stripe and a thin brown outer tarsal stripe, and lacks a row of low distinct tubercles along the posterior ventrolateral edge of the forearm and contrasting vertical bars on the upper lip. *Smilisca sordida* lacks contrasting vertical bars on the upper lip and a brown postorbital bar or stripe and has more webbing on Finger IV (only about 1 segment free of webbing). *Smilisca sordida* is also a smaller frog (males to 45 mm SVL, females to 64 mm). Females of all other genera of Mosquitia hylids lack the postorbital dark bar or stripe.
**General geographic distribution:** *Smilisca baudinii* occurs at low, moderate, and intermediate elevations from extreme southern Texas, USA, to eastern Costa Rica on the Atlantic versant and from southern Sonora, Mexico, to southeastern Costa Rica on the Pacific versant (including the Islas de Tres Marías, Mexico).
**Distribution in Honduras:** This species is widespread in the country, including Islas de Barbareta, Guanaja, Roatán, and Utila and the Cayos Cochinos. It is known from about sea level to 1610 m elevation.
**Distribution in the Mosquitia:** Colón—Las Champas (BMNH); Río Guaraska (BMNH); Quebrada Machín (USNM). El Paraíso—1.5–2.0 km E of Arenales (USNM); Arenales (LACM); Boca Español (USNM). Gracias a Dios—Caño Awalwás (SMF; USNM); Awasbila (USNM); Caño Awawás (USNM); Baltiltuk (UNAH); Barra Patuca (USNM); Brus Laguna (UNAH); Karasangkan (USNM); Kaska Tingni (USNM); Krahkra (USNM); Krausirpe (LSUMZ); Mocorón (UNAH); Rus Rus (UF; USNM); Tánsin (LSUMZ); confluence of Ríos Wampú and Patuca (USNM); between mouth of Río Wampú and Yapuwás (USNM); confluence of Quebrada Waskista with Río Wampú (USNM); between Quebrada Waskista and mouth of Río Wampú (USNM). Olancho—confluence of Ríos Aner and Wampú (USNM); Kauroahuika (USNM); Quebrada Kuilma Tingni (USNM); Quebrada de Las Marías (SMF; UNAH; USNM); Matamoros (USNM); Quebrada El Mono (USNM); Nueva Esperanza (USNM); Qururia (USNM); confluence of Ríos Sausa and Wampú (USNM); Subterráneo (USNM).
**Natural history comments:** *Smilisca baudinii* occurs in primary to completely denuded evergreen broadleaf forest and broadleaf swamp forest and in pine savanna in the Mosquitia. The species breeds in inundated areas and in temporary and permanent ponds, or in virtually any body of standing water. Tadpoles of this species, in addition to being found in inundated areas and temporary and permanent ponds, have been found in the Mosquitia in small water-filled depressions in trails made by human and pack animal traffic and in a water-filled tree buttress (McCranie and Wilson, 2002). *Smilisca baudinii* has an extended reproductive season, but our experience in late May and early June during periods of intermittent rain at the end of the dry season indicates that it does not form breeding aggregations at that time, as do some other hylid species (e.g., *Hyla loquax*, *H. microcephala*, *Scinax staufferi*). Males call from low emergent vegetation above the breeding sites. It is also not unusual to see solitary individuals of this species sitting in trees overhanging streams and rivers in the primary evergreen broadleaf forests of the Mosquitia. *Smilisca baudinii* also occurs regularly in and around villages. The species is active at night.

*Smilisca phaeota* **(Cope, 1862d)**
**Common name(s):** None
**Description (Plate 43):** This moderately large frog (males to 65 mm SVL, females to 78 mm; Duellman, 2001) has paired subgular vocal sacs in the males. The pupil is horizontally elliptical. The snout is rounded in lateral profile. Fingers are moderately webbed (basal between Fingers I–II, remaining modal webbing formula **II** 2—3 **III** 2 1/2—2 **IV**) and the toes are extensively webbed (modal webbing formula **I** 1—2 **II** 3/4—2 **III** 3/4—2 **IV** 2—3/4 **V**). Fingers and toes have large disc pads with rounded disc covers. A row of low, distinct tubercles is absent along the posterior ventrolateral edge of the forearm. Dorsal surfaces are some shade of brown or green. A brown interorbital bar and dorsal body blotches are occasionally present. A distinct dark brown to black postorbital bar or broad stripe extends above the tympanum and then downward onto the dorsolateral portion of the body at least to the level

**Plate 43.** *Smilisca phaeota.* Photograph by McCranie.

of the axilla. A narrow yellow to cream labial stripe is present and contrasting dark brown vertical lip bars are absent. Flanks are yellow to cream with fine dark brown venation present. A thin brown stripe is present along the posterior ventrolateral edge of the forearms and along the outer edge of the tarsus.

**Similar species:** *Smilisca phaeota*, and its congenerics *S. baudinii* and *S. sordida*, are the only Mosquitia hylids with paired subgular vocal sacs in males. *Smilisca baudinii* has contrasting vertical bars on the upper lip and a row of distinct tubercles along the posterior ventrolateral edge of the forearm, and lacks a narrow pale labial stripe and a thin brown outer tarsal stripe. *Smilisca sordida* lacks a brown postorbital bar or stripe and has more webbing on Finger IV (only about 1 segment free of webbing). *Smilisca sordida* is also a smaller frog (males to 45 mm SVL, females to 64 mm). Females of all other genera of Mosquitia hylids lack the postorbital dark bar or stripe.

**General geographic distribution:** *Smilisca phaeota* is found at low and moderate elevations from eastern Honduras to north-central Colombia on the Atlantic versant and from northwestern Costa Rica to northwestern Ecuador on the Pacific versant.

**Distribution in Honduras:** This frog is known from low and moderate elevations (40 to 1100 m) in the eastern portion of the country.

**Distribution in the Mosquitia:** Colón—Quebrada Machín (USNM). El Paraíso—Boca Español (USNM). Gracias a Dios—Caño Awalwás (UF; USNM); Awasbila (USNM); Caño Awawás (USNM); Mocorón (UNAH); Rus Rus (USNM); Bodega de Río Tapalwás (USNM); Warunta Tingni Kiamp (USNM). Olancho—Quebrada El Guásimo (USNM); Río Kosmako (USNM); Quebrada de Las Marías (SMF; UNAH; USNM); Matamoros (SMF; USNM).

**Natural history comments:** *Smilisca phaeota* occurs in primary to heavily disturbed evergreen broadleaf forest (including gallery forest through pine savanna) in the Mosquitia. The species breeds in swampy areas, flooded fields and other inundated areas, side pools of small streams, water filled road ruts, and large water-filled cavities in fallen logs. Males call while floating on the water surface or while sitting in shallow water. *Smilisca phaeota* is active at night. Solitary individuals are sometimes found sitting in trees above rivers and streams in primary forest.

*Smilisca sordida* **(W. Peters, 1863b)**

**Common name(s):** None

**Description (Plate 44):** This moderately large frog (males to 45 mm SVL, females to 64 mm; Duellman, 2001) has paired subgular vocal sacs in the males. The pupil is horizontally elliptical. The snout is rounded in lateral profile. Fingers are moderately webbed (basal between Fingers I–II, remaining modal webbing formula **II** 1—2 1/3 **III** 2⁻—1 **IV**) and the toes are extensively webbed (modal webbing formula **I** 3/4—1⁻ **II** 3/4—1 **III** 3/4—1 **IV** 1—3/4 **V**). Fingers and toes have large disc pads with rounded disc covers. A row of low, distinct tubercles is usually present along the posterior ventrolateral edge of the forearm. Dorsal surfaces are brown. A darker brown interorbital bar and

**Plate 44.** *Smilisca sordida.* Photograph by McCranie.

dorsal blotches are present. A postorbital bar or stripe and contrasting vertical lip bars are absent. Flanks are pinkish brown with scattered small dark brown spots; pale blue mottling can also be present in the groin. A brown outer tarsal stripe is absent.
**Similar species:** *Smilisca sordida*, and its congenerics *S. baudinii* and *S. phaeota*, are the only Mosquitia hylids with paired subgular vocal sacs in males. *Smilisca baudinii* is a larger frog (males to 76 mm SVL, females to 90 mm) that has contrasting vertical lip bars, a brown postorbital bar or stripe, and less webbing on Finger IV (2 segments free of webbing). *Smilisca phaeota* has a narrow pale labial stripe and a thin brown outer tarsal stripe, and lacks a row of low distinct tubercles along the posterior ventrolateral edge of the forearm. Females of the Mosquitia species of *Hyla* (except the unmistakeable *H. miliaria*) have an axillary membrane and are smaller frogs (maximum of 23–47 mm SVL). Female *Ptychohyla hypomykter* have less webbing (modal webbing formula of fingers **II** 2—2 3/4 **III** $2^+$—2 **IV**, that of the toes **I** $1^+$—2 **II** $1^-$—2 **III** 1—2 **IV** 2—1 **V**). Females of both species of *Scinax* have protruding snouts.
**General geographic distribution:** *Smilisca sordida* is found at low and moderate elevations from northeastern Honduras to western Panama on the Atlantic versant and from northwestern Costa Rica to western Panama on the Pacific versant.
**Distribution in Honduras:** This frog is known only in the Mosquitia from 30 to 220 m elevation.
**Distribution in the Mosquitia:** Colón—Empalme Río Chilmeca (KU). Gracias a Dios—Baltiltuk (formerly in UNAH, now lost); Raudal Pomokir (KU); Walpunpansilpi (KU). Olancho—confluence of Quebrada Siksatara with Río Wampú (USNM).
**Natural history comments:** Our only experience with *Smilisca sordida* has been along a single stream through primary evergreen broadleaf forest during periods of heavy rainfall. Two specimens were collected one night in September and another on a night in July in low vegetation above the stream. Males were not calling. The species is known to breed in streams in Costa Rica during the dry season and can be a common species at those times (Savage, 2002).

## Family Leptodactylidae

The family Leptodactylidae has no known synapomorphies (Pough et al., 2003) and, thus, may not be monophyletic. Leptodactylids are highly variable in morphology, habits, and life history (Pough et al., 2003). Members of this family in the Mosquitia are distinguished by the combination of having the fingers unwebbed and the toe webbing absent, basal, or only slightly developed. The members of this family occur from southeastern Arizona, southern New Mexico, south-central Texas, and extreme southern Texas, USA, to southern Chile and southern Argentina. The family also occurs throughout the West Indies. Outside of the natural range of the family, it has been widely introduced in Florida and Hawaii, USA, and on Bermuda. Forty-nine genera containing 1131 species were included in this family by Frost (2004), but Crawford and Smith (2005) resurrected the generic name *Craugastor* for the "Middle American clade" formerly placed in *Eleutherodactylus*. Four genera with 35 species are known to occur in Honduras. Three genera containing 13 species are found in the Mosquitia.

### *Craugastor epochthidius* (McCranie and Wilson, 1997a)

**Common name(s):** None
**Description (Plate 45):** This small frog (males to 27 mm SVL, females to 37 mm; McCranie and Wilson, 2002) has the dorsal surfaces wrinkled and covered with numerous tiny to small tubercles. Short postocular ridges are present and cranial crests are absent. Ventral surfaces of the body are smooth. The snout is rounded to nearly vertical in lateral profile. The tympanum is indistinct to

**Plate 45.** *Craugastor epochthidius*. Photograph by McCranie.

absent. Fingers are unwebbed and toes are slightly webbed (modal webbing formula **I** 2—2 3/4 **II** 2—3 1/2 **III** 3—4⁺ **IV** 4⁺—2 1/2 **V**). All fingers and toes have expanded disc pads and the disc covers are rounded on Fingers III–IV and on all toes. Fingers and toes lack supernumerary tubercles. Finger I is shorter than Finger II and Toe III is longer than Toe V. An inner tarsal fold is absent and vomerine teeth are present. Males have paired vocal slits and a colorless, granular thumb pad. Dorsal surfaces are usually some shade of brown, although the dorsum of one specimen was brick red with a dark brown middorsal hourglass figure. A dark eye mask is absent. Flanks are brown, except that the groin region is usually yellow. Posterior surfaces of the thighs are brown, with yellow to pale brown tiny to small spots present. The belly is yellow with brown flecking.

**Similar species:** *Craugastor epochthidius* is the only Mosquitia *Craugastor* that has an indistinct to absent tympanum and wrinkled dorsal surfaces that are covered with numerous tiny to small tubercles.

**General geographic distribution:** *Craugastor epochthidius* is found at low and moderate elevations of the Sierra de Agalta, Olancho, northeastward to the Montaña de Las Marías, Olancho, and tributaries of the ríos Paulaya and Plátano, Colón, on the Atlantic versant of east-central and northeastern Honduras.

**Distribution in Honduras:** See General geographic distribution. This species is known from 150 to 1450 m elevation.

**Distribution in the Mosquitia:** Colón—Río Guaraska (BMNH); Quebrada Machín (USNM). Olancho—Quebrada de Las Marías (USNM); Nueva Esperanza (USNM).

**Natural history comments:** *Craugastor epochthidius* occurs along montane streams (or at least fast flowing streams originating in montane areas) in primary to moderately disturbed evergreen broadleaf forest. The species is active at night in the Mosquitia and has been collected in July and August in the region. Most specimens were on the ground along streams or on emergent rocks in streams. A few were in low vegetation along streams. The species has disappeared from its known localities in the Sierra de Agalta to the west of the Mosquitia (McCranie and Wilson, 2002).

*Craugastor fitzingeri* **(O. Schmidt, 1857)**
**Common name(s):** None

**Description (Plate 46):** This moderate-sized frog (males to 37 mm SVL [McCranie and Wilson, 2002], females to 53 mm [Lynch and Myers, 1983]) lacks cranial crests and a dark brown eye mask. Short postocular ridges and/or short ridges on the back are usually present. Dorsal surfaces have scattered small to moderate-sized tubercles. Ventral surfaces of the body are smooth. The snout is rounded in lateral profile and subelliptical in dorsal aspect in males and subovoid in dorsal aspect in females. The canthus is angular. The tympanum is prominent. Fingers are unwebbed and toes are slightly webbed (modal webbing formula **I** 2—2⁺ **II** 2—3 **III** 2 3/4—4 **IV** 4—2 **V**). All fingers and toes have expanded disc pads with those on Fingers III–IV broadly expanded (disc on Finger III about 2.5 to 3.3 times width of digit just proximal to disc). Disc covers on Fingers III–IV are truncated and those on all toes are somewhat truncated. Fingers and toes lack supernumerary tubercles. Finger I is longer than, or equal in length to Finger II and Toe III is longer than Toe V. An inner tarsal fold and vomerine teeth are present. Males have paired vocal slits and a colorless, granular thumb pad. Dorsal surfaces are some shade of brown or gray. A broad pale middorsal stripe extending from the snout to the vent is commonly present, especially in females. Upper lips are usually distinctly barred. The throat is usually gray or brown, with a white, irregular stripe evident medially. Posterior surfaces of the thighs are brown with pale yellow spots or a reticulated pattern. The belly is white, usually with scattered dark brown flecking.

**Similar species:** *Craugastor epochthidius* has wrinkled dorsal surfaces that are covered with

**Plate 46.** *Craugastor fitzingeri*. Photograph by McCranie.

numerous tiny to small tubercles and an indistinct to absent tympanum. *Craugastor lauraster* has well-developed supernumerary tubercles on the fingers and toes and the finger and toe discs are not expanded. *Craugastor megacephalus* has cranial crests and *C. mimus* and *C. noblei* have a distinct dark brown eye mask and a slightly protruding snout in lateral profile. *Craugastor pechorum* has a snout that is nearly rounded in dorsal aspect, a rounded canthus, the disc on Finger III ≤2.3 times the width of the digit just proximal to the disc, and rounded disc covers on the toes. *Eleutherodactylus cerasinus*, *E. diastema*, and *E. ridens* have Toe V longer than Toe III.

**General geographic distribution:** *Craugastor fitzingeri* occurs at low, moderate, and rarely intermediate elevations on the Atlantic versant from eastern Honduras to the inter-Andean valleys of Colombia, and from northwestern Costa Rica to western Colombia on the Pacific versant.

**Distribution in Honduras:** This species is known only in the Mosquitia from 5 to 700 m elevation.

**Distribution in the Mosquitia:** Colón—Quebrada Machín (USNM). El Paraíso—Boca Español (USNM). Gracias a Dios—Caño Awalwás (SMF; UF; USNM); Awasbila (USNM); Caño Awawás (USNM); Baltiltuk (UNAH); Crique Curamaira (USNM); Kalila Plapan Tingni (USNM); Kaska Tingni (USNM); Kasunta (USNM); Mocorón (UNAH); Rus Rus (UF; USNM); Río Sutawala (USNM); Bodega de Río Tapalwás (UF; USNM); Urus Tingni Kiamp (USNM); Cerro Wahatingni (UF; USNM); Wakling Kiamp (USNM); Warunta Tingni Kiamp (USNM); confluence of Quebrada Waskista with Río Wampú (USNM); Crique Yulpruan (USNM). Olancho—confluence of Ríos Aner and Wampú (USNM); Caobita (SMF; USNM); Quebrada El Guásimo (SMF; USNM); Río Kosmako (USNM); Quebrada Kuilma Tingni (SMF; USNM); Quebrada de Las Marías (SMF; USNM); Matamoros (SMF; USNM); Quebrada El Mono (SMF; USNM); Qururia (USNM); confluence of Ríos Sausa and Wampú (USNM); confluence of Quebrada Siksatara with Río Wampú (USNM); Subterráneo (USNM); confluence of Ríos Yanguay and Wampú (USNM).

**Natural history comments:** *Craugastor fitzingeri* is an extremely common frog in primary to lightly disturbed evergreen broadleaf forests of the Mosquitia (including gallery forest through pine savanna). The species also occurs in lesser numbers in heavily disturbed evergreen broadleaf forest and in broadleaf swamp forest. *Craugastor fitzingeri* is primarily nocturnal, but can also be found active during the day. It can be found on the ground in the forest and along streams, on emergent rocks in streams, and on low vegetation in the forest and along streams. Males call in late afternoon and during the early night from low vegetation. These calling males are usually shielded by overhanging leaves. An adult female (SVL 40.3 mm) was found on 18 May while guarding an egg clutch beneath leaf litter in primary evergreen broadleaf forest. The egg clutch (UF) contains 32 eggs with an average diameter of 4.5 mm.

*Craugastor lauraster* **(Savage, McCranie, and Espinal, 1996)**

**Common name(s):** None

**Description (Plate 47):** This small frog (males to 20 mm SVL, females to 24 mm) has the finger and toe discs not expanded (although the discs on Fingers III–IV and Toes III–IV can be somewhat swollen with spadate disc covers) and well-developed supernumerary tubercles on the fingers and toes. The thenar tubercle is much smaller than the palmar tubercle. Postocular ridges and cranial crests are absent. Dorsal surfaces are smooth to tuberculate (tubercles and/or rugosities are usually most obvious posteriorly on the body and upper eyelids). Ventral surfaces of the body are weakly to coarsely areolate. The snout is rounded in lateral profile. The tympanum is prominent. Fingers and toes are unwebbed, except that extremely basal webbing is sometimes present between Toes II–III–IV. Finger I is shorter than Finger II and Toe III is longer than Toe V. A weak inner tarsal fold and

**Plate 47.** *Craugastor lauraster*. Photograph by McCranie.

vomerine teeth are present. Male vocal slits and thumb pads are absent. Dorsal surfaces are brown with darker brown spots or blotches present dorsally and dorsolaterally. A dark brown supratympanic stripe is usually present and an indistinct dark brown, but incomplete eye mask can be present. Flanks and groin are flesh colored to pale brown and darker brown blotches are usually present on the flanks. Posterior surfaces of the thighs are mottled pale brown and yellowish cream or are an essentially unmarked pale brown. The belly is pale yellow to flesh color.
**Similar species:** *Craugastor lauraster* is the only *Craugastor* in the Mosquitia with well-developed supernumerary tubercles on the fingers and toes and the finger and toe discs not expanded.
**General geographic distribution:** *Craugastor lauraster* occurs at low and moderate elevations on the Atlantic versant from north-central Honduras to north-central Nicaragua.
**Distribution in Honduras:** This frog is known from the eastern half of the country from 40 to 1200 m elevation.
**Distribution in the Mosquitia:** Gracias a Dios—Caño Awalwás (UF; USNM); Awasbila (USNM); Cabeceras de Río Rus Rus (USNM); Kaska Tingni (USNM); Mocorón (UNAH); Bodega de Río Tapalwás (UF; USNM); Urus Tingni Kiamp (USNM); Cerro Wahatingni (USNM); Warunta Tingni Kiamp (USNM); confluence of Quebrada Waskista with Río Wampú (USNM). Olancho—Caobita (SMF; USNM); Quebrada El Guásimo (SMF; USNM); Río Kosmako (USNM).
**Natural history comments:** *Craugastor lauraster* is a common species in the leaf litter of primary and lightly disturbed evergreen broadleaf forest in the Mosquitia. The species is active primarily during the day; however, it is occasionally taken while active at night. It can also be found by raking through the leaf litter both during the day and at night.
**Remarks:** Köhler (2001) discussed variation in Nicaraguan populations of this frog in the diagnostic characters used by Savage et al. (1996) to define the species. All specimens from the Honduran Mosquitia agree completely with the diagnosis of *Craugastor lauraster* provided by Savage et al. (1996).

*Craugastor megacephalus* **(Cope, 1875)**
**Common name(s):** None
**Description (Plate 48):** This moderately large frog (males to 43 mm SVL, females to 70 mm; Savage, 2002) has paired cranial crests in the frontoparietal region. Ridges are also present in the suprascapular and laterosacral regions. The species has a noticeably broad head. The snout is nearly vertical with a rounded upper end in lateral profile. The tympanum is prominent. Dorsal surfaces are smooth with scattered small tubercles (in addition to the ridges) and the ventral surfaces of the body are smooth. Fingers and toes are unwebbed. Supernumerary tubercles are absent on the fingers and toes. Finger I is longer than Finger II and Toe III is longer than Toe V. Finger and toe discs are present, those on the fingers are not expanded, those on the toes are narrowly expanded. An inner tarsal fold is absent and vomerine teeth are present. Males lack vocal slits and thumb pads. Dorsal surfaces of the head and body are brown. The suprascapular and laterosacral ridges are partially outlined with darker brown. A dark brown supratympanic stripe is present. Flanks are brown with a few orange-brown spots. A dark brown seat patch mark is also present. Posterior surfaces of the thighs are brown with darker brown mottling. The belly is grayish white with brown mottling and reticulations.
**Similar species:** *Craugastor megacephalus* is the only leptodactylid in the Mosquitia with frontoparietal crests.
**General geographic distribution:** *Craugastor megacephalus* is found at low and moderate elevations from eastern Honduras to western Panama on the Atlantic versant and marginally on the Pacific versant in northwestern Costa Rica.
**Distribution in Honduras:** This frog is known

**Plate 48.** *Craugastor megacephalus.* Photograph by McCranie.

only from three low elevation (130–360 m) localities in the Mosquitia.
**Distribution in the Mosquitia:** El Paraíso—Arenales (LACM). Gracias a Dios—Bodega de Río Tapalwás (UF). Olancho—Río Kosmako (USNM).
**Natural history comments:** We have collected only one specimen of *Craugastor megacephalus* in the Mosquitia. An adult female was found at night in July while active on the ground in primary evergreen broadleaf forest on a hillside. Another was collected for us in primary evergreen broadleaf forest in October. According to Savage (2002), adults of this species in Costa Rica hide in burrows during the day and at night they commonly sit at the burrow entrance and ambush passing prey.
**Remarks:** Honduran specimens of this species were previously called *Eleutherodactylus biporcatus* (see McCranie and Wilson, 2002), but a systematic revision of the *C. biporcatus* group (as *Eleutherodactylus*) by Savage and Myers (2002) demonstrated that the correct name for the Honduran populations is *C. megacephalus*.

*Craugastor mimus* **(Taylor, 1955)**
**Common name(s):** None
**Description (Plate 49):** This moderate-sized frog (males to 45 mm SVL, females to 58 mm; see Remarks) has a dark brown eye mask extending from the snout across the eye and above the tympanum to the level of the axilla or beyond. A dark brown seat patch mark is also present. Dorsal surfaces are smooth to weakly granular, except for paired suprascapular tubercles and several small tubercles on the upper eyelids. Cranial crests are absent. Ventral surfaces of the body are smooth. The snout is slightly protruding with a rounded upper edge in lateral profile. The tympanum is prominent. Fingers are unwebbed and toes are slightly webbed (modal webbing formula **I** 2—2 **II** $2^-$—3 **III** $3^-$—4 **IV** 4—2 2/3 **V**) with distinct fleshy lateral keels present on the unwebbed portions of the toes. All fingers and toes have narrowly expanded disc pads. Disc covers on Fingers III–IV are usually palmate and those on all toes vary from rounded to palmate. Fingers and toes lack supernumerary tubercles. Finger I is longer than Finger II and Toe III is longer than Toe V. An inner tarsal fold and vomerine teeth are present. Males lack vocal slits and thumb pads. Dorsal surfaces are brown with a narrow pale brown middorsal line (see above for eye mask and seat patch coloration). Posterior surfaces of the thighs are uniformly brown. A dark brown stripe is present on the anterior surface of the shanks from the knees to near the ankles, this dark brown stripe extending onto the anterior surface of the thighs near the knee. The belly is white with a purplish tinge.

**Plate 49.** *Craugastor mimus.* Photograph by McCranie.

**Similar species:** *Craugastor mimus* and *C. noblei* are the only Mosquitia *Craugastor* with distinct dark brown eye masks and a slightly protruding snout in lateral profile. *Craugastor noblei* has the discs on Fingers III–IV much larger than those on Fingers I–II, less toe webbing (modal webbing formula **I** $2^+$—2 3/4 **II** $2^+$—3 1/2 **III** $3^+$—4 1/2 **IV** $4^+$—2 3/4 **V**), and non-fleshy lateral keels on the unwebbed portions of the toes. It also lacks a seat patch mark.
**General geographic distribution:** *Craugastor mimus* occurs at low and moderate elevations on the Atlantic versant from eastern Honduras to eastern Costa Rica.
**Distribution in Honduras:** This species is known only in the Mosquitia from 70 to 700 m elevation.
**Distribution in the Mosquitia:** Gracias a Dios—Caño Awalwás (USNM); Karasangkan (USNM); Bodega de Río Tapalwás (UF; USNM); Urus Tingni Kiamp (USNM); Cerro Wahatingni (UF; USNM); Warunta Tingni Kiamp (USNM). Olancho—confluence of Ríos Aner and Wampú (USNM); Quebrada de Las Marías (USNM).
**Natural history comments:** *Craugastor mimus* occurs in primary to lightly disturbed evergreen broadleaf forest. The species is primarily nocturnal in the Mosquitia, but is said to be primarily diurnal in Costa Rica (Savage, 2002). The few Mosquitia adults were taken on the forest floor, but subadults are usually found on low vegetation. We have found

the species only in the forest away from the environs of streams.
**Remarks:** Savage (2002) recorded a maximum size of 37 mm SVL for males of *Craugastor mimus.* A single Mosquitia male is considerably larger (44.9 mm SVL) than the other known males of this species. A second adult male from the Mosquitia has a SVL of 30.0 mm. The largest known Mosquitia female has a SVL of 46.1 mm, whereas Savage (2002) stated that females from Costa Rica reached 58 mm SVL.

*Craugastor noblei* **(Barbour and Dunn, 1921)**
**Common name(s):** None
**Description (Plate 50):** This moderate-sized frog (males to 48 mm SVL, females to 66 mm; Savage, 2002) has a dark brown eye mask extending from the snout across the eye and above the tympanum to the level of the axilla or beyond. Dorsal surfaces are granular, usually with several small tubercles on the upper eyelids and above the tympanum. Cranial crests are absent. Ventral surfaces of the body are smooth. The snout is slightly protruding with a rounded upper edge in lateral profile. The tympanum is prominent. Fingers are unwebbed and toes are slightly webbed (modal webbing formula **I** $2^+$—2 3/4 **II** $2^+$—3 1/2 **III** $3^+$—4 1/2 **IV** $4^+$—2 3/4 **V**), with non-fleshy lateral keels present on the unwebbed portions of the toes. All toes and Fingers I–II have narrowly expanded disc pads, with the disc covers rounded to palmate. Disc pads on Fingers III–IV are broadly expanded with usually palmate disc covers. Fingers and toes lack supernumerary tubercles. Finger I is longer than Finger II and Toe III is longer than Toe V. An inner tarsal fold and vomerine teeth are present. Male vocal slits and thumb pads are absent. Dorsal surfaces are brown to orange-brown, usually with a brown hourglass mark present on the back. A narrow pale brown middorsal line is usually present, at least posteriorly on the back. A dark brown seat patch mark is absent (see above for eye mask coloration). Posterior surfaces of the thighs are reddish brown with paler brown mottling. There is no dark brown stripe on the anterior surfaces of the shanks and thighs, although a few dark brown spots are usually present near the knees. The belly is pale yellow to white.

**Plate 50.** *Craugastor noblei.* Photograph by McCranie.

**Similar species:** *Craugastor mimus* and *C. noblei* are the only Mosquitia *Craugastor* with distinct dark brown eye masks and slightly protruding snouts in lateral profile. *Craugastor mimus* has more toe webbing (modal webbing formula **I** 2—2 **II** $2^-$—3 **III** $3^-$—4 **IV** 4—2 2/3 **V**), fleshy lateral keels on the unwebbed portions of the toes, a dark seat patch mark, and the discs on Fingers III–IV not noticeably larger than those on Fingers I–II.
**General geographic distribution:** *Craugastor noblei* is found at low and moderate elevations from north-central Honduras to western Panama on the Atlantic versant and from west-central Costa Rica to west-central Panama on the Pacific versant.
**Distribution in Honduras:** This species is known from the northern slopes of the Cordillera Nombre de Dios in Atlántida and Colón, and from northwestern Olancho to south-central and southern Gracias a Dios. It is known from 40 to 1170 m elevation.
**Distribution in the Mosquitia:** Colón—Quebrada Machín (USNM). Gracias a Dios—Caño Awalwás (USNM); Mocorón (UNAH); Bodega de Río Tapalwás (USNM); Urus Tingni Kiamp (USNM); Warunta Tingni Kiamp (USNM). Olancho—Caobita (SMF; USNM).
**Natural history comments:** *Craugastor noblei* occurs in primary to lightly disturbed evergreen broadleaf forest in the Mosquitia. Most of the Mosquitia specimens we have found were active on low vegetation at night, but we also found several that were active on the forest floor during the day. Several of the specimens seen at night on low vegetation were positioned on the edges of steep slopes or ridges, so that one leap would launch the frog down these inclines. Savage (2002) stated that the species is diurnal in Costa Rica.

*Craugastor pechorum* **(McCranie and Wilson, 1999)**
**Common name(s):** None
**Description (Plate 51):** This moderate-sized frog (males to 43 mm SVL, females to 62 mm; McCranie and Wilson, 2002) lacks cranial crests and a dark brown eye mask. Postocular ridges vary from well developed to weakly developed, and extend to the level of the axilla. Dorsal surfaces are smooth to granular, except distinct pustular tubercles are present on the posterior portion of the back and on the upper eyelids. Ventral surfaces of the body are smooth. The snout is rounded in lateral profile and nearly rounded in dorsal aspect. The canthus is rounded. The tympanum is prominent. Fingers are unwebbed and toes are slightly webbed (modal webbing formula **I** 2—2 1/2 **II** 2—3 1/2 **III** 3—4 1/3 **IV** 4 1/3—3 **V**). All fingers and toes have expanded disc pads (disc on Finger III about 1.9 to 2.3 times width of digit just proximal to disc), with the disc covers on Fingers III–IV somewhat truncated; those on Fingers I–II and on all toes are rounded. Fingers and toes lack supernumerary tubercles. Finger I is longer than Finger II and Toe III is longer than Toe V. An inner tarsal fold and vomerine teeth are present. Males have paired vocal slits and a colorless, granular thumb pad. Dorsal surfaces are brown with slightly darker brown mottling. A pale middorsal stripe is absent. Posterior surfaces of the thighs are dark brown with pale gold spots and/or blotches. Upper lips are usually distinctly barred. The throat is white, heavily to lightly flecked with brown; a pale medial stripe is absent. The belly is some shade of yellow and lightly flecked with brown.

**Plate 51.** *Craugastor pechorum.* Photograph by McCranie.

**Similar species:** *Craugastor epochthidius* has wrinkled dorsal surfaces that are covered with numerous tiny to small tubercles and an indistinct to absent tympanum. *Craugastor lauraster* has well-developed supernumerary tubercles on the fingers and toes, and the finger and toe discs are not expanded. *Craugastor megacephalus* has cranial crests. *Craugastor fitzingeri* has a snout that is subelliptical in dorsal aspect in males and subovoid in dorsal aspect in females, an angular canthus, the disc on Finger III ≥2.5 times the width of the digit just proximal to the disc, and somewhat truncated disc covers on the toes. *Craugastor mimus* and *C. noblei* have a distinct dark brown eye mask and a slightly protruding snout in lateral profile. *Eleutherodactylus cerasinus*, *E. diastema*, and *E. ridens* have Toe V longer than Toe III.
**General geographic distribution:** *Craugastor pechorum* occurs at low and moderate elevations in the Mosquitia on the Atlantic versant of the northeastern and eastern portions of the Honduran departments of Olancho and Colón, respectively.
**Distribution in Honduras:** See General geographic distribution. The species is known from about 150 to 680 m elevation.
**Distribution in the Mosquitia:** Colón—Río Cuyamel (BMNH); Quebrada Machín (USNM). Olancho—Quebrada de Las Marías (USNM); Nueva Esperanza (USNM).
**Natural history comments:** *Craugastor pechorum* is a streamside species that occurs in primary to heavily disturbed evergreen broadleaf forest; however, only one specimen has been taken in heavily disturbed areas. The species is active at night and is usually found on the ground along streams or on emergent rocks in streams; however, a few specimens were 1–2 m above the ground on broad leaves and palm tree trunks about 10–20 m from the nearest stream (McCranie and Wilson, 2002).

*Eleutherodactylus cerasinus* **(Cope, 1875)**
**Common name(s):** None
**Description (Plate 52):** This small frog (males to 25 mm SVL, females to 35 mm; Savage, 2002) has Toe V longer than Toe III, with the tip of Toe V usually not reaching the level of the distal subarticular tubercle on Toe IV (the tip of Toe V occasionally reaches the level of the distal subarticular tubercle on Toe IV). Dorsal surfaces are smooth to weakly granular, usually with suprascapular ridging (occasionally with only

**Plate 52.** *Eleutherodactylus cerasinus*. Photograph by McCranie.

scattered tubercles in suprascapular region). Upper eyelids usually have small tubercles along the outer edges. A distinct pointed or pustular tubercle is present on each heel. Cranial crests are absent. Ventral surfaces of the body are coarsely areolate. The snout is rounded or vertical with a rounded upper edge in lateral profile. The tympanum is usually distinct, occasionally indistinct. Fingers and toes are not webbed. The finger and toe disc pads are distinctly expanded, with the disc covers on Fingers III–IV and those on the toes somewhat truncated. Fingers and toes lack supernumerary tubercles. Some subarticular tubercles on Finger III and Toes III–IV are pungent or pointed. Finger I is usually shorter than Finger II. An inner tarsal tubercle or short fold is present. Several outer tarsal tubercles are usually present. Vomerine teeth are on low, short, indistinct ridges, with the vomerine teeth not evident in some males. Males have paired vocal slits and white thumb pads. Dorsal surfaces are yellowish brown to dark brown, occasionally with a darker W or Y-shaped suprascapular mark. The upper lip is usually distinctly barred. Flanks, groin, and anterior surfaces of the thighs are usually pinkish brown to brown. The posterior surfaces of the thighs are brown with pale brown or yellow spots. The heels are sometimes a pale copper color. The belly is white to pale gray.
**Similar species:** *Eleutherodactylus cerasinus* is the only Mosquitia species of *Eleutherodactylus* that has a distinct pointed to pustular heel tubercle. All Mosquitia species of *Craugastor* have Toe V shorter than Toe III.

**General geographic distribution:** *Eleutherodactylus cerasinus* is found at low and moderate elevations on the Atlantic versant from eastern Honduras to eastern Panama and marginally on the Pacific versant in northwestern Costa Rica.
**Distribution in Honduras:** This frog is known only in the Mosquitia from 150 to 680 m elevation.
**Distribution in the Mosquitia:** Colón—Quebrada Machín (USNM). Gracias a Dios—Bodega de Río Tapalwás (UF; USNM); Cerro Wahatingni (USNM); Warunta Tingni Kiamp (USNM). Olancho—Quebrada de Las Marías (USNM).
**Natural history comments:** *Eleutherodactylus cerasinus* occurs in primary to heavily disturbed evergreen broadleaf forest, and is extremely common in one primary forest area (Bodega de Río Tapalwás). The species is active at night on low vegetation in the forest. Males call from the upper surfaces of vegetation. The species is also occasionally found under leaf litter during the day. It is most active on nights following heavy rains.
**Remarks:** This species was included in McCranie and Wilson (2002) as Eleutherodactylus operosus. That nominal form was synonymized with *E. cerasinus* by McCranie and Wilson (2003).

*Eleutherodactylus diastema* **(Cope, 1875)**
**Common name(s):** None
**Description (Plate 53):** This small frog (males to 21 mm SVL, females to 24 mm; Savage, 2002) has Toe V longer than Toe III, with the tip of Toe V extending to the level of the distal subarticular tubercle on Toe IV. Dorsal surfaces are smooth, except that occasional specimens have a few small

**Plate 53.** *Eleutherodactylus diastema*. Photograph by McCranie.

low tubercles on the upper eyelids. Heels are smooth, lacking a distinct tubercle. Cranial crests are absent. Ventral surfaces of the body are coarsely areolate. The snout is rounded to nearly vertical with a rounded upper end in lateral profile. The tympanum is indistinct to distinct. Fingers and toes are not webbed. The finger and toe disc pads are distinctly expanded, with most disc covers palmate. Fingers and toes lack supernumerary tubercles. Finger I is shorter than Finger II. An inner tarsal fold or tubercle and outer tarsal tubercles are absent. Vomerine teeth are present, but on short, low, indistinct ridges. Males have paired vocal slits, but lack thumb pads. Dorsal surfaces vary from pale brown to gray. A paler colored interorbital bar is commonly present. Paired pale colored longitudinal dorsolateral stripes are also commonly present. Flanks, groin, and anterior surfaces of the thighs are mottled with pale brown and brown or pale gray and gray. Posterior surfaces of the thighs are brown with paler brown mottling. The belly is pale brown with numerous dark brown spots or heavy flecking.
**Similar species:** *Eleutherodactylus cerasinus* has a distinct pointed to pustular heel tubercle and thumb pads in males. *Eleutherodactylus ridens* has rounded disc covers and lacks vomerine teeth. All Mosquitia species of *Craugastor* have Toe V shorter than Toe III.
**General geographic distribution:** *Eleutherodactylus diastema* is found at low and moderate elevations from eastern Honduras to eastern Panama on the Atlantic versant and on the Pacific versant from northwestern Costa Rica to western Ecuador.
**Distribution in Honduras:** This species is known only in the Mosquitia from 60 to 190 m elevation.
**Distribution in the Mosquitia:** Gracias a Dios—Caño Awalwás (USNM); Awasbila (USNM); Bodega de Río Tapalwás (UF; USNM); Urus Tingni Kiamp (USNM); Cerro Wahatingni (UF; USNM); Warunta Tingni Kiamp (USNM); Crique Yulpruan (USNM).
**Natural history comments:** *Eleutherodactylus diastema* occurs in primary to moderately disturbed evergreen broadleaf forest. The species is nocturnal and is found on low vegetation in the forest. Males call from the upper surfaces of vegetation, from inside bromeliads, or from under loose bark on tree trunks. The species is most active on nights following heavy rains. It can be extremely abundant where it occurs.
**Remarks:** This species was recently reported for the first time from Honduras by McCranie, Nicholson, and Castañeda (2002).

*Eleutherodactylus ridens* **(Cope, 1866)**
**Common name(s):** None
**Description (Plate 54):** This small frog (males to 19 mm SVL, females to 26 mm; McCranie and Wilson, 2002) has Toe V longer than Toe III, with the tip of Toe V extending to the level of the distal subarticular tubercle on Toe IV. Dorsal surfaces are smooth, except that there are several low tubercles present on the upper eyelids. Heels are smooth to rugose, lacking a distinct tubercle. Cranial crests are absent. Ventral surfaces of the body are coarsely areolate. The snout is rounded in lateral profile. The tympanum is distinct to indistinct in males, indistinct to very indistinct in females. Fingers and toes are not webbed. Finger and toe disc pads are distinctly expanded, with rounded disc covers. Fingers and toes lack supernumerary tubercles. Finger I is shorter than Finger II. A weak or very abbreviated inner tarsal fold is present and vomerine teeth are absent. Outer tarsal tubercles are absent. Males have paired vocal slits, but lack thumb pads. Dorsal surfaces are pale olive to brown. A slightly darker X-shaped mark in the suprascapular region is sometimes present. A dark brown supratympanic stripe is usually present. The groin and anterior and ventral surfaces of the thighs are usually reddish orange; sometimes, these surfaces are brown. Posterior surfaces of the thighs are pale to dark brown. The belly varies from nearly uniformly pale yellow to heavily flecked with dark brown.
**Similar species:** *Eleutherodactylus cerasinus* has

**Plate 54.** *Eleutherodactylus ridens.* Photograph by McCranie.

a distinct pointed to pustular heel tubercle and thumb pads in males. *Eleutherodactylus diastema* has most disc covers palmate and indistinct vomerine teeth ridges. All Mosquitia species of *Craugastor* have Toe V shorter than Toe III.
**General geographic distribution:** *Eleutherodactylus ridens* is found at low and moderate elevations from northern Honduras to central Panama on the Atlantic versant and from northwestern Costa Rica to western Colombia on the Pacific versant.
**Distribution in Honduras:** This frog is known from about sea level to 1180 m elevation from eastern Atlántida eastward to northern Olancho and southern Gracias a Dios.
**Distribution in the Mosquitia:** Colón—Río Guaraska (BMNH); Quebrada Machín (USNM); Tulito (BMNH). Gracias a Dios—Auka Kiamp (USNM); Caño Awalwás (UF); Mocorón (UNAH); Rus Rus (UF; USNM); Bodega de Río Tapalwás (UF; USNM); Urus Tingni Kiamp (USNM); Cerro Wahatingni (UF); Warunta Tingni Kiamp (USNM). Olancho—Caobita (SMF; USNM); Quebrada El Guásimo (SMF; USNM); Río Kosmako (USNM); Quebrada de Las Marías (SMF; USNM); confluence of Quebrada Siksatara with Río Wampú (USNM).
**Natural history comments:** *Eleutherodactylus ridens* occurs in primary to recently cleared evergreen broadleaf forest (including gallery forest through pine savanna) in the Mosquitia. The species is active at night and is found on vegetation in the forest. It is most active on nights following heavy rains.

*Leptodactylus fragilis* **(Brocchi, 1877)**
**Common name(s):** None
**Description (Plate 55):** This moderate-sized frog (males to 43 mm SVL, females to 44 mm; Heyer, 1978) lacks expanded finger and toe tips and a digital grove around the tips of the fingers and toes. Fingers are unwebbed and webbing is absent between Toes I–II and IV–V; webbing is basal between Toes II–III–IV. Lateral keels are absent on all toes, or only weakly developed on one or more of Toes II–IV. The tongue is only slightly notched posteriorly. Male thumb spines and hypertrophied arms are absent. Males have paired vocal slits. The skin of the dorsal surfaces is smooth to weakly granular. Dorsolateral ridges vary from absent to distinct. Numerous dirty white to cream (in preservative) tubercles are present on the ventral surfaces of the tarsal segments. Dorsal surfaces are some shade of brown with darker brown spots or blotches on the back. A pale yellow longitudinal stripe (pale brown to cream in preservative) is present on the posterior surfaces of the thighs. Ventral surfaces are white to pale yellow.

**Plate 55.** *Leptodactylus fragilis*. Photograph by McCranie.

**Similar species:** *Leptodactylus melanonotus* has well-developed lateral fleshy fringes on the toes and two thumb spines in adult males and lacks a pale longitudinal stripe on the posterior surfaces of the thighs. *Leptodactylus pentadactylus* is a much larger species (males >100 mm SVL) that has a single thumb spine and strongly hypertrophied arms in adult males and lacks a pale longitudinal stripe on the posterior surfaces of the thighs. All species of *Rana* have extensively webbed toes and a tongue that is deeply notched posteriorly.
**General geographic distribution:** *Leptodactylus fragilis* occurs at low, moderate, and intermediate elevations from extreme southern Texas, USA, to central Colombia and northern Venezuela on the Atlantic versant (disjunct in much of the area from Nicaragua southward) and from Colima, Mexico, to central Panama on the Pacific versant.
**Distribution in Honduras:** This species is widely distributed through much of the country. It is known from about sea level to 1530 m elevation.
**Distribution in the Mosquitia:** Gracias a Dios—Ahuás (LACM); Caño Awalwás (SMF; USNM); Awasbila (USNM); Caño Awawás (USNM); near Calpo (UF); Kasunta (USNM); Krausirpe (LSUMZ); Mocorón (UNAH); Prumnitara (UF); Rus Rus (UF; USNM); Swabila (UF); Tánsin (LACM); Tikiraya (UF). Olancho—Kauroahuika (USNM); Matamoros (USNM).

**Natural history comments:** *Leptodactylus fragilis* occurs in highly disturbed evergreen broadleaf and broadleaf swamp forests, pine savanna, freshwater marshes, and coastal strand in the Mosquitia. Males call at night from temporary ponds and puddles and from inundated areas during the rainy season. Males call from concealed places and can be difficult to locate. The species occurs in heavily polluted areas in villages and towns, including Puerto Lempira. In addition to being nocturnal, this terrestrial species can also be found active during rainy days.
**Remarks:** This frog has usually been called *Leptodactylus labialis* in the recent literature. However, Heyer (2002) concluded that the correct name for this species was *L. fragilis*.

*Leptodactylus melanonotus* **(Hallowell, "1860" [1861])**
**Common name(s):** None
**Description (Plate 56):** This moderate-sized frog (males to 46 mm SVL, females to 50 mm [Heyer, 1970]; Honduran specimens are smaller, however, with the largest known male being 44 mm SVL and the largest known female being 43 mm SVL) lacks expanded finger and toe tips and a digital grove around the tips of the fingers and toes. Fingers are unwebbed and basal webbing is present between the toes. Well-developed lateral fleshy fringes are present on the toes. The tongue is only slightly notched posteriorly. Adult males have two thumb spines, but almost always lack hypertrophied arms. Males have paired vocal slits. The skin of the dorsal surfaces is smooth to weakly granular, usually with scattered coni apicales; occasionally small scattered tubercles can be present. Dorsolateral ridges are absent. Coni apicales are present on the ventral surfaces of the tarsal segments. Dorsal surfaces are brown to gray with indistinct darker spots present in the paler specimens. Posterior surfaces of the thighs are brown, mottled with paler brown, and never have a pale longitudinal stripe. Ventral surfaces are white to cream with scattered dark flecking. Brown to orange ventrolateral glands are usually evident.

**Plate 56.** *Leptodactylus melanonotus*. Photograph by McCranie.

**Similar species:** *Leptodactylus fragilis* lacks well-developed lateral fleshy fringes on the toes and thumb spines in adult males and has a pale longitudinal stripe on the posterior surface of the thighs. *Leptodactylus pentadactylus* is a much larger species (adults >100 mm SVL) that has a single thumb spine in adult males, the arms strongly hypertrophied in adult males, dorsolateral ridges, and adults lack lateral fleshy fringes on the toes. Juvenile *L. pentadactylus* lack coni apicales. All species of *Rana* have extensively webbed toes and a tongue that is deeply notched posteriorly.
**General geographic distribution:** *Leptodactylus melanonotus* is found at low, moderate, and intermediate elevations from Tamaulipas, Mexico, to central Panama on the Atlantic versant and from Sonora, Mexico, to Ecuador on the Pacific versant.
**Distribution in Honduras:** This frog is widely distributed at low and moderate elevations (about sea level to 1280 m) on the mainland (exclusive of the extreme southwestern portion) and on the Islas de la Bahía and Cayos Cochinos.
**Distribution in the Mosquitia:** El Paraíso—2.0 km E of Arenales (USNM); Boca Español (USNM). Gracias a Dios—Awasbila (USNM).
**Natural history comments:** *Leptodactylus melanonotus* is known in the Mosquitia only from highly disturbed areas formerly cloaked in evergreen broadleaf forest. Males call at night and, to a lesser extent, during the day from temporary ponds and puddles and inundated areas in the rainy season. Males call from concealed places and can be difficult to locate. Females are active on the ground at night.

*Leptodactylus pentadactylus* **(Laurenti, 1768)**
**Common name(s):** Burka* (Miskito)
**Description (Plate 57):** This large to huge frog (adults >100 mm SVL) lacks expanded finger and toe tips and a digital grove around the tips of the fingers and toes. Fingers and toes are unwebbed in adults; juveniles can have basal toe webbing.

**Plate 57.** *Leptodactylus pentadactylus.* Photograph by McCranie.

Lateral keels are absent or very weak on the toes in adults; juveniles have well-developed lateral keels on the toes. The tongue is only slightly notched posteriorly. Adult males have a single thumb spine, hypertrophied arms, and paired vocal slits. The skin of the dorsal surfaces is smooth to weakly granular. Dorsolateral ridges are present. Tubercles are absent on the ventral surfaces of the tarsal segments. Dorsal surfaces are brown to rust-red. Posterior surfaces of the thighs are dark brown with pale brown spots or mottling, never with a pale yellow longitudinal stripe. Ventral surfaces vary from nearly uniformly brown to brown with cream mottling.
**Similar species:** *Leptodactylus pentadactylus* is a much larger species than *L. fragilis* and *L. melanonotus. Leptodactylus fragilis* differs from juvenile *L. pentadactylus* in having a pale longitudinal stripe on the posterior surface of the thighs. *Leptodactylus melanonotus* differs from juvenile *L. pentadactylus* in having scattered coni apicales on the dorsal surfaces of the body and the ventral surfaces of the tarsal segments. All species of *Rana* have extensively webbed toes and a tongue that is deeply notched posteriorly.
**General geographic distribution:** *Leptodactylus pentadactylus* is found at low and moderate elevations from north-central Honduras to Peru and Brazil on the Atlantic versant and from southwestern Nicaragua to Ecuador on the Pacific versant (see Remarks).
**Distribution in Honduras:** This species is known from about the eastern half of the country from about sea level to 660 m elevation.
**Distribution in the Mosquitia:** Colón—Quebrada Machín (USNM). El Paraíso—about 1 km E of Arenales (USNM). Gracias a Dios—Caño Awalwás (USNM); Caño Awawás (USNM); Baltiltuk (UNAH); Bil Almuk (MCZ); Krahkra (USNM); Mocorón (CF); Rus Rus (USNM); Swabila (UF); Bodega de Río Tapalwás (UF; USNM); Tikiraya (UF); Urus Tingni Kiamp (USNM); Walpunpansilpi (formerly in UNAH, now lost); Warunta Tingni Kiamp (USNM). Olancho—Quebrada El Guásimo (USNM); Río Kosmako (USNM); Quebrada de Las Marías (SMF; USNM); Matamoros (SMF); near Quebrada El Mono (USNM); Nueva Esperanza (USNM); confluence of Quebrada Siksatara with Río Wampú (USNM); El Torno (USNM); confluence of Ríos Yanguay and Wampú (USNM).
**Natural history comments:** *Leptodactylus pentadactylus* occurs in primary to highly disturbed evergreen broadleaf (including gallery forest through pine savanna) and broadleaf swamp forests in the Mosquitia. Adult males call in late afternoon and at night from beneath large logs or inside holes in the ground. They seem to call only following heavy rains. Adult females apparently hide by day inside holes in the ground. At night, females frequently sit outside their daytime retreats and hop into the hole when approached. Other females appear to wander some distance from their daytime retreats. Like most other anurans in the Mosquitia, this species is most active during the rainy season. Although this species has virulent skin secretions, adults are eaten by the snake *Chironius grandisquamis.* A juvenile found by McCranie beneath a log played dead upon capture. The frog stayed belly up in his open hand for about a minute before it was placed in a collecting bag.
**Remarks:** The range given in the General geographic distribution section probably encompasses ranges of more than one species (Heyer, 1998).

## Family Ranidae

This family lacks any known synapomorphies (Pough et al., 2003), so it may be polyphyletic. Members of this family in the Mosquitia are distinguished by the combination of having the fingers unwebbed, the toes extensively webbed, the tongue deeply notched posteriorly, and parotoid glands absent. The members of this family range in the Western Hemisphere from northern Alaska, USA, on the west and northern Quebec, Canada, on the east to north-central Bolivia and eastern Brazil.

Outside of the Western Hemisphere, this family is generally lacking only from Saharan and southern Africa, most of Australia, New Zealand, and high latitude regions. Thirty-nine genera containing 663 species were included in this family by Frost (2004), but the taxonomy of this family "is still very problematic" (Dubois, 1999:81). Five species placed in a single genus occur in Honduras, with four species recorded from the Mosquitia.

*Rana brownorum* **Sanders, 1973**
**Common name(s):** None
**Description (Plate 58):** This large frog (males to 88 mm SVL, females to 117 mm; McCranie and Wilson, 2002) lacks expanded digital tips and a digital groove. Fingers are unwebbed and toes are extensively webbed (modal webbing formula **I** 1/4—2 **II** 1/4—2 1/3 **III** 1—2$^{+}$ **IV** 2 1/2—1/4 **V**). Lateral keels or fleshy fringes are present on the unwebbed portions of the toes. An outer metatarsal tubercle is absent. The tongue is deeply notched posteriorly. Adult males have a well-developed gray thumb pad. Adult males usually have small, poorly developed, paired vocal slits and paired, lateral vocal sacs located posterior to the angle of the jaw. The skin of the dorsal surfaces is smooth to weakly granular, except that the skin is occasionally denticulate on the lower back and on the hind limbs. Distinct dorsolateral ridges are present. Dorsal surfaces are pale green to brown, almost always with distinct dark brown spots or blotches on the back. Posterior surfaces of the thighs are mottled dark and pale brown, or have small pale brown spots on a darker brown ground color. Ventral surfaces are pale yellow to white; small brown spots or flecking is occasionally present on the chin, throat, and chest.

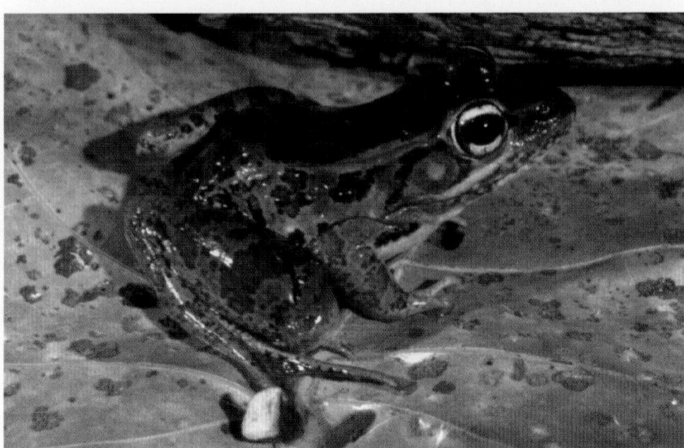

**Plate 58.** *Rana brownorum.* Photograph by McCranie.

**Similar species:** *Rana warszewitschii* has a small outer metatarsal tubercle, well-defined digital discs with marginal grooves laterally, a dark eye mask, large yellowish-brown spots and/or vertical bars on the posterior surfaces of the thighs, and lacks distinct dorsal spots or blotches. *Rana maculata* and *R. vaillanti* have denticulate dorsal surfaces, slightly expanded toe tips, and lack distinct dorsal spots or blotches. All Mosquitia *Leptodactylus* lack toe webbing, or have only basal toe webbing, and have a tongue that is only slightly notched posteriorly.
**General geographic distribution:** *Rana brownorum* occurs at low, moderate, and intermediate elevations on the Atlantic versant from southern Veracruz, Mexico, to northern Nicaragua (see Remarks).
**Distribution in Honduras:** This species is widely distributed on the mainland, exclusive of the southwestern, south-central, and extreme southern portions. It also occurs on Islas de Roatán and Utila, Islas de la Bahía, and is known from about sea level to 1650 m elevation.
**Distribution in the Mosquitia:** El Paraíso—Boca Español (USNM). Gracias a Dios—Barra de Caratasca (KU); Barra Patuca (USNM); near Calpo (UF); Krahkra (USNM); Mocorón (UTA); Rus Rus (USNM); Swabila (UF); Tikiraya (UF). Olancho—Casamacoa (USNM); Quebrada de Las Marías (USNM); Matamoros (SMF); Quebrada El Mono (USNM).
**Natural history comments:** *Rana brownorum* occurs in moderately to heavily disturbed broadleaf forest (both evergreen and swamp forest), pine savanna, fresh water marshes, and coastal strand in the Mosquitia. It occurs on the ground around and in permanent ponds, swamps, and river overflow areas. The species is active both during the day and at night, but males call only at night. It is probably active throughout the year in the Mosquitia.
**Remarks:** We follow Frost (2004) in using the name *Rana brownorum* for the Honduran Atlantic versant populations of the *R. pipiens* complex, although noting that the dorsolateral folds are broken and inset medially in the Honduran populations (dorsolateral folds continuous or short and not inset medially in *R. brownorum* according to Sanders, 1973). Clearly, the Central American populations of this complex need to be studied in detail using both molecular and morphological data

(also see McCranie and Wilson, 2002, as *R. berlandieri*).

*Rana maculata* **Brocchi, 1877**
**Common name(s):** None
**Description (Plate 59):** This large frog (males to 82 mm SVL [McCranie and Wilson, 2002], females to 113 mm [Hillis and de Sá, 1988]) has slightly expanded digital tips without marginal grooves. Fingers are unwebbed and toes are extensively webbed (modal webbing formula **I** 1/4—$2^-$ **II** 1/4—2 **III** 1/4—2 **IV** $2^-$—1/4 **V**). Lateral fleshy fringes are present on the unwebbed portions of the toes. An outer metatarsal tubercle is absent. The tympanum is moderately large (tympanum length/eye length <0.700). The tongue is deeply notched posteriorly. Adult males have a well-developed thumb pad that is usually darker than the rest of the thumb. Adult males have small, poorly developed, paired vocal slits and internal, paired vocal sacs. The skin of the dorsal surfaces is almost always denticulate. Distinct dorsolateral ridges are present. Dorsal surfaces are mottled green and brown or are nearly uniformly brown. A dark brown eye mask extends from the tip of the snout to past the tympanum. A pale yellow supralabial stripe is present. Posterior surfaces of the thighs are mottled dark and pale brown, or have small pale brown spots on a darker brown ground color. Ventral surfaces are white, lightly flecked with brown on the chin, throat, and chest.
**Similar species:** *Rana brownorum* has smooth skin on the back, unexpanded digital tips, and distinct dorsal spots. *Rana vaillanti* has a larger tympanum (tympanum length/eye length >0.700).

**Plate 59.** *Rana maculata*. Photograph by McCranie.

*Rana warszewitschii* has a small outer metatarsal tubercle, well-defined digital discs with marginal grooves laterally, large yellowish-brown spots and/or vertical bars on the posterior surfaces of the thighs, and lacks distinct dorsal spots or blotches. All Mosquitia *Leptodactylus* lack toe webbing, or have only basal toe webbing, and have a tongue that is only slightly notched posteriorly.
**General geographic distribution:** *Rana maculata* is found at low, moderate, intermediate, and high elevations from Chiapas, Mexico, to central Nicaragua on the Atlantic versant and from eastern Oaxaca, Mexico, to Honduras on the Pacific versant.
**Distribution in Honduras:** This frog is widely distributed at low, moderate, and intermediate elevations (40–1980 m) of mountainous regions from along the borders with Guatemala and El Salvador eastward to eastern Olancho and southeastern Colón.
**Distribution in the Mosquitia:** Colón—Quebrada Machín (USNM). Olancho—Quebrada El Guásimo (USNM); Quebrada de Las Marías (USNM); Matamoros (USNM); Quebrada El Mono (SMF); Nueva Esperanza (USNM).
**Natural history comments:** *Rana maculata* occurs in primary to highly disturbed evergreen broadleaf forest in the Mosquitia. The species occurs on the ground or on rocks along streams and is active at night. It is essentially a montane species, but does occur along streams in hilly areas in the lowlands. *Rana maculata* has not been collected in flat areas in the Mosquitia. The species is probably active throughout the year in the Mosquitia.

*Rana vaillanti* **Brocchi, 1877**
**Common name(s):** None
**Description (Plate 60):** This large frog (males to 94 mm SVL, females to 125 mm; Hillis and de Sá, 1988) has slightly expanded digital tips without marginal grooves. Fingers are unwebbed and toes are extensively webbed (modal webbing formula **I** 1/4—1 1/3 **II** 1/4—$2^-$ **III** 1/4—$2^-$ **IV** 1 1/2—1/4 **V**). Lateral fleshy fringes are present on unwebbed portions of the toes. An outer metatarsal tubercle is absent. The tympanum is large (tympanum length/eye length >0.700). The tongue is deeply notched posteriorly. Adult males have a well-developed thumb pad that is usually not darker than the rest of the thumb. Adult males usually have small, poorly developed, paired vocal slits and internal,

**Plate 60.** *Rana vaillanti*. Photograph by McCranie.

paired vocal sacs are usually present. The skin of the dorsal surfaces is denticulate. Distinct dorsolateral ridges are present. Dorsal surfaces are some shade of brown, usually with a greenish color anteriorly. A dark eye mask is usually absent. A pale supralabial stripe is usually absent; when present, a pale stripe is usually located only posterior to the eye. Posterior surfaces of the thighs are mottled dark and pale brown. Ventral surfaces are white with a bronze sheen (cream to white in preservative), usually lightly flecked with gray or brown, occasionally densely flecked or mottled with dark brown.

**Similar species:** *Rana brownorum* has smooth skin on the back, unexpanded digital tips, and distinct dorsal spots. *Rana maculata* has a smaller tympanum (tympanum length/eye length <0.700). *Rana warszewitschii* has a small outer metatarsal tubercle, well-defined digital discs with marginal grooves laterally, large yellowish-brown spots and/ or vertical bars on the posterior surfaces of the thighs, and lacks distinct dorsal spots or blotches. All Mosquitia *Leptodactylus* lack toe webbing, or have only basal toe webbing, and have a tongue that is only slightly notched posteriorly.

**General geographic distribution:** *Rana vaillanti* is found at low and moderate elevations from north-central Veracruz and northern Oaxaca, Mexico, to central Panama on the Atlantic versant. On the Pacific versant, it occurs in southeastern Oaxaca and northwestern Chiapas, Mexico, from northwestern Nicaragua to northwestern Costa Rica, and from western to eastern Panama.

**Distribution in Honduras:** This frog is widely distributed in about the northern half of the country. It also occurs on Isla de Guanaja, Islas de la Bahía. Its known elevational range is from about sea level to 880 m.

**Distribution in the Mosquitia:** Colón—Empalme Río Chilmeca (formerly in UNAH, now lost); Río Guaraska (BMNH). Gracias a Dios—Caño Awalwás (UF; USNM); Awasbila (USNM); Caño Awawás (USNM); Laguna Bacalar (BMNH); Barra Río Plátano (formerly in UNAH, now lost); Crique Curamaira (USNM); Karasangkan (USNM); Kaska Tingni (USNM); Mocorón (UNAH); Rus Rus (USNM); Sin Sin Warra (formerly in UNAH, now lost); Tánsin (LACM; LSUMZ); Bodega de Río Tapalwás (USNM); Tikiraya (UF); Urus Tingni Kiamp (USNM); Crique Wahatingni (UF; USNM); Wakling Kiamp (USNM); Warunta Tingni Kiamp (USNM). Olancho—Casamacoa (SMF; USNM); Kauroahuika (USNM); Quebrada Kuilma Tingni (USNM); Quebrada El Mono (USNM); confluence of Ríos Sausa and Wampú (SMF; USNM); confluence of Ríos Yanguay and Wampú (SMF; USNM); Yapuwás (USNM).

**Natural history comments:** *Rana vaillanti* occurs in primary to highly disturbed evergreen broadleaf forest, lightly disturbed broadleaf swamp forest, and pine savanna in the Mosquitia. The species occurs on the ground around and in streams, river overflow areas, permanent and temporary swamps, and low areas that are inundated by heavy rains. It is active at night. *Rana vaillanti* usually occurs in relatively flat areas in the Mosquitia, but is sympatric with the closely related *R. maculata* in river overflow areas in the hilly region at Quebrada El Mono, Olancho. The species is probably active throughout the year in the Mosquitia.

*Rana warszewitschii* **(O. Schmidt, 1857)**
**Common name(s):** None
**Description (Plate 61):** This moderately large frog (males to 52 mm SVL [Savage, 2002], females to 63 mm [Hillis and de Sá, 1988]) has well-defined digital discs with marginal grooves laterally. Fingers are unwebbed and toes are extensively webbed (modal webbing formula **I** 1/2—2 **II** 1/2—$2^+$ **III** 3/4—$3^-$ **IV** 2 1/2—3/4 **V**). Lateral fleshy fringes are present on the unwebbed portions of the toes. A small outer metatarsal tubercle is present. The tongue is deeply notched posteriorly. Adult males have a well-developed thumb pad that is not darker than the rest of the thumb. Adult males lack vocal slits and vocal sacs. The skin of the dorsal surfaces is weakly granular to weakly denticulate. Distinct

**Plate 61.** *Rana warszewitschii.* Photograph by McCranie.

dorsolateral ridges are present. Dorsal surfaces are brown with small darker brown spots on the back. A dark brown eye mask is usually present. A pale yellow supralabial stripe is present. Posterior surfaces of the thighs are brown with yellowish-brown large spots and/or vertical bars. Ventral surfaces are white to pale brown with brown flecking along the anterior edges.
**Similar species:** *Rana warszewitschii* is the only Mosquitia *Rana* with an outer metatarsal tubercle, well-defined digital discs with marginal grooves laterally, and large yellowish-brown spots and/or vertical bars on the posterior surfaces of the thighs. All Mosquitia *Leptodactylus* lack toe webbing, or have only basal toe webbing, and have a tongue that is only slightly notched posteriorly.
**General geographic distribution:** *Rana warszewitschii* occurs at low, moderate, and intermediate elevations from northeastern Honduras to central Panama on the Atlantic versant and from northwestern Costa Rica to eastern Panama on the Pacific versant.
**Distribution in Honduras:** This species is known only in the Mosquitia from 60 to 200 m elevation.
**Distribution in the Mosquitia:** Gracias a Dios—Auka Kiamp (USNM); Caño Awalwás (UF; USNM); Awasbila (USNM); Bodega de Río Tapalwás (USNM); Crique Wahatingni (UF; USNM). Olancho—confluence of Ríos Aner and Wampú (USNM); Quebrada El Guásimo (SMF; USNM); Río Kosmako (USNM).
**Natural history comments:** *Rana warszewitschii* occurs in primary to lightly disturbed evergreen broadleaf forest. It occurs on the forest floor in the vicinity of small streams and is active both during the day and at night.

## Class Reptilia (Reptiles)

### Order Crocodylia (Crocodilians)

Both species of crocodilians known from Honduras (Wilson and McCranie, 2002) occur in the Mosquitia. Crocodilians are large, lizard-like reptiles in general appearance that live in association with rivers, swamps, and lagoons in the Mosquitia.

#### Family Alligatoridae

Alligatorids have the teeth of the lower jaw fitting into pits in the upper jaw, so that they cannot be seen when the jaws are closed (Pough et al., 2003). The Mosquitia representative of this family is also easily distinguished from the other Mosquitia crocodilian in having an elevated, crescent-shaped, transverse preorbital ridge on top of the head. The members of this family of crocodilians, in the Western Hemisphere, range in the southeastern United States and from extreme southern Mexico to northern Argentina. In the Eastern Hemisphere, a single, highly endangered species (*Alligator sinensis)* is found in the Yangtze River drainage in eastern China. Three genera containing eight species are presently included in this family (Pough et al., 2003). One species is known to occur in Honduras, including the Mosquitia.

*Caiman crocodilus* **(Linnaeus, 1758)**
**Common name(s):** Caimán, Lagarto (Spanish); Karas* (Miskito); Agari* (Garífuna)
**Description (Plate 62):** A small to medium-sized crocodilian that can reach over 2 m TL (usually 1.25 to 1.75 m TL) and weigh over 50 kg. Hatchlings range in total length from 20 to 26 cm. The snout is relatively short and broad with the fourth mandibular tooth concealed in the upper jaw when the mouth is closed. A prominent transverse preoccipital ridge is present. There are 2 to 4 transverse rows of 6 to 10 irregularly arranged postoccipital scutes and 4 or 5 transverse rows of 2 to 4 nuchal scales. There are 17 to 19 transverse rows of dorsal scutes in 8 to 13 longitudinal rows. Ventral scales are in 20 to 27 transverse rows. The dental formula is 5+14–15/18–20. Adult coloration is pale brown or olive-brown. Ventral scales are uniformly yellow or creamy white and there are often dark dorsal and caudal bands that fade with age.

**Plate 62.** *Caiman crocodilus* (juvenile). Photograph by McCranie.

**Similar species:** *Crocodylus acutus* has the fourth tooth of the lower jaw visible with the mouth closed and lacks a preoccipital ridge.
**General geographic distribution:** *Caiman crocodilus* occurs at low elevations from extreme southeastern Chiapas, Mexico, to western Ecuador on the Pacific versant (apparently absent from the Pacific versant of Honduras) and from northwestern Honduras to eastern Peru and eastern and central Brazil on the Atlantic versant. The species also occurs on the islands of Trinidad and Tobago and has been introduced on Isla de Juventud, Cuba, Puerto Rico, and in southern Florida, USA.
**Distribution in Honduras:** This crocodilian is known only from near the north coast from sea level to 55 m elevation.
**Distribution in the Mosquitia:** Colón—Anzuelo Bridge (O'Shea, 1986a). Gracias a Dios—Crique Amatingni (UF); Laguna Bacalar (UF); Laguna Biltamaira (Klein, 1979); Laguna de Brus (UF); Río La Criba (UF); Crique La Culebra (King et al., 1990); Laguna de Ébano (King et al., 1990); Crique Las Flores (King et al., 1990); Crique Gabú Dende (King et al., 1990); Laguna Jolamaya (King et al., 1990); Laguntara (Klein, 1979); Mocorón (CF); near mouth of Río Negro (UF); Palacios (O'Shea, 1986a); Río Palacios (UF); Laguna Paptatingni (King et al., 1990); near mouth of Río Patuca (UF); Criques Plaplaya (King et al., 1990); near mouth of Río Plátano (UF); about 2 km S of Río Rus Rus (COHDEFOR); Laguna Siksa (Klein, 1979); Laguna Tampatingni (King et al., 1990); Laguna de Tánsin (LACM; LSUMZ); Laguna Tilbalacán (Klein, 1979); Laguna Tinguitara (King et al., 1990); Laguna de Warunta (Klein, 1979).
**Natural history comments:** *Caiman crocodilus* is a secretive, aquatic species that occurs in freshwater or brackish conditions in rivers, swamps, and lagoons in the Mosquitia. It can sometimes be seen basking on shore.
**Remarks:** This species is placed on the CITES Appendix II list.

## Family Crocodylidae

In crocodylids, the fourth tooth in the lower jaw is accommodated in a notch in the upper jaw, so as to be visible when the jaws are closed (Pough et al., 2003). The Mosquitia representative of this family is also easily distinguished from the other Mosquitia crocodilian in lacking a crescent-shaped preorbital ridge on top of the head. In the Western Hemisphere, the members of this family range in coastal southern Florida and the Florida Keys, USA, coastal Cuba (and adjacent islands), Hispaniola, Jamaica, and the Cayman Islands, both coasts of Mexico from northern Sinaloa and central Tamaulipas southward through Central America to northern South America from Colombia to the mouth of the Orinoco River in Venezuela on the Atlantic side and Colombia to extreme northwestern Peru on the Pacific side. In the Eastern Hemisphere, they are distributed in tropical Africa, India, southern China, Indochina, and northern Australia. Two genera containing 13 species are presently included in this family (Pough et al., 2003). One species is known to occur in Honduras, including the Mosquitia.

*Crocodylus acutus* **Cuvier, 1807**
**Common name(s):** Cocodrilo, Lagarto (Spanish); Tura* (Miskito); Gangadili, Agarewa** (Garífuna)
**Description (Plate 63):** *Crocodylus acutus* is a large crocodile that can reach lengths in excess of 6 m (adults usually 3 to 4 m TL) and weigh over 1,000 kg. At the time of hatching they measure 20 to 35 cm TL. The snout is long and pointed, with the fourth tooth of the lower jaw clearly visible when the mouth is closed. A preorbital transverse ridge is absent. There are 2 to 4 postoccipital scutes arranged in a single transverse row and 0 to 6 nuchal scales (usually 4 in 2 juxtaposed pairs). There are 14 to 18 transverse rows of dorsal scutes in 2 to 6 (usually 4) longitudinal rows at midbody. Ventral scales are in 25 to 35 transverse rows. The

**Plate 63.** *Crocodylus acutus* (juvenile). Photograph by Gunther Köhler.

dental formula is 5+13–14/15. Adults are gray, brownish gray, or olive dorsally, with dark markings or banding on the body and tail. Ventrals are cream to white.

**Similar species:** *Caiman crocodilus* has a transverse ridge across the head just anterior to the eyes and the fourth tooth of the lower jaw concealed when the mouth is closed.

**General geographic distribution:** *Crocodylus acutus* occurs at low and moderate elevations from Sinaloa, Mexico, to extreme northwestern Peru on the Pacific versant and from Tabasco, Mexico, to northeastern Venezuela on the Atlantic versant. The species is also known from southern Florida, USA, and the islands of Cuba (including Isla de Juventud and other satellites), Little Cayman, Cayman Brac, Jamaica, Hispaniola, Martinique, and Margarita.

**Distribution in Honduras:** This crocodilian was formerly widespread along both coasts (including the Islas de la Bahía) and well inland along rivers from sea level to 650 m elevation.

**Distribution in the Mosquitia:** Gracias a Dios—Laguna Bacalar (King et al., 1990); Laguna Biltamaira (Klein, 1979); Laguna de Brus (King et al., 1990); Río Coco, near Kyras, Nicaragua (sight record); Río Coco, near mouth of Caño Awawás (UF photograph); Laguna de Ébano (King et al., 1990); Crique Las Flores (King et al., 1990); near mouth of Río Negro (King et al., 1990); Laguna Paptatingni (King et al., 1990); Laguna Siksa (Klein, 1979); Laguna de Tánsin (Klein, 1979); Bodega de Río Tapalwás (sight record); Laguna de Warunta (Klein, 1979); Laguntara (Klein, 1979). Olancho—Caobita (Nicholson et al. 2000); Río Cuyamel at Quebrada El Mono (Nicholson et al., 2000).

**Natural history comments:** *Crocodylus acutus* is an aquatic species that occurs in freshwater and brackish conditions in mangrove forest, coastal lagoons, and rivers (which it can inhabit many miles inland) in the Mosquitia. It frequently basks on shore. A 1.5 m subadult was seen at night in May while active in the Río Tapalwás, a tributary of the Río Rus Rus, which is in turn a tributary of the Río Coco. A long time resident of Rus Rus who was with us at the time had never seen *Crocodylus* before in the Río Rus Rus system.

**Remarks:** Populations of *Crocodylus acutus* in Honduras have been severely depleted due to overhunting for meat and skins (King et al., 1990). Despite being placed on the CITES Appendix I list, which severely limits the legal trade in crocodile skins and products, the illegal exploitation of *C. acutus* in the Mosquitia continues. Robust populations of *C. acutus* were present along the Río Patuca near Yapuwás in 1992 (McCranie pers. observ.). However, these populations were under heavy hunting pressure by a group of hunters being paid by several people living in San Pedro Sula, Honduras. As a result, these populations are now severely depleted. Several large *C. acutus* (3 m +) as well as several smaller crocodiles were seen by the authors along the Río Coco in the Tawahka-Asangni Biosphere Reserve in 2001. A marked increase in ladino settlement and deforestation along this part of the river was evident in 2002 and 2003 and fewer crocodiles were seen along the Río Coco at those times.

## Order Testudines (Turtles)

Turtles are reptiles that possess a shell composed of a dorsal portion (the carapace) and a ventral portion (the plastron). "The shell is composed of dermal ossifications incorporating the ribs, vertebrae [except for those of the neck and tail], and portions of the pectoral girdle" (Pough et al., 2003:97). The ribs are fused to the lateral portion of the carapace and enclose the pectoral and pelvic girdles, a unique arrangement among vertebrate animals (Pough et al., 2003). The bony portions of the shell are overlain usually by keratinous scutes. In a few cases, as in the leatherback sea turtle, for example, the dermal bony elements are covered with a leathery skin (Pough et al., 2003). Fourteen species of terrestrial, fresh-water, or marine turtles are known from Honduras or its territorial waters (Wilson and McCranie, 2002). Of these, 12 species are known from the Mosquitia or its coastal waters.

Family Cheloniidae

The limbs are modified into fully webbed paddles and the members of this family of turtles are wholly marine, save for the females that come ashore to lay eggs (Pough et al., 2003). This family ranges circumglobally in temperate and tropical oceans. The paddle-like limbs are unique to this family and the family Dermochelyidae among the turtles known to occur in the Mosquitia. Five genera containing six species are currently included in this family (Pough et al., 2003). Four species placed in four genera are known to occupy Honduran waters. Three species occur in the coastal Caribbean waters of the Mosquitia. Additional research focusing on sea turtle activity along the coast of the Mosquitia is needed to assess the area's importance as nesting habitat. Wilber (1996:36) stated that "Beaches within the reserve [Río Kruta Biological Reserve] are important nesting grounds for four species of marine turtles." These four species of marine turtles are the three members of the family Cheloniidae plus *Dermochelys coriacea* of the family Dermochelyidae.

*Caretta caretta* **(Linnaeus, 1758)**
**Common name(s):** Caguama (Spanish); Lagrit*, Lisiks (Miskito); Gawámu* (Garífuna)
**Description (Plate 64):** Most adults of this large sea turtle have a carapace length of 700 to 1000 mm and weigh 70 to 160 kg (Savage, 2002). The shield-shaped carapace is widest towards the anterior end, has serrate margins, and non-overlapping scutes (except scutes imbricate in some young specimens). There are 5 pairs of costal scutes, with the first pair in contact with the nuchal scute. The juvenile carapace is tricarinate, with the median keel knobbed. Adults lack keels on the carapace. The plastron is unhinged, and hatchlings often have 2 longitudinal plastral ridges. There are 12 plastral scutes arranged in 6 pairs, and a small intergular scute can be present or absent. Two pairs of prefrontal scales are present that sometimes form a median suture, but most often an additional azygous scale or scales are present. The large, robust head has a smooth-margined lower jaw. Limbs are developed into

**Plate 64.** *Caretta caretta*. Photograph by McCranie.

paddle-like flippers, each with 2 small claws. The tail of males extends beyond the carapacial margin, whereas the tail of females barely reaches the carapacial margin. The carapace is reddish-brown, often with algae or barnacles attached. The plastron ranges from yellowish white to yellowish brown. The head can be various shades of brown, with some lateral scales having some shade of red centrally and with yellow on the margins. Limbs and the tail are brown dorsally and yellow ventrally.
**Similar species:** *Chelonia mydas* and *Eretmochelys imbricata* have 4 pairs of costal scutes, with the first pair separated from the nuchal scute. Additionally, *C. mydas* has only a single claw on each limb and a serrated lower jaw. *Eretmochelys imbricata* also has imbricate dorsal scutes. *Dermochelys coriacea* has the carapace and plastron covered by soft skin over a layer of connective tissue.
**General geographic distribution:** This species is circumglobal in distribution, "...inhabiting continental shelves, bays, estuaries, and lagoons in the temperate, subtropical, and tropical waters of the Atlantic, Pacific, and Indian oceans. Major nesting grounds are generally located in warm temperate and subtropical regions" (Dodd, 1990:483.2).
**Distribution in Honduras:** *Caretta caretta* is known only from Caribbean waters and coastal regions.
**Distribution in the Mosquitia:** Gracias a Dios—Barra Patuca (USNM); Plaplaya (UF photograph). Also reported by Marin (1984) from Laguna de Brus, near mouth of Río Kruta, near mouth of Río Negro, and Laguna Tata (= Laguntara), all in

Gracias a Dios. Wilber (1996) reported that this species nests on beaches in the Río Kruta Biological Reserve.

**Natural history comments:** *Caretta caretta* is strictly a marine turtle, with only the females coming ashore, and then only to excavate a nest and lay eggs. This species nests during the warmest months of the year, but the nesting season tends to be extended in tropical areas and can range from April to September or even longer (Dodd, 1988). Females can lay 1–6 nests, with 40–160 eggs each, during a nesting season, with a general consensus that there are 2–3 years between nesting seasons (Dodd, 1988). *Caretta caretta* is omnivorous and has a highly variable diet that was well summarized by Dodd (1988).

**Remarks:** *Caretta caretta* is known to nest along the beach near Plaplaya, and nests there are relocated to a locally operated hatchery along with those of *Dermochelys coriacea* (see Remarks for that species). In 1995, five *C. caretta* nests were relocated to the hatchery and in 1996 parts of two nests were relocated (J. Peskin, unpubl. data). Miskito turtle hunters in Nicaragua do not typically utilize *C. caretta* as a source of food or in any commercial capacity and usually release loggerheads that are caught in their nets, sometimes after knocking the turtle unconscious to avoid being bitten (C. Lagueux and C. Campbell, pers. comm.).

*Chelonia mydas* **(Linnaeus, 1758)**

**Common name(s):** Tortuga Verde (Spanish); Turtle (English-speaking Miskito); Lih (Miskito); Gadáru* (Garífuna)

**Description (Plate 65):** This large sea turtle typically reaches a carapace length between 900 and 1220 mm, but has been reported to reach 1530 mm and weigh 295 kg or more (Savage, 2002). The somewhat rounded, heart shaped carapace is broad and low with smooth margins. Dorsal scutes are juxtaposed. There are 4 pairs of costal scutes, with the first pair separated from the nuchal scute. Hatchlings usually have a middorsal keel on the carapace, whereas adults lack dorsal keels or ridges. The plastron is unhinged, and hatchlings often have 2 longitudinal plastral keels. There are 6 pairs of plastral scutes and a large intergular scute. One pair of prefrontal scales is present. The lower jaw is serrate. Limbs are developed into paddle-like flippers, each with usually a single small claw. The tail of males has a flattened,

**Plate 65.** *Chelonia mydas*. Photograph by Cathi L. Campbell.

keratinized tip and extends well beyond the margin of the carapace, whereas the tail of females lacks a keratinized tip and does not exceed the margin of the carapace. The carapace is usually brown, often with infusions of darker mottling, wavy lines, or blotches. The plastron is cream or pale yellow. Scales on the dorsal surfaces of the head, limbs, and tail are dark brown or grayish black with pale margins. Ventral surfaces are cream or pale yellow.

**Similar species:** The only other turtles in the Mosquitia with paddle-like limbs are *Caretta caretta*, *Eretmochelys imbricata*, and *Dermochelys coriacea*, all of which are also marine turtles. *Caretta caretta* and *Eretmochelys imbricata* have 2 claws on each limb and a smooth-margined lower jaw. In addition, *C. caretta* has 5 or more pairs of costal scutes, with the first pair in contact with the nuchal scute and *E. imbricata* has imbricate carapacial scutes, two pairs of prefrontal scales, and a slightly hooked upper jaw. *Dermochelys coriacea* lacks bony carapacial and plastral scutes, instead having a carapace and plastron covered by soft skin over a layer of connective tissue.

**General geographic distribution:** This species occurs in tropical and subtropical seas, normally between the 20°C isotherms.

**Distribution in Honduras:** *Chelonia mydas* has been reported in both the Pacific and Caribbean coastal waters.

**Distribution in the Mosquitia:** Reported to nest on beaches in the Río Plátano Biosphere Reserve (Cruz, 1986) and the Río Kruta Biological Reserve (Wilber, 1996).

**Natural history comments:** *Chelonia mydas* is strictly marine, with the exception of females that come ashore to dig their nest and lay eggs. Most green turtles in the western Caribbean nest between June and November on the beaches near Tortuguero, Costa Rica (Savage, 2002). Females typically have 2–7 nests per season, with a 2–4 year interval between nesting seasons (Carr et al., 1978). The diet of *C. mydas* generally consists of turtle grass (*Thalassia testudinum*) and other sea grasses (Savage, 2002).

**Remarks:** Green turtles have been harvested for food by Miskitos for at least 500 years and this practice has been well documented in Nicaragua (Nietschmann, 1973, 1979). The extent to which *C. mydas* is utilized by Honduran Miskitos has not been documented, however Lagueux (1998) reported that during 29 months between February 1994 and April 1997 at least 43 *C. mydas* that were harvested by turtlers from Dákura and Sandy Bay, Nicaragua were taken to market in Iralaya, Depto. Gracias a Dios, Honduras. An additional 102 *C. mydas* were reported to be taken to market during the same time period at "Cabo Gracias a Dios" and "Río Coco," which could indicate villages along either side of the border (Lagueux, 1998). Green turtles taken to Honduras were either sold or traded for coconuts or beef (C. Lagueux and C. Campbell, pers. comm.). Most information on *C. mydas* nesting in the western Caribbean results from the work started by Archie F. Carr, Jr. in 1955 at Tortuguero, Costa Rica (Carr et al., 1978). That work continues today, and over 20,000 *C. mydas* have been tagged at that beach (Savage, 2002).

*Eretmochelys imbricata* **(Linnaeus, 1766)**

**Common name(s):** Carey (Spanish); Aksbil* (Miskito); Garáru*(Garífuna)

**Description (Plate 66):** This medium-sized sea turtle typically reaches a carapace length of between 750 and 900 mm, but has been reported to reach 1140 mm and weigh up to 127 kg (Savage, 2002). The carapace is relatively long and narrow in adults, and more heart-shaped in juveniles. The margins are strongly serrated posteriorly, and in most individuals the dorsal scutes are imbricate (juveniles and very old animals have dorsal scutes that do not overlap). There are 4 pairs of costal scutes, with the first pair not in contact with the nuchal scute. Hatchlings usually have a middorsal keel on the carapace. The plastron is unhinged, and hatchlings often have 2 longitudinal plastral ridges. There are 6 pairs of plastral scutes and a large intergular scute. The relatively narrow head has 2 pairs of prefrontal scales, a somewhat hooked upper jaw, and a lower jaw with a smooth margin. Limbs are paddle-like, each usually with 2 small claws. Males have long tails that extend well beyond the margin of the carapace, whereas the tail of females extends to the edge of or just slightly beyond the margin of the carapace. Carapacial scutes are brown with a distinct black, tan, and cream pattern, and can have a glossy sheen. The plastron is yellow or yellow-orange. Dorsal scales on the head and appendages are generally brown or reddish-brown, with pale colored margins. Ventral surfaces of the head and appendages are pale yellow.

**Plate 66.** *Eretmochelys imbricata*. Photograph by McCranie.

**Similar species:** The only other turtles in the Mosquitia region with broad paddle-like limbs are *Caretta caretta*, *Chelonia mydas*, and *Dermochelys coriacea*, all of which are also sea turtles. *Caretta caretta* and *C. mydas* have non-overlapping carapacial scutes. *Caretta caretta* also has 5 pairs of costal scutes, with the first pair in contact with the nuchal scute. *Chelonia mydas* also usually has only a single claw per limb, has a serrated lower jaw, a single pair of prefrontal scales, and a non-hooked upper jaw. *Dermochelys coriacea* has the carapace and plastron covered by soft skin over a layer of connective tissue.

**General geographic distribution:** *Eretmochelys imbricata* occurs circumglobally in tropical and subtropical seas, and occasionally ranges into some temperate seas.

**Distribution in Honduras:** This marine turtle is known from the Golfo de Fonseca on the Pacific and from the Caribbean waters and coastal areas.

**Distribution in the Mosquitia:** Reported to nest

on beaches in the Río Plátano Biosphere Reserve (Cruz, 1986) and the Río Kruta Biological Reserve (Wilber, 1996).

**Natural history comments:** *Eretmochelys imbricata* is strictly a marine turtle, with only the females leaving the water and then only to lay eggs. There is a large *E. imbricata* rookery in the Pearl Cays, Nicaragua, where 154–158 nests were recorded annually between April and November of 2000, 2001, and 2002 (Lagueux et al., 2003). These nests had between 50 and 229 eggs each (Lagueux et al., 2003). This species spends much of its time in the relatively shallow waters near coral reefs, feeding primarily upon sponges and other sessile animals (Meylan, 1984).

**Remarks:** This turtle species has been heavily exploited for its meat, eggs, and shell by the coastal Miskitos since at least the 1600s (Offen, 1999), and the utilization of *E. imbricata* in Nicaragua continues today (Lagueux et al., 2003). In 2003, we recovered sea turtle tags in Tikiraya, Gracias a Dios, a Miskito village along the Río Kruta, that were from an *E. imbricata* taken by a Miskito fisherman during a trip to the vicinity of Cayo Gorda, a small island on a bank approximately 125 km northeast of Barra Kruta. The tags were originally placed on a juvenile *E. imbricata* in Jaragua National Park, Dominican Republic in 1998 and during a recapture at the same location in 1999 (Y. Leon, pers. comm.). The fisherman who caught the turtle reported to us that he captured the turtle by hand while it was in the water.

## Family Chelydridae

Chelydrids are freshwater turtles with large heads and powerful jaws. The head, neck, and limbs are incapable of being retracted fully within the shell. They move about primarily by walking on the bottom, inasmuch as they are not strong swimmers (Pough et al., 2003). The Mosquitia representative of this family is easily distinguished from all other Mosquitia turtles by having a reduced plastron that is cruciform in shape. In the Western Hemisphere, this family of turtles occurs from southern Canada through the eastern and central United States, thence from southern Mexico through Central America to western Ecuador. In the Eastern Hemisphere, it occurs from southeastern China to Burma and Thailand. Three species placed in three genera are presently included in this family (Pough et al., 2003; but see Remarks in *Chelydra serpentina* account). One species is known to occur in Honduras, including the Mosquitia.

### *Chelydra serpentina* (Linnaeus, 1758)

**Common name(s):** Tortuga Lagarto, Sambunango (Spanish)

**Description (Plate 67):** This large freshwater turtle can reach 494 mm in carapace length and weigh 34 kg (Savage, 2002). The carapace is tricarinate, with large knobby keels, and the posterior margin is strongly serrated. The plastron is reduced, cruciform and unhinged, with 5 pairs of scutes (humerals, pectorals, femorals, anals, and the widely separated abdominals of the bridge elements) and one unpaired or sometimes paired gular scute. Much of the soft ventral surfaces of the body are exposed due to the reduced plastron. The head is robust and the upper jaw is strongly hooked. A pair of large barbels is present anteriorly on the undersurface of the lower jaw; 1 or 2 smaller pairs of barbells can also be present at about the midlength of the lower jaw. Feet are fully webbed, with heavy claws. The tail is long (over one-half length of the carapace), with 3 rows of tubercles on the dorsal surface (median row most prominent) and 2 rows of large, flat plates on the subcaudal surface. The carapace is a patternless brown to black and the plastron is yellow to brown. Dorsal surfaces of the head and body are typically dark gray or brown, with the ventral surfaces pale tan to pale brown. Many tubercles on the neck and limbs are cream-colored.

**Similar species:** No other species of turtle in the Mosquitia has a cruciform plastron, the tail with a

**Plate 67.** *Chelydra serpentina*. Photograph by Gunther Köhler.

dorsal median row of large triangular scales, a long tail about one-half or more the length of the carapace, and a strongly serrated posterior margin of the carapace.

**General geographic distribution:** *Chelydra serpentina* occurs from "Nova Scotia, New Brunswick, southern Quebec and southern Alberta [Canada] southward east of the Rocky Mountains to Florida and the Texas coast [USA]" (Gibbons et al., 1988:420.1). The species also occurs at low elevations from central Veracruz, Mexico, to northwestern Colombia on the Atlantic versant and from northwestern Costa Rica to southwestern Ecuador on the Pacific versant (but see Remarks).

**Distribution in Honduras:** This large turtle is widely distributed in the Atlantic drainages across the northern and eastern portions of the country from about sea level to 660 m elevation.

**Distribution in the Mosquitia:** El Paraíso—near Arenales (LACM). Gracias a Dios—Awasbila (USNM); vicinity of Tikiraya (UF); Warunta Tingni Kiamp (USNM). Olancho—near confluence of Ríos Cuyamel and Patuca (USNM).

**Natural history comments:** The natural history of *Chelydra serpentina* in the Mosquitia is poorly known. The Olancho specimen was taken in a temporary rain-filled pond in lightly disturbed evergreen broadleaf forest near the Río Patuca in August. The Tikiraya specimens are plastrons only; the turtles were eaten by people in that village. These turtles were taken from a muddy-bottomed slow-moving tributary of the Río Kruta that passes through broadleaf swamp forest. The Warunta Tingni Kiamp specimen was taken in a shallow river during the night as it was feeding on the remains of a peccary (*Tayassu pecari*). The species is also reported to live in rivers and freshwater lagoons in the Mosquitia.

**Remarks:** This species occurs in two widely disjunct populations, separated by about a 950 km gap between the eastern and southern North America populations and the more or less continuous populations from Veracruz, Mexico, south to Ecuador. Further study of these populations may determine that more than one species is involved. Fishermen in Awasbila, along the Río Coco, related that these turtles are not sought for their meat, despite the value placed on other species of turtle. However, people in other parts of the Mosquitia eat these turtles (see above).

Family Dermochelyidae

As with the members of the family Cheloniidae, these marine turtles have limbs that are modified into fully webbed paddles and live their entire life in the ocean, save for when the females come ashore to lay eggs (Pough et al., 2003). This family ranges circumglobally in tropical, subtropical, temperate, and even occasionally in subarctic oceans. It is monotypic, with the species known to occupy Honduran waters, including the coastal waters of the Mosquitia. This family is so distinctive that it is considered by some to represent a separate suborder (see Lee, 1996).

*Dermochelys coriacea* **(Vandelli, 1761)**

**Common name(s):** Baula (Spanish); Lisiksa (Miskito); Abadawa (Garífuna)

**Description (Plate 68):** This huge sea turtle, the largest of all extant turtles, typically reaches a carapace length between 1280 and 1750 mm in Costa Rica, but has been reported to reach 1830 mm and weigh about 680 kg (Savage, 2002). In all examples other than recent hatchlings, the carapace and plastron are covered by soft skin over a layer of connective tissue. The carapace has 7 knobby longitudinal keels. There are also 5 plastral keels in many subadults, but they are almost or completely obliterated in large adults (Savage, 2002). In small juveniles, epidermal scales are present, and the carapacial and plastral keels are formed by yellow or white scales. In large adults, the upper jaw has a large triangular

**Plate 68.** *Dermochelys coriacea* (hatchling). Photograph by Jocelyn Peskin.

cusp on each side below the nostril. The lower jaw has a median hook that fits into a notch at the upper jaw symphysis. Limbs are paddle-like and lack claws. Dorsal surfaces are dark brown or black, uniform or with white, cream, or pink blotches and spots laterally. Margins of the limbs can be cream or white. Ventral surfaces are white and pale pink.
**Similar species:** The only other turtles in the Mosquitia region that have the limbs modified into paddles are *Caretta caretta*, *Chelonia mydas*, and *Eretmochelys imbricata*. These three species have hard carapacial and plastral scutes.
**General geographic distribution:** *Dermochelys coriacea* occurs worldwide in tropical, subtropical, temperate and occasionally in subarctic oceans.
**Distribution in Honduras:** This marine turtle is known from Caribbean coastal waters.
**Distribution in the Mosquitia:** Laguna de Ébano (photograph; see Remarks); Plaplaya (UF photograph). It is also reported to nest on the beaches in the Río Kruta Biological Reserve (Wilber, 1996).
**Natural history comments:** *Dermochelys coriacea* is strictly a marine turtle, with only the females coming ashore to excavate their nests and lay eggs. Females are rather fecund, depositing at least 5–7 nests of 70–90 eggs each per nesting season, with a 2–3 year interval between nesting seasons (Eckert, 2001). Leatherbacks are typically found in deep offshore waters and are reported to feed primarily on soft-bodied cnidarians and tunicates (Eckert, 2001).
**Remarks:** The Laguna de Ébano record is based on a photograph taken by Nereyda Estrada in March 2000 of a dead turtle on the beach. There is a *Dermochelys coriacea* nesting beach in the Río Plátano Biosphere Reserve between Palacios and Plaplaya, and MOPAWI along with the local Garífuna communities manage a turtle hatchery at Plaplaya. Between 15 April and 31 May 1995, 38 *D. coriacea* nests were relocated from this stretch of beach to the hatchery for protection from poachers and predators, but only 8 were located and moved during the same period in 1996 (J. Peskin, unpubl. data). During those 2 years at least 66 additional nests were lost to natural causes or human harvest (J. Peskin, unpubl. data). The wide difference in nest numbers from year to year may be at least partially attributed to the 2–3 + year intervals between the nesting seasons for individual female leatherbacks.

## Family Emydidae

Emydid turtles are primarily aquatic to semiaquatic, occurring in both fresh and brackish water environments, although a few members are terrestrial (Pough et al., 2003). The single Mosquitia emydid has a solid, large and unhinged plastron. This family ranges in the Western Hemisphere from southern Canada, through much of the USA, much of Mexico and Central America, and into South America as far south as southern Brazil, Uruguay, and northeastern Argentina (the South American distribution is highly disjunct); it is also distributed in the Bahamas and the Greater Antilles. In the Eastern Hemisphere, the family occurs in Europe, western Asia, and northwestern Africa. About 12 genera containing 40 species are included in this family (Pough et al., 2003). One species is known to occur in Honduras, including the Mosquitia. Seidel (2002) split the polytypic species *Trachemys scripta* into 15 allopatric species (one of which is *T. venusta*), and this species group will likely undergo further revision upon future study.

### *Trachemys venusta* (Gray, 1855)

**Common name(s):** Jicotea (Spanish); Kuswa* (Miskito); Bagudura*, Gawalasi** (Garífuna)
**Description (Plate 69):** This moderate-sized turtle exhibits strong sexual size dimorphism, with adult females reaching 600 mm in carapace length, and males reaching a maximum of 340 mm (Savage, 2002). The carapace has a well-defined

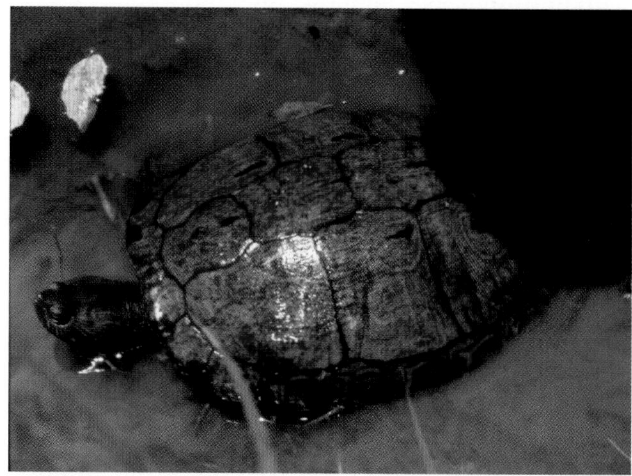

**Plate 69.** *Trachemys venusta*. Photograph by McCranie.

median keel in juveniles, the keel becoming reduced to absent in older individuals. The posterior margin of the carapace is serrate. The plastron is unhinged and posteriorly notched, and lacks a pronounced concavity in the plastron of adult males. There are 12 plastral scutes arranged in 6 pairs. The upper jaw is notched and the alveolar surface is broad and ridged. Feet are extensively webbed. The carapace is green to gray, with ocellate yellow-orange lines with dark borders and centers on the costal and vertebral scutes. The plastron is yellow with a dark brown lined symmetrical figure and with dark ocelli on the underside of the marginals. The head is green to gray with a well-defined yellow supratemporal stripe that contacts the eye. A broad yellow or reddish orange supratympanic stripe is also present and in contact with the eye. Numerous narrow yellow (with black borders) stripes are also present on all surfaces of the head (all head stripes can become obscure or absent in old individuals). Soft parts are generally greenish gray with streaks of yellow and black. The tail has paired yellow stripes above and below, with the dorsal stripes fusing distally.

**Similar species:** *Chelydra serpentina* has a cruciform plastron and a tail over one-half the length of the carapace. *Kinosternon leucostomum* and *K. scorpioides* have 11 plastral scutes and hinged plastrons. All species of *Rhinoclemmys* lack a ridge on the alveolar surface of the upper jaw and the green to gray head with yellow and black stripes. In addition, *R. annulata*, *R. areolata*, and *R. pulcherrima* have unwebbed or only slightly webbed feet, and *R. annulata* and *R. funerea* have a black or dark brown plastron with a yellow border.

**General geographic distribution:** *Trachemys venusta* occurs at low and moderate elevations on the Atlantic versant from northern Tamaulipas, Mexico, to extreme northern Colombia and on the Pacific versant from southern Oaxaca, Mexico, to southwestern Guatemala, southern El Salvador, and from west-central Costa Rica to northwestern Colombia.

**Distribution in Honduras:** This turtle is widely distributed along the Atlantic versant in the northern and eastern portions of the country. It is also known from Islas de Roatán and Utila and from Cayo Cochino Grande in the Islas de la Bahía. Its known elevational range is from near sea level to 650 m.

**Distribution in the Mosquitia:** Colón—Río Blanquito (USNM). Gracias a Dios—Caño Awalwás (USNM); Awasbila (USNM); Calpo (UF); Canco (UF); Río Coco (USNM); Laguna Kohunta (UF); Río Kruta (UF photograph); Mocorón (UTA); Río Paulaya (BMNH); Puerto Lempira (LACM, LSUMZ); Rus Rus (USNM); Tánsin (LSUMZ); Tikiraya (UF). Olancho—Río Patuca across from Quebrada El Guásimo (SMF); confluence of Ríos Wampú and Patuca (USNM).

**Natural history comments:** *Trachemys venusta* is an aquatic turtle that is typically found in large rivers, where it can be observed sunning on exposed logs, rocks, or along the bank. We have seen this turtle in the ríos Coco, Kruta, and Patuca, but rarely was it seen in tributaries of these rivers. These sites were in areas where primary to lightly disturbed evergreen broadleaf forest and denuded broadleaf swamp forest occurred. It can also occur in brackish-water habitats, such as mangrove swamps (Moll and Moll, 1990) and estuaries (Moll and Moll, 1990; pers. observ.), as well as in freshwater lagoons. This species reportedly is most abundant in areas with some degree of disturbance in bankside habitat and is uncommon in bodies of water with unbroken evergreen broadleaf forest along the banks, the latter of which provide poor basking and nesting habitat (Moll and Moll, 1990).

**Remarks:** We follow the taxonomy proposed by Seidel (2002) partitioning the wide-ranging megaspecies *T. scripta* into 15 allopatric species, 8 of which (including *T. venusta*) remain polytypic. This species is exploited as a food source by locals in the Mosquitia, who are known to hunt the turtles with rifles, nets, and by snorkeling when the water is clear.

## Family Geoemydidae

Most geoemydids are aquatic to semiaquatic, including both fresh and brackish water. However, some geoemydids are terrestrial (Pough et al., 2003; as Bataguridae). All Mosquitia members of this turtle family have solid, unhinged, and large plastrons. This family ranges in the Western Hemisphere from southern Sonora and southern Veracruz, Mexico, through Central America to western Ecuador and northeastern Brazil. In the Eastern Hemisphere, it occurs in "northwestern Africa, Europe to western Asia and the Middle East, across southern Asia to China, Japan, the Philippines, and islands of the Sunda Shelf" (Pough et al., 2003:109; as Bataguridae). This family is usually called the Bataguridae in the literature; however, Bour and Dubois (1986) have shown that the correct name for this family is Geoemydidae (also see Bour and Dubois, in David, 1994). About 23 genera comprising 65 species were included in this family (as Bataguridae) by Pough et al. (2003). However, controversy exists about the number of genera and species in this family. New species and new generic names or arrangements are being proposed on a regular basis. One genus containing four species occurs in Honduras, all of which are known from the Mosquitia.

*Rhinoclemmys annulata* **(Gray, 1860)**
**Common name(s):** Swarin* (Miskito)
**Description (Plate 70):** This small turtle can reach 204 mm carapace length, with no sexual size dimorphism present (Ernst, 1980a). The high-domed, medially flattened carapace has a low middorsal keel. The posterior margin is slightly serrate, becoming smoother with age and wear. The ovate plastron is large and lacks hinges. There are 6 pairs of plastral scutes, and the plastron is notched posteriorly. The plastron is concave in males and flat in females; both sexes have the plastron upturned anteriorly. The upper jaw is hooked, unnotched, laterally serrate, and the alveolar surface lacks a ridge. Feet are unwebbed to slightly webbed. The tail is short, with males having longer tails than females. The carapace ranges from tan to black in ground color, often with yellow or orange blotches present on the costal and vertebral scutes. The bridge is brown or black. The plastron is uniform brown or black with a yellow border. The head has a wide yellow, orange, or red stripe extending from the eye onto the neck, and a smaller stripe from the lower edge of the eye to the tympanum. There is a small stripe sometimes present from the anterior edge of the eye to the tip of the snout. All of these stripes can vary in intensity between individuals and fade with age. The gular region is yellow with brown mottling. Forelimbs have yellow and dark brown stripes or rows of spots, the hind limbs are brown on the outside surface and yellow on the inside surface. The tail has yellow stripes on the brown dorsal surface.

**Plate 70.** *Rhinoclemmys annulata*. Photograph by McCranie.

**Similar species:** *Chelydra serpentina* has a cruciform plastron and a tail over one-half the length of the carapace. *Kinosternon leucostomum* and *K. scorpioides* have 11 plastral scutes and a hinged plastron. *Trachemys venusta* has a ridge on the alveolar surface of the upper jaw, a plastron figure composed of dark symmetrical lines, and fully webbed feet. *Rhinoclemmys areolata*, *R. funerea*, and *R. pulcherrima* have notched upper jaws. *Rhinoclemmys areolata* also has a mostly yellow bridge, *R. funerea* has fully webbed feet, and *R. pulcherrima* has a red stripe crossing the tip of the snout.
**General geographic distribution:** *Rhinoclemmys annulata* occurs at low and moderate elevations from north-central Honduras to northwestern Colombia on the Atlantic versant and from central Panama to western Ecuador on the Pacific versant.
**Distribution in Honduras:** This species is known from the northeastern and north-central portions of the country from 20 to 540 m elevation.
**Distribution in the Mosquitia:** Colón—Quebrada Machín (USNM). Gracias a Dios—Mocorón (CF); Rus Rus (USNM); Bodega de Río Tapalwás (USNM); Warunta Tingni Kiamp (USNM). Olancho—Quebrada El Guásimo (SMF).
**Natural history comments:** In the Mosquitia, *Rhinoclemmys annulata* has been collected in primary evergreen broadleaf forest. Most specimens were found during the day while active on the forest floor. One individual was found at night while partially buried in a muddy backwater area of a small stream.

*Rhinoclemmys areolata* **(A.M.C. Duméril and Bibron, in A.M.C. Duméril and Duméril, 1851)**
**Common name(s):** None
**Description (Plate 71):** This small turtle can reach 206 mm in carapace length, with no sexual

**Plate 71.** *Rhinoclemmys areolata.* Photograph by John B. Iverson.

size dimorphism apparent (Ernst, 1980b). The high-domed ovoid carapace has a low middorsal keel and flared margins, with the posterior margin being slightly serrate. The carapace can be somewhat rugose in juveniles, becoming smooth with old age. The plastron is large, lacks hinges, and is notched posteriorly. There are 6 pairs of plastral scutes. The plastron is concave in males and flat in females; both sexes have the plastron slightly upturned anteriorly. The upper jaw is notched and the alveolar surface lacks a ridge. Feet are slightly webbed. The tail is short, with males having longer tails than females. The carapace is usually olive or brown with black seams and moderately extensive yellow mottling; some individuals have mostly tan to black carapaces. The bridge is yellow. The plastron is yellow with a brown to black central blotch and brown to black seams. The head has a yellow or red stripe extending from the eye onto the neck; a smaller stripe extends from the eye to the tympanum. There are usually 2 oval yellow or red blotches on the dorsolateral surface of the neck. The lower jaw and chin are yellow with brown or black spots or ocelli. Soft areas are olive, brown, or yellow with large yellow, black-spotted scales present on the forelimbs.

**Similar species:** *Chelydra serpentina* has a cruciform plastron and a long tail that is more than one-half the length of the carapace. *Kinosternon leucostomum* and *K. scorpioides* have 11 plastral scutes and a hinged plastron. *Trachemys venusta* has a ridge on the alveolar surface of the upper jaw, a plastron figure composed of dark symmetrical lines, and fully webbed feet. *Rhinoclemmys annulata* has a hooked and unnotched upper jaw and a brown or black bridge. *Rhinoclemmys funerea* has extensively webbed feet and a mostly brown or black bridge. *Rhinoclemmys pulcherrima* has 2 or 3 yellow or red supratemporal stripes, a red stripe crossing the snout, and a brown or black bridge.

**General geographic distribution:** *Rhinoclemmys areolata* occurs at low elevations on the Atlantic versant from southern Veracruz, Mexico, to the San Pedro Sula region of northwestern Honduras. There is also an isolated record in the Mosquitia of extreme northeastern Honduras.

**Distribution in Honduras:** See General geographic distribution. Its known elevational range is from near sea level to 100 m.

**Distribution in the Mosquitia:** Gracias a Dios—Segovia River (= Río Coco) (USNM).

**Natural history comments:** This species is typically found in open savanna habitat and marsh areas, but is known to enter adjacent dense woodlands (Ernst and Barbour, 1989). The inclusion of this species in the herpetofauna of the Mosquitia is based on a single specimen from "Segovia River" that was collected in 1887. There is little reason to doubt this record, as several other reptile and bird species that are well known from the Mosquitia carrying the same locality data were collected in the same year by the same collector (Charles H. Townsend). The specimen is most likely to have been collected either in the open freshwater marshes or *llanos* that extend near the coast between the Río Coco (Segovia) and Río Kruta or in the pine savannas adjacent to the Río Coco. Monroe (1968:29) noted that birds collected by Townsend in 1887 and labeled "Segovia River" are "representative of the species and races found exclusively in the lowland pine savanna of the Mosquitia." Thus, we have included *Rhinoclemmys areolata* in pine savanna in Table 3.

*Rhinoclemmys funerea* **(Cope, 1875)**

**Common name(s):** Tortuga Negra (Spanish); Kuswa Kuiwi* (Miskito)

**Description (Plate 72):** This moderate-sized turtle can reach 325 mm carapace length, with no sexual size dimorphism present (Ernst, 1981). The high-domed, ovoid carapace has a low median keel (becoming obscure in old individuals) and a serrate posterior margin. Posterior marginals are flared. The plastron is large, unhinged, and has a posterior notch. There are 6 pairs of plastral scutes. The plastron is concave in males and flat in females,

**Plate 72.** *Rhinoclemmys funerea*. Photograph by Townsend.

and upturned anteriorly in both sexes. The upper jaw is serrated laterally and notched medially, and the alveolar surface lacks a ridge. The tail is short with the males having longer, thicker tails than do the females. Feet are extensively webbed. The carapace is dark brown to black and the plastron is black with a yellow midseam in adults. The bridge is uniformly dark brown or dark brown with a yellow bar on the lateral edges of each marginal. The dorsal surface of the head is black with a wide yellow stripe extending posteriorly from the eye to above the tympanum; 2 other yellow lines extend from the eye and corner of the mouth to the tympanum. These head stripes can be obscure in old individuals. The lower jaw and gular area is yellow with black spots. Forelimbs are yellow with black spots on the inside surfaces and dark brown on the outer surfaces. Hind limbs are dark brown on the outside surfaces and yellow with dark brown spots on the inside surfaces. The tail is yellow with dark brown stripes.
**Similar species:** *Chelydra serpentina* has a cruciform plastron and a tail over one-half the length of the carapace. *Kinosternon leucostomum* and *K. scorpioides* have 11 plastral scutes and hinged plastrons. *Trachemys venusta* has a ridge on the alveolar surface of the upper jaw and a plastron figure composed of dark symmetrical lines. *Rhinoclemmys annulata*, *R. areolata*, and *R. pulcherrima* have unwebbed or slightly webbed feet.
**General geographic distribution:** *Rhinoclemmys funerea* occurs at low elevations from the drainages of the Río Plátano in Honduras to central Panama on the Atlantic versant.
**Distribution in Honduras:** This species is known only from the drainages of the ríos Coco and Plátano. It is known from 90 to 100 m elevation.
**Distribution in the Mosquitia:** Gracias a Dios—Caño Awalwás (USNM); Boca de Caño Awalwás (USNM); Río Coco near Krasa (LACM); Río Plátano (Sletto, 1999); Río Rus Rus (UF).
**Natural history comments:** *Rhinoclemmys funerea* is a primarily aquatic turtle that comes onto land at night to feed. We found an adult that was foraging on low herbaceous plants at night near a tributary river of the Caño Awalwás that flows through primary evergreen broadleaf forest. Another was taken near the confluence of Caño Awalwás and the Río Coco, in an area with high turbidity due to the mixing of the clear water from the caño and the muddy waters of the Río Coco. The vegetation along the confluence of these two rivers was lightly disturbed evergreen broadleaf forest. Tomás Manzanares collected two specimens for us by snorkeling in the Río Rus Rus near the village of Rus Rus. These turtles were collected during the dry season in January and May.
**Remarks:** This species is prized by locals in the Mosquitia for its meat and is actively hunted with rifles and by snorkeling during the dry season when the water is clear. Photographs of eggs and an adult of *Rhinoclemmys funerea* to be used as food by people in the Río Plátano Biosphere Reserve are in Sletto (1999).

*Rhinoclemmys pulcherrima* **(Gray, 1855)**
**Common name(s):** None
**Description (Plate 73):** This small turtle reaches 206 mm carapace length, with males smaller than

**Plate 73.** *Rhinoclemmys pulcherrima*. Photograph by McCranie.

females and reaching a maximum of 181 mm carapace length (Ernst, 1978). The high-domed, somewhat flattened, ovoid carapace has a middorsal keel and a slightly serrated posterior margin (the middorsal keel and serrated margin can become obscure in old individuals). The plastron is large, unhinged, and notched posteriorly. There are 12 plastral scutes arranged in 6 pairs. The plastron is concave in males and flattened in females, and slightly upturned anteriorly in females. The upper jaw is serrated laterally and notched medially, and the alveolar surface is unridged. Feet are unwebbed or only slightly webbed. The short tail is longer in males than in females. The carapace is brown with dark brown bordered yellow, orange, or red ocelli on the costal scutes. Vertebral scutes are uniform in color or flecked with dark brown. The plastron is yellow with a brown mottled central blotch. The bridge is brown with a yellow bar on each marginal. The head has an olive brown ground color with 3 red stripes dorsally; the red stripe extending anteriorly from each eye crosses the tip of the snout. There are also red stripes present extending from the upper jaw to the tympanum, from the nostril to the eye, and from the eye to the tympanum. The chin and gular area are yellow and marked with red or brown lines, ocelli, or spots. Forelimbs have yellow, orange, or red scales with rows of black spots. Hind limbs are brown on the outside surfaces and yellow or orange with dark brown spots on the inside surfaces. The tail is yellow, orange, or red with dark dorsal stripes.
**Similar species:** *Chelydra serpentina* has a cruciform plastron and a tail over one-half the length of the carapace. *Kinosternon leucostomum* and *K. scorpioides* have 11 plastral scutes and hinged plastrons. *Trachemys venusta* has a ridge on the alveolar surface of the upper jaw and a plastron figure composed of dark symmetrical lines. *Rhinoclemmys annulata* has a hooked and unnotched upper jaw. *Rhinoclemmys funerea* has extensively webbed feet. *Rhinoclemmys areolata* has one supratemporal stripe and a yellow bridge, and lacks a red stripe crossing the tip of the snout.
**General geographic distribution:** *Rhinoclemmys pulcherrima* occurs at low and moderate elevations from southern Sonora, Mexico, to central Costa Rica on the Pacific versant. The species also occurs on the Atlantic versant in several interior valleys of Honduras and Guatemala.
**Distribution in Honduras:** This turtle occurs in the southern part of the country as well as in several central interior valleys. It is known from near sea level to 1480 m elevation.
**Distribution in the Mosquitia:** Olancho—Quebrada El Guásimo (USNM).
**Natural history comments:** The one specimen collected in the Mosquitia was found active in a small stream within primary evergreen broadleaf forest, a habitat considered unusual for this species by Nicholson et al. (2000). It is possible that the Mosquitia specimen, found about one year after Hurricane Mitch occurred, was washed down the Río Patuca from subhumid areas of the Río Guayape-Guayambre valley where this turtle is known to occur. This species normally lives in subhumid areas, not in primary evergreen broadleaf forest.

## Family Kinosternidae

Kinosternid turtles are generally small (110 to 200 mm in carapace length), although some tropical species can reach nearly 400 mm. They possess cloacal glands that release a foul-smelling musk. They tend to walk along the bottoms of slow-moving rivers and streams and ponds and are poor swimmers. The Mosquitia members of this family are the only turtles in the area with a double-hinged plastron that completely closes the shell. The distribution of this family is limited to the Western Hemisphere. It occurs from the eastern, central and southwestern USA, through Mexico and Central America, to South America as far south as northern Argentina. Three genera containing 22 species were included in this family by Pough et al. (2003). Two genera comprising three species are known to range into Honduras. Two species placed in a single genus occur in the Mosquitia.

### *Kinosternon leucostomum* (A.M.C. Duméril and Bibron, in A.M.C. Duméril and Duméril, 1851)

**Common name(s):** Tortuga (Spanish); Siakwa* (Miskito); Agaga, Aragaga* (Garífuna)
**Description (Plate 74):** This small turtle can exceed 175 mm in carapace length in adult males of some populations, with females being slightly smaller (Berry and Iverson, 2001a). The ovoid carapace is unicarinate (keel can be absent or indistinct in some old individuals) and the marginals anterior and posterior to the bridge are moderately to distinctly flared. The plastron has 2

**Plate 74.** *Kinosternon leucostomum.* Photograph by McCranie.

hinges, the anterior hinge more kinetic than the posterior hinge. These hinges allow for complete closure of the shell in the Mosquitia populations. There are 11 plastral scutes, arranged in 5 pairs plus a single intergular scute that is broader on the dorsal surface of the plastron than on the ventral surface. The plastron is usually slightly smaller and more concave in males than in females. The upper jaw is hooked and both the upper and the lower jaw margins are smooth. One or more pairs of small barbels are present in the gular region. Feet are webbed, and adult males have patches of spiny scales on the posterior surfaces of the calves and thighs of the hind limbs that are used to clasp females during mating. The tail is short, but longer in males than in females. Both sexes have a terminal spine on the tail which is larger in males. The carapace is brown to black and the plastron is yellow to pale brown, with some seams dark brown. The head is dark brown to gray dorsally and laterally with cream to pale brown spots and/or reticulations present laterally and usually dorsally. A cream, yellow, or pale brown stripe extending from the upper posterior portion of the eye onto the lateral area of the neck can be present (distinct or obscure) or absent altogether. The jaw sheaths are cream to yellow with dark vertical lines present in some older males. The limbs and soft parts are brown or gray dorsally and yellowish brown to pale brown ventrally.

**Similar species:** *Chelydra serpentina* has a cruciform plastron and a tail over one-half the length of the carapace. All other turtles in the Mosquitia, except *Kinosternon scorpioides,* have 12 plastral scutes and a solid plastron. *Kinosternon scorpioides* has 3 keels on the carapace (usually only indicated posteriorly in old individuals), and the intergular scute not broader on the dorsal surface than on the ventral surface, and adult males lack opposable patches of spines on the thigh and calf.

**General geographic distribution:** *Kinosternon leucostomum* occurs at low and moderate elevations from central Veracruz, Mexico, to north-central Colombia on the Atlantic versant and from west-central Costa Rica to extreme northwestern Peru on the Pacific versant. The species also occurs on Isla del Maíz Grande, Nicaragua, and Cayo Cochino Grande, Honduras.

**Distribution in Honduras:** This turtle is widely distributed across the northern and eastern portions of the mainland as well as on Cayo Cochino Grande. Its known elevational range is from near sea level to 1120 m.

**Distribution in the Mosquitia:** Gracias a Dios—Caño Awalwás (UF; USNM); Awasbila (USNM); Caño Awawás (USNM); Laguna Baraya (ROM); Cauquira (UF); Río Coco (USNM); Kaska Tingni (USNM); about 30 km S of Mocorón (UTA); Mocorón (UTA); Raudal Pomokir (formerly in UNAH, now lost); Crique Sikiatingni (UF); Tánsin (LACM, LSUMZ); Bodega de Río Tapalwás (USNM); Tikiraya (UF); Crique Wahatingni (UF); Warunta Tingni Kiamp (USNM). Olancho—Callejón (LACM); Quebrada El Guásimo (USNM); Río Kosmako (USNM).

**Natural history comments:** *Kinosternon leucostomum* occurs in various permanent, semi-permanent, and temporary aquatic habitats, primarily at lower elevations throughout its range (Berry and Iverson, 2001a). In the Mosquitia, this species is often seen while active at night in and around shallow rivers and streams through primary to moderately disturbed evergreen broadleaf forest. It also occurs in streams and swamps in broadleaf swamp forest and in water-filled depressions in coastal strand. It typically occurs in slower moving waters and is a bottom walker. Adults can also be found active during the day on the forest floor well away from surface water. One hatchling was collected in July on a muddy trail that ran through poorly drained pasture that was cut from primary evergreen broadleaf forest.

**Remarks:** Some residents of Tikiraya stated that they use *K. leucostomum* for food.

*Kinosternon scorpioides* **(Linnaeus, 1766)**
**Common name(s):** Tortuga (Spanish); Siakwa* (Miskito); Agaga, Aragaga* (Garífuna)
**Description (Plate 75):** This small turtle can exceed 205 mm in carapace length in adult males, with females slightly smaller (Berry and Iverson, 2001b). The ovoid carapace is tricarinate (keels can be present only posteriorly in old individuals) and the marginals anterior and posterior to the bridge are slightly flared. The plastron has 2 hinges, the anterior hinge more kinetic than the posterior hinge. These hinges allow for complete closing of the shell in the Mosquitia populations. The plastral scutes number 11, with 5 paired scutes plus a single intergular scute that is not broader on the dorsal surface of plastron than it is on the ventral surface. The plastron is usually slightly smaller and more concave in males than in females. The upper jaw is weakly to strongly hooked, usually more strongly so in males, and both the upper and lower jaw margins are smooth. Two or 3 pairs of small barbels are present in the gular region. Feet are webbed, and males lack patches of spiny scales on the calf and thigh of the hind limbs. The tail is short, but longer in males than in females. Both sexes have a terminal spine on the tail which is larger in males. The carapace is brown to black and the plastron is yellow to orange with dark brown seams. Dorsal and lateral head coloration is variable, generally gray, brown, or black with cream, yellow, orange, or red mottling, spots, or reticulations. Jaws are pale brown, orange, or red, with or without brown vertical streaks. Limbs and soft parts are gray or brown, usually with small darker spots or mottling.

**Plate 75.** *Kinosternon scorpioides*. Photograph by McCranie.

**Similar species:** *Chelydra serpentina* has a cruciform plastron and a tail over one-half the length of the carapace. All other turtles in the Mosquitia, except *K. leucostomum*, have 12 plastral scutes and a solid plastron. *Kinosternon leucostomum* has a unicarinate carapace, an intergular scute that is broader on the dorsal surface than on the ventral surface, and opposable patches of spines present on the thigh and calf in adult males.
**General geographic distribution:** *Kinosternon scorpioides* is a widespread species, found at low and moderate elevations from southern Tamaulipas, Mexico, to eastern Nicaragua and from eastern Panama to northern Argentina on the Atlantic versant and on the Pacific versant from the Isthmus of Tehuantepec region, Oaxaca, Mexico, to eastern Panama. In addition, it occurs throughout the Atlantic drainages of northern and eastern South America, as well as on the islands of Cozumel, San Andrés, and Trinidad.
**Distribution in Honduras:** This turtle occurs on the Pacific versant in the southern portion of the country and at several open forest or sub-humid localities on the Atlantic versant in the central and northeastern portions of the country. It is known from near sea level to 1240 m elevation.
**Distribution in the Mosquitia:** Gracias a Dios—42 km E of Awasbila (USNM); Calpo (UF); Canco (UF); Mocorón (CF); 1.2 km SW of road to Pranza on Rus Rus-Puerto Lempira road (USNM); Rus Rus (USNM); between Rus Rus and Awasbila (UF); Crique Sikiatingni (UF); Tánsin (LACM, LSUMZ); Tikiraya (UF).
**Natural history comments:** *Kinosternon scorpioides* is associated with low-lying wet areas and small seasonal ponds in pine savanna habitat in the Mosquitia. It also occurs in permanent swampy areas in freshwater marshes and broadleaf swamp forest. This turtle is apparently abundant in the llanos and freshwater lagoons of the eastern Mosquitia, where it has been collected in the same water bodies as the turtles *K. leucostomum* and *Trachemys venusta*. This species also can be regularly found in and around large, semi-permanent puddles on the Puerto Lempira-Rus Rus-Awasbila road. We have observed this species active both during the day and at night.
**Remarks:** *Kinosternon scorpioides* is eaten by some people in the Mosquitia. We found numerous shells of this species, along with those of *Trachemys venusta*, in a dump in Canco. In

addition, some people in Tikiraya stated that they also eat these turtles.

### Order Squamata (Lizards and Snakes)

The Order Squamata contains the lizards and snakes, as well as the amphisbaenians (no amphisbaenians occur in the Mosquitia). Typically, squamates have a highly kinetic skull, compared to that of turtles, crocodilians, and the New Zealand tuatara. In addition, they possess a pair of male copulatory organs called hemipenes, which are outpocketings of the posterior wall of the cloaca residing in the base of the tail (Pough et al., 2003). Amphisbaenians and snakes are groups nested within the Scleroglossa, a group of squamates also including several lizard families (Pough et al., 2003). Thus, the traditional separation of squamate reptiles into two suborders is not substantiated on evolutionary grounds. Nonetheless, in the region covered by this book, snakes can easily be distinguished from lizards, inasmuch as the lizards all have four well-developed limbs and the snakes do not (although *Boa constrictor* and *Corallus annulatus* do have cloacal spurs, which are external remnants of posterior limbs). The lizards and snakes are dealt with in separate sections, as follows.

### Lizards

Eighty-nine species of lizards, placed in 12 families, are recorded from Honduras (Wilson and McCranie, 2002; McCranie, 2005). Of these, 31 species in nine families and 18 genera are known from the Mosquitia.

#### Family Gekkonidae

Species of the family Gekkonidae (following the classification of Kluge, 1987) are covered dorsally by small granular scales and have skin that is fragile and tears easily. Many species have greatly expanded subdigital toe pads containing setae that allow for exceptional climbing abilities. One lineage (containing *Gonatodes* and *Sphaerodactylus* in the Mosquitia) has expanded subdigital lamellae, but lack the greatly expanded toe pads, although they still retain good climbing abilities. The members of this family are found in the Western Hemisphere from southern California, USA, to the southern tip of Baja California, Mexico, and from Sonora and Veracruz, Mexico, southward to Chile and southern Argentina. They also occur on the Galapagos Islands, in southeastern Florida, USA, the Greater and Lesser Antilles, Trinidad and Tobago, and on many islands on both coasts of Middle America. They range throughout the Eastern Hemisphere south of about 42°N latitude to the southern tips of Africa, Australia, and New Zealand. A number of gecko species have been widely introduced into tropical and sub-tropical environments around the world, including Honduras. About 75 genera containing 800+ species were said to be in this family (Pough et al., 2003). Six genera comprised of 14 species are known to occupy Honduran territory, with four species in four genera known to occur in the Mosquitia. Members of this family found in the Mosquitia can be differentiated from other lizards in the area by the combination of having the dorsal surface of the head covered with granular scales and by lacking moveable eyelids.

*Gonatodes albogularis* **(A.M.C. Duméril and Bibron, 1836)**
**Common name(s):** Akak* (Miskito)
**Description (Plate 76):** *Gonatodes albogularis* is a small gecko (both sexes to 48 mm SVL) with a relatively short tail (about 1.0 to 1.2 times SVL). The eyes are relatively large with round pupils. Moveable eyelids are absent. Dorsal surfaces of the head and body are covered with small conical, granular scales. Ventral scales are flat, imbricate, and larger than the dorsals. Males have numerous enlarged escutcheon scales on the venter and underside of the thighs. Digits lack expanded pads,

**Plate 76.** *Gonatodes albogularis.* Photograph by McCranie.

and have a nonretractable claw articulated between a superior and an inferior terminal scale. Subdigital lamellae are not divided, and there are 18 to 22 lamellae on Digit IV of the hind limb (Savage, 2002). The median subcaudal scales are enlarged. Femoral and preanal pores are absent. This species is sexually dichromatic. Males have black to dark gray or gray-brown bodies, often with blue lateral spots; the head and neck are yellow to red-orange with a blue line on the white supralabials; the ventral surface is blackish blue anteriorly, fading to gray posteriorly. Females are grayish white to tan with irregular dark mottling or spots dorsally; the head is similar in color to the dorsum of the body; the ventral surface is dirty white to tan. Males normally have a white tip to their tail, if the tail is undamaged.
**Similar species:** *Hemidactylus frenatus* and *Thecadactylus rapicauda* have strongly expanded subdigital toe pads. *Sphaerodactylus millepunctatus* has a retractable claw that is displaced laterally between an enlarged terminal pilose pad and several smaller terminal scales and 10 to 11 subdigital lamellae on Digit IV of the hind limb.
**General geographic distribution:** *Gonatodes albogularis* occurs at low and moderate elevations from southeastern Chiapas, Mexico, to western Colombia on the Pacific versant and from eastern Guatemala to western Venezuela on the Atlantic versant. The species also occurs on the Greater and Lesser Antilles and Curaçao. Reportedly introduced in the Miami and Key West areas, Florida, USA, and in Belize City, Belize.
**Distribution in Honduras:** This species is found at a number of widely scattered localities from near sea level to about 1000 m elevation.
**Distribution in the Mosquitia:** Gracias a Dios—Río Plátano (CM); Rus Rus (UF; USNM).
**Natural history comments:** *Gonatodes albogularis* is a habitat generalist that is usually found in edificarian situations. The Rus Rus locality is a village in pine savanna and the specimens taken there were in piles of lumber under a stilt house or active on the walls of buildings.

*Hemidactylus frenatus* **Schlegel, in A.M.C. Duméril and Bibron, 1836**
**Common name(s):** Geco (Spanish); Akak* (Miskito)
**Description (Plate 77):** *Hemidactylus frenatus* is a moderate-sized gecko (males to 65 mm SVL, females to 60 mm) with a relatively short tail

**Plate 77.** *Hemidactylus frenatus.* Photograph by McCranie.

(about 1.0 to 1.2 times SVL). The eyes are large, with vertical pupils. Moveable eyelids are absent. The head and dorsal body scales are granular, with some enlarged, weakly keeled scales scattered among the granules on the body. Ventral scales are smooth, imbricate, and much larger than the dorsal scales. Limbs are short and stocky. Digits lack basal webbing, and 9 or 10 expanded, medially divided, subdigital lamellae are present on Digit IV of the hind limb. The claw is terminally located on each digit and is non retractable. The tail is flattened, with 6 longitudinal rows of enlarged, keeled tubercles. These rows of enlarged tubercles are separated by 8 rows of smooth scales. The median row of subcaudal scales is enlarged and platelike. About 25 to 36 total femoral and precloacal pores are present in males (these pores are absent in females). Dorsal coloration varies from day to night. Nighttime color can be buff, pinkish-tan, tan, or brown with scattered dark spots. Daytime color tends to be darker. The ventral surface is uniformly creamy white, yellow, or tan.
**Similar species:** *Thecadactylus rapicauda* has 12 to 25 subdigital lamellae on Digit IV of the hind limb, basal webbing between the digits, a retractable claw, and adults that reach 126 mm SVL. All other geckos known from the Mosquitia lack medially divided subdigital lamellae on expanded toe pads.
**General geographic distribution:** *Hemidactylus frenatus* occurs in "Taiwan, Hong Kong, Guangdong, Hainan, and southern Yunnan, China. Southern and eastern Africa, Madagascar, Mauritius, South and southeastern Asia,

Philippines, Japan (Ryukyu and Bonin islands), Indoaustralian Archipelago east to New Guinea and northern Australia; Oceania and Mexico. Introduced into Mariana Islands (Guam) and USA (Hawaiian Islands)" (Zhao and Adler, 1993:184). The species is also widely introduced in Central America, and introduced populations have also been reported from Florida and Texas, USA.
**Distribution in Honduras:** This species has become widely introduced in cities, towns, and villages on the mainland. It has also been introduced on Isla de Utila in the Islas de la Bahía. Its known elevational range is from near sea level to 930 m.
**Distribution in the Mosquitia:** Gracias a Dios—Puerto Lempira (UF; USNM).
**Natural history comments:** *Hemidactylus frenatus* occurs in edificarian situations along the coast in the Mosquitia, and can be observed moving across the walls of buildings at night. These geckos are often seen around electric lights feeding on the insects that are attracted to them. This species has a voice and frequently squeaks while active.
**Remarks:** This species was not collected in Honduras until 1997, but has subsequently been collected or seen on or in buildings in scattered localities throughout much of the country.

*Sphaerodactylus millepunctatus* **Hallowell, "1860" (1861)**
**Common name(s):** Akak* (Miskito)
**Description (Plate 78):** *Sphaerodactylus millepunctatus* is a small gecko (males to 30 mm SVL, females to 31 mm) with a relatively short tail (about 0.9 to 1.0 times SVL). The head is covered with small granular scales. Eyes are small with nearly round pupils. Moveable eyelids are absent. Dorsal body scales are oval, keeled, and imbricate. Ventral scales are round, smooth, imbricate, and are larger than the dorsals. The median subcaudal scales are greatly enlarged, forming a continuous longitudinal row. Adult males have enlarged escutcheon scales on the venter and usually on the undersides of the thighs. Digits lack expanded pads, are dorsolaterally compressed at the distal end, and have 9 to 13 undivided subdigital lamellae on Digit IV of the hind limb. Claws are retractable and are displaced laterally between an enlarged terminal pilose pad and several smaller terminal scales. Femoral and precloacal pores are absent. Adults are brown

**Plate 78.** *Sphaerodactylus millepunctatus.* Photograph by McCranie.

with small darker brown spots dorsally on the body and usually dark brown lines and spots on the head. Dark sacral and nuchal spots or bands are present in juveniles; these markings can be retained into adulthood, but usually are lost in larger individuals.
**Similar species:** *Hemidactylus frenatus* and *Thecadactylus rapicauda* have greatly expanded subdigital toe pads with divided lamellae. *Gonatodes albogularis* has a nonretractable and terminally placed claw on the toes.
**General geographic distribution:** *Sphaerodactylus millepunctatus* occurs at low and moderate elevations from the Isthmus of Tehuantepec, and Oaxaca, Mexico, to northern Costa Rica on the Atlantic versant and in northwestern Costa Rica on the Pacific versant. The species also occurs on the Bay Islands of Honduras, Isla Cozumel, Mexico, and Isla de Maíz Grande, Nicaragua.
**Distribution in Honduras:** This lizard is widely distributed across the northern half of the country and on the Islas de la Bahía. It is also known from a single locality in south-central Honduras. Its known elevational range is from near sea level to 930 m.
**Distribution in the Mosquitia:** Colón—near Barranco (UMMZ). Gracias a Dios—Caño Awalwás (UF); Awasbila (USNM); Cauquira (UF); Palacios (BMNH); Rus Rus (UF; USNM). Olancho—Matamoros (USNM); confluence of Ríos Sausa and Wampú (USNM).
**Natural history comments:** *Sphaerodactylus millepunctatus* occurs in primary to highly disturbed evergreen broadleaf forest, coastal

strand, and pine savanna in the Mosquitia. These diminutive, primarily diurnal geckos are often found in association with human habitation, including inside houses, under piles of debris, and in one case on a steep riverbank at the edge of a village. However, it can also be found in leaf litter in evergreen broadleaf forest well away from human habitation, as well as under coconut fronds in coastal strand. One specimen was collected at night while feeding on insects attracted to an electrical light bulb.

*Thecadactylus rapicauda* **(Houttuyn, 1782)**
**Common name(s):** Talconete (Spanish); Akak* (Miskito)
**Description (Plate 79):** *Thecadactylus rapicauda* is the largest gecko found in the Mosquitia (males to 125 mm SVL, females to 126 mm [A. Russell and Bauer, 2002]) and has a relatively short tail (about 0.6 to 0.9 times SVL). Eyes are large with vertically elliptical pupils. Movable eyelids are absent. Dorsal scales of the head and body are small, uniform, and granular. Ventral scales are round to oval, imbricate, smooth, and are larger than the dorsal scales. Subcaudal scales are squarish, flat, and larger than the ventral scales. Limbs are short and stocky. Digits have large expanded toe pads and are basally webbed, with 14 to 25 medially divided subdigital lamellae on Digit IV of the hind limb. The claw is retractable into a fleshy sulcus. The tail is easily lost and most adults have regenerated tails that have the proximal part fleshy and much wider than the base of the tail, and the distal part tapering to a blunt tip. Femoral and precloacal pores are absent.

**Plate 79.** *Thecadactylus rapicauda*. Photograph by McCranie.

Coloration is highly variable and can change with fluctuations in environmental or physiological conditions. Dorsal body and tail coloration can range from creamy white to different shades of gray or brown, or even black, and can possess a number of different dorsal patterns including chevrons, spots, or bars. Ventral surfaces are creamy white or beige.
**Similar species:** *Hemidactylus frenatus* does not exceed 65 mm SVL, lacks basal webbing between the toes, and has a nonretractable terminal claw on each toe and 9 or 10 subdigital lamellae on Digit IV of the hind limb. All other geckos known from the Mosquitia lack medially divided subdigital lamellae on expanded toe pads.
**General geographic distribution:** *Thecadactylus rapicauda* has the most extensive natural range of any Western Hemisphere gecko (A. Russell and Bauer, 2002). It occurs at low and moderate elevations from the Yucatán Peninsula and Chiapas, Mexico, to northeastern Bolivia, and much of Amazonian Brazil on the Atlantic versant and from west-central Costa Rica to western Ecuador on the Pacific versant. It is also found marginally in northwestern Costa Rica on the Pacific versant and also occurs on most major islands in the Lesser Antilles and on St. Croix and Necker Island in the Virgin Islands and on Trinidad and Tobago, several small islands off the coast of Venezuela, Isla de Utila, Honduras, Islas del Maíz, Nicaragua, and Islas de las Perlas, Panama.
**Distribution in Honduras:** This lizard is known from across the northern portion of the mainland and from Isla de Utila, Islas de la Bahía. It occurs from near sea level to 750 m elevation.
**Distribution in the Mosquitia:** Gracias a Dios—Crique Ibantara (USNM); Karasangkan (USNM); Palacios (BMNH); Bodega de Río Tapalwás (UF; USNM); Cerro Wahatingni (USNM); Warunta Tingni Kiamp (USNM). Olancho—Matamoros (SMF, USNM).
**Natural history comments:** This nocturnal species is found in primary to highly disturbed evergreen broadleaf forest in the Mosquitia. Adults were collected on the walls and thatched roof of a building and subadults were collected in primary forest on a limestone boulder, on a large fallen tree, and on a palm frond.
**Remarks:** People living in the area of Matamoros, Olancho, believe that *Thecadactylus rapicauda* is capable of inflicting a venomous sting with the tip of its tail (Nicholson et al., 2000).

## Family Corytophanidae

Corytophanid lizards are characterized by the presence of well-developed head crests or casques (Pough et al., 2003, who recognize this group as a subfamily within the Iguanidae). These crests or casques are sexually dimorphic in the genus *Basiliscus* (well developed only in adult males), whereas they are about equally developed in both sexes of the other genera (including juveniles). The members of this family (*sensu* Frost and Etheridge, 1989, and Frost et al., 2001; see Schulte et al., 2003, for an opposing taxonomy) are limited in distribution to the Western Hemisphere, within which they range from Tamaulipas and Jalisco, Mexico, southward through Central America into South America as far south as west-central Venezuela east of the Andes and western Ecuador west of the Andes. Three genera containing nine species are currently included in this family (Pough et al., 2003). All three genera comprising seven species are known to occur in Honduras. Two genera containing three species occur in the Mosquitia.

*Basiliscus plumifrons* **Cope, 1875**
**Common name(s):** Charancaco (Spanish); Bibat*, Swain* (Miskito)
**Description (Plate 80):** This large lizard (males to 250 mm SVL, females to 174 mm [Savage, 2002]) has a very long tail (about 2.4 to 3.0 times SVL). Adult males have bilobed, laterally compressed head crests, the anterior lobe is small and narrow, and the posterior lobe is large and extends posteriorly to about the midlength of the neck. Adult females have smaller head crests that are bilobed only in the largest individuals; the rest of the females and subadult males have head crests consisting of a small knob on the posterior portion of the head. The tympanum is distinct and is higher than long and there is no much enlarged scale below the tympanic region. Supralabials number 7 or 8 and infralabials 7. Dorsal body scales are smooth to weakly keeled and imbricate. Adult males have strongly raised middorsal and caudal crests that are supported by bony rays; these crests are also present in adult females, but are much lower and less developed. Ventral scales are smooth and imbricate. Caudal autotomy is absent, as are femoral and precloacal pores. A lateral flap of scales is present on the outer edge of each hind toe. The fourth toe is much longer than the third toe. Dorsal and ventral surfaces are primarily green in life. The iris is yellow.

**Plate 80.** *Basiliscus plumifrons.* Photograph by McCranie.

**Similar species:** *Basiliscus vittatus* has keeled ventral scales and a dorsal ground color of some shade of brown. *Iguana iguana* has a very large scale below the tympanic region.
**General geographic distribution:** *Basiliscus plumifrons* occurs at low and moderate elevations from northeastern Honduras to northwestern Panama on the Atlantic versant and in southeastern Costa Rica on the Pacific versant.
**Distribution in Honduras:** This species is known from low elevations (60 to 225 m) only in the Mosquitia.
**Distribution in the Mosquitia:** Colón—Empalme Río Chilmeca (formerly in UNAH, now lost); Subterráneo del Río Plátano (formerly in UNAH, now lost). Gracias a Dios—Caño Awalwás (UF; USNM); Awasbila (USNM); Río Coco (USNM); Kalila Plapan Tingni (USNM); Kaska Tingni (USNM); Mocorón (CF); Bodega de Río Tapalwás (UF; USNM); Urus Tingni Kiamp (USNM). Olancho—Caño El Cajón (USNM); Quebrada El Guásimo (SMF; USNM); Río Kosmako (USNM); Matamoros (SMF; USNM); Quebrada El Mono (USNM); Qururia (USNM).
**Natural history comments:** *Basiliscus plumifrons* occurs along streams and rivers in primary and lightly disturbed evergreen broadleaf forest. Adults and juveniles are active during sunny days on both the ground and in trees, however, adults are more arboreal than are juveniles. Adults and juveniles are commonly found sleeping on vegetation at night.

*Basiliscus vittatus* **Wiegmann, 1828**
**Common name(s):** Charancaco (Spanish); Bibat*, Swain* (Miskito); Wagaga, Wagánga, Wügüri** (Garífuna)
**Description (Plate 81):** This moderately large lizard (males to 170 mm SVL, females to 134 mm) has a long tail (about 2.3 to 3.2 times SVL). Adult males have a single lobed, laterally compressed head crest. The head crest of adult females consists of a small knob on the posterior portion of the head. The tympanum is distinct and higher than long, and there is no much enlarged scale below the tympanic region. Supralabials number 7 or 8 and the infralabials 7 to 9. Dorsal body scales are keeled and imbricate. Adult males have a raised middorsal crest that is supported by bony rays in larger individuals; females and subadult males have a middorsal crest consisting of a row of serrated scales. Adults of both sexes have a low, serrated dorsal caudal keel. Ventral scales are keeled and imbricate. Caudal autotomy is absent, as are femoral and precloacal pores. A lateral flap of scales is present on the outer edge of each hind toe. The fourth toe is much longer than the third toe. Dorsal ground color is usually pale brown to dark brown; darker brown crossbands are usually present in females. A pair of pale brown dorsolateral stripes is usually present. Ventral surfaces are tan to gray with some pinkish orange-to-orange pigment. The iris is orange to brown.
**Similar species:** *Basiliscus plumifrons* has smooth ventral scales and green dorsal and ventral surfaces. *Iguana iguana* has a very large scale below the tympanic region and usually green dorsal and ventral surfaces.

**Plate 81.** *Basiliscus vittatus.* Photograph by McCranie.

**General geographic distribution:** *Basiliscus vittatus* occurs at low and moderate elevations from southern Tamaulipas, Mexico, to northwestern Colombia on the Atlantic versant and from northwestern Jalisco, Mexico, to west-central Nicaragua and from central Panama to northwestern Colombia on the Pacific versant. It has also been introduced into southern Florida, USA.
**Distribution in Honduras:** This lizard is widely distributed through much of the country, including the Islas de la Bahía. It is known from sea level to 1400 m elevation.
**Distribution in the Mosquitia:** Colón—Cañon Subterráneo del Río Plátano (formerly in UNAH, now lost). El Paraíso—Arenales (LACM); Boca Español (USNM). Gracias a Dios—Awasbila (USNM); Baltiltuk (formerly in UNAH, now lost); Barra Patuca (USNM); Canco (UF); Crique Canco (USNM); Cauquira (UF); Río Coco (USNM); Crique Curamaira (USNM); Kaska Tingni (USNM); Kasunta (sight record); Krahkra (USNM); Krausirpe (LSUMZ); about 15 km S of Mocorón (UTA); about 3 km S of Mocorón (UTA); Mocorón (UTA); Rus Rus (UF; USNM); Tánsin (LACM; LSUMZ); Tikiraya (UF); Wampusirpe (LSUMZ); confluence of Quebrada Waskista with Río Wampú (USNM). Olancho—Casamacoa (USNM); Quebrada El Guásimo (USNM); Kauroahuika (USNM); Matamoros (SMF; USNM); Quebrada El Mono (USNM); confluence of Ríos Sausa and Wampú (USNM); confluence of Quebrada Siksatara with Río Wampú (USNM); confluence of Ríos Yanguay and Wampú (USNM); Yapuwás (USNM); confluence of Ríos Yapuwás and Patuca (LSUMZ).
**Natural history comments:** *Basiliscus vittatus* occurs along streams, rivers, swamps, ponds, and road puddles in primary to denuded evergreen broadleaf forest and pine savanna in the Mosquitia. It also occurs in broadleaf swamp forest, freshwater marshes, and coastal strand. This diurnal species is active during sunny periods. When active, adults are usually seen in vegetation, whereas juveniles are primarily terrestrial. *Basiliscus vittatus* is capable of bipedal locomotion (using only its two hind limbs) across the surface of water, and uses this method of locomotion to escape from potential predators. Adults and juveniles are commonly seen sleeping on vegetation at night.

*Corytophanes cristatus* **(Merrem, 1820)**
**Common name(s):** Aya-pasi, Swain* (Miskito)
**Description (Plate 82):** This moderate-sized

lizard (males to 124 mm SVL, females to 123 mm) has a long tail (about 1.8 to 2.5 times SVL). A triangular head casque that projects posteriorly past the head is present in all individuals, the head casque is continuous with a well-developed nuchal crest. The tympanum is distinct and is higher than long and there is no very enlarged scale below the tympanic region. Supralabials number 11 to 15 and infralabials 10 to 13. Dorsal body scales are usually smooth (occasional dorsal scales are keeled) and imbricate. A serrated middorsal crest with triangular scales is present. Ventral scales are strongly keeled and imbricate. Caudal autotomy is absent, as are femoral and precloacal pores. There is no lateral flap of scales on the outer edges of the toes. The fourth toe is much longer than the third toe. Dorsal surfaces usually have some pale olive green to darker green pigment present, with some shade of brown pigment present as well. Olive brown to black crossbands are usually present on the body. Ventral surfaces are pale brown. The iris is ocher to copper colored.

**Similar species:** No other species of lizard in the Mosquitia has a triangular head casque that projects posteriorly past the head.

**General geographic distribution:** *Corytophanes cristatus* occurs at low and moderate elevations from the Yucatán Peninsula and Chiapas, Mexico, to northwestern Colombia on the Atlantic versant and from west-central Costa Rica to central Panama on the Pacific versant. The species also occurs marginally on the Pacific versant in northwestern Costa Rica.

**Distribution in Honduras:** This species is widespread in the northern and eastern portions of the country (near sea level to 1300 m elevation).

**Distribution in the Mosquitia:** Colón—Empalme Río Chilmeca (formerly in UNAH, now lost); Cañon Subterráneo del Río Plátano (formerly in UNAH, now lost); Río Guaraska (BMNH); Quebrada Machín (USNM). Gracias a Dios—Caño Awalwás (UF; USNM); Awasbila (USNM); Río Coco (USNM); Mocorón (CF); Palacios (BMNH); between Río Patuca and Río Coco (MCZ); Rus Rus (UF); Río Sutawala (USNM); Bodega de Río Tapalwás (UF; USNM); trail to Bodega de Río Tapalwás (UF); near confluence of Ríos Tapalwás and Rus Rus (USNM); Urus Tingni Kiamp (USNM); Cerro Wahatingni (UF); Wakling Kiamp (USNM); Warunta Tingni Kiamp (USNM). Olancho—Quebrada El Guásimo (USNM); Río Kosmako (USNM); Quebrada de Las Marías (USNM); Qururia (USNM); confluence of Quebrada Siksatara with Río Wampú (USNM); Subterráneo (USNM).

**Natural history comments:** *Corytophanes cristatus* occurs in primary evergreen broadleaf forest or old second growth evergreen broadleaf forest near primary forest in the Mosquitia. This diurnal species is usually found sitting motionless on tree trunks. Females can also be found sleeping or active on the ground near trees during the day. Adults are also found sleeping on tree trunks at night, whereas juveniles were found sleeping on leafy vegetation at night. A recently hatched juvenile was found sleeping at dusk in a small cave through which a small stream flowed. A juvenile at Bodega de Río Tapalwás was covered with sporangia of the slime mold *Physarum pusillum*, representing the first recorded instance of a slime mold inhabiting the body of any living animal (Townsend et al., 2005).

**Plate 82.** *Corytophanes cristatus.* Photograph by McCranie.

## Family Iguanidae

Iguanids are generally moderate-sized to large terrestrial, rock-dwelling, or arboreal, primarily herbivorous lizards as adults (Pough et al., 2003, who recognize this group as a subfamily within the Iguanidae). The two Mosquitia species of this family (*sensu* Frost and Etheridge, 1989, and Frost et al., 2001; see Schulte et al., 2003, for an opposing taxonomy) are the largest lizards in the region. The members of this family range in the Western Hemisphere from southeastern California, southern Nevada, and southwestern and south-central Utah in the USA, southward to the southern tip of the Baja California Peninsula (excepting the northwestern sector), the coastlands of western Mexico, and Tamaulipas, Mexico, thence on through Central America into South America as far south as Ecuador west of the Andes and southeastern Brazil east of the Andes. They also occur on the Bahama Islands, Cuba, Jamaica, Hispaniola, the Cayman Islands, Mona Island, the Lesser Antilles, and the Galapagos Islands. The family has also been introduced into southern Florida and Hawaii, USA. In the Eastern Hemisphere, they are distributed on Fiji and Tonga Islands in the southwestern Pacific Ocean. Eight genera (Frost and Etheridge, 1989) containing about 43 species are currently included in this family. Two genera comprised of 6 species are known to occupy Honduras, of which 2 species in both genera occur in the Mosquitia.

*Ctenosaura similis* **(Gray, 1831)**
**Common name(s):** Garrobo (Spanish); Islu*, Iswili* (Miskito); Guab, Serewei* (Garífuna)
**Description (Plate 83):** This large and heavy bodied lizard (males to 490 mm SVL, females to 400 mm) has a long tail (about 1.5 to 2.4 times SVL, proportionally longer in juveniles). Head crests or casques are absent. The tympanum is distinct and higher than long, and there is no much enlarged scale below the tympanic region. Supralabials and infralabials number 10 to 15. Dorsal body scales are keeled and imbricate. A distinct middorsal crest consisting of enlarged serrated scales is present; this crest is best developed in adult males. Ventral scales are smooth and imbricate. The tail has whorls of large spinous scales and intercalary scales between the whorls. Two complete rows of intercalary scales are present between the third and fifth tail whorls. Caudal autotomy is absent. Six to 18 total femoral pores are present. Scales on the anterodorsal surface of the shank are not enlarged. A lateral flap of scales is absent on the hind toes. Adults have a dorsal ground color of pale brown, tan, or gray (or various colors in between), with 4 to 6 darker crossbands present on the body. Juveniles have green dorsal surfaces, usually with a few, incomplete brown to black crossbands.
**Similar species:** No other species of lizard in the Mosquitia has tail whorls with spinous scales.
**General geographic distribution:** *Ctenosaura similis* occurs at low and moderate elevations on the Atlantic versant from central Tabasco and the Yucatán Peninsula, Mexico, to northeastern Honduras and in western Nicaragua, eastern Costa Rica, and central Panama (including numerous islands in the Caribbean Sea). It also occurs from southeastern Oaxaca, Mexico, to west-central Panama on the Pacific versant and has also been introduced into southern Florida, USA.
**Distribution in Honduras:** This large lizard is widespread in open habitats on the mainland and also occurs on Islas de Guanaja, Utila, and Zacate Grande. It is known from near sea level to about 1200 m elevation.
**Distribution in the Mosquitia:** Gracias a Dios—Barra Patuca (USNM); Canco (sight record); Palacios (BMNH); Prumnitara (sight records); Puerto Lempira (sight records); Tánsin (LACM).
**Natural history comments:** *Ctenosaura similis* is a diurnal, terrestrial to arboreal species that occurs in open habitats along the coast in the Mosquitia. Several adults were seen on trees with hollows in them. We saw a young adult in a sea grape tree (*Coccoloba* sp.) growing just above the high tide mark in Puerto Lempira. Others were on lumber piles in that same town. In other parts of Honduras, this species occurs on or in rocky outcrops, rock walls (especially those used as fence rows), fallen logs, and trees with hollows in them.

**Plate 83.** *Ctenosaura similis.* Photograph by McCranie.

*Iguana iguana* **(Linnaeus, 1758)**
**Common name(s):** Iguana (Spanish); Kakamuk (Miskito); Wayamaga* (Garífuna)
**Description (Plate 84):** This large and heavy bodied lizard (males to 580 mm SVL, females to 411 mm) has a long tail (about 2.7 to 3.2 times SVL). Raised scales can be present on the posterior portion of the head, but crests or casques are absent. The tympanum is distinct and higher than

**Plate 84.** *Iguana iguana.* Photograph by McCranie.

long, and there is an extremely enlarged scale present below the tympanic region. Seven to 9 supralabials and infralabials are present to the level below the center of the eye. Many individuals have 1 or 2 raised scales on the top of the snout. Dorsal body scales are granular, most are keeled, and imbricate. A distinct middorsal crest consisting of enlarged serrated scales is present; this crest is best developed in adult males. Ventral scales are small, smooth, and imbricate. Whorls with large spinous scales are absent on the tail. Caudal autotomy is absent in adults. Nine to 23 total femoral pores are present. A lateral flap of scales is absent on the hind toes. Most individuals have the dorsal surfaces of the head and body green, frequently with darker, obscure wavy crossbands on the body. Some large males can have gray dorsal surfaces. Ventral surfaces are usually pale green. The iris is usually some shade of orange or tan.

**Similar species:** No other species of lizard in the Mosquitia has a very large scale below the tympanic region.

**General geographic distribution:** *Iguana iguana* occurs at low and moderate elevations on the Atlantic versant from northern Veracruz, Mexico, to south-central Brazil and Paraguay and from southern Sinaloa, Mexico, to extreme northwestern Peru on the Pacific versant. The species also occurs in the Lesser Antilles. It also occurs on numerous Caribbean islands and several islands off the Pacific coast. This species has also been introduced into southern Florida and Hawaii, USA, Puerto Rico, the Virgin Islands, and Anguilla.

**Distribution in Honduras:** This large lizard occurs along rivers and streams across the mainland. It also occurs on Islas de Barbareta, Guanaja, Roatán, and Utila, and on the Islas del Cisne. It is known from near sea level to 880 m elevation.

**Distribution in the Mosquitia:** Colón—Barranco (ANSP). Gracias a Dios—Caño Awalwás (sight record); Caño Awawás (sight record); Barra Patuca (USNM); Río Coco (USNM); Raudal Kiplatara (formerly in UNAH, now lost); Mocorón (CF); Tánsin (LSUMZ); Urus Tingni Kiamp (photograph); Crique Wahatingni (sight record). Olancho—confluence of Ríos Aner and Wampú (USNM); Quebrada El Guásimo (UNAH); Quebrada Kuilma Tingni (sight record).

**Natural history comments:** *Iguana iguana* is a diurnal, mostly arboreal species as adults; however, juveniles are more terrestrial. The species occurs in primary to lightly disturbed evergreen broadleaf forest in the Mosquitia. Adults are active in trees along rivers and large streams, into which they dive when approached. They can also be seen sleeping in trees near watercourses at night. Adults and their eggs are a prized food source among the people of the Mosquitia, thus they can be rarely seen in some areas.

## Family Phrynosomatidae

Phrynosomatids are morphologically and ecologically diverse lizards (Pough et al., 2003). Thus, they are difficult to characterize as a group on the basis of their external appearance. However, the two species of this family (*sensu* Frost and Etheridge, 1989, and Frost et al., 2001; see Schulte et al., 2003, for an opposing taxonomy) in the Mosquitia have more strongly keeled dorsal scales than any other lizards in the area. The members of this family occur only within the Western Hemisphere, where they range from extreme southern British Columbia, Alberta, and Saskatchewan, Canada, southward through most of the western USA and most of the eastern USA from southern Illinois, southern Indiana, southern Ohio, southern Pennsylvania, and southern New Jersey, on through Mexico and into Central America to eastern and southern Honduras, and from northwestern Nicaragua to west-central Panama. Nine genera containing about 125 species are currently included in this family (Pough et al., 2003). Three species in one genus are known to occur in Honduras, with two species occupying the Mosquitia.

*Sceloporus malachiticus* **Cope, 1864**
**Common name(s):** Sungsung* (Miskito)
**Description (Plate 85):** This moderately small lizard (males to 98 mm SVL, females to 94 mm) has a moderately long tail (about 0.8 to 1.3 times SVL [Köhler and Heimes, 2002]). Head crests, casques, or raised scales on the head are absent. The ear opening (tympanum is deeply recessed) is distinct and higher than long, and there is no very enlarged scale below the tympanic region. There are 3 to 5 supralabials and 4 to 6 infralabials to the level below the center of the eye. Dorsal body scales are strongly keeled and mucronate. There is no middorsal crest. Ventral scales are smooth with notched or rounded posterior edges. Caudal autotomy is present. There are 22 to 34 total femoral pores present. A postfemoral dermal pocket is absent as is a lateral flap of scales on the outer edges of the hind toes. Dorsal ground color varies from bright green to greenish tan to gray or black. A black collar is usually present on the sides of the neck. Adult males have paired black-bordered longitudinal dark blue ventral patches; adult females lack or have blue (but not black-bordered) ventral patches.
**Similar species:** *Sceloporus variabilis* is the only other lizard in the Mosquitia with strongly keeled and mucronate dorsal body scales. That species has a postfemoral dermal pocket and usually paired pale longitudinal dorsolateral stripes on a tan background.
**General geographic distribution:** *Sceloporus malachiticus* occurs at low (at upper limits), moderate, and intermediate elevations on the Atlantic versant from western Honduras to western Panama. The species also occurs on the Pacific versant in northern El Salvador and from southwestern to south-central Honduras, in central Costa Rica, and marginally in northwestern Costa Rica.
**Distribution in Honduras:** This species occurs primarily at moderate and intermediate elevations in the mountainous regions of the country; however, in some locations in the western end of the Mosquitia it can occur at the higher end of the low elevational range. The known elevational range is 540 to 2530 m.
**Distribution in the Mosquitia:** Colón—Quebrada Machín (USNM). Olancho—between La Llorona and confluence of Ríos Lagarto and Wampú (USNM); Quebrada de Las Marías (USNM).
**Natural history comments:** *Sceloporus malachiticus* is a montane species that only marginally occurs in the Mosquitia. Mosquitia localities of this diurnal, arboreal species are in heavily disturbed to denuded evergreen broadleaf forest areas.
**Remarks:** The range given in the general geographic distribution section probably encompasses ranges of more than one species.

*Sceloporus variabilis* **Wiegmann, 1834**
**Common name(s):** Sungsung* (Miskito)
**Description (Plate 86):** This moderately small lizard (males to 76 mm SVL, females to 68 mm [Köhler and Heimes, 2002; Savage, 2002]) has a moderately long tail (about 1.0 to 1.5 times SVL). Head crests, casques, or raised scales on the head are absent. The ear opening (tympanum is deeply recessed) is distinct and higher than long, and

**Plate 85.** *Sceloporus malachiticus.* Photograph by McCranie.

**Plate 86.** *Sceloporus variabilis.* Photograph by McCranie.

there is no very enlarged scale below the tympanic region. There are 3 to 5 supralabials and infralabials to the level below the center of the eye. Dorsal body scales are strongly keeled and mucronate. There is no middorsal crest. Ventral scales are smooth with notched or rounded posterior edges. Caudal autotomy is present. There are 14 to 34 total femoral pores present. A postfemoral dermal pocket is present. There is no lateral flap of scales on the outer edges of the hind toes. Dorsal ground color is some shade of brown. A paler brown longitudinal dorsolateral stripe is usually present on each side of the body. Adult males have paired blue-bordered pink ventrolateral patches; most adult females lack ventral patches.
**Similar species:** *Sceloporus malachiticus* is the only other lizard in the Mosquitia with strongly keeled and mucronate dorsal body scales. That species lacks a postfemoral dermal pocket and paired pale longitudinal dorsolateral stripes and usually has a dorsal ground color of some shade of green in life.
**General geographic distribution:** *Sceloporus variabilis* occurs at low and moderate elevations on the Atlantic versant from south-central Texas, USA, to northeastern and southwestern Nicaragua and from the Isthmus of Tehuantepec region of Mexico to northwestern Costa Rica and marginally in central Costa Rica on the Pacific versant.
**Distribution in Honduras:** This species is found at low and moderate elevations (near sea level to 1510 m) across much of the country.
**Distribution in the Mosquitia:** Gracias a Dios—Krausirpe (LSUMZ); Mavita (USNM); Mocorón (CF); Rus Rus (USNM); Tánsin (LSUMZ); Walpatá (LACM).
**Natural history comments:** *Sceloporus variabilis* occurs in pine savanna in the Mosquitia. This diurnal species is usually seen on the ground or on pine tree trunks near the ground.

## Family Polychrotidae

Polychrotids have a mental scale that is partially or completely divided by a mental groove and a male dewlap (dewlap also present in females of some species). This family includes the anoles and the genus *Polychrus* (Frost et al., 2001). The anoles are the only non-gekkonid lizards in the Mosquitia with expanded subdigital pads. Members of this family are limited in distribution to the Western Hemisphere, where they range from the southeastern USA through Gulf coastal and Pacific coastal Mexico, thence southward through Central America to southeastern Brazil and Paraguay. They also occur on the the Greater and Lesser Antilles, Trinidad and Tobago, and on several other small Caribbean and Pacific islands. About 330 species are presently included in this family; the number of genera is controversial. Three genera containing 37 species are known to occupy Honduras, of which two genera comprised of 12 species are known from the Mosquitia.

*Norops biporcatus* **(Wiegmann, 1834)**
**Common name(s):** None
**Description (Plate 87):** This is a large anole (males and females to 105 mm SVL) with a long tail (about 2.0 to 2.4 times SVL). The ear opening is vertically oval. One to 3 scales separate the well-defined supraorbital semicircles at the narrowest point, and suboculars and supralabials are in contact, or are separated by 1 scale. The anterior nasal scale is divided, both the upper and lower scales are separated from the rostral by 1 or 2 scales. Postmentals number 5 to 7. The lateral head scales anterior to the ear opening are slightly larger than those posterior to the ear opening. Dorsal body scales are keeled or tuberculate, with the two middorsal rows slightly enlarged; the rest of the dorsals are similar in size to the small laterals. Ventral scales are keeled and most are mucronate. Femoral pores are absent and the fourth toe is much longer then the third toe. Caudal autotomy is present. The male

**Plate 87.** *Norops biporcatus*. Photograph by McCranie.

dewlap is moderately large, extending posteriorly to the level of the axillae. The female dewlap is nearly as large as the male dewlap. Enlarged postcloacal scales and a tubelike axillary pocket are absent. Dorsal surfaces are green in life, but the species can quickly change to brown when stressed. The male dewlap is tricolor, with the basal area white, the central area largely powder blue, and the outer area yellowish orange or reddish orange. The female dewlap is white with some blue or pale brown streaking centrally.

**Similar species:** *Norops capito* lacks a uniformly bright green dorsum in life and has flat and smooth dorsal body scales and a cinnamon, buff yellow, greenish yellow, or greenish white male dewlap. All other anoles in the Mosquitia are much smaller, in addition to having brown dorsal surfaces in life. *Polychrus gutturosus* has femoral pores and the third and fourth toe about equal in length.

**General geographic distribution:** *Norops biporcatus* occurs at low and moderate elevations on the Atlantic versant from southern Veracruz, Mexico, to western Venezuela and on the Pacific versant from northwestern Costa Rica to northwestern Ecuador, including Isla Gorgona, Colombia. The species also occurs marginally on or very near the Pacific versant in western Nicaragua.

**Distribution in Honduras:** This species occurs from near sea level to 950 m elevation in about the northern two-thirds of the country.

**Distribution in the Mosquitia:** Colón—Río Guaraska (BMNH); Quebrada Machín (USNM); Río Paulaya (BMNH). Gracias a Dios—Caño Awalwás (USNM); Kasunta (USNM); Krahkra (USNM); about 30 km S of Mocorón (UTA color slide); Mocorón (CF); Palacios (BMNH); Rus Rus (UF; USNM); Swabila (UF); Bodega de Río Tapalwás (UF; USNM); Urus Tingni Kiamp (USNM); Warunta Tingni Kiamp (USNM). Olancho—confluence of Quebrada Siksatara with Río Wampú (USNM); Cerro Wampú (USNM); between mouth of Río Wampú and Yapuwás (USNM).

**Natural history comments:** *Norops biporcatus* is a diurnal, highly arboreal species that occurs in primary to lightly disturbed evergreen broadleaf forest (including gallery forest through pine savanna) and in lightly disturbed broadleaf swamp forest in the Mosquitia. This species is most often seen while sleeping at night in trees about 3 to 10 m above the ground in the forest and along streams and rivers.

*Norops capito* **(W. Peters, 1863a)**

**Common name(s):** Waganga Würi** (Garífuna)

**Description (Plate 88):** This is a large anole (males to 90 mm SVL, females to 96 mm) with a long tail (about 1.5 to 2.0 times SVL) and an extremely short head. The ear opening is vertically oval. One to 3 scales separate the well-defined supraorbital semicircles at the narrowest point and the suboculars are separated from the supralabials by 1 or 2 scale rows. The anterior nasal scale is divided with the scales separated from the rostral and first supralabial by 1 or 2 scales. Postmentals number 4 to 8. The lateral head scales anterior to the ear opening are larger than those posterior to the ear opening. Dorsal body scales are flat, smooth, and hexagonal or pentagonal; the rest of the dorsals grade into the slightly smaller laterals. Ventral scales are distinctly keeled, mucronate, and imbricate. Femoral pores are absent and the fourth toe is much longer then the third toe. Caudal autotomy is present. The male dewlap is small, not extending posteriorly to the level of the axillae. The female dewlap is rudimentary or absent. Enlarged postcloacal scales and a tubelike axillary pocket are absent. Dorsal surfaces of the head and body have a ground color of brown, yellowish green, or olive. Dorsal body pattern is complex. It can have lichenose-like dark brown marbling in the form of vague crossbands, be nearly uniform, or have a broad pale brown or brown middorsal stripe. The male dewlap is variable, and can be cinnamon, buff-yellow, greenish yellow, or greenish white.

**Similar species:** *Norops biporcatus* has a bright green dorsum in life, keeled or tuberculate dorsal

**Plate 88.** *Norops capito*. Photograph by McCranie.

body scales, and a tricolor male dewlap that is white basally, largely powder blue centrally, and yellowish orange or reddish orange on the outer portion. *Norops lionotus* has the lateral body scales much smaller than the middorsals, a normal-shaped head, a pale lateral stripe on each side of the body, and an orangish yellow male dewlap. *Norops pentaprion* has smooth ventral scales and a red to purple dewlap in both sexes. All other anoles in the Mosquitia are much smaller and have normally shaped heads.

**General geographic distribution:** *Norops capito* occurs at low and moderate elevations on the Atlantic versant from Tabasco, Mexico, to eastern Panama and from southeastern Costa Rica to central Panama on the Pacific versant.

**Distribution in Honduras:** This species is found from near sea level to 1250 m elevation in the northern and eastern portions of the country.

**Distribution in the Mosquitia:** Colón—Cañon del Chilmeca (formerly in UNAH, now lost); Empalme Río Chilmeca (formerly in UNAH, now lost); Río Guaraska (BMNH); Quebrada Machín (USNM); Tulito (BMNH). Gracias a Dios—Auka Kiamp (USNM); Caño Awalwás (UF; USNM); Awasbila (USNM); about 30 km S of Mocorón (UTA); Mocorón (CF); Río Sutawala (USNM); Bodega de Río Tapalwás (UF; USNM); trail to Bodega de Río Tapalwás (UF); Urus Tingni Kiamp (USNM); Cerro Wahatingni (UF); Warunta Tingni Kiamp (USNM). Olancho—confluence of Ríos Aner and Wampú (USNM); Quebrada El Guásimo (SMF; USNM); Río Kosmako (USNM); Quebrada de Las Marías (USNM); confluence of Ríos Sausa and Wampú (USNM); confluence of Ríos Yanguay and Wampú (USNM).

**Natural history comments:** *Norops capito* is a diurnal, arboreal species that occurs in primary to lightly disturbed evergreen broadleaf forest in the Mosquitia. This species is active on lower parts of tree trunks, usually with the head pointed downward. It can also be found sleeping at night on tree trunks and leaves. The species occurs both in the forest and along streams.

*Norops dariense* **(Fitch and Seigel, 1984)**

**Common name(s):** None

**Description (Plate 89):** This is a small anole (males to 50 mm SVL, females to 52 mm) with a long tail (about 1.5 to 2.0 times SVL). The ear opening is vertically oval. One to 3 scales separate the well-defined supraorbital semicircles at the narrowest point and the suboculars are usually separated from the supralabials by 1 scale row (occasionally 1 subocular is in contact with a supralabial). The anterior nasal scale is divided with the lower scale contacting the rostral and usually the first supralabial. Postmentals number 5 to 9. The lateral head scales anterior and posterior to the ear opening are about subequal in size. Dorsal body scales are faintly keeled, with 0 to 2 median rows slightly enlarged; the rest of the dorsals grade into the granular and homogeneous laterals. Ventral scales are weakly to strongly keeled, juxtaposed and subimbricate or imbricate. Femoral pores are absent and the fourth toe is much longer then the third toe. Caudal autotomy is present. The male dewlap is very large, extending posteriorly well onto the venter nearly to the level of the elbows when the forelimbs are extended alongside the body. The female dewlap is absent. Enlarged postcloacal scales and a tubelike axillary pocket are absent. Dorsal surfaces of the head and body are some shade of brown, usually with a yellowish brown or pale brown lateral stripe on each side of the body. The male dewlap is bicolor, with an outer area that is some shade of brown and a darker brown basal spot.

**Plate 89.** *Norops dariense*. Photograph by McCranie.

**Similar species:** *Norops quaggulus*, *N. tropidonotus*, and *N. wampuensis* have deep tubelike axillary pockets. *Norops limifrons* and *N. pentaprion* have smooth ventral scales and male dewlaps that are white with an orangish yellow basal spot and red to purple, respectively. *Norops capito* and *N. lionotus* have flat and usually juxtaposed middorsal body scales and different colored male dewlaps (cinnamon, buff yellow, greenish yellow, or greenish white in *N. capito* and orangish yellow in *N. lionotus*). *Norops biporcatus* has green dorsal surfaces, a larger size (to 105 mm SVL in both sexes), and a male dewlap that is white basally, mostly powder blue centrally, and yellowish or reddish orange on the outer portion. *Norops lemurinus* has conspicuous dark brown lines radiating outward from the eye, a conspicuous dark brown interorbital bar, and a pinkish orange to reddish orange male dewlap. *Norops sericeus* has the suboculars in broad contact with the supralabials, 6 to 8 median dorsal scale rows slightly enlarged, and a male dewlap that is yellowish orange with a blue or purple central spot.

**General geographic distribution:** *Norops dariense* occurs at low and moderate elevations on the Atlantic versant from north-central Honduras to south-central Nicaragua.

**Distribution in Honduras:** This species is widespread in central and eastern Honduras from near sea level to 1250 m elevation.

**Distribution in the Mosquitia:** Colón—Quebrada Machín (USNM). El Paraíso—Arenales (LACM). Gracias a Dios—Caño Awalwás (UF; USNM); Awasbila (USNM); Caño Awawás (USNM); Karasangkan (USNM); Kaska Tingni (USNM); Kasunta (USNM); Krahkra (USNM); Rus Rus (USNM); Swabila (UF); Bodega de Río Tapalwás (UF; USNM); trail to Bodega de Río Tapalwás (UF); Tikiraya (UF); Crique Wahatingni (USNM); Warunta Tingni Kiamp (USNM). Olancho—confluence of Ríos Aner and Wampú (USNM); Raudal La Caldera (USNM); Quebrada El Guásimo (SMF; USNM); Río Kosmako (USNM); Qururia (USNM); Yapuwás (USNM).

**Natural history comments:** *Norops dariense* is a diurnal, terrestrial to arboreal species that occurs in primary to lightly disturbed broadleaf forests (both evergreen and swamp forest) in the Mosquitia. The species is active on the ground or on low tree trunks. Those active on the ground retreat to the nearest tree and climb the trunk when pursued. It can also be found sleeping at night on leaves of low vegetation. In evergreen broadleaf forest, it is usually seen away from streams and rivers, whereas it occurs on emergent vegetation in swamp forest.

**Remarks:** Savage (2002) suggested elevating *Norops cupreus dariense* to a full species, a suggestion we follow here. *Norops dariense* has smaller scales, longer hind limbs, and a different colored dewlap than typical *N. cupreus*.

## *Norops lemurinus* (Cope, 1861)

**Common name(s):** None

**Description (Plate 90):** This is a moderate-sized anole (males and females to 79 mm SVL) with a long tail (about 1.7 to 2.7 times SVL). The ear opening is vertically oval. Zero to 3 scales separate the well-defined supraorbital semicircles at the narrowest point and the suboculars are separated from the supralabials by 0 or 1 scale row. The anterior nasal scale is divided with the lower scale contacting the rostral and first supralabial. Postmentals number 6 to 8. The lateral head scales anterior to the ear opening are slightly larger than those posterior to the ear opening. Dorsal body scales are distinctly keeled, with about 2 median rows slightly enlarged; the rest of the dorsals grade into the granular and homogeneous laterals. Ventral scales are strongly keeled, mucronate, and imbricate. Femoral pores are absent and the fourth toe is much longer then the third toe. Caudal autotomy is present. The male dewlap is large, extending posteriorly slightly beyond the level of the axillae. The female dewlap is rudimentary or absent. Enlarged postcloacal scales are absent, as is a tubelike axillary pocket (although a shallow axillary pocket can be present). Dorsal surfaces of the head and body are some shade of brown. Distinct dark brown lines radiate outward from the eye and a distinct dark brown interorbital bar is present. A dark brown lyriform mark is usually present in the occipital region, however this mark can be obscure or absent altogether. The male dewlap is pinkish orange to reddish orange.

**Similar species:** *Norops quaggulus*, *N. tropidonotus*, and *N. wampuensis* have deep tubelike axillary pockets. *Norops limifrons* and

**Plate 90.** *Norops lemurinus*. Photograph by McCranie.

*N. pentaprion* have smooth ventral scales and male dewlaps that are white with an orangish yellow basal spot and red to purple, respectively. *Norops capito* and *N. lionotus* have flat and usually juxtaposed middorsal body scales and different colored male dewlaps (cinnamon, buff yellow, greenish yellow, or greenish white in *N. capito* and orangish yellow in *N. lionotus*). *Norops biporcatus* has green dorsal surfaces, a larger size (to 105 mm SVL in both sexes), and a male dewlap that is white basally, mostly powder blue centrally, and yellowish or reddish orange on the outer portion. *Norops dariense* lacks conspicuous dark brown lines radiating outward from the eye and a conspicuous dark brown interorbital bar and has a male dewlap that is some shade of brown with a darker brown basal spot. *Norops sericeus* lacks conspicuous dark brown lines radiating outward from the eye and a conspicuous dark brown interorbital bar and has a male dewlap that is yellowish orange with a blue or purple central spot.

**General geographic distribution:** *Norops lemurinus* is found at low and moderate elevations on the Atlantic versant from central Veracruz, Mexico, to central Panama and disjunctly from northwestern Costa Rica to central Panama on the Pacific versant.

**Distribution in Honduras:** This species occurs in the northern portion of the country, including the Cayos Cochinos. It is known from near sea level to 960 m elevation

**Distribution in the Mosquitia:** Colón—Amarillo (BMNH). El Paraíso—Boca Español (USNM). Gracias a Dios—Baltiltuk (formerly in UNAH, now lost); Barra Patuca (USNM); Krausirpe (LSUMZ); Mocorón (UTA); Palacios (BMNH); Río Plátano (CM); Rus Rus (UF); Urus Tingni Kiamp (USNM). Olancho—Caobita (SMF); Matamoros (USNM); Quebrada El Mono (SMF).

**Natural history comments:** *Norops lemurinus* is a diurnal, terrestrial to arboreal species that occurs in primary to heavily disturbed evergreen broadleaf forest in the Mosquitia. The species is active on the ground or on low tree trunks. One was also found active in a thatched roof. It can sometimes be found sleeping on leaves at night. The species can be found some distance from streams and rivers as well as along stream and river banks.

*Norops limifrons* **(Cope, 1862c)**

**Common name(s):** None

**Description (Plate 91):** This is a small anole (males to 43 mm SVL, females to 45 mm) with a long tail (about 1.7 to 2.5 times SVL). The ear opening is vertically oval. One to 3 scales separate the well-defined supraorbital semicircles at the narrowest point and there are about 2 suboculars in contact with the posterior-most supralabials. The anterior nasal scale is single. Postmentals number 6 or 7. The lateral head scales anterior and posterior to the ear opening are subequal in size. Dorsal body scales are faintly keeled, with about 2 median rows slightly enlarged; the rest of the dorsals grade into the granular and homogeneous laterals. Ventral scales are smooth, slightly conical with rounded posterior edges, and subimbricate. Femoral pores are absent and the fourth toe is much longer then the third toe. Caudal autotomy is present. The male dewlap is small, extending posteriorly to the level of the axillae. The female dewlap is absent. Enlarged postcloacal scales are present in males. A tubelike axillary pocket is absent. Dorsal surfaces of the head and body are some shade of brown. The dorsal surface of the tail is usually strongly banded with pale and dark brown. The male dewlap is white with an orangish yellow basal spot.

**Similar species:** The only other anole in the Mosquitia with smooth or slightly conical ventral scales is *Norops pentaprion*. That species has a red to purple dewlap that is well developed in both males and females and a larger size (males to 79 mm SVL, females to 63 mm).

**General geographic distribution:** *Norops limifrons* is found at low and moderate elevations on the Atlantic versant from northeastern Honduras (east of the Cordillera Nombre de Dios) to central Panama and from west-central Costa

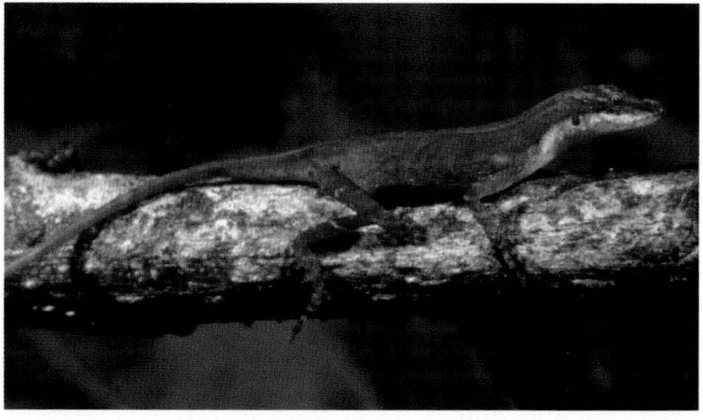

**Plate 91.** *Norops limifrons*. Photograph by McCranie.

Rica to eastern Panama on the Pacific versant.
**Distribution in Honduras:** This small anole occurs in the eastern portion of the country east of the Cordillera Nombre de Dios. It is known from near sea level to 710 m elevation.
**Distribution in the Mosquitia:** Colón—Empalme Río Chilmeca (formerly in UNAH, now lost); Río Guaraska (BMNH); Río Kinikisne (BMNH); Quebrada Machín (USNM); Río Paulaya (BMNH); Tulito (BMNH). El Paraíso—Boca Español (USNM). Gracias a Dios—Caño Awalwás (UF; USNM); Awasbila (USNM); Laguna Baraya (ROM); Crique Curamaira (USNM); Kalila Plapan Tingni (USNM); Kaska Tingni (USNM); Krahkra (USNM); Karasangkan (USNM); Krausirpe (LSUMZ); Mocorón (UTA); Rus Rus (USNM); Cabeceras de Río Rus Rus (USNM); Río Sutawala (USNM); Bodega de Río Tapalwás (UF; USNM); Urus Tingni Kiamp (USNM); Cerro Wahatingni (UF); confluence of Ríos Wampú and Patuca (USNM); Warunta Tingni Kiamp (USNM); confluence of Quebrada Waskista and Río Wampú (SMF; USNM). Olancho—confluence of Ríos Aner and Wampú (SMF; USNM); Caobita (SMF); Quebrada El Guásimo (SMF; USNM); Río Kosmako (USNM); Quebrada Kuilma Tingni (USNM); Quebrada de Las Marías (USNM); Matamoros (SMF; USNM); Quebrada El Mono (USNM); Nueva Esperanza (USNM); Qururia (USNM); confluence of Ríos Sausa and Wampú (SMF; USNM); confluence of Quebrada Siksatara with Río Wampú (USNM); along Río Wampú between Ríos Aner and Sausa (USNM); confluence of Ríos Yanguay and Wampú (USNM); Yapuwás (USNM).
**Natural history comments:** *Norops limifrons* is a diurnal, terrestrial or arboreal species that occurs in primary to secondary evergreen broadleaf forest (including gallery forest through pine savanna) and in lightly disturbed broadleaf swamp forest in the Mosquitia. It is active on the ground, on logs, and on low tree trunks and leaves. The species is commonly seen sleeping at night on leaves of low vegetation both in the forest and near streams.

*Norops lionotus* **(Cope, 1861)**
**Common name(s):** None
**Description (Plate 92):** This is a moderate-sized anole (males to 85 mm SVL, females to 68 mm [Savage, 2002]) with a long tail (about 1.7 to 2.1 times SVL). The ear opening is vertically oval. One to 3 scales separate the rather well defined supraorbital semicircles at the narrowest point and the suboculars are separated from the supralabials by 1 or 2 scale rows. The anterior nasal scale is divided and separated from the rostral by 1 scale; the lower scale can contact the first supralabial or be separated from it by 1 scale. Postmentals number 5 to 7. The lateral head scales anterior to the ear opening are larger than those posterior to the ear opening. Dorsal body scales are flattened, weakly keeled or smooth, hexagonal or pentagonal, and mostly juxtaposed, with about 18 to 24 median rows slightly enlarged; the rest of the dorsals grade into the much smaller laterals. Ventral scales are keeled and most are subimbricate. Femoral pores are absent and the fourth toe is much longer then the third toe. Caudal autotomy is present. The male dewlap is large, extending posteriorly onto the belly to about one-third distance from the axilla to the groin. The female dewlap is absent. Enlarged postcloacal scales are present in males and a tubelike axillary pocket is absent. Dorsal surfaces of the head and body are brown. A pale (yellow or white) lateral stripe is present on each side of the body. The male dewlap is orangish yellow.
**Similar species:** The only other species of anole in the Mosquitia with flattened, smooth to weakly keeled, and usually juxtaposed dorsal body scales is *Norops capito*. That species has the lateral body scales only slightly smaller than the middorsals, a short head, and a male dewlap that is cinnamon, buff-yellow, greenish yellow, or greenish white. *Norops capito* also lacks a pale lateral stripe on each side of the body.
**General geographic distribution:** *Norops lionotus* occurs at low elevations on the Atlantic versant from northeastern Honduras to western

**Plate 92.** *Norops lionotus*. Photograph by McCranie.

Panama and from northwestern Costa Rica to south-central Costa Rica on the Pacific versant.
**Distribution in Honduras:** This species is restricted to the Mosquitia and is known from 85 to 225 m elevation.
**Distribution in the Mosquitia:** Gracias a Dios—Awasbila (USNM); Kaska Tingni (USNM); confluence of Quebrada Waskista with Río Wampú (SMF; USNM). Olancho—Caño El Cajón (SMF); Caobita (USNM); Quebrada El Guásimo (SMF; USNM); Río Kosmako (USNM); Matamoros (USNM); Quebrada El Mono (USNM); Qururia (USNM); confluence of Quebrada Siksatara with Río Wampú (USNM).
**Natural history comments:** *Norops lionotus* is a diurnal, semi-aquatic species that occurs in primary to lightly disturbed evergreen broadleaf forest. The species is usually active on low vegetation and will jump into the water and attempt to swim to the other side when pursued. If allowed, they will take refuge among tree roots, other low vegetation, or under debris on the ground. It can also be found sleeping on low streamside vegetation at night.
**Remarks:** This species has frequently been called *Norops oxylophus* in the literature.

*Norops pentaprion* **(Cope, 1862c)**
**Common name(s):** None
**Description (Plate 93):** This is a moderate-sized anole (males to 79 mm SVL, females to 63 mm) with a long tail (about 1.1 to 1.4 times SVL). The ear opening is vertically oval. Zero to 2 (usually 1) scales separate the well-defined supraorbital semicircles at the narrowest point. Suboculars and supralabials are in contact. The anterior nasal scale is divided and separated from the rostral by 1 scale. Postmentals number 5 to 7. The lateral head scales anterior to the ear opening are slightly larger than those posterior to the ear opening. Dorsal body scales are small (2 to 4 middorsal rows slightly enlarged), most are smooth, and the laterals scales are heterogeneous. Ventral scales are smooth and slightly conical. Femoral pores are absent and the fourth toe is much longer then the third toe. Caudal autotomy is present. The male dewlap is moderately large, extending posteriorly slightly beyond the level of the axillae. The female dewlap is well developed and is only slightly smaller than the male dewlap. Enlarged postcloacal scales are absent, as is a tubelike axillary pocket. Dorsal surfaces of the head and body have a lichenose pattern and a color repertory from some shade of brown to white or pale green. Both the male and female dewlaps are red to purple.

**Plate 93.** *Norops pentaprion.* Photograph by McCranie.

**Similar species:** The only other anole in the Mosquitia with smooth or slightly conical ventral scales is *Norops limifrons.* That species has a white male dewlap with a basal orangish yellow spot and a smaller size (males to 43 mm SVL, females to 45 mm).
**General geographic distribution:** *Norops pentaprion* is found at low and moderate elevations on the Atlantic versant from Tabasco, Mexico, to northwestern Colombia and from northwestern Costa Rica to northwestern Colombia on the Pacific versant. It also occurs on the Pearl Islands in the Gulf of Panama.
**Distribution in Honduras:** This lizard occurs in the northern and eastern portions of the country and is known from near sea level to 1400 m elevation.
**Distribution in the Mosquitia:** Gracias a Dios—Caño Awalwás (USNM); Palacios (BMNH).
**Natural history comments:** *Norops pentaprion* is a diurnal, arboreal species that occurs in primary evergreen broadleaf forest in the Mosquitia. We have only collected one specimen of this lizard in the Mosquitia. It was sleeping at night on vegetation about 2 m above the ground.

*Norops quaggulus* **(Cope, 1885)**
**Common name(s):** None
**Description (Plate 94):** This is a small anole (males to 37 mm SVL, females to 41 mm) with a long tail (about 1.3 to 1.7 times SVL). The ear opening is vertically oval. One to 3 scales separate the poorly defined supraorbital semicircles at the

**Plate 94.** *Norops quaggulus*. Photograph by McCranie.

narrowest point and 1 scale row is present between the suboculars and supralabials. The anterior nasal scale is divided with the lower scale contacting the rostral and first supralabial. Postmentals number 4 to 7. The lateral head scales anterior and posterior to the ear opening are subequal in size. Dorsal body scales are distinctly keeled, with about 7 to 10 median rows greatly enlarged; the rest of the dorsals grade into the granular and homogeneous laterals. Ventral scales are keeled and imbricate. Femoral pores are absent and the fourth toe is much longer then the third toe. Caudal autotomy is present. The male dewlap is large, extending posteriorly to a level slightly beyond the axillae. The female dewlap is absent or rudimentary. Enlarged postcloacal scales are absent. A deep tubelike axillary pocket is present. Dorsal surfaces of the head and body are some shade of brown, with or without darker brown middorsal markings on the body. The male dewlap is reddish orange to red with a yellow margin.
**Similar species:** All other species of anoles in the Mosquitia, except *Norops tropidonotus* and *N. wampuensis,* lack a deep tubelike axillary pocket. *Norops tropidonotus* and *N. wampuensis* have the scales anterior to the ear opening distinctly larger than those posterior to the ear opening.
**General geographic distribution:** *Norops quaggulus* is found at low and moderate elevations on the Atlantic versant from eastern Honduras to extreme northern Costa Rica.
**Distribution in Honduras:** This lizard occurs only in the eastern portion of the country. It is known from 60 to 840 m elevation.
**Distribution in the Mosquitia:** Colón—Quebrada Machín (USNM). Gracias a Dios—Bodega de Río Tapalwás (UF; USNM); Urus Tingni Kiamp (USNM); Warunta Tingni Kiamp (USNM). Olancho—Quebrada El Guásimo (SMF; USNM); Río Kosmako (USNM); Quebrada de Las Marías (SMF; USNM); Matamoros (SMF; USNM); near Quebrada El Mono (USNM); Yapuwás (SMF).
**Natural history comments:** *Norops quaggulus* is a diurnal, terrestrial species that occurs in primary to lightly disturbed evergreen broadleaf forest in the Mosquitia. It is usually found active in leaf litter. Occasionally it can be found sleeping at night on leafy vegetation just above the ground.
**Remarks:** Mosquitia specimens of this species have usually been called *Norops* (or *Anolis*) *humilis* in the literature. However, Köhler et al. (2003) demonstrated that the correct name for the Mosquitia populations is *N. quaggulus.*

*Norops sericeus* **(Hallowell, "1856" [1857])**
**Common name(s):** None
**Description (Plate 95):** This is a small anole (males to 52 mm SVL, females to 47 mm [Savage, 2002]) with a long tail (about 1.8 to 2.3 times SVL). The ear opening is oval. Zero to 2 (usually 1) scales separate the well-defined supraorbital semicircles at the narrowest point and the suboculars are in broad contact with the supralabials. The anterior nasal scale is single or divided with the lower edge or the lower scale contacting the rostral. Postmentals number 5 to 7. The lateral head scales anterior to the ear opening are slightly larger than those posterior to the ear opening. Dorsal body scales are keeled, with 6 to 8 median rows slightly

**Plate 95.** *Norops sericeus*. Photograph by McCranie.

enlarged; the rest of the dorsals grade into the granular and homogeneous laterals. Ventral scales are keeled and imbricate. Femoral pores are absent and the fourth toe is much longer then the third toe. Caudal autotomy is present. The male dewlap is moderately large, extending posteriorly slightly past the level of the axillae. The female dewlap is rudimentary. Enlarged postcloacal scales and a tubelike axillary pocket are absent. Dorsal surfaces of the head and body are gray to bronze with a silky sheen. A few indistinct darker brown spots or reticulations can be present on the body. The male dewlap is yellowish orange with a blue or purple central spot.

**Similar species:** *Norops quaggulus*, *N. tropidonotus*, and *N. wampuensis* have deep tubelike axillary pockets. *Norops limifrons* and *N. pentaprion* have smooth ventral scales and male dewlaps that are white with an orangish yellow basal spot and red to purple, respectively. *Norops capito* and *N. lionotus* have flat and usually juxtaposed middorsal body scales and different colored male dewlaps (cinnamon, buff yellow, greenish yellow, or greenish white in *N. capito* and orangish yellow in *N. lionotus*). *Norops biporcatus* has green dorsal surfaces, a larger size (to 105 mm SVL in both sexes), and a male dewlap that is white basally, mostly powder blue centrally, and yellowish or reddish orange on the outer portion. *Norops lemurinus* has conspicuous dark brown lines radiating outward from the eye and a conspicuous dark brown interorbital bar, and a pinkish orange to reddish orange male dewlap. *Norops dariense* usually has 1 scale row between the suboculars and supralabials (occasionally 1 subocular contacts a supralabial), 0 to 2 middorsal scale rows slightly enlarged, and a male dewlap that is some shade of brown with a darker brown basal spot.

**General geographic distribution:** *Norops sericeus* is found at low and moderate elevations on the Atlantic versant from central Tamaulipas, Mexico, to northeastern and southwestern Nicaragua and extreme northern Costa Rica and from eastern Oaxaca, Mexico, to west-central Costa Rica on the Pacific versant. An apparently disjunct population also occurs on the Atlantic versant in southeastern Costa Rica. The species also occurs on Isla del Maíz Grande, Nicaragua, Isla de Utila, Honduras, and Isla Mujeres, Quintana Roo, Mexico.

**Distribution in Honduras:** This small lizard occurs in open habitats throughout much of the mainland. It also occurs on Isla de Utila in the Islas de la Bahía and is known from near sea level to 1320 m elevation.

**Distribution in the Mosquitia:** Gracias a Dios—Awasbila (USNM); Barra Patuca (USNM); Río Coco (USNM); Karasangkan (USNM); Krausirpe (USNM); Mocorón (UTA); Palacios (BMNH); Rus Rus (UF; USNM); Swabila (UF); Tánsin (LACM).

**Natural history comments:** *Norops sericeus* is a diurnal, arboreal species that occurs in pine savanna (including open savanna with scattered shrubs) and in denuded broadleaf swamp forest in the Mosquitia. It is active on low leafy vegetation and also can be found sleeping at night on stems and small branches in low vegetation.

*Norops tropidonotus* **(W. Peters, 1863a)**

**Common name(s):** None

**Description (Plate 96):** This is a moderate-sized anole (males to 60 mm SVL, females to 55 mm) with a long tail (about 1.4 to 1.7 times SVL). The ear opening is vertically oval. One or 2 scales separate the poorly defined supraorbital semicircles at the narrowest point and 1 scale row is present between the suboculars and supralabials. The anterior nasal scale is divided with the lower scale contacting the rostral and first supralabial. Postmentals number 4 to 6. The lateral head scales anterior to the ear opening are distinctly larger than those posterior to the ear opening. Dorsal body scales are distinctly keeled, with about 9 to 12 median rows greatly enlarged; the rest of the dorsals grade into the granular and homogeneous laterals. Ventral scales are distinctly keeled and imbricate. Femoral pores are absent and the fourth toe is much longer then the third toe. Caudal autotomy is present. The male dewlap is large,

**Plate 96.** *Norops tropidonotus.* Photograph by McCranie.

extending posteriorly slightly beyond the level of the axillae. The female dewlap is absent or rudimentary. Enlarged postcloacal scales are absent. A deep tubelike axillary pocket is present. Dorsal surfaces of the head and body are brown, usually with pale brown middorsal chevrons on the body. The male dewlap is orange-red with a yellow margin and a distinct dark central streak of burnt orange or brilliant red.
**Similar species:** All other species of anoles in the Mosquitia, except *Norops quaggulus* and *N. wampuensis*, lack a deep tubelike axillary pocket. *Norops quaggulus* has the lateral head scales anterior and posterior to the ear opening subequal in size. *Norops wampuensis* is a smaller species (males to 50 mm SVL, females to 51 mm) that lacks a distinct dark central streak in the male dewlap.
**General geographic distribution:** *Norops tropidonotus* is found at low, moderate, and intermediate elevations on the Atlantic versant from central Veracruz, Mexico, to north-central Nicaragua and on the Pacific versant in extreme northern El Salvador and from southwestern to south-central Honduras.
**Distribution in Honduras:** This species occurs throughout much of the country. It is known from sea level to 1900 m elevation.
**Distribution in the Mosquitia:** Colón—Barranco (ANSP); Río Paulaya (BMNH). El Paraíso—Arenales (LACM). Gracias a Dios—Krausirpe (LSUMZ); Palacios (BMNH). Olancho—Quebrada de Las Marías (SMF).
**Natural history comments:** *Norops tropidonotus* is a diurnal, terrestrial to arboreal species that, based on our experience, is known only from denuded areas formerly cloaked in evergreen broadleaf forest in the Mosquitia. We have never found this species in primary, or even moderately disturbed, evergreen broadleaf forest in the Mosquitia. Unlike many species of *Norops*, this species does not sleep on vegetation at night, rather it sleeps in leaf litter.

*Norops wampuensis* **(McCranie and Köhler, 2001)**
**Common name(s):** None
**Description (Plate 97):** This is a small anole (males to 50 mm SVL, females to 51 mm) with a long tail (about 1.4 to 1.7 times SVL). The ear opening is vertically oval. One or 2 scales separate the poorly defined supraorbital semicircles at the narrowest point and 1 scale row is present between the suboculars and supralabials. The anterior nasal scale is divided with the lower scale contacting the rostral and first supralabial. Postmentals number 4 to 6. The lateral head scales anterior to the ear opening are distinctly larger than those posterior to the ear opening. Dorsal body scales are distinctly keeled, with about 9 or 10 median rows greatly enlarged; the rest of the dorsals grade into the granular and homogeneous laterals. Ventral scales are distinctly keeled and imbricate. Femoral pores are absent and the fourth toe is much longer then the third toe. Caudal autotomy is present. The male dewlap is moderately large, extending posteriorly slightly beyond the level of the axillae. The female dewlap is absent or rudimentary. Enlarged postcloacal scales are absent. A deep tubelike axillary pocket is present. Dorsal surfaces of the head and body are brown, usually with pale brown middorsal chevrons on the body. The male dewlap is orange-red with a yellow margin; a dark central streak is absent.

**Plate 97.** *Norops wampuensis*. Photograph by McCranie.

**Similar species:** All other species of anoles in the Mosquitia, except *Norops quaggulus* and *N. tropidonotus*, lack a deep tubelike axillary pocket. *Norops quaggulus* has the lateral head scales anterior and posterior to the ear opening subequal in size. *Norops tropidonotus* is a larger species (males to 60 mm SVL, females to 55 mm) that has a distinct dark central streak in the male dewlap.
**General geographic distribution:** *Norops wampuensis* is found at low elevations near the Río Wampú in the Mosquitia.

**Distribution in Honduras:** See General geographic distribution. The species is known from 95 to 110 m elevation.
**Distribution in the Mosquitia:** Olancho—confluence of Ríos Aner and Wampú (SMF; USNM); confluence of Ríos Sausa and Wampú (USNM); confluence of Quebrada Siksatara with Río Wampú (SMF; USNM); along Río Wampú between Ríos Aner and Sausa (SMF).
**Natural history comments:** *Norops wampuensis* is a diurnal, terrestrial or arboreal species that is known from primary evergreen broadleaf forest, with the exception of two specimens collected from the edge of a cornfield recently carved from primary evergreen broadleaf forest. The species is active on the ground or in low vegetation. It can also be found at night while sleeping on low vegetation. This species is known from only one small area on the western side of the Mosquitia.

*Polychrus gutturosus* **Berthold, 1845**
**Common name(s):** None
**Description (Plate 98):** This is a large lizard (males to 135 mm SVL, females to 170 mm [Savage, 2002]) with an extremely long tail (about 3.0 to 3.5 times SVL). The ear opening is vertically oval. One scale separates the poorly defined supraorbital semicircles at the narrowest point and the suboculars are in broad contact with the supralabials. The nasal scale is single or partially divided and contacting the postrostral, the second supralabial, and 2 loreals. There are 2 large postmentals. The lateral head scales anterior to the ear opening are slightly larger than, or about the same size as, those posterior to the ear opening. Toe IV is about the same length as, or only slightly longer than, Toe III. Dorsal body scales are distinctly keeled, with the median rows slightly larger than, or about the same size as, the homogeneous laterals. About 18 to 25 total femoral pores are present. Ventral scales are strongly keeled (multicarinate in adults) and imbricate. Caudal autotomy is absent. The male dewlap is large, extending posteriorly to about the level of the axillae. The female dewlap is rudimentary. Enlarged postcloacal scales are absent, as is a tubelike axillary pocket. Dorsal surfaces of the head, body, and limbs are some shade of green in life with brown or white crossbands on the body. A longitudinal pale lateroventral stripe is frequently present on each side. A pale brown or white postorbital spot or stripe is also frequently present on each side. The belly is some shade of green. This species is capable of dramatic color changes in life with the green pigment changing to dark brown.

**Plate 98.** *Polychrus gutturosus.* Photograph by McCranie.

**Similar species:** *Polychrus gutturosus* is the only species of lizard in the Mosquitia with a tail more than three times the length of the head and body. In addition, *Iguana iguana* has a large, smooth subtympanic scale, and *Basiliscus plumifrons*, *B. vittatus*, and all species of *Norops* have the fourth toe much longer than the third toe and lack femoral pores.
**General geographic distribution:** *Polychrus gutturosus* is found at low and moderate elevations on the Atlantic versant from northern Honduras to northwestern Colombia and from northwestern Costa Rica to western Ecuador on the Pacific versant. It also occurs marginally on the Pacific versant in northwestern Costa Rica.
**Distribution in Honduras:** This lizard is known from a few scattered localities in the northern portion of the country from 10 to 190 m elevation.
**Distribution in the Mosquitia:** Gracias a Dios—Río Plátano (Anonymous, 2002); Rus Rus (UF); Bodega de Río Tapalwás (UF); Wakling Kiamp (USNM).
**Natural history comments:** *Polychrus gutturosus* is a diurnal and arboreal species that occurs in primary to heavily disturbed evergreen broadleaf forest (including gallery forest through pine savanna) in the Mosquitia. The species is apparently a canopy dweller that only occasionally ventures to the lower tree trunks. An adult female that laid eight eggs (with an average length of about 27.5 mm) in the collecting bag was found in

September about chest high among vines leading to the canopy of a tree. Another adult was found sleeping at night in vegetation about 5 m above a small stream. A juvenile was collected in a tree along a river.

## Family Scincidae

Skinks are exceedingly variable, but most are characterized by smooth, shiny cycloid scales underlain by osteoderms comprised of a mosaic of smaller bones, giving the body a very hard exterior (Pough et al., 2003). This adaptation gives skinks an increased dispersal capability, and, as a result, the members of this family are found nearly worldwide. In the Western Hemisphere, they occur from southern British Columbia, Canada, and most of the United States southward through Mexico and Central America to western Ecuador west of the Andes and to north-central Argentina east of the Andes. Members also occur on Trinidad and Tobago, Jamaica, Hispaniola, Puerto Rico and nearby islands, the Virgin Islands, the Turks and Caicos Islands, and the Lesser Antilles. They range throughout the Eastern Hemisphere south of about 42°N latitude to the southern tips of Africa, Australia, and New Zealand. About 115 genera containing 1260 species were included in this family by Pough et al. (2003). Four genera comprised of six species are known to occupy Honduras. Two species in two genera range into the Mosquitia.

*Mabuya unimarginata* **Cope, 1862c**
**Common name(s):** Tonagule Heve (Garífuna)
**Description (Plate 99):** This medium-sized lizard (56 to 91 mm SVL [Savage, 2002]) has a moderately long tail (about 1.4 times SVL). The narrow head is barely distinct from the attenuate body and has enlarged, symmetrical scales dorsally. The snout is pointed when viewed dorsally, and the lower eyelid possesses a translucent disk. Two supranasal (internasal) and 2 frontoparietal scales are present. The tympanum is distinct and deeply recessed. Dorsal, lateral, and ventral scales are smooth, cycloid, and imbricate, and are uniform in size. The slender tail is round in crosssection, with smooth, cycloid, and imbricate scales on the dorsal, lateral, and subcaudal surfaces. Femoral pores are absent. This shiny lizard has a metallic appearance, with gray to brown dorsal surfaces and a broad, deep brown or black lateral stripe extending from the snout, across the eye and tympanum, to the area of the hind limb. Below the dark stripe is a pale gray, cream, or iridescent green stripe extending from the tip of the snout to the groin area. The belly is a patternless gray, tan, cream, or pale green. The iris is black.

**Plate 99.** *Mabuya unimarginata*. Photograph by McCranie.

**Similar species:** *Sphenomorphus cherriei* does not exceed 68 mm SVL, lacks supranasal scales, and has a single frontoparietal scale.
**General geographic distribution:** *Mabuya unimarginata* is found at low, moderate, and rarely intermediate elevations on the Atlantic versant from northeastern Hidalgo, Mexico, to Panama and from southern Jalisco, Mexico, to Panama on the Pacific versant (see Remarks). The species also occurs on the Islas de la Bahía, Honduras, and on islands off the coast of Belize and Quintana Roo, Mexico.
**Distribution in Honduras:** *Mabuya unimarginata* is widespread in open habitats (near sea level to 1510 m elevation) throughout much of the mainland. It also occurs on Islas de Guanaja, Roatán, and Utila.
**Distribution in the Mosquitia:** Colón—Barranco (ANSP). Gracias a Dios—Awasbila (USNM); Cauquira (UF); Dursuna (USNM); Krahkra (USNM); near Mocorón (UTA); Mocorón (UTA); Palacios (BMNH); Quiguastara (LACM); Rus Rus (UF; USNM); Swabila (UF); Tánsin (LACM); Tikiraya (UF). Olancho—confluence of Quebrada Siksatara and Río Wampú (USNM).
**Natural history comments:** This diurnal, terrestrial to semiarboreal species is highly adaptable and can be found in a variety of habitats in the Mosquitia, including primary to disturbed broadleaf forests (both evergreen and swamp

forest), pine savanna, and coastal strand. Although frequently active on the ground, it also climbs onto tree trunks, fence posts, and brush piles to bask. A subadult of the snake *Oxyrhopus petola* regurgitated an adult *Mabuya unimarginata*.
**Remarks:** Savage (2002) discussed taxonomic and nomenclatural uncertainties regarding the name *Mabuya unimarginata*, and used that name for the Mexican and Central America populations of *Mabuya*.

*Sphenomorphus cherriei* **(Cope, 1893)**
**Common name(s):** None
**Description (Plate 100):** This small lizard (males to 58 mm SVL, females to 68 mm [Savage, 2002]) has a moderately long tail (about 1.4 to 1.5 times SVL). The short, broad head is slightly distinct from the body, and has enlarged symmetrical scales dorsally. The snout is short and rounded when viewed dorsally, and the lower eyelid usually lacks a translucent disk. The tympanum is distinct and deeply recessed. One frontoparietal plate is present. Supranasal (internasal) scales are absent. Dorsal, lateral, and ventral scales are smooth, cycloid, and imbricate, and all are about the same size. The slender tail is round in crosssection, with smooth, cycloid, and imbricate scales on the dorsal, lateral, and subcaudal surfaces. Femoral pores are absent. Dorsal color is brown and the lateral surfaces are usually a paler shade of brown. The upper lip is spotted with dark brown. A black lateral stripe extends posteriorly from the tip of the snout, across the eye and tympanum, onto the body where it breaks up into smaller black dots or disappears altogether. This stripe is bordered ventrally by a narrow white or yellow stripe that diffuses posteriorly. The belly is uniformly gray, tan, or cream. The iris is black.

**Plate 100.** *Sphenomorphus cherriei.* Photograph by McCranie.

**Similar species:** *Mabuya unimarginata* reaches 91 mm SVL and has paired supranasal (internasal) and frontoparietal scales.
**General geographic distribution:** *Sphenomorphus cherriei* is found at low, moderate, and occasionally intermediate elevations on the Atlantic versant from central Veracruz, Mexico, to extreme western Panama and from northwestern Costa Rica to extreme western Panama on the Pacific versant. Apparently isolated populations also occur on the outer end and central portion of the Yucatán Peninsula, Mexico. The species also occurs on Isla del Maíz Grande, Nicaragua, and on Cayo Cochino Pequeño, Honduras
**Distribution in Honduras:** This lizard occurs in the northern two-thirds of the country and is known from near sea level to 1860 m elevation.
**Distribution in the Mosquitia:** Colón—Quebrada Machín (USNM); Tulito (BMNH). El Paraíso—Arenales (LACM). Gracias a Dios—Caño Awalwás (UF; USNM); Rus Rus (USNM); Bodega de Río Tapalwás (UF; USNM); Urus Tingni Kiamp (USNM); Cerro Wahatingni (UF); Crique Wahatingni (USNM); Warunta Tingni Kiamp (USNM). Olancho—confluence of Ríos Aner and Wampú (USNM); Caobita (SMF); Quebrada El Guásimo (SMF); Quebrada de Las Marías (USNM); confluence of Ríos Sausa and Wampú (USNM); along Río Wampú between Ríos Aner and Sausa (USNM); confluence of Ríos Yanguay and Wampú (USNM).
**Natural history comments:** This species can be found in primary to disturbed evergreen broadleaf forest (including gallery forest) and adjacent pine savanna. *Sphenomorphus cherriei* is diurnal and terrestrial, and is typically found in areas with abundant leaf litter.

## Family Gymnophthalmidae

The combination of having infralingual plicae and the lack of eyelids will distinguish the gymnophthalmid representative from all lizards of the other families in the Mosquitia. This family is restricted in distribution to the Neotropics, where it occurs from southern Chiapas, Mexico, and Belize southward to northwestern Peru west of the Andes and central Argentina east of the Andes. The family also occurs on Trinidad and Tobago and the Lesser Antilles (many Lesser Antilles populations are introduced). Thirty-seven genera containing 178 species were included in this family by Pellegrino et al. (2001). One species occurs in Honduras.

*Gymnophthalmus speciosus* **(Hallowell, "1860" [1861])**
**Common name(s):** None
**Description (Plate 101):** This small lizard attains a maximum known SVL of 42 mm in males and 44 mm in females. The tail is long (about 1.7 to 2.0 times SVL). The dorsal surface of the head is covered with large plates. Moveable eyelids are absent. The gular scales are cycloid in shape. Supralabials number 5 to 7 and infralabials 6 to 8. Dorsal and ventral body scales are smooth and cycloid in shape. Limbs are short and small, and only 4 digits are present on the forelimbs. Four to 13 total femoral pores are present in males; femoral pores are absent in females. The dorsum is some shade of brown, usually with a metallic sheen. A pale brown or white longitudinal line is usually present along the upper border of the dark brown lateral surface. The tail is bright red in juveniles and reddish orange in adults, if not regenerated. The belly varies from white in many subadults to heavily suffused with black in adult males.
**Similar species:** The only other lizard species in the Mosquitia that has the dorsal surface of the head covered with enlarged platelike scales and lacks moveable eyelids is *Lepidophyma flavimaculatum*. That species has 5 digits on the forelimbs, squarish ventral scales, and numerous dorsal tubercles.

**Plate 101.** *Gymnophthalmus speciosus*. Photograph by McCranie.

**General geographic distribution:** *Gymnophthalmus speciosus* is found at low and moderate elevations on the Atlantic versant from northern Belize to Guyana and from eastern Oaxaca, Mexico, to Panama on the Pacific versant. It also occurs on Trinidad and Tobago and Islas de Guanaja and Roatán (and several satellite islands) in the Islas de la Bahía, Honduras (see Remarks).
**Distribution in Honduras:** This species occurs in open habitats throughout much of the mainland in addition to Islas de Barbareta, Guanaja, Morat, and Roatán in the Islas de la Bahía. It is known from near sea level to 1320 m elevation.
**Distribution in the Mosquitia:** Colón—Las Champas (BMNH). Gracias a Dios—Rus Rus (USNM); Tánsin (LACM).
**Natural history comments:** *Gymnophthalmus speciosus* is a terrestrial or semifossorial, diurnal species. Our only experience with the species in the Mosquitia was in pine savanna at Tánsin and in transition forest between pine savanna and gallery forest at Rus Rus.
**Remarks:** The range given in the General geographical distribution section probably encompasses ranges of more than one species (Kizirian and Cole, 1999).

Family Teiidae

The combination of having infralingual plicae and moveable eyelids will distinguish the teiids from all other lizard families in the Mosquitia. The members of this family are restricted in distribution to the Western Hemisphere, where they are found from Maryland westward to Idaho and Oregon, USA, southward through Mexico and Central America to central Chile west of the Andes and central Argentina east of the Andes. Members also occur on the Bahama Islands, the Greater and Lesser Antilles, and Trinidad and Tobago. Nine genera containing 125 species were included in this family by Pough et al. (2003). Three genera consisting of six species are known to occupy Honduras, with all three genera containing four species occurring in the Mosquitia.

*Ameiva festiva* **(Lichtenstein and von Martens, 1856)**
**Common name(s):** Talyapti* (Miskito)
**Description (Plate 102):** This moderate-sized lizard attains a maximum known SVL of 129 mm in both sexes (Savage, 2002). The tail is long (about

**Plate 102.** *Ameiva festiva*. Photograph by McCranie.

1.4 to 1.8 times SVL). The dorsal surface of the head is covered with large plates. Moveable eyelids are present. The central gular scales are much enlarged, irregular in arrangement, and there is a gradual reduction in size of the scales radiating outward from the enlarged gular scales. There is a transverse row of abruptly enlarged mesoptychial scales. Supralabials number 12 to 18 and infralabials 8 to 15. Dorsal body scales are granular and smooth. Ventral scales are large, platelike and smooth, and are in 8 transverse rows. There is a single row of greatly enlarged scales on the anterior dorsolateral surface of the upper arm. Limbs are large and have 5 digits each. There are 32 to 55 total femoral pores. The middorsal ground color is brown with a pale (blue in juveniles, turning to yellowish-brown to orange in many adults, fading to white or yellow with age) vertebral stripe present in all but the largest individuals. A chestnut to dark brown paramiddorsal stripe is present. Yellow to pale brown longitudinal dashes or spots are present laterally on the body. The belly ground color varies from pinkish brown to pale blue.

**Similar species:** *Ameiva undulata* never has a pale vertebral stripe and has a lateral body pattern of pale vertical stripes alternating with dark vertical bars. *Aspidoscelis deppii* and *Cnemidophorus lemniscatus* have several rows of enlarged scales on the dorsolateral surface of the upper arm.

**General geographic distribution:** *Ameiva festiva* is found at low and moderate elevations on the Atlantic versant from Tabasco, Mexico, to north-central Colombia and on the Pacific versant marginally in northwestern Costa Rica and from south-central Costa Rica to northwestern and north-central Colombia.

**Distribution in Honduras:** This species occurs in the northern half of the country and is known from near sea level to 1400 m elevation.

**Distribution in the Mosquitia:** Colón—Empalme Río Chilmeca (formerly in UNAH, now lost); Quebrada Machín (USNM). Gracias a Dios—Caño Awalwás (UF); Barra Río Plátano (formerly in UNAH, now lost); Río Coco (USNM); Kalila Plapan Tingni (USNM); Mocorón (UTA); Río Sutawala (USNM); Bodega de Río Tapalwás (USNM); Urus Tingni Kiamp (USNM); Warunta Tingni Kiamp (USNM). Olancho—confluence of Ríos Aner and Wampú (USNM); Caobita (SMF; USNM); Quebrada El Guásimo (SMF; USNM); between La Llorona and confluence of Ríos Lagarto and Wampú (USNM); confluence of Ríos Sausa and Wampú (USNM); confluence of Quebrada Siksatara with Río Wampú (USNM); confluence of Ríos Yanguay and Wampú (USNM); confluence of Ríos Yapuwás and Patuca (LSUMZ).

**Natural history comments:** *Ameiva festiva* is a terrestrial, diurnal, heliothermic species that is found in primary to moderately disturbed evergreen broadleaf forest in the Mosquitia (including gallery forest through pine savanna). The species is active in sunny areas within the forest. Inactive individuals can be found under logs and rocks.

*Ameiva undulata* **(Wiegmann, 1834)**

**Common name(s):** Talyapti* (Miskito)

**Description (Plate 103):** This moderate-sized lizard attains a maximum known SVL of 129 mm in males and 111 mm in females (Echternacht, 1971). The tail is long (about 1.4 to 1.8 times SVL). The dorsal surface of the head is covered with large plates. Moveable eyelids are present. The central gular scales vary from slightly to moderately enlarged, are irregular to regular in arrangement, and there is a gradual reduction in size of the scales radiating outward from the enlarged gular scales. There is a transverse row of abruptly enlarged mesoptychial scales. Supralabials number 12 to 18 and infralabials 7 to 14. Dorsal body scales are granular and smooth. Ventral scales are large, platelike and smooth, and are in 8 to 12 (usually 8) transverse rows. There is a single row of greatly enlarged scales on the anterior dorsolateral surface of the upper arm. Limbs are large and have 5 digits

**Plate 103.** *Ameiva undulata.* Photograph by Townsend.

each. There are 22 to 48 total femoral pores. The middorsal ground color varies from gray-green to leaf green anteriorly and golden brown to brown posteriorly. A pale vertebral stripe is never present. The lateral body pattern consists of bluish white to greenish white vertical stripes alternating with dark brown to black vertical bars. The belly ground color can be white, blue, or pale pinkish orange.
**Similar species:** *Ameiva festiva* has a pale vertebral stripe in all but the largest individuals and yellow to pale brown longitudinal dashes or spots present laterally on the body. *Aspidoscelis deppii* and *Cnemidophorus lemniscatus* have several rows of enlarged scales on the dorsolateral surfaces of the upper arm.
**General geographic distribution:** *Ameiva undulata* is found at low, moderate, and intermediate elevations on the Atlantic versant from southern Tamaulipas, Mexico, to southern Nicaragua and from southern Nayarit, Mexico, to central and west-central Costa Rica on the Pacific versant. The species also occurs on Isla del Maíz Grande, Nicaragua, and a few islands and cays off the coast of Belize and Quintana Roo, Mexico.
**Distribution in Honduras:** This species occurs in open habitats at low and moderate elevations throughout most of the country. It is known from near sea level to 1240 m elevation.
**Distribution in the Mosquitia:** El Paraíso—Arenales (LACM). Gracias a Dios—Barra Patuca (USNM); Krausirpe (LSUMZ); Mocorón (UTA); Rus Rus (UF; USNM); Tánsin (LACM); Wampusirpe (LSUMZ). Olancho—Quebrada Kuilma Tingni (sight record).
**Natural history comments:** *Ameiva undulata* is a terrestrial, diurnal species that usually is found in pine savanna in the Mosquitia. This species is active only during sunny periods and is heliothermic. Several individuals were seen in an area of open, low vegetation growing in a sandy and rocky area along the Río Coco; the vegetation away from the immediate vicinity of the river was second growth evergreen broadleaf forest. The Arenales locality is a denuded area formerly cloaked in evergreen broadleaf forest.

*Aspidoscelis deppii* **(Wiegmann, 1834)**
**Common name(s):** Irakaya*, Rikaya* (Miskito)
**Description (Plate 104):** This moderately small lizard attains a maximum known SVL of 93 mm in males and 87 mm in females (Duellman and Wellman, 1960). The tail is long (about 2.2 to 2.4 times SVL). The dorsal surface of the head is covered with large plates. Moveable eyelids are present. There are 2 parietal scales and 1 interparietal scale present. The anterior and central gular scales are much larger than the posterior ones. There are 2 to 4 regular to irregular transverse rows of enlarged mesoptychial scales. Supralabials and infralabials number 6 to 7. Dorsal body scales are granular and smooth. Ventral scales are large, platelike and smooth, and are in 8 transverse rows. There are 2 or 3 rows of enlarged scales on the dorsolateral surfaces of the upper arm. Limbs are large and have 5 digits each. There are 29 to 44 total femoral pores. A preanal spur is absent. Juveniles and adult females have 8 to 10 yellowish or creamy white longitudinal stripes on the dorsal and lateral surfaces of the body. Adult males have the paravertebral stripes fused to form

**Plate 104.** *Aspidoscelis deppii.* Photograph by McCranie.

a vertebral stripe, which stripe can be obscured in some individuals. Also, the ventrolateral stripes in adult males are broken up into bluish white spots. The middorsal ground color between these pale stripes is suffused with green or is dark brown. The belly is black in males and white to bluish white in juveniles and adult females.
**Similar species:** *Cnemidophorus lemniscatus* has 4 parietal scales and males have a preanal spur at each side of the preanal plate. *Ameiva festiva* and *A. undulata* have a single row of greatly enlarged scales on the anterior dorsolateral surface of the upper arm.
**General geographic distribution:** *Aspidoscelis deppii* is found at low and moderate elevations on the Pacific versant from Michoacán, Mexico, to west-central Costa Rica. It also crosses the Isthmus of Tehuantepec to reach northern Veracruz and western Campeche, Mexico, on the Atlantic versant. The species also occurs disjunctly on the Atlantic versant from southeastern Campeche, Mexico, to northeastern Nicaragua and southwestern Nicaragua.
**Distribution in Honduras:** This lizard occurs in open habitats throughout much of the country and is known from near sea level to 900 m elevation.
**Distribution in the Mosquitia:** Gracias a Dios—Mocorón (see McCranie, Castañeda, and Nicholson, 2002); Prumnitara (UF); Tánsin (LACM; LSUMZ). Olancho—Quebrada Kuilma Tingni (sight record).
**Natural history comments:** *Aspidoscelis deppii* is a terrestrial, diurnal, and heliothermic species that has been collected in pine savanna and coastal strand in the Mosquitia. However, we saw, but were unable to collect, several individuals of this species in an area of open, low vegetation growing in a sandy and rocky area along the Río Coco; the vegetation away from the vicinity of the river was second growth evergreen broadleaf forest.

*Cnemidophorus lemniscatus* **(Linnaeus, 1758)**
**Common name(s):** Irakaya*, Rikaya* (Miskito)
**Description (Plate 105):** This moderate-sized lizard attains a maximum known SVL of 113 mm in males and 93 mm in females (Savage, 2002). The tail is long (about 1.9 to 2.6 times SVL). The dorsal surface of the head is covered with large plates. Moveable eyelids are present. There are 4 parietal scales and 1 interparietal scale present. The anterior gular scales are much larger than the posterior ones; the central gular scales are not greatly enlarged. There are 3 or 4 regular transverse rows of enlarged mesoptychial scales. Supralabials number 6 to 9 and infralabials 5 to 9. Dorsal body scales are granular and smooth. Ventral scales are large, platelike and smooth, and are in 8 to 10 (usually 8) transverse rows. There are 2 or 3 rows of enlarged scales on the dorsolateral surfaces of the upper arms. Limbs are large and have 5 digits each. There are 30 to 66 total femoral pores. A preanal spur is present on each side of the preanal plate in males. Juveniles and adult females have dorsal and lateral ground colors of brown or black, or these colors are suffused with green, and have 7 to 10 pale longitudinal stripes. Adult males have a middorsal body ground color of brown and the flanks are pinkish tan, rust-red, or yellowish brown (or various colors in between). There are about 3 rows of yellow to white spots on the lateral surfaces and usually no more than 4 pale stripes on the dorsal and dorsolateral areas in adult males. The belly is some shade of green in males and white in juveniles and adult females; a bluish tinge to the belly color can be present in both sexes.

**Plate 105.** *Cnemidophorus lemniscatus*. Photograph by McCranie.

**Similar species:** *Aspidoscelis deppii* has 2 parietal scales and males lack a preanal spur. *Ameiva festiva* and *A. undulata* have a single row of greatly enlarged scales on the anterior dorsolateral surface of the upper arm.
**General geographic distribution:** *Cnemidophorus lemniscatus* occurs at low elevations of the Atlantic versant from southern Belize to eastern Honduras, and from eastern Panama to northern Brazil and on the Pacific versant in central and eastern Panama. The species also occurs on Trinidad and Tobago, the Bay

Islands of Honduras, and several other Caribbean Islands (see Remarks). It has also been introduced into southern Florida, USA.
**Distribution in Honduras:** This species is found along the northern coastal plain of the mainland (it occasionally ranges inland along river valleys), as well as on Islas de Roatán and Utila and Cayo Cochino Pequeño in the Islas de la Bahía. It is known from sea level to 400 m elevation.
**Distribution in the Mosquitia:** Gracias a Dios—Barra Río Plátano (formerly in UNAH, now lost); Laguna Bacalar (BMNH); Cauquira (UF).
**Natural history comments:** *Cnemidophorus lemniscatus* is a terrestrial, diurnal, and heliothermic species that occurs in sandy areas in coastal strand in the Mosquitia.
**Remarks:** The range given in the General geographic distribution section probably encompasses ranges of more than one species (Reeder et al., 2002).

Family Xantusiidae

Xantusiids lack movable eyelids and have relatively flat bodies and heads (Pough et al., 2003). The members of this family of lizards are found only in the Western Hemisphere, where they occur from southern Utah, southern Nevada, southern California, and central and western Arizona, USA, southward through Baja California (save for the northwestern portion) and northwestern Sonora, Mexico. Populations also occur in the central Chihuahuan Desert region and the Sierra Madre Oriental, Mexico, and from Guerrero and Veracruz, Mexico, southward to the Canal Zone region of Panama. An isolated genus also occurs in eastern Cuba. Three genera comprised of about 23 species are currently included in this family. One species is known to occur in Honduras, which ranges into the Mosquitia.

*Lepidophyma flavimaculatum* **(A.H. A. Duméril, in A.M.C. Duméril and Duméril, 1851)**
**Common name(s):** None
**Description (Plate 106):** This medium-sized lizard (maximum SVL 127 mm [Bezy and Camarillo, 2002]) has a moderately long tail (about 1.3 to 1.5 times SVL). The distinct head is large and covered with enlarged smooth plates. The snout is somewhat pointed in dorsal aspect, moveable eyelids are lacking, and the pupils are vertically elliptical. The dorsal surface of the body and the gular region are covered by a combination of enlarged tubercles and small granular scales. Ventral surface of the body is covered with large, rectangular platelike scales that are slightly imbricate. Five digits are present on each limb. The tail has transverse rows of enlarged keeled scales that are separated by 3 or 4 rows of small scales. There are 26 to 33 total femoral pores present. Dorsal ground color is black, dark brown, or dark gray, with distinct yellow or tan spots or blotches on the body and tail. The labial area is yellow or tan with well-defined dark spots or bars. Ventral surfaces are yellow, cream, or tan with some brown mottling. The iris is dark brown.

**Plate 106.** *Lepidophyma flavimaculatum*. Photograph by McCranie.

**Similar species:** The only other species of lizard known from the Mosquitia that lacks moveable eyelids and has the dorsal surface of the head covered with enlarged, platelike scales is *Gymnophthalmus speciosus*. That species has only 4 digits on the forelimbs and cycloid ventral scales.
**General geographic distribution:** *Lepidophyma flavimaculatum* is found at low and moderate elevations on the Atlantic versant from southern Veracruz, Mexico, to central Panama and on the Pacific versant in central Panama and marginally in northwestern Costa Rica (but see Remarks).
**Distribution in Honduras:** This lizard occurs in the northern portion of the country. It is known from near sea level to about 1400 m elevation.
**Distribution in the Mosquitia:** Colón—near Las Champas (BMNH); Quebrada Machín (USNM). Gracias a Dios—Caño Awalwás (UF; USNM); Bodega de Río Tapalwás (USNM); Cerro Wahatingni (UF).

**Natural history comments:** *Lepidophyma flavimaculatum* is a primarily nocturnal, fossorial species that can be found in its diurnal retreats under logs and leaf litter, in rock crevices, or in holes in the ground. We have seen this species active at night on tree trunks with hollows in them. This species is found in primary evergreen broadleaf forest in the Mosquitia.
**Remarks:** Bezy (1989) and Bezy and Camarillo (2002) pointed out that northern populations (Veracruz to Honduras) of the *Lepidophyma flavimaculatum* complex contain both males and females, whereas southern populations (southern Nicaragua to Panama) appear to be all-female, with the exception of a few male individuals present at localities in southern Nicaragua and northern Costa Rica. Bezy and Camarillo (2002:19) stated "The term complex is used for the aggregation of *Lepidophyma flavimaculatum* populations to denote that it may contain more than one species. The populations in Panamá and most of Costa Rica lack males but do not appear to differ significantly in allozymes, karyotype, scalation, or color pattern from the populations to the northwest that contain males."

## Snakes

The snake fauna of Honduras is known to include 122 species placed in nine families and 66 genera (McCranie, in prep.). Of these, 63 species in six families and 45 genera are known from the Mosquitia.

### Family Anomalepididae

The family Anomalepididae includes the fossorial, insectivorous snakes referred to as blind worm snakes (Savage, 2002). They resemble the members of other scolecophidian snake families in possessing smooth, shiny cycloid scales on the body and tail of the same size on the venter as on the dorsum. Furthermore, they have short tails and vestigial eyes located under an ocular scale (Savage, 2002). Insofar as is known, these snakes are oviparous (Savage, 2002). The family members differ from those of other scolecophidian snake families by having the following combination of internal characters: maxillae moveable, toothed; a small dentary bearing 1 to 3 teeth; hyoid apparatus an M-shaped element; tracheal lung present and left lung absent; pelvic vestiges, if present, cartilaginous (Savage, 2002). The members of this family occur in the Western Hemisphere from northeastern Honduras southward through the remainder of Central America and disjunctly into South America as far south as eastern Paraguay, northeastern Argentina, and southern Brazil (Pough et al., 2003). Four genera containing 15 species are included in this family (McDiarmid et al., 1999). One species is known to occupy Honduras and to range into the Mosquitia.

#### *Anomalepis mexicanus* Jan, *in* Jan and Sordelli, 1860

**Common name(s):** None
**Description (Plate 107):** *Anomalepis mexicanus* is a tiny (to 180 mm TL) fossorial blind worm snake with an extremely short tail (0.02 of TL). The body is subcylindrical, with the head the same width as the neck. The snout is rounded in lateral and dorsal profiles. The rostral is short, reaching nearly to the level of the nostril. The rostral width is about 27 percent of the head width. Nostrils are not visible from above. Nasals are divided with the supranasal much larger than the infranasal. Prefrontals are paired, large, and in contact with the rostral, supranasals, upper preoculars, supraoculars, and frontal. Supraoculars are much smaller than the prefrontals. A single loreal is present. Preoculars number 2, the upper the largest and larger than the ocular, the lower about the same size as the ocular. The lower preocular is in contact with supralabial 3. The frontal is slightly larger than each prefrontal. The eye is visible beneath the skin and is located at the anterior edge

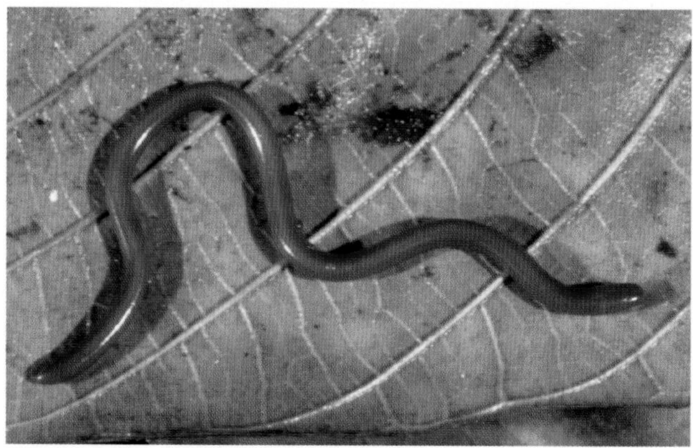

**Plate 107.** *Anomalepis mexicanus*. Photograph by McCranie.

of the ocular. Suboculars are single. The rostral, prefrontals, frontals, and supraoculars are each larger than any of the dorsal body scales. Supralabials number 4 and infralabials 3. A small mental is present. Scales around body are (22–24)–(22–24)–22 in the Honduran specimens, with all rows of equal size. Median dorsal scales from the prefrontal to the tail cone number 261 to 262 (261 to 272). The median subcaudal series is 6 to 7. Enlarged, paired precloacal scales are present. Dorsal and ventral surfaces are uniformly chestnut, with the internal organs visible through the translucent ventral skin. The iris is black.

**Similar species:** *Anomalepis mexicanus* and *Typhlops costaricensis* are the only two snakes in the Mosquitia that possess smooth, cycloid scales throughout the body and tail of the same size on the ventral as on the dorsal side of the body. Furthermore, they have vestigial eyes located beneath an ocular scale. *Typhlops costaricensis* has 20 scale rows around the body and the prefrontal scales fused with the prenasal scales.

**General geographic distribution:** *Anomalepis mexicanus* is found at low elevations on the Atlantic versant from northeastern Honduras to central Panama and on the Pacific versant from northwestern Costa Rica to central Panama. The species has also been reported from northwestern Peru.

**Distribution in Honduras:** This tiny snake is known only from 150 m elevation in the Mosquitia in southwestern Gracias a Dios.

**Distribution in the Mosquitia:** Gracias a Dios—Urus Tingni Kiamp (UF).

**Natural history comments:** *Anomalepis mexicanus* is a fossorial inhabitant of undisturbed evergreen broadleaf forest in the Mosquitia. One of the two Mosquitia specimens was found under a rotten log on a stream bank in December and the other was inside a rotten log on a steep hillside in May. Both situations were moist from recent heavy rains.

**Remarks:** This species was recently reported from Honduras by McCranie (2004b).

## Family Typhlopidae

The family Typhlopidae contains the fossorial, insectivorous snakes called blind snakes (Savage, 2002). They are like the members of other scolecophidian snake families in having smooth, shiny cycloid scales on the body and tail of the same size on the venter as on the dorsum. In addition, they have blunt heads, short tails, and vestigial eyes located under an ocular scale (Savage, 2002; Pough, et al. 2003). Most family members are apparently oviparous (Savage, 2002). This family differs from other scolecophidian snake families by having the following combination of internal characters: maxillae moveable, toothed; a small toothless dentary; hyoid apparatus wishbone shaped; usually a tracheal lung present, left lung vestigial or absent; pelvic vestiges usually consisting of usually ossified ischia (Savage, 2002). The members of this family occupy the Western Hemisphere from central Veracruz, Mexico, through Central America into South America to northern Argentina east of the Andes and to northwestern Ecuador west of the Andes, as well as the West Indies. In the Eastern Hemisphere, it occurs in southeastern Europe, tropical and many subtropical parts of Africa, southeastern Asia, Australia, and islands in the Pacific Ocean. Six genera containing 203 species are included in this family (McDiarmid et al., 1999). Two species placed in one genus are known to occupy Honduras with one species occurring in the Mosquitia.

### *Typhlops costaricensis* Jiménez and Savage, 1962

**Common name(s):** None

**Description (Plate 108):** *Typhlops costaricensis* is a moderate-sized (to 360 mm TL) fossorial blind snake with an extremely short tail (0.02 of TL). The body is subcylindrical, with the head the same width as the neck. The snout is rounded in lateral profile and broadly rounded in dorsal aspect. The rostral is long, reaching nearly to the level of the

**Plate 108.** *Typhlops costaricensis*. Photograph by McCranie.

eye. The rostral width is about 26 percent of the head width. The upper nasals and prefrontals are fused, reaching to a level slightly posterior to the rostral and the level of the anterior part of the eye. Nostrils are not visible from above. Nasals are completely divided by a suture extending in a curved line from the dorsal point of contact between the first and second supralabials through the nostril to the rostral above nostril. Nasals-prefrontals are separated medially by the rostral. Supraoculars are each about the same size as the frontal. There is no loreal. The preocular is about equal in size to the ocular; both are wider than long. The preocular contacts supralabials 2 and 3. The eye is visible beneath the skin and is located anterior to and above the center of the ocular, near the edge of the preocular. Suboculars are absent. Median and posterior head series of scales (supraoculars, frontal, interparietals, and parietals) are each larger than any of the dorsal body scales. Supralabials number 4 with the anteriormost one tiny. Infralabials number 4. A small mental is present. Scales around the body number 20–20–20, with all rows of equal size. Median dorsal scales from the prefrontal to the tail cone number 417 in the single Honduran specimen examined (394 to 417). The median subcaudal series is 8. Enlarged precloacal scales are absent. Dorsal surfaces are uniformly dark brown, except for the snout region, which has pale pinkish tan pigment along the seams of the rostral and nasals. The undersurface of the snout is pale pinkish tan. Ventral surfaces are fuscous. The iris is black.
**Similar species:** *Anomalepis mexicanus* and *Typhlops costaricensis* are the only two snakes in the Mosquitia that possess smooth, cycloid scales throughout the body and tail of the same size on the ventral as on the dorsal side of the body. Furthermore, they have vestigial eyes located beneath an ocular scale. *Anomalepis mexicanus* has 20 to 24 scale rows around the body and paired prefrontal scales.
**General geographic distribution:** *Typhlops costaricensis* is found at low and moderate elevations on both versants in south-central Honduras, the Atlantic versant of northeastern Honduras and north-central Nicaragua, and both versants in north-central Costa Rica.
**Distribution in Honduras:** This species is known from two nearby localities in Francisco Morazán and one locality in Gracias a Dios (150 to somewhere between 1100 to 1500 m elevation).
**Distribution in the Mosquitia:** Gracias a Dios—Warunta Tingni Kiamp (UF).
**Natural history comments:** *Typhlops costaricensis* is a fossorial inhabitant of undisturbed evergreen broadleaf forest in the Mosquitia. The single Mosquitia specimen was found under the root mass of a decaying small tree in May.

## Family Boidae

The family Boidae includes the snakes typically referred to as boas, sand boas, and pythons. The largest snakes in the world belong to this family, but some boas are rather small. The boas have many small scales on the dorsum of the head, retain externally visible remnants of posterior limbs, give birth to living young (viviparity), and constrict their prey. Some boas have infrared-sensitive labial pits. The members of this family are found in the Western Hemisphere from southern British Columbia and extreme southwestern Alberta, Canada, southward into Baja California and from central Tamaulipas and southern Sonora, Mexico, through Central America and into South America to about latitude 35°S, as well as the West Indies. In the Eastern Hemisphere, they occur from southeastern Europe to Asia Minor, then southward into northern, central, and eastern Africa, Madagascar, and Reunion Island, and eastward through the Arabian Peninsula, central and southwestern Asia to India and Sri Lanka, as well as the Moluccas and New Guinea through Melanesia to Samoa. Ten genera (McDiarmid et al., 1999; Austin, 2000) containing 41 species (McDiarmid et al., 1999) were included in this family in the most recent summaries. Two genera containing two species are known to occupy Honduras and to range into the Mosquitia.

### *Boa constrictor* Linnaeus, 1758

**Common name(s):** Boa, Mazacuate (Spanish); Waula* (Miskito); Ugrwe, Hágani Garádun** (Garífuna)
**Description (Plate 109):** This boa is a large terrestrial to arboreal snake (to about 5500 mm TL) with no enlarged plates on the dorsum of the head or any labial pits. It possesses 64 to 79 (55 to 95) dorsal scale rows at midbody and 19 to 22 (17 to 25) supralabials. Ventral scales are relatively narrow and do not reach the lateral edges of the venter; they number 229 to 251 (223 to 288). Subcaudals number 51 to 64 (43 to 70). A pair of

**Plate 109.** *Boa constrictor.* Photograph by McCranie.

horny spurs is present on either side of the vent in both males and females, but is better developed in males. The pupil is vertically elliptical. The head is well set off from the neck, as a consequence of the massive jaw muscles. The dorsum of the length of the body is gray to tan with a series of anteriorly H-shaped dark brown dorsal blotches. The dorsum of the head is the same ground color as the body, with a dark brown median line extending from the snout to the nape. The venter is pale gray to tan with dark lateral blotches.
**Similar species:** *Boa constrictor* and *Corallus annulatus* are the only two snakes in the Mosquitia that have relatively narrow ventral scales that never reach the lateral edge of the venter, more than 48 dorsal scale rows at midbody, and visible paracloacal spurs at the vent. *Corallus annulatus* has a well-developed series of pits on the posterior labial scales.
**General geographic distribution:** *Boa constrictor* occurs at low and moderate elevations from central Tamaulipas, Mexico, on the Atlantic versant and from northern Sonora, Mexico, on the Pacific versant through Central America to central Argentina east of the Andes and northwestern Peru west of the Andes. The species also occurs on numerous islands along both coasts.
**Distribution in Honduras:** This snake is widespread throughout much of the mainland (near sea level to 1370 m elevation). It also occurs on Islas de Barbareta, Guanaja, Roatán, Utila, and Cayo Cochino Grande in the Islas de la Bahía.
**Distribution in the Mosquitia:** Colón—Las Champas (BMNH). Gracias a Dios—Laguna Bacalar (BMNH); Barra Patuca (USNM); Río Coco (USNM); Mistruk (LSUMZ); Mocorón (CF); near confluence of Ríos Palacios and Negro (BMNH); Rus Rus (COHDEFOR); Tikiraya (USNM); Crique Turalka (USNM); Urus Tingni Kiamp (sight records); Waumpusirpi (LSUMZ). Olancho—Quebrada El Guásimo (UNAH).
**Natural history comments:** *Boa constrictor* is a terrestrial, nocturnal inhabitant of disturbed and undisturbed evergreen broadleaf forest and broadleaf swamp forest, as well as pine savanna, in the Mosquitia. We have found this species coiled by day among rocks on a riverbank and in debris beneath a stilt house. One adult crawled into a camp site at about 1000 h in the Warunta area and another was in a tree about 3 m above the ground in the same area. The latter was eating a large rat at about 2100 h.

*Corallus annulatus* **(Cope, 1875)**
**Common name(s):** Boa (Spanish)
**Description (Plate 110):** This tree boa is a moderately large arboreal snake (to about 1500 mm TL) without enlarged plates on the dorsum of the head. It possesses a well-developed series of pits on the posterior labials. The body is laterally compressed and the tail is prehensile. The head is distinctly set off from the neck. The single Mosquitia specimen examined has 49 (49 to 57) dorsal scale rows at midbody and 14 (14 or 15) supralabials. Ventrals number 262 (251 to 268) and are relatively narrow, not reaching the lateral edges of the venter. There are 80 (79 to 88) subcaudals. Paracloacal spurs are present. The pupil is vertically elliptical. An adult from Bodega de Río Tapalwás was olive gray dorsally with a series of

**Plate 110.** *Corallus annulatus.* Photograph by McCranie.

pale orange-edged grayish olive alternating blotches. The venter was cream with grayish olive smudging. The iris was gray with brown reticulations. Spurs were very dark brown. A subadult from Caño Awalwás was brown above, with a series of dark brown-edged brown lateral blotches, some joined at dorsal midline with those on other side of the body; some lateral blotches with white flecking at lower edge. The venter was pale brown with small, scattered dark brown blotches. The dorsum of the tail was slightly darker than most of body. The head was pale brown with scattered dark brown markings, including a dark postocular stripe. The chin was pale brown and the iris cinnamon brown.

**Similar species:** *Boa constrictor* and *Corallus annulatus* are the only two snakes in the Mosquitia that have relatively narrow ventral scales that never reach the lateral edge of the venter, 49 or more dorsal scale rows at midbody, and visible paracloacal spurs at the vent. *Boa constrictor* lacks labial pits.

**General geographic distribution:** *Corallus annulatus* occurs at low elevations on the Atlantic versant from eastern Guatemala southward to northwestern Colombia. It also occurs on the Pacific versant in central and southern Panama and northwestern Colombia.

**Distribution in Honduras:** The distribution of this snake in Honduras is unclear (see Remarks), although it is known for certain only from 100 to 190 m elevation in the Mosquitia.

**Distribution in the Mosquitia:** Gracias a Dios—Caño Awalwás (Wilson et al., 2003); Bodega de Río Tapalwás (USNM); Urus Tingni Kiamp (photographs).

**Natural history comments:** *Corallus annulatus* is a nocturnal inhabitant of primary evergreen broadleaf forest in the Mosquitia. One specimen was crawling down a vine leading to the canopy and another was about 8 m above the ground coiled on a vine next to a tree (both at Bodega de Río Tapalwás). Another was active in a tree about 4 m above a small river (Caño Awalwás). In addition, three individuals were seen at night in trees along Urus Tingni Kiamp; all were in a head down position and appeared to be alert.

**Remarks:** This tree boa was originally reported from Honduras (E. Smith and Acevedo, 1997) on the basis of an adult female and her 14 captive-born offspring collected for a Honduran animal dealer and sent to a dealer in the United States. Conflicting information about the origin of these specimens were apparently given to the USA animal dealer and to our colleague Mario R. Espinal. Contrary to the statements in Henderson et al. (2001), it is unlikely that these specimens came from the locality for which they were reported by E. Smith and Acevedo (1997) and Henderson et al. (2001). The locality given by these authors does not occur in the department in which the adult was purported to have been collected, but there is a locality of the same name in an adjacent department. Thus, the specimen reported by McCranie, Castañeda, and Nicholson (2002) is the first with unequivocal locality data. Individuals have been subsequently collected or seen at several localities in the Mosquitia.

## Family Colubridae

The family Colubridae has no known synapomorphies and may be paraphyletic (Pough et al., 2003). Consequently, characterization of the family is difficult or impossible. This family of snakes is the most specious of "approximately 15 families" recognized (Pough et al., 2003:147). It is distributed in the Western Hemisphere from Canada throughout the United States, Mexico, Central America, South America, and the West Indies. In the Eastern Hemisphere, colubrids are found throughout Europe, Africa, Asia, Australia, and some islands of Oceania. Approximately 320 genera comprised of more than 1800 species are included in this family (Pough et al., 2003). Fifty genera comprised of 98 species are known to range into Honduras (including the Swan Islands). Thirty-seven genera containing 53 species are known to occur in the Mosquitia.

### *Adelphicos quadrivirgatum* Jan, 1862

**Common name(s):** None

**Description (Plate 111):** This semifossorial snake is small (to about 390 mm TL) and has a relatively short tail (0.14 to 0.21 of TL). The head is relatively small, conical in shape, and not or only slightly distinct from the neck. There is only a single, elongate scale (a loreal) present between the postnasal and the eye. Supralabials usually number 7, with the third and fourth bordering the eye. Infralabials number 6 to 8, usually 7, with the third infralabial scale greatly reduced or absent. Anterior chinshields are greatly enlarged, paired, and are in contact with the lip or not. A mental groove is

**Plate 111.** *Adelphicos quadrivirgatum*. Photograph by McCranie.

present and the pupil is circular. Ventral scales number from 117 to 132 (117 to 155) and the subcaudals from 31 to 47 (29 to 50). The cloacal scute is divided. Dorsal scales are smooth, without apical pits, and in 15 rows throughout the body. Dorsal body coloration consists of one to five dark grayish brown longitudinal stripes on a brownish gray, yellowish orange, or red background. The venter is cream to pale yellow in color, marked with a variable amount of dark pigment. The head is colored as is the dorsal ground color, with dark grayish brown mottling. Supralabials and the chin are yellowish tan. The iris is black.
**Similar species:** No other snake in the Mosquitia has the greatly enlarged chinshields of this species or a third infralabial scale greatly reduced or absent. Mosquitia members of the genus *Coniophanes* have 19 to 21 (sometimes 23) dorsal scales at midbody. *Enuliophis sclateri* has an unlined dorsum and a white head band. *Geophis hoffmanni* has a uniformly dark gray dorsum, five supralabials, and a single cloacal scute. *Ninia maculata* and *N. sebae* have keeled dorsal scales, nonlineate dorsal patterns, and a vertically subelliptical pupil. *Rhadinaea decorata* has 17–17–17 dorsal scale rows, 85 to 124 subcaudals, and pale postorbital and nuchal markings. *Tantilla taeniata* lacks a loreal scale, but does have a preocular scale; in addition, it has a dorsal pattern of pale stripes on a dark ground color and a pale nuchal band. *Tantillita lintoni* lacks a loreal scale, but does have a preocular scale; in addition, it has a uniformly brown dorsum. *Urotheca decipiens* and *U. guentheri* have 17 dorsal scale rows, a dorsal pattern of pale longitudinal stripes on the body and tail, and immaculate venters.

**General geographic distribution:** *Adelphicos quadrivirgatum* occurs at low, moderate, and occasionally intermediate elevations on the Atlantic versant from southern Tamaulipas, Mexico, to northeastern Honduras and on the Pacific versant from central Oaxaca, Mexico, to central Guatemala.
**Distribution in Honduras:** This species is widespread in the northern and southwestern portions of the country and is known from near sea level to 1740 m elevation.
**Distribution in the Mosquitia:** Colón—Quebrada Machín (USNM). Gracias a Dios—Caño Awalwás (USNM); Caño Awawás (USNM); Kaska Tingni (USNM).
**Natural history comments:** *Adelphicos quadrivirgatum* is a semifossorial snake, typically encountered underneath or within rotten logs in undisturbed evergreen broadleaf forest in the Mosquitia.

*Chironius grandisquamis* **(W. Peters, 1868)**
**Common name(s):** Tamagás Negro (Spanish)
**Description (Plate 112):** This is a large snake (to 2718 mm TL) with a long tail (0.36 to 0.38 of TL). The head is distinctly set off from the neck. Two scales (a loreal and a preocular) are located between the postnasal (or nasal when it is undivided) and the eye. Supralabials number 8 or 9, usually 9, with usually the fourth, fifth, and sixth (sometimes the fourth and fifth or fifth and sixth) bordering the eye. Infralabials number 9 to 12, usually 10 or 11. The enlarged chinshields are paired, a mental groove is present, and the pupil is circular. Ventrals range from 156 to 163 (151 to 167) and subcaudals from 125 to 146 (125 to 155). The

**Plate 112.** *Chironius grandisquamis*. Photograph by McCranie.

cloacal scute is divided. Dorsal scales are normally in 10–10–8 rows. In males, the paravertebral scales are strongly keeled with a total of 6 to 8 keeled rows. In females, the paravertebral rows are weakly keeled. The color pattern is of two basic types in adults. Some adults are uniform black on the dorsum, posterior venter, and subcaudal surface with the chin and anterior venter white. Other adults retain a semblance of the juvenile pattern. These latter individuals have the head and sometimes the anterior portion of the body black, grading to dark salmon with black crossbands posteriorly; the lower portion of the supralabials is white; and the venter is white to pale pinkish orange anteriorly, grading to salmon posteriorly in some individuals or to salmon and then black on the posterior portion and the underside of the tail. The iris is dark to very dark gray in both phases. Juveniles of the black phase have the dorsum of the head and the anterior body black, grading to cinnamon brown with darker crossbands on the remainder of the body. The chin is pale cream grading to cream and then to pale orange on the posterior half of the body; pale orange lateral blotches are present on the ventrals of the anterior half of the body.

**Similar species:** *Spilotes pullatus* is one of only two other colubrid snake species in the Mosquitia with an even number of dorsal scale rows; those rows number 14 to 18 at midbody. In addition, this species has a yellow and black dorsum. *Nothopsis rugosus* has 26 to 30 dorsal scale rows at midbody and the upper head surface broken up into many, small, keeled or tuberculate scales.

**General geographic distribution:** *Chironius grandisquamis* is found at low, moderate, and occasionally intermediate elevations on the Atlantic versant from northwestern Honduras to north-central Colombia and on the Pacific versant from west-central Costa Rica to northwestern Ecuador.

**Distribution in Honduras:** This snake occurs at low and moderate elevations (near sea level to 990 m) in the north-central and eastern portions of the country.

**Distribution in the Mosquitia:** Colón—Quebrada Machín (USNM); Tulito (BMNH). El Paraíso—Arenales (LACM). Gracias a Dios—Caño Awalwás (USNM); Caño Awawás (USNM); Mocorón (CF); Bodega de Río Tapalwás (UF; USNM); Urus Tingni Kiamp (UF); Cerro Wahatingni (UF). Olancho—Quebrada de Las Marías (USNM).

**Natural history comments:** *Chironius grandisquamis* is a diurnal species found in primary to lightly disturbed evergreen broadleaf forest, where it is found on the ground and in trees and understory vegetation along water courses in the Mosquitia. It is most frequently seen at night while sleeping in vegetation and trees along streams and rivers.

**Remarks:** Adults females of this species from the region of the Río Coco retain the juvenile pattern of pale bands on a darker ground color, as has been reported for specimens from other portions of the range (Dixon et al., "1993" 1995). In the remainder of the range of this snake in Honduras, the adults are usually shiny black above, as was the single adult male from the Río Coco region.

*Clelia clelia* **(Daudin, 1803)**

**Common name(s):** Matsiksa (Miskito)

**Description (Plates 113 and 114):** *Clelia clelia* is a large (to 2471 mm TL) terrestrial snake with a relatively short tail (0.17 to 0.21) and the head not significantly broader than the neck. Two scales (a loreal and a preocular) are usually present between the postnasal and the eye, although the anterior scale can be absent. Supralabials number 7 or 8, usually 7, with the third and fourth bordering the eye. Infralabials range from 7 to 9, with 8 the usual number. The enlarged chinshields are paired and a mental groove is present. The pupil is vertically elliptical. Ventrals range from 212 to 247 (198 to 247) and subcaudals from 73 to 89 (57 to 93). The cloacal scute is single. Dorsal scales are smooth, with paired apical pits, and in 19 rows at midbody and 17 rows at the vent. The color pattern of this snake varies ontogenetically. Juveniles have a coral

**Plate 113.** *Clelia clelia* (adult). Photograph by McCranie.

**Plate 114.** *Clelia clelia* (juvenile). Photograph by McCranie.

red dorsum, with each dorsal scale usually tipped with dark red, and a dark head cap and nape blotch (the latter not extending onto the ventrals) separated by a white, cream, or yellow nuchal collar beginning on the parietal scales. Adults are uniformly shiny bluish black to dark gray with a purplish sheen on the dorsum. Scales of the lower neck region are pink. The lower portion of the supralabials and the venter are pale pearl gray.
**Similar species:** Black adult individuals of *Chironius grandisquamis* have 10 dorsal scale rows at midbody and a circular pupil. *Drymarchon melanurus* has 17 dorsal scale rows at midbody, a divided cloacal scute, a circular pupil, and a dorsal pattern including a gray to brown anterior dorsum, with an oblique, elongate dark mark on the neck, grading to a dark gray to black posterior portion. *Hydromorphus concolor* has the internasals fused, a divided cloacal scute, and 157 to 186 ventrals. *Masticophis mentovarius* has 17 dorsal scales at midbody, a divided cloacal scute, a circular pupil, and a gray, tan, or brown dorsum. *Mastigodryas melanolomus* has 17 dorsal scale rows at midbody, a divided cloacal scute, 160 to 195 ventrals, a circular pupil, and a salmon red venter. In comparison with juvenile *C. clelia*, *Ninia sebae* is a small snake with keeled scales and usually some indication of yellow-outlined black transverse markings on the dorsum, and *Oxyrhopus petola* has black transverse bands on the dorsum.
**General geographic distribution:** *Clelia clelia* is found at low and moderate elevations from northern Guatemala and Belize on the Atlantic versant and from northwestern Costa Rica on the Pacific versant to central Bolivia and northern Brazil east of the Andes and western Peru west of the Andes. It also occurs on the islands of Trinidad and Grenada.
**Distribution in Honduras:** This species is widespread across the northern portion of the country. It is known from near sea level to 990 m elevation.
**Distribution in the Mosquitia:** El Paraíso—Arenales (LACM). Gracias a Dios—Kaska Tingni (USNM); Mocorón (UTA); Rus Rus (USNM); Warunta Tingni Kiamp (USNM). Olancho—Quebrada de Las Marías (USNM); Matamoros (USNM); confluence of Quebrada Siksatara with Río Wampú (USNM); Bodega de Río Tapalwás (USNM); Cerro Wahatingni (USNM).
**Natural history comments:** *Clelia clelia* is a nocturnal, terrestrial inhabitant of primary evergreen broadleaf forest in the Mosquitia. One subadult *C. clelia* was collected from a wet hole in sandy soil under a partially buried rock next to a stream and had a partially digested *Ameiva festiva* in its stomach. Active individuals have been found swimming in rivers and streams, crawling on the forest floor near and well away from streams, among tree roots in a cavity in a stream bank, and on a hill in karst limestone.

*Coniophanes bipunctatus* **(Günther, 1858)**
**Common name(s):** None
**Description (Plate 115):** This snake is medium-sized (to about 750 mm TL) and has a tail of moderate length (0.29 to 0.36 of TL). The head is moderately distinct from the neck. Two scales (a loreal and a preocular) are present between the postnasal and the eye. Supralabials number 7 to 9,

**Plate 115.** *Coniophanes bipunctatus*. Photograph by McCranie.

usually 8, with the fourth and fifth bordering the eye. Infralabials number 7 to 11, usually 9 or 10. The enlarged chinshields are paired, a mental groove is present, and the pupil is circular. Ventrals range from 124 to 137 (124 to 145) and the subcaudals from 78 to 96 (72 to 101). The cloacal scute is divided. Dorsal scales are smooth, without apical pits, and usually in 21–21–17 or 21–21–19 rows. The dorsum of the body is pale to dark brown to reddish brown with dark brown stripes on rows 4 and 5 and sometimes row 3, as well as a dark brown stripe on the middorsal row. The venter is cream to yellow anteriorly, grading to pinkish orange posteriorly, with circular dark brown to black spots, usually one pair to a ventral, decreasing in size posteriorly. The dorsum of the head is colored as is the dorsum of the body; the supralabials are cream mottled with brown spotting. The chin is cream with dark mottling and longitudinal streaking.

**Similar species:** *Adelphicos quadrivirgatum* has a small and conical head, no preocular scale, and 15 dorsal scale rows throughout the body. *Coniophanes fissidens* has an immaculate venter, or one with numerous small black dots or with one pair of small spots per ventral scale, and a poorly defined middorsal stripe that is often broken into a series of dots. *Coniophanes imperialis* has 19 dorsal scale rows at midbody. *Conophis lineatus* has three dark stripes on the head, one medial and one on each side, the lateral stripes continuing for some distance onto the side of the body; in addition, it has 149 to 180 ventrals and 19 dorsal scale rows at midbody. *Rhadinaea decorata* has 17–17–17 dorsal scale rows. *Tantilla taeniata* lacks a loreal scale and has a pattern of a middorsal and lateral pale stripes on a darker ground color, and 15 dorsal scale rows throughout the body. *Urotheca decipiens* and *U. guentheri* have distinct pale longitudinal stripes on either side of the body and 17 dorsal scale rows throughout the body.

**General geographic distribution:** *Coniophanes bipunctatus* is found at low and moderate elevations on the Atlantic versant from southern Veracruz, Mexico, to northwestern Panama. The species also occurs on Isla de Roatán, Honduras, and Isla Escudo de Veraguas, Panama.

**Distribution in Honduras:** This snake is known from several localities (from near sea level to 1370 m elevation) in the northern portion of the mainland and on Isla de Roatán.

**Distribution in the Mosquitia:** Gracias a Dios—near Saúpuka (LACM; see Remarks).

**Natural history comments:** We have not encountered *Coniophanes bipunctatus* in the Mosquitia, but elsewhere in Honduras we have found it around small streams, flood plains of a river, and swampy areas. The species is nocturnal. Saúpuka apparently lies in pine savanna (see map in Parsons, 1955).

**Remarks:** Saúpuka lies on the Nicaraguan side of the Río Coco. H. Campbell and Howell (1965) first reported *Coniophanes bipunctatus* from Saúpuka; these authors stated (p. 131) "records from localities along the Río Coco may apply to Nicaragua or Honduras." Thus, we are including this species in the herpetofauna of the Honduran Mosquitia. Wilson and Meyer (1985) also included that locality record in their work on the Honduran snake fauna.

*Coniophanes fissidens* **(Günther, 1858)**

**Common name(s):** None

**Description (Plate 116):** This snake is small to medium-sized (to about 800 mm TL) and has a long tail (0.26 to 0.35 of TL). The head is moderately distinct from the neck. Two scales (a loreal and preocular) are usually present between the postnasal and the eye, with the one nearest the eye (preocular) single or divided. Supralabials number 7 or 8, usually 8, with the fourth and fifth bordering the eye. Infralabials number 9 or 10. The enlarged chinshields are paired, a mental groove is present, and the pupil is circular. Ventrals range from 115 to 129 (109 to 146) and subcaudals from 66 to 88 (57 to 103). The cloacal scute is divided. Dorsal scales are smooth, without apical

**Plate 116.** *Coniophanes fissidens.* Photograph by McCranie.

pits, and usually in 21–21–17 rows. The dorsum of the body is pale brown to brown with a dark brown stripe on row 5 or row 6. An indistinct dark brown stripe can be present on the middorsal scale row or not. The venter is cream medially and pale orange to pinkish orange laterally and can be immaculate, have numerous small black spots, or have one pair of small spots per ventral scale. The head is rust brown to brown above. A cream stripe is present along some portion of the upper part of the supralabials; the remainder of the supralabials is heavily stippled with gray. The iris is orangish red to brown.
**Similar species:** *Adelphicos quadrivirgatum* has a small and conical head, no preocular scale, and 15 dorsal scale rows throughout the body. *Coniophanes bipunctatus* has a pair of large, rounded dark brown to black spots on each ventral scale and usually a well-defined middorsal dark stripe. *Coniophanes imperialis* has 19 dorsal scale rows at midbody. *Conophis lineatus* has three dark stripes on the head, one medial and one on each side, the lateral stripes continuing for some distance onto the side of the body; in addition, it has 149 to 180 ventrals and 19 dorsal scale rows at midbody. *Rhadinaea decorata* has 17–17–17 dorsal scale rows. *Tantilla taeniata* lacks a loreal scale and has a pattern of a middorsal and lateral pale stripes on a darker ground color, and 15 dorsal scale rows throughout the body. *Urotheca decipiens* and *U. guentheri* have distinct pale longitudinal stripes on either side of the body and 17 dorsal scale rows throughout the body.
**General geographic distribution:** *Coniophanes fissidens* occurs at low, moderate, and intermediate elevations from southern San Luis Potosí, Mexico, on the Atlantic versant and from southern Michoacán, Mexico, on the Pacific versant to extreme northwestern Peru.
**Distribution in Honduras:** This species is found at low and moderate elevations (near sea level to 1300 m) in the northern and central portions of the country.
**Distribution in the Mosquitia:** Colón—Río Guaraska (BMNH). Gracias a Dios—Oscana (USNM); Caño Sucio (USNM); Bodega de Río Tapalwás (UF; USNM).
**Natural history comments:** Specimens were collected in primary evergreen broadleaf forest in the Mosquitia. Most were crawling in leaf litter, whereas one was on a bare riverbank. All were active during the day.

*Coniophanes imperialis* **(Baird and Girard, *in* Baird, 1859)**
**Common name(s):** None
**Description (Plate 117):** This is a medium-small snake (to about 550 mm TL) with a long tail (about 0.30 to 0.39 of TL). The head is slightly distinct from the neck. Two scales (a loreal and a preocular) are usually present between the postnasal and the eye, with the one nearest the eye (preocular) single or divided. Supralabials number 7 or 8, usually 8, with the fourth and fifth bordering the eye. Infralabials number 8 to 10. The enlarged chinshields are paired, a mental groove is present, and the pupil is circular. Ventrals range from 114 to 128 (114 to 141) and subcaudals from 69 to 88 (62 to 94). The cloacal scute is divided. Dorsal scales are smooth, without apical pits, and in 19–19–17 or 19–19–15 rows. The dorsum of the body is medium brown from the upper half of dorsal row 4 to the middorsal row and dark brown from the lower half of dorsal row 4 to the edge of the venter, these two areas separated by a very dark brown line on the middle of row 4. A dark brown line follows the middorsal scale row. The venter is cream on the chin (speckled with dark brown) and anterior body grading to pinkish orange at about midbody. The head is brown above with a dark brown-edged tan line beginning on the nasals and terminating on the upper posterior temporal. The side of the head is brown, except for the supralabials, which are ivory cream, bounded above by a very dark brown line and speckled with very dark brown. The iris is tan above and brown below.
**Similar species:** *Adelphicos quadrivirgatum* has a small and conical head, no preocular scale, and 15

**Plate 117.** *Coniophanes imperialis.* Photograph by McCranie.

dorsal scale rows throughout the body. *Coniophanes bipunctatus* and *C. fissidens* have 21 (sometimes 23) dorsal scales at midbody. *Conophis lineatus* has three dark stripes on the head, one medial and one on each side, the lateral stripes continuing for some distance onto the side of the body; in addition, it has 149 to 180 ventrals. *Rhadinaea decorata* has 17–17–17 dorsal scale rows. *Tantilla taeniata* lacks a loreal scale and has a pattern of a middorsal and lateral pale stripes on a darker ground color, and 15 dorsal scale rows throughout the body. *Urotheca decipiens* and *U. guentheri* have distinct pale longitudinal stripes on either side of the body and 17 dorsal scales throughout the body.

**General geographic distribution:** *Coniophanes imperialis* is found at low and moderate elevations on the Atlantic versant from southern Texas, USA, to northeastern Honduras. It also occurs on Isla de Utila and Cayo Cochino Pequeño in the Honduran Bay Islands. In addition, it occurs on the Pacific versant in Oaxaca, Mexico.

**Distribution in Honduras:** This species is known from the northern portion of the country from near sea level to 650 m elevation.

**Distribution in the Mosquitia:** Gracias a Dios—Swabila (UF); Tikiraya (UF).

**Natural history comments:** One specimen was found inside a log in a cattle pasture cut from broadleaf swamp forest in the Mosquitia. *Coniophanes imperialis* is active during the day in other parts of Honduras.

*Conophis lineatus* **(A.M.C. Duméril, Bibron, and Duméril, 1854b)**

**Common name(s):** Guarda Camino (Spanish)

**Description (Plate 118):** This is a medium-sized snake (to 1167 mm TL) with a moderately long tail (0.20 to 0.25 of TL). The head is not distinctly wider than the neck. Two scales (a loreal and a preocular) are present between the postnasal and the eye. Supralabials number 7 or 8, usually 8, with the third and fourth or fourth and fifth bordering the eye. Infralabials number 8 to 11, usually 9 or 10. The enlarged chinshields are paired, a mental groove is present, and the pupil is circular. Ventrals range from 153 to 178 (149 to 180) and subcaudals from 60 to 80 (56 to 80). The cloacal scute is divided. Dorsal scales are smooth, without apical pits, and in 19 rows at midbody and 17 rows at the vent. The color pattern in specimens from the Mosquitia is a reduced form of the variable lineate pattern seen elsewhere in the country. The dorsum is gray with narrow, indistinct dark gray stripes on the neck and sometimes the posterior body. The middorsum of the head is grayish brown flanked by gray areas confluent with the dorsal ground color. A dark grayish brown-edged olive stripe begins on the snout and continues onto the temporal region of the head. The venter is pale grayish white with gray smudging on the otherwise white chin.

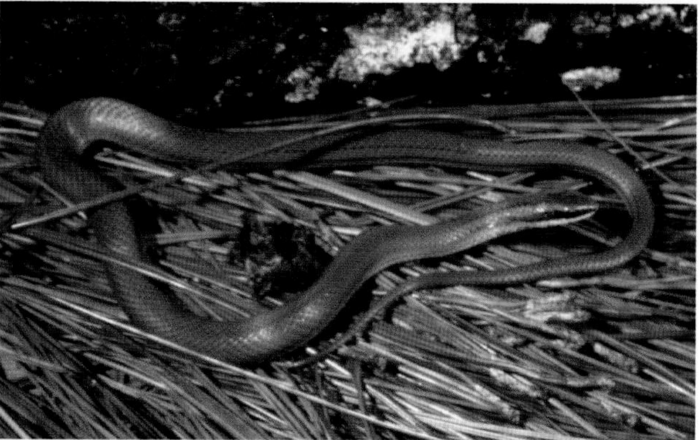

**Plate 118.** *Conophis lineatus*. Photograph by McCranie.

**Similar species:** Mosquitia members of the genus *Coniophanes* (*bipunctatus*, *fissidens*, and *imperialis*) have 146 or fewer ventrals. *Tantilla taeniata* is a smaller snake with a pattern of three pale stripes on a darker ground color and lacks a loreal scale. *Thamnophis proximus* is a more slender snake with keeled scales and a pattern of three pale stripes on a darker ground color. *Urotheca decipiens* is a smaller snake and has a prominent zigzag white stripe on the lower body and 17 dorsal scale rows throughout the body. *Urotheca guentheri* is a smaller snake with a pattern of two lateral pale stripes on a darker ground color, an immaculate bright orange to red venter, and black-bordered pale ocelli on each parietal plate and on either side of the neck.

**General geographic distribution:** *Conophis lineatus* is found at low and moderate elevations on the Atlantic versant from northern Veracruz, Mexico, to north-central Nicaragua and on the Pacific versant from southern Guatemala to north-central Costa Rica.

**Distribution in Honduras:** This species occurs in disjunct populations in open habitats throughout much of the country. It is known from near sea level to 1000 m elevation.

**Distribution in the Mosquitia:** Gracias a Dios—

Barra Patuca (USNM); Oscana (USNM); Puerto Lempira (CAS); Rus Rus (UF; USNM).
**Natural history comments:** *Conophis lineatus* is a diurnal, terrestrial inhabitant of pine savanna in the Mosquitia. One was under a log in a savanna that had recently burned.

*Dendrophidion percarinatum* **(Cope, 1893)**
**Common name(s):** None
**Description (Plate 119):** This snake is moderate-sized (to 1175 mm TL), with a long tail (0.40 to 0.45 of TL). The head is distinctly set off from the neck. Two scales (a loreal and a preocular) are present between the postnasal and the eye. Supralabials number 8 to 10, usually 9, with the fourth, fifth, and sixth bordering the eye. Infralabials number 9 to 11, usually 10. The enlarged chinshields are paired, a mental groove is present, and the pupil is circular. Ventrals range from 152 to 159 (152 to 169) and subcaudals from 143 to 163 (133 to 164). The cloacal scute is divided. Dorsal scales are keeled (less strongly so laterally), with paired apical pits, and in 17–17–15 rows. The dorsum of the body is brown with narrow pale brown crossbands anteriorly (less than one scale long). Pale crossbands are outlined with dark brown. The dorsal surface of the head is brown. Lateral surfaces of the head are brown, except for the supralabials, which are white with dark brown dorsal edges anterior and posterior to the eye. The dorsal surface of the tail is brown with dark brown spotting. Ventral surfaces of the body and tail are orangish yellow. The ventral surface of he head is white. The iris is brownish gray with a golden brown inner rim.

**Plate 119.** *Dendrophidion percarinatum.* Photograph by McCranie.

**Similar species:** *Dendrophidion vinitor* has more strongly keeled dorsal scales, a single cloacal scute, less than 130 subcaudals, and broader pale crossbands on the neck (one and one-half to two dorsal scales long). Some juvenile *Masticophis mentovarius* also have a pattern of narrow, transverse bands on the neck, but have smooth dorsal scales. Juvenile *Mastigodryas melanolomus* have a pattern of pale crossbands, often broken into spots, on a darker ground color, but have smooth dorsal scales.
**General geographic distribution:** *Dendrophidion percarinatum* occurs at low and moderate elevations on the Atlantic versant from northern Honduras to northwestern Colombia and on the Pacific versant from west-central Costa Rica to southwestern Ecuador. It also occurs marginally on the Pacific versant in northwestern Costa Rica. Isolated populations are also found on the Atlantic versant in north-central Colombia.
**Distribution in Honduras:** This species is known from the northern and eastern portions of the country from 20 to 685 m elevation.
**Distribution in the Mosquitia:** Gracias a Dios—Rus Rus (USNM); Bodega de Río Tapalwás (UF; USNM); Warunta Tingni Kiamp (USNM). Olancho—Quebrada El Guásimo (USNM); confluence of Ríos Yanguay and Wampú (USNM).
**Natural history comments:** *Dendrophidion percarinatum* is a diurnal, terrestrial inhabitant of primary evergreen broadleaf forest in the Mosquitia. One specimen was crawling on the forest floor next to a stream in the morning, another was sleeping at night in understory vegetation about 1.5 m above the ground next to a stream, and two others were under logs on heavily overcast days.

*Dendrophidion vinitor* **H. Smith, 1941**
**Common name(s):** None
**Description (Plate 120):** This snake is moderate-sized and slender (to about 1100 mm TL), with a long tail (0.34 to 0.37 of TL). The head is distinctly set off from the neck. Two scales (a loreal and a preocular) are present between the postnasal and the eye. Supralabials number 8 to 10, usually 9, with the fourth, fifth, and sixth bordering the eye. Infralabials number 8 to 11, usually 9 or 10. The enlarged chinshields are paired, a mental groove is present, and the pupil is circular. Ventrals range from 152 to 162 (148 to 165) and subcaudals from 116 to 119 (111 to 128). The cloacal scute is entire.

**Plate 120.** *Dendrophidion vinitor.* Photograph by McCranie.

Dorsal scales are strongly keeled, except those of lowermost row, with paired apical pits, and in 17–17–15 rows. Dorsal coloration of adults consists of dark brown-edged pale crossbands (pale portion about one and one-half scales long on the neck) on a darker ground color. The ground color is dark reddish brown, with the skin between the scales pale blue. The first few pale crossbands are rust red, those following on the anterior quarter of the body are brown grading to yellowish red on the remainder of the body. Scales of the middorsum are edged with bright yellow. The tail is colored as is the posterior portion of the body. The dorsal and lateral surfaces of the head are brown. Lower portions of the supralabials are bright yellow, as are the infralabials. Chinshields are largely white. The venter is bright yellow, grading to yellow-orange posteriorly, which color continues onto the underside of the tail. The iris is pale brown above, brown below. Juveniles have a grayish brown anterior dorsum with dark brown and mahogany red-edged gray crossbands, grading to a brown dorsum with dark gray-edged gray crossbands at midbody and posteriorly. The dorsum of the head is grayish brown. The posterior supralabials are pale yellow, edged dorsally with dark gray. Infralabials are pale yellow and the chinshields are white. The throat is pale yellow grading to pale cream posteriorly. The iris is tan dorsally, gray-brown laterally and ventrally.

**Similar species:** *Dendrophidion percarinatum* has more lightly keeled dorsal scales, a divided cloacal scute, more than 140 subcaudals, and narrower pale crossbands on the neck (less than one dorsal scale row in length). Some juvenile *Masticophis mentovarius* also have a pattern of narrow, transverse bands on the neck, but have smooth dorsal scales and a divided cloacal scute. Juvenile *Mastigodryas melanolomus* have a pattern of pale crossbands, often broken into spots, on a darker ground color, but have smooth dorsal scales and a divided cloacal scute.

**General geographic distribution:** *Dendrophidion vinitor* is found at low and moderate elevations on the Atlantic versant from southern Veracruz, Mexico, disjunctly to western Panama and on the Pacific from west-central Costa Rica to western Colombia.

**Distribution in Honduras:** This snake is known only from 70 to 180 m elevation in the southeastern portion of the Mosquitia.

**Distribution in the Mosquitia:** Gracias a Dios—Caño Awalwás (USNM); Crique Ibantara (USNM); Bodega de Río Tapalwás (USNM); Warunta Tingni Kiamp (USNM).

**Natural history comments:** *Dendrophidion vinitor* occurs in primary evergreen broadleaf forest in the Mosquitia where it is diurnal and terrestrial. Two specimens were active at about midday and late afternoon on the forest floor and two others were sleeping at night on understory vegetation in the forest.

**Remarks:** This species was recently reported from Honduras by Wilson et al. (2003).

*Dipsas bicolor* **(Günther, 1895)**

**Common name(s):** None

**Description (Plate 121):** This snake is medium small (to 482 mm TL) with a long tail (0.32 to 0.37 of TL). The head is distinctly set off from the neck.

**Plate 121.** *Dipsas bicolor.* Photograph by McCranie.

Two scales (a loreal and a preocular) are present between the nasal and the eye. Supralabials number 9 or 10, usually 10, with the fourth, fifth, sixth, and seventh bordering the eye. Infralabials number 10 to 12. The enlarged chinshields are unpaired. No mental groove is present. The pupil is vertically elliptical. Ventrals range from 181 to 202 (181 to 202) and subcaudals from 112 to 122 (111 to 129). The cloacal scute is single. Dorsal scales are smooth, without apical pits, and in 15 rows throughout the body; the vertebral row is not to slightly enlarged. The body is patterned with dark brown rings separated by pale pinkish tan interspaces or pale interspaces with a red dorsal saddle. Scales of the middorsum of the interspaces are edged with brownish orange. The anterior portion of the head is dark brown; this dark head cap is followed by a tan nuchal band.
**Similar species:** *Imantodes cenchoa* is a much more slender snake with a pattern of dark crossbands on a paler ground color and a divided cloacal scute. *Leptodeira septentrionalis* has a dorsal pattern of dark crossbands on a paler ground color, usually 8 supralabials (with the fourth and fifth bordering the eye), and a divided cloacal scute. Snakes of the genus *Oxybelis* (*aeneus*, *brevirostris*, and *fulgidus*) have an elongate, pointed head, a circular pupil, and dorsal scale row numbers that reduce to 13 at the vent. *Rhinobothryum bovallii* has a very large nostril, 21–19–17 dorsal scale rows, which are smooth anteriorly and keeled on rows 9 to 13 posteriorly, and a divided cloacal scute. Snakes of the genus *Sibon* (*annulatus*, *longifrenis*, *nebulatus*, and *Sibon* sp.) have a mental groove and paired chinshields. *Sibon annulatus* also has a dorsal pattern of dark edged pale crossbands or rings. *Sibon longifrenis* also has a dorsal pattern of black-bordered pinkish to rust-colored single or paired blotches on a grayish green to olive green ground color. *Sibon nebulatus* also has a dorsal pattern of irregular, narrow white-outlined dark bands or rings on a pale brown, brownish gray, or dark gray ground color. *Sibon* sp. also lacks red or pink in its dorsal color pattern. *Tropidodipsas sartorii* has 17 weakly keeled dorsal scale rows throughout the body, a mental groove, and paired chinshields.
**General geographic distribution:** *Dipsas bicolor* occurs at low and moderate elevations on the Atlantic versant from northeastern Honduras to eastern Costa Rica and marginally on the Pacific versant in northwestern Costa Rica.
**Distribution in Honduras:** This snake is known from 365 to 1000 m elevation at a few scattered localities in the eastern portion of the country.
**Distribution in the Mosquitia:** El Paraíso—Arenales (CAS). Gracias a Dios—Cabeceras de Río Rus Rus (USNM); Urus Tingni Kiamp (USNM); Warunta Tingni Kiamp (USNM). Olancho—Nueva Esperanza (USNM).
**Natural history comments:** *Dipsas bicolor* is a nocturnal, arboreal inhabitant of recently disturbed and undisturbed evergreen broadleaf forest in the Mosquitia. Three Mosquitia specimens were active in understory vegetation and another was in a palm in the process of eating a snail.

*Drymarchon melanurus* **(A.M.C. Duméril, Bibron, and Duméril, 1854a)**
**Common name(s):** Zumbadora (Spanish); Siakwani* (Miskito)
**Description (Plate 122):** This is a large snake (to 2950 mm TL) with a moderately long tail (0.17 to 0.20 of TL). The head is distinctly set off from the neck. Two scales (a loreal and a preocular) are present between the nasal and the eye. Supralabials number 7 to 9, usually 8, with the fourth and fifth bordering the eye. Infralabials number 7 to 10, usually 8. The enlarged chinshields are paired, a mental groove is present, and the pupil is circular. Ventrals range from 193 to 207 (182 to 215) and subcaudals from 64 to 80 (55 to 88). The cloacal scute is entire. Dorsal scales are smooth, with paired apical pits, and in 19 to 17 rows anteriorly, 17 rows at midbody, and 13 to 15 rows posteriorly. The dorsum is olive green,

**Plate 122.** *Drymarchon melanurus.* Photograph by McCranie.

grading to black on the posterior portion of the body and the tail. A diagonal black mark about one and one-half scales long begins on about the fifth scale row on the neck and extends onto the lateral portion of the ventrals. The anterior venter is pale yellow, with a few black markings on the lateral edges of some of the ventral scales, gradually becoming increasingly infused with black near the vent. The head is olive green, with black pigment on the posterior edges of supralabials 4, 5, 6, and 7. The chin is cream, save for the posterior edges of infralabials 4, 5, and 6, which are black.
**Similar species:** The adults of other rapidly moving, terrestrial racer-like snakes are generally much shorter and more slender. Members of the genus *Dendrophidion* (*percarinatum* and *vinitor*) and *Drymobius* (*margaritiferus* and *melanotropis*) have keeled dorsal scales. In addition, *D. margaritiferus* has a dorsal pattern of pale spots on each of the otherwise dark dorsal scales, and *D. melanotropis* adults have a bright green dorsum and lemon yellow venter. *Masticophis mentovarius* is a fairly large snake, but usually has 7 supralabial scales, with a single one bordering the eye, and lacks an oblique dark mark on the side of the neck. *Mastigodryas melanolomus* lack an oblique dark mark on the side of the neck and has a divided cloacal scute.
**General geographic distribution:** *Drymarchon melanurus* occurs at low, moderate, and occasionally intermediate elevations from south-central Texas, USA, on the Atlantic versant and from southern Sonora, Mexico, on the Pacific versant to northern Venezuela and northwestern Peru. It also occurs on the following islands: Tres Marías, Nayarit, Mexico; and Islas de la Bahía, Honduras (see Remarks).
**Distribution in Honduras:** This species is widespread (near sea level to 1555 m elevation) throughout much of the country, as well as on the Bay Islands.
**Distribution in the Mosquitia:** El Paraíso—1.7 km E of Arenales (USNM). Gracias a Dios—Tánsin (LSUMZ).
**Natural history comments:** *Drymarchon melanurus* is a diurnal, terrestrial species that is known from highly disturbed evergreen broadleaf forest and pine savanna in the Mosquitia. One specimen was crossing a dirt road and the other was in an inundated area.
**Remarks:** This species is usually referred to in the scientific literature as *Drymarchon corais*. Recently, however, that taxon has been considered composite and has been divided into a number of species (Wüster et al., 2001), one of which is *D. melanurus*.

*Drymobius margaritiferus* **(Schlegel, 1837)**
**Common name(s):** Tamagás Verde (Spanish); Aubana (Garífuna)
**Description (Plate 123):** This snake is medium-large (to about 1340 mm TL) with a long tail (0.31 to 0.36 of TL). The head is moderately set off from the neck. Two scales (a loreal and a preocular) are present between the postnasal and the eye. Supralabials number 8 to 10, usually 9, with the fourth, fifth and sixth bordering the eye. Infralabials number 9 to 12, usually 10. The enlarged chinshields are paired, a mental groove is present, and the pupil is circular. Ventrals range from 137 to 153 (137 to 158) and subcaudals from 98 to 129 (98 to 138). The cloacal scute is divided. Dorsal scales are keeled, with paired apical pits, and in 17–17–15 rows. Scales of the dorsum are pale green at the base and dark gray on the remainder; posteriorly, the keels of the dorsal scales become infused with cinnamon so that the scales are tricolored. The head is olive gray, save for the supralabials, which are cream with black posterior borders. The venter of the body and tail is pale yellow with dark gray posterolateral edges. The iris is brown.
**Similar species:** *Drymobius melanotropis* adults have a bright green dorsum and a lemon yellow venter. Members of the genus *Dendrophidion* (*percarinatum* and *vinitor*) have dorsal patterns consisting of pale crossbands on a darker ground

**Plate 123.** *Drymobius margaritiferus*. Photograph by McCranie.

color. *Drymarchon melanurus* is a larger snake with a single cloacal scute, a black diagonal mark on the neck, and a dorsal ground color grading from gray, brown, or gray to dark gray to black posteriorly. *Masticophis mentovarius* usually has 7 supralabial scales, with a single one bordering the eye, and dorsal scales in 19–17–13 rows. *Mastigodryas melanolomus* has smooth dorsal scales and a more-or-less uniform dorsal coloration and a salmon red venter.

**General geographic distribution:** *Drymobius margaritiferus* is found at low, moderate, and intermediate elevations from southern Texas, USA, to northern Colombia on the Atlantic versant and from southern Sonora, Mexico, to central Panama on the Pacific versant. It also occurs on Isla del Maíz Grande, Nicaragua.

**Distribution in Honduras:** This species occurs at low and moderate elevations (near sea level to 1450 m) throughout much of the country.

**Distribution in the Mosquitia:** Gracias a Dios—Awasbila (USNM); Barra Patuca (USNM); Karasangkan (USNM); Mocorón (CF); Rus Rus (UF; USNM); Tánsin (LSUMZ); Tikiraya (UF).

**Natural history comments:** *Drymobius margaritiferus* is found in lightly disturbed to denuded broadleaf forest (both evergreen and swamp forest) and pine savanna in the Mosquitia, where it is diurnal and terrestrial. Specimens we have collected were crawling on the ground in the morning.

*Drymobius melanotropis* **(Cope, 1875)**

**Common name(s):** Tamagás Verde (Spanish); Aubana (Garífuna)

**Description (Plate 124):** This snake is medium-sized (to about 1300 mm TL) with a long tail (0.26 to 0.27 of TL). The head is distinctly set off from the neck. Two scales (a loreal and a preocular) are present between the postnasal and the eye. Supralabials number 9, with the fourth, fifth, and sixth bordering the eye. Infralabials number 9 to 11, usually 10. The enlarged chinshields are paired, a mental groove is present, and the pupil is circular. Ventrals number 154 to 160 (150 to 161) and subcaudals 95 to 97 (90 to 108). The cloacal scute is divided. Dorsal scales are keeled, with paired apical pits, and in 17–17–15 or 17–15–15 rows. The dorsum of adults is green and the venter is yellow (the dorsal coloration invades about the lateral one quarter of the venter). Juveniles have narrow black crossbands or black spots on a green dorsum. Keels of the median 3 dorsal scale rows are black.

**Plate 124.** *Drymobius melanotropis.* Photograph by Gunther Köhler.

**Similar species:** *Drymobius margaritiferus* has a dorsal pattern of pale spots on each of the otherwise dark dorsal scales. Members of the genus *Dendrophidion* (*percarinatum* and *vinitor*) have dorsal patterns consisting of pale crossbands on a darker ground color. *Drymarchon melanurus* is a larger snake with a single cloacal scute, a diagonal black mark on the neck, and a dorsal ground color grading from gray, brown, or gray to dark gray to black posteriorly. *Masticophis mentovarius* usually has 7 supralabial scales, with a single one bordering the eye, and dorsal scales in 19–17–13 rows. *Mastigodryas melanolomus* has smooth dorsal scales and a more-or-less uniform dorsal coloration and a salmon red venter.

**General geographic distribution:** *Drymobius melanotropis* occurs at low and moderate elevations on the Atlantic versant from north-central Honduras to eastern Costa Rica.

**Distribution in Honduras:** This species is known from three localities (about 200 to 1030 m elevation) in eastern Colón and northwestern Olancho.

**Distribution in the Mosquitia:** Colón—along Río Guraska (KU); Cañon Subterráneo del Río Plátano (UNAH; specimen now lost).

**Natural history comments:** *Drymobius melanotropis* is a diurnal, terrestrial inhabitant of primary evergreen broadleaf forest in the Mosquitia. We have not collected this snake in the Mosquitia.

*Enuliophis sclateri* **(Boulenger, 1894)**
**Common name(s):** None
**Description (Plate 125):** This is a small snake (to about 700 mm TL) with an extremely long (0.36 to 0.42 of TL), thick tail that is frequently broken and incomplete. The head is scarcely distinct from the neck. A single scale (an elongate loreal) is present between the postnasal and the eye. Supralabials number 7, rarely 6, with the third and fourth bordering the eye. Infralabials number 7. The enlarged chinshields are paired, a mental groove is present, and the pupil is circular. Ventrals range from 134 to 146 (129 to 151) and subcaudals are 101 (96 to 103) in single Honduran specimen with a complete tail. The cloacal scute is divided. Dorsal scales are smooth, with paired apical pits, and in 15–15–15 rows. The dorsum of the body is uniformly black, except that the ventral coloration extends dorsad to all but the upper tip of dorsal scale row 1. The venter is pale gray (cream in preservative). The head and nuchal region are white, except for the snout and the area around the eye or the anterior portion of the head to the level of the posterior edge of the supraoculars, which are black. The iris is black.
**Similar species:** *Adelphicos quadrivirgatum* has a dorsal pattern of narrow dark longitudinal stripes on a brownish gray to red background and a pair of much enlarged chinshields with the third infralabial scale greatly reduced or absent. *Geophis hoffmanni* has a short tail, relatively few subcaudals (24 to 37), usually 5 supralabials, and a single cloacal scute. *Hydromorphus concolor* is a larger snake with the internasals scales usually fused and 31 to 54 subcaudals. Snakes of the genus *Ninia* (*maculata* and *sebae*) have keeled dorsal scales, a vertically subelliptical pupil, and dark transverse markings on a paler ground color. *Tantilla taeniata* has a pattern of three pale stripes on a darker ground color and lacks a loreal scale (but has a preocular scale). *Tantillita lintoni* lacks a loreal scale but has a preocular scale; in addition, it has 103 to 116 ventrals and 40 to 56 subcaudals. *Urotheca decipiens* and *U. guentheri* have a pair of pale stripes on a dark dorsum, 17 dorsal scale rows throughout the body, and two scales between the postnasal and the eye.
**General geographic distribution:** *Enuliophis sclateri* is found at low and moderate elevations on the Atlantic versant from northeastern Honduras to central Colombia and on the Pacific versant from western Costa Rica to eastern Panama.
**Distribution in Honduras:** This species is known from three low elevation (60 to 190 m) localities in the Río Coco drainage system in the Mosquitia.
**Distribution in the Mosquitia:** Gracias a Dios—Caño Awalwás (UF); Rus Rus (USNM); Bodega de Río Tapalwás (UF).
**Natural history comments:** *Enuliophis sclateri* is a semifossorial inhabitant of primary to lightly disturbed evergreen broadleaf forest (including gallery forest through pine savanna) in the Mosquitia. All Mosquitia specimens were crawling in leaf litter, two at night and two during the day.
**Remarks:** This species was recently reported from Honduras by McCranie et al. (2003b).

**Plate 125.** *Enuliophis sclateri*. Photograph by McCranie.

*Erythrolamprus mimus* **(Cope, "1868" [1869])**
**Common name(s):** Coral (Spanish); Silbiera* (Miskito)
**Description (Plate 126):** This snake is medium-sized (to 650 mm TL) with a relatively short tail (0.13 to 0.16 of TL). The head is scarcely distinct from the neck. Two scales (a loreal and a preocular) are present between the nasal and the eye. Supralabials usually number 7 (5 to 7), with the third and fourth bordering the eye. Infralabials number 7 to 10, usually 9. The enlarged chinshields are paired, a mental groove is present, and the pupil is circular. Ventrals range from 174 to 180 (171 to 199) and subcaudals from 44 to 51 (42 to 56). The cloacal scute is divided. Dorsal scales are smooth, without apical pits, and in 15 rows throughout. The dorsal coloration consists of black rings alternating with very pale greenish blue-edged red rings, the scales of which are heavily tipped with black. Middorsal scales inside the black

**Plate 126.** *Erythrolamprus mimus.* Photograph by Louis Porras.

rings are very pale greenish blue, each tipped with black. The ventral portion of the red rings is smudged with black. The head is black to just behind the eyes. A pale parietal band is suffused with red and is followed by a black nape band. The iris is black.

**Similar species:** Several species with a pattern of red (or orange or white) and black, or red (or orange), black, and yellow rings or dorsal crossbands occur in the Mosquitia. *Dipsas bicolor* lacks a mental groove and has unpaired chinshields and a vertically elliptical pupil; in addition, the pale rings are white with a red dorsal saddle. *Lampropeltis triangulum* has 19 to 23 dorsal scale rows, a single cloacal scute, and solid black rings (lacking white spotting). *Ninia sebae* has keeled dorsal scales in 19 rows throughout the body and transverse crossbands that do not cross the venter. *Oxyrhopus petola* has 19 dorsal scale rows at midbody, a vertically elliptical pupil, and dark crossbands that do not cross the venter. Snakes of the genus *Pliocercus* (*elapoides* and *euryzonus*) have 17 dorsal scale rows throughout the body. *Rhinobothryum bovallii* has a very large nostril, 239 to 246 ventrals, 115 to 125 subcaudals, a vertically elliptical pupil, and 19 dorsal scales at midbody, rows 9 to 13 of which are keeled. *Scaphiodontophis annulatus* has 127 to 166 ventrals, 93 to 149 subcaudals, usually has 17 dorsal scale rows throughout the body, a dorsal pattern of red, black, and yellow, white, or gray bands that do not cross the venter usually only on a variable amount of the anterior portion of the body, and usually a grayish or brownish posterior portion of the body with three dark interrupted, longitudinal stripes. *Tropidodipsas sartorii* has 17 weakly keeled dorsal scale rows throughout the body, a vertically elliptical pupil, a single cloacal scute, and a bicolor pattern. The venomous coral snakes of the genus *Micrurus* have paired fixed fangs in the anterior portion of the mouth and only a single scale between the postnasal and the eye.

**General geographic distribution:** *Erythrolamprus mimus* occurs at low and moderate elevations on the Atlantic versant from northwestern Honduras to central Colombia. It also occurs on the Pacific versant from southeastern Costa Rica to northwestern Ecuador.

**Distribution in Honduras:** This species is known from the northwestern, central, and eastern portions of the country at elevations of 60 to 1400 m.

**Distribution in the Mosquitia:** El Paraíso—near Arenales (LACM). Gracias a Dios—Crique Ibantara (USNM); Mocorón (CF); Rus Rus (USNM); Walpatanta (USNM). Olancho—Quebrada de Las Marías (USNM).

**Natural history comments:** *Erythrolamprus mimus* occurs in primary to disturbed evergreen broadleaf forest in the Mosquitia. It is diurnal and terrestrial. One specimen was taken in a banana patch recently carved from the forest and two others were on the ground near small streams in the forest.

*Geophis hoffmanni* **(W. Peters, 1859)**

**Common name(s):** None

**Description (Plate 127):** This snake is small (to 300 mm TL) with a relatively short tail (0.12 to 0.17 of TL). The head is scarcely set off from the neck.

**Plate 127.** *Geophis hoffmanni.* Photograph by McCranie.

One scale (an elongate loreal) is present between the postnasal and the eye. Supralabials usually number 5, rarely 4, with the third and fourth bordering the eye. Infralabials number 5 or 6, usually 6. The enlarged chinshields are paired, a mental groove is present, and the pupil is circular. Ventrals range from 115 to 127 (115 to 135) and subcaudals from 25 to 33 (24 to 37). The cloacal scute is single. Dorsal scales are smooth, except a few scales are keeled above the vent in males, with paired apical pits, and in 15 rows throughout the body. The dorsum is dark gray. The venter is pale gray. The underside of the tail is dark gray. A pale nuchal collar is present in juveniles, gradually disappearing or becoming obscure as the snake grows older.
**Similar species:** *Adelphicos quadrivirgatum* has a lined dorsum, a divided cloacal scute, and an enlarged chin shield with the third infralabial reduced or absent. *Enuliophis sclateri* has 129 to 151 ventrals and 96 to 103 subcaudals, and usually has 7 supralabials. *Hydromorphus concolor* is a larger snake that has the internasal scales usually fused, a divided cloacal scute, and 157 to 186 ventrals. Snakes of the genus *Ninia* (*maculata* and *sebae*) have keeled dorsal scales, a vertically subelliptical pupil, and a brown or dull red dorsum with dark transverse bands. *Tantilla taeniata* has a pattern of three pale stripes on a darker ground color, a preocular and no loreal, and a divided cloacal scute. *Tantillita lintoni* has a preocular and no loreal and a divided cloacal scute. *Rhadinaea decorata*, *Urotheca decipiens*, and *U. guentheri* have stripes on the body, 17 dorsal scale rows throughout the body, and two scales between the postnasal and the eye.
**General geographic distribution:** *Geophis hoffmanni* is found at low and moderate elevations on the Atlantic versant from northeastern Honduras to central Panama and on the Pacific versant from west-central Costa Rica to central Panama.
**Distribution in Honduras:** This species occurs at low elevations (200 to 600 m) in the eastern portion of the country.
**Distribution in the Mosquitia:** Colón—Empalme Río Chilmeca (was in UNAH, now lost); Quebrada Machín (USNM). El Paraíso—Arenales (CAS; LACM). Gracias a Dios—Rus Rus (USNM); Bodega de Río Tapalwás (USNM); Urus Tingni Kiamp (USNM); Warunta Tingni Kiamp (USNM). Olancho—Mata de Maíz (UNAH).

**Natural history comments:** *Geophis hoffmanni* is a semifossorial, diurnal inhabitant of undisturbed evergreen broadleaf forest in the Mosquitia. Specimens were collected inside and under rotten logs, under rocks, and in decaying root masses. This species is abundant in the environs of Urus Tingni and Warunta Tingni Kiamps, as about 75 individuals were seen within the course of three short trips to those areas.

*Hydromorphus concolor* **W. Peters, 1859**
**Common name(s):** Li-pyutka* (Miskito)
**Description (Plate 128):** This snake is medium-sized (to 797 mm TL) with a relatively short tail (0.13 to 0.18 of TL). The head is barely set off from the neck. The nostrils are dorsolaterally placed. There are 1 or 2 scales (a loreal and sometimes a preocular) between the nasal and the eye. Internasal scales are usually fused. The supralabials usually number 6, occasionally 5 or 7, with the third bordering the eye. Infralabials number 6 to 9, usually 8 or 9. The enlarged chinshields are paired and a mental groove is present (rarely evident only between first pair of infralabials). The pupil of this species was said to be circular by Savage (2002), but the Mosquitia specimens have vertically subelliptical pupils. Ventrals range from 160 to 177 (157 to 186) and subcaudals from 37 to 51 (31 to 54). The cloacal scute is divided. Dorsal scales are smooth, with paired apical pits (Savage, 2002), or without apical pits (the Mosquitia specimens), and usually in 19–17–15 or 17–17–15 rows, but ranging from 15 to 17 rows at midbody. The dorsum is dark brownish olive, with darker dashes on row 6. The venter is

**Plate 128.** *Hydromorphus concolor.* Photograph by McCranie.

tan with grayish brown midventral blotches. The underside of the tail is grayish brown.
**Similar species:** *Adelphicos quadrivirgatum* is a smaller snake that has a lined dorsum, enlarged chinshields, with the third infralabial reduced or absent, and usually 7 supralabials, with the third and fourth bordering the eye. *Enuliophis sclateri* is a smaller snake that has a white head band, 96 to 103 subcaudals, and 15 dorsal scales throughout the body. *Geophis hoffmanni* is a smaller snake that has 115 to 135 ventrals, a single cloacal scute, and 15 dorsal scales throughout the body. Snakes of the genus *Ninia* (*maculata* and *sebae*) are smaller snakes that have keeled dorsal scales and a brown or red dorsum with dark transverse bands. *Tantilla lintoni* is a much smaller snake with 103 to 116 ventrals and 40 to 56 subcaudals. *Tretanorhinus nigroluteus* has 127 to 152 ventrals, 56 to 82 subcaudals, 21 dorsal scale rows at midbody, and usually 8 supralabials. All of these above mentioned species also have paired internasal scales.
**General geographic distribution:** *Hydromorphus concolor* occurs at low and moderate elevations on the Atlantic versant from eastern Guatemala to central Panama and on the Pacific versant from central and west-central Costa Rica to central Panama.
**Distribution in Honduras:** This species is known from few, widely disjunct localities from 100 to 1400 m elevation in the northern portion of the country.
**Distribution in the Mosquitia:** Gracias a Dios—Urus Tingni Kiamp (USNM). Olancho—Quebrada El Guásimo (USNM).
**Natural history comments:** *Hydromorphus concolor* is an aquatic inhabitant of streams in undisturbed evergreen broadleaf forest in the Mosquitia, although its distribution appears to be spotty. This species is active at night when it can be seen in slower moving parts of streams.

*Imantodes cenchoa* **(Linnaeus, 1758)**
**Common name(s):** Bejuquillo (Spanish); Andris Taya* (Miskito); Üwuri** (Garífuna)
**Description (Plate 129):** This snake is moderate-sized (to 1250 mm TL), elongate and slender, with a long tail (0.28 to 0.35 of TL). The head is very distinctly set off from the neck. Two scales (a loreal and a preocular) are present between the postnasal and the eye. Supralabials number 7 to 9, usually 8, with the fourth and fifth, third, fourth, and fifth, or fourth, fifth, and sixth bordering the eye. Infralabials number 9 to 12, usually 10. The enlarged chinshields are paired and a mental groove is present. The pupil is vertically elliptical. Ventrals range from 228 to 261 (228 to 288) and subcaudals from 134 to 170 (134 to 195). The cloacal scute is divided. Dorsal scales are smooth, without apical pits, and in 19–17–17, 17–17–17, or 17–17–15 rows. The vertebral dorsal scale row is conspicuously enlarged, about 3 to 5 times the size of the lateral body scales. The dorsum of the body and tail is beige with dark brown-outlined brown blotches. The venter is pale pinkish tan with extensive dark brown flecking. The head is brown and the iris olive green.

**Plate 129.** *Imantodes cenchoa*. Photograph by Townsend.

**Similar species:** Only a few snakes in the Mosquitia even approach *I. cenchoa* in degree of slenderness. *Dipsas bicolor* lacks a mental groove and has unpaired, rectangular chinshields; in addition, the supralabials usually number 10, the dorsal scales are in 15 rows throughout the body, and the cloacal scute is single. *Leptodeira septentrionalis* has 170 to 211 ventrals, 60 to 107 subcaudals, and usually 21 or 23 dorsal scale rows at midbody. Snakes of the genus *Leptophis* (*ahaetulla*, *mexicanus*, and *nebulosus*) have an

elongate head, a striped or uniform dorsal pattern, keeled dorsal scales, and a circular pupil. Snakes of the genus *Oxybelis* (*aeneus*, *brevirostris*, and *fulgidus*) have an elongate, pointed head, a circular pupil, and a more-or-less uniform gray, brown, or green dorsum. Snakes of the genus *Sibon* (*annulatus*, *longifrenis*, *nebulatus*, and *Sibon* sp.) have 15 scale rows throughout the body and a single cloacal scute.
**General geographic distribution:** *Imantodes cenchoa* occurs at low, moderate, and intermediate elevations on the Atlantic versant from southern Tamaulipas, Mexico, to northeastern Argentina and on the Pacific versant from southeastern Chiapas, Mexico, to Guatemala and from northwestern Costa Rica (exclusive of the Pacific lowlands in Costa Rica) to northwestern Ecuador. It also occurs on Isla de Utila, Honduras, Isla del Venado, Nicaragua, Isla del Rey, Panama, and Trinidad and Tobago.
**Distribution in Honduras:** This species is widely distributed in the northern portion of the country and is known from near sea level to 1620 m elevation.
**Distribution in the Mosquitia:** Colón—Quebrada Machín (USNM). Gracias a Dios—Auka Kiamp (USNM); Awasbila (USNM); Laguna Bacalar (BMNH); Crique Curamaira (USNM); between Ríos Patuca and Warunta (MCZ); Swabila (UF); Tánsin (LSUMZ); Bodega de Río Tapalwás (UF; USNM); Urus Tingni Kiamp (USNM). OLANCHO: Caobita (USNM); Quebrada El Guásimo (USNM).
**Natural history comments:** *Imantodes cenchoa* is found in primary to lightly disturbed evergreen broadleaf forest and broadleaf swamp forest in the Mosquitia. It is nocturnal and arboreal and is found on understory vegetation in the forest, both well away from streams and along streams.

*Lampropeltis triangulum* **(Lacepède, 1789)**
**Common name(s):** Coral (Spanish); Silbiera* (Miskito)
**Description (Plate 130):** This is a large snake (to almost 2000 mm TL) with a relatively short tail (0.13 to 0.17 of TL). The head is slightly distinct from the neck. Two scales (usually a loreal [rarely absent] and a preocular] are usually present between the postnasal and the eye. Supralabials number 6 to 9, usually 7, with the third and fourth bordering the eye. Infralabials number 7 to 11, usually 9. The enlarged chinshields are paired, a mental groove is present, and the pupil is circular.

**Plate 130.** *Lampropeltis triangulum.* Photograph by McCranie.

Ventrals range from 223 to 242 (152 to 244) and subcaudals from 49 to 60 (31 to 63). The cloacal scute is single. Dorsal scales are smooth, with paired apical pits, and usually in 19 to 23 rows at the neck and midbody and 17 or 19 at the vent. The dorsal coloration consists of tricolor rings of red or reddish orange, black, and cream or yellow. The longer red rings are bounded by narrower black rings that are separated by cream or yellow rings. The head is black with pale snout and nuchal bands.
**Similar species:** *Lampropeltis triangulum* is one of several species with a pattern of red (or orange) and black rings, or red (or orange), black, and yellow rings that occur in the Mosquitia. *Dipsas bicolor* lacks a mental groove and has unpaired chinshields and a vertically elliptical pupil. *Erythrolamprus mimus* has 15 dorsal scale rows at midbody, a divided cloacal scute, and white spotting on the black rings. *Ninia sebae* has keeled dorsal scales in 19 rows throughout the body, a vertically subelliptical pupil, and transverse crossbands that do not cross the venter. *Oxyrhopus petola* has dark crossbands that do not cross the venter and a vertically elliptical pupil. Snakes of the genus *Pliocercus* (*elapoides* and *euryzonus*) have 17 dorsal scale rows throughout the body. *Rhinobothryum bovallii* has a very large nostril, a vertically elliptical pupil, 115 to 125 subcaudals, and rows 9 to 13 on the dorsum keeled. *Scaphiodontophis annulatus* has 17 or 15 dorsal scale rows at midbody, 127 to 166 ventrals, 93 to 149 subcaudals, a dorsal pattern of red, black, and yellow, white, or gray bands that do not cross the venter usually only on a variable amount of the anterior portion of

the body, and usually a grayish or brownish posterior portion of the body with three dark interrupted, longitudinal stripes. *Tropidodipsas sartorii* have 17 weakly keeled dorsal scale rows throughout the body and a bicolor pattern. The species of venomous coral snakes of the genus *Micrurus* have a pair of fixed fangs in the anterior portion of the mouth and 15 dorsal scale rows throughout the body.

**General geographic distribution:** *Lampropeltis triangulum* occurs at low, moderate, and intermediate elevations on both versants from southeastern Canada, much of about the eastern three-quarters of the United States, and much of Mexico (exclusive of Baja California, all of the Sonoran Desert, and most of the Chihuahuan Desert, but including the Islas Tres Marías) to north-central Venezuela and northwestern Ecuador.

**Distribution in Honduras:** This species is known from low and moderate elevations (near sea level to 1370 m) throughout much of the country (excluding the southwestern, extreme southern, and extreme eastern portions).

**Distribution in the Mosquitia:** Olancho—Caobita (USNM).

**Natural history comments:** *Lampropeltis triangulum* is a diurnal and nocturnal terrestrial species that has been taken in lightly disturbed evergreen broadleaf forest in the Mosquitia. The single Mosquitia specimen was crawling on the forest floor in the early afternoon.

*Leptodeira annulata* **(Linnaeus, 1758)**

**Common name(s):** Sulkat* (Miskito)

**Description (Plate131):** This snake is medium-sized (to 1038 mm TL) with a moderately long tail (0.18 to 0.26 of TL). The head is distinctly set off from the neck. Two scales (a loreal and a preocular) are present between the postnasal and the eye. Supralabials number 7 to 9, usually 8, with the fourth and fifth bordering the eye. Infralabials number 9 to 12, usually 10. The enlarged chinshields are paired and a mental groove is present. The pupil is vertically elliptical. Ventrals range from 160 to 175 (151 to 204) and subcaudals from 62 to 82 (54 to 102). The cloacal scute is divided. Dorsal scales are smooth (males occasionally with weak keels in the supracloacal region), with paired apical pits, and in 17 to 25 rows at midbody and 11 to 19 rows at the vent. The dorsal coloration varies from orange with a slight brownish tinge to medium brown. The dorsal

**Plate 131.** *Leptodeira annulata.* Photograph by McCranie.

blotches (21 to 56) are black, narrowly outlined with pale yellowish green, and do not extend to the ventrals. Brown lateral spots alternate with the dark dorsal blotches. The venter is cream to pale creamy orange. The head is brown above, with some very dark brown blotching and a dark brown temporal stripe. The chin is white. The iris is olive tan.

**Similar species:** *Leptodeira nigrofasciata* has a dorsal pattern of 21 or fewer dark crossbands, which extend to the lateral edges of the ventral scales. *Leptodeira septentrionalis* has more than186 ventral scales in Honduran specimens. Juvenile *Chironius grandisquamis* have 10 dorsal scale rows at midbody. *Imantodes cenchoa* is extremely slender with a blunt head well set off from the extremely slender neck, 228 to 288 ventrals, and 134 to 195 subcaudals. *Oxybelis aeneus* has an elongate, pointed head and a gray to brown dorsum without dark dorsal blotches. *Pseustes poecilonotus* has 181 to 220 ventrals, a single cloacal scute, 95 to 147 subcaudals, and a circular pupil. *Xenodon rabdocephalus* has a single cloacal scute, a circular pupil, and ventral blotching and peppering.

**General geographic distribution:** *Leptodeira annulata* occurs at low and moderate elevations on the Atlantic versant from central Tamaulipas, Mexico, to northeastern Argentina and southeastern Brazil and on the Pacific versant from southwestern Guerrero, Mexico, to southwestern Colombia. It also occurs on Trinidad and Tobago, several islands off the coast of Venezuela, and Isla del Rey, Panama.

**Distribution in Honduras:** This species is

widespread throughout much of the country. It is known from near sea level to 1530 m elevation.
**Distribution in the Mosquitia:** Gracias a Dios—Barra Patuca (USNM); Canco (UF); Karasangkan (USNM); Kokotá (LSUMZ); Mocorón (UTA); Puerto Lempira (CAS); Rus Rus (UF; USNM); Tánsin (LSUMZ).
**Natural history comments:** *Leptodeira annulata* is a nocturnal arboreal and terrestrial inhabitant of pine savanna and freshwater marshes in the Mosquitia. One specimen was found in a pile of lumber and another in a pile of tin beneath stilt houses. Others were crawling on the ground near marshy or swampy areas.

*Leptodeira nigrofasciata* **(Günther, 1868)**
**Common name(s):** None
**Description (Plate 132):** This snake is medium small (to 581 mm TL) with a moderately long tail (0.23 to 0.38 of TOL; Savage, 2002). The head is distinctly set off from the neck. Two scales (a loreal and a preocular) are present between the postnasal and the eye. Supralabials number 7 to 9, usually 8, with the fourth and fifth bordering the eye. Infralabials number 9 to 11, usually 10. The enlarged chinshields are paired and a mental groove is present. The pupil is vertically elliptical. Ventrals range from 167 to 175 (161 to 196) and subcaudals from 57 to 74 (50 to 76). The cloacal scute is divided. Dorsal scales are smooth, with paired apical pits, and usually in 19–19–17 rows, but sometimes in 17–17–17, 17–19–17, or 19–19–15 rows. The dorsum of the body is cream to grayish tan to yellow with broad dark brown to black crossbands extending to the lateral edges of the ventrals. The venter is otherwise cream to pale grayish tan. The head is dark brown to black to the posterior edge of the parietals. A pale nuchal band separates the head cap from the first crossband on the body.
**Similar species:** *Leptodeira annulata* and *L. septentrionalis* have dorsal patterns of 20 or more dark blotches, which do not extend to the venter. Juvenile *Chironius grandisquamis* have 10 dorsal scale rows at midbody. *Imantodes cenchoa* is extremely slender with a blunt head well set off from the extremely slender neck, 228 to 288 ventrals, and 134 to 195 subcaudals. *Oxybelis aeneus* has an elongate, pointed head, a circular pupil, and a gray to brown dorsum without dark dorsal blotches. *Pseustes poecilonotus* has 181 to 220 ventrals, a single cloacal scute, 95 to 147 subcaudals, and a circular pupil. *Xenodon rabdocephalus* has a single cloacal scute, a circular pupil, and ventral blotching and peppering.
**General geographic distribution:** *Leptodeira nigrofasciata* is known from low and moderate elevations on the Pacific versant from south-central Guerrero, Mexico, to northwestern Costa Rica. It also occurs on the Atlantic versant in interior valleys in Chiapas, Mexico, Guatemala, and Honduras.
**Distribution in Honduras:** This species occurs in open habitats in the central and southern portions of the country. It is known from sea level to 1300 m elevation.
**Distribution in the Mosquitia:** El Paraíso—near Arenales (LACM 20486).
**Natural history comments:** The only Mosquitia locality for *Leptodeira nigrofasciata* is in an area of denuded evergreen broadleaf forest. We have not encountered this species in the Mosquitia.

**Plate 132.** *Leptodeira nigrofasciata*. Photograph by Louis Porras.

*Leptodeira septentrionalis* **(Kennicott, *in* Baird, 1859)**
**Common name(s):** None
**Description (Plate 133):** This snake is medium-sized to medium large (to 1055 mm TL) with a moderately long tail (0.22 to 0.30 of TL). The head is distinctly set off from the neck. Two scales (a loreal and a preocular) are present between the postnasal and the eye. Supralabials number 7 to 9, usually 8, with the fourth and fifth bordering the eye. Infralabials number 9 to 12, usually 10. The enlarged chinshields are paired and a mental groove is present. The pupil is vertically elliptical. Ventrals range from 189 to 206 (170 to 211) and subcaudals from 83 to 106 (60 to 107). The cloacal

**Plate 133.** *Leptodeira septentrionalis.* Photograph by McCranie.

scute is divided. Dorsal scales are smooth, with paired apical pits, and usually in 21 or 23 rows at midbody and 15 or 17 rows at the vent. The dorsum of the body is cinnamon brown, with a series (20 to 70) of dark brown dorsal blotches. The venter is pale pinkish tan. The top of the head is brown and the chin pale cream. The iris is copper.
**Similar species:** *Leptodeira annulata* has fewer than 186 ventral scales in Honduran specimens. *Leptodeira nigrofasciata* has a dorsal pattern of 21 or fewer dark blotches, which extend to the lateral edges of the venter. Juvenile *Chironius grandisquamis* have 10 dorsal scale rows at midbody. *Imantodes cenchoa* is extremely slender with a blunt head well set off from the extremely slender neck, has 228 to 288 ventrals, 134 to 195 subcaudals, and 17 dorsal scale rows at midbody. *Oxybelis aeneus* has an elongate, pointed head, a circular pupil, and a gray to brown dorsum without dark dorsal blotches. *Pseustes poecilonotus* has a single cloacal scute and a circular pupil. *Xenodon rabdocephalus* has a single cloacal scute, a circular pupil, and ventral blotching and peppering.
**General geographic distribution:** *Leptodeira septentrionalis* is found at low, moderate, and intermediate elevations on the Atlantic versant from southern Texas, USA, to Peru. It is also discontinuously distributed on the Pacific versant from southern Sinaloa, Mexico, to Peru (see Remarks).
**Distribution in Honduras:** This species occurs in the western and northern portions of the country and is known from near sea level to 1940 m elevation. It is also known from Cayo Cochino Pequeño off the north coast.
**Distribution in the Mosquitia:** Colón—Quebrada Machín (USNM). Gracias a Dios—Caño Awalwás (USNM); Kaska Tingni (USNM); Mocorón (CF); Bodega de Río Tapalwás (USNM); Urus Tingni Kiamp (USNM); Warunta Tingni Kiamp (USNM). Olancho—Quebrada de Las Marías (USNM).
**Natural history comments:** *Leptodeira septentrionalis* is a nocturnal, arboreal inhabitant of disturbed and undisturbed evergreen broadleaf forest in the Mosquitia. This species seems to be most active on rainy nights when it can be seen in understory vegetation around ponds and along streams apparently searching for frogs or their eggs to eat.
**Remarks:** More than one species may be included within the general range as given above. Savage (2002) briefly discussed this matter.

*Leptophis ahaetulla* **(Linnaeus, 1758)**
**Common name(s):** Tamagás Verde (Spanish); Aubana (Garífuna)
**Description (Plate 134):** This is a large snake (to 2243+ mm TL) with a long tail (0.33 to 0.40 of TL). The head is distinctly set off from the neck. Two scales (a preocular and a lateral extension of each prefrontal) are present between the postnasal and the eye. Supralabials number 7 to 10, usually 8, with the fourth and fifth bordering the eye. Infralabials number 7 to 12, usually 10 or 11. The enlarged chinshields are paired, a mental groove is present, and the pupil is circular. Ventrals range from 165 to 178 (147 to 183) and subcaudals from 163 to 182 (137 to 189). The cloacal scute is divided. Dorsal scales are keeled, save for the first scale

**Plate 134.** *Leptophis ahaetulla.* Photograph by McCranie.

row and the middorsal scale row, with a single apical pit, and in 15–15–11 rows. The dorsum is leaf green, with the keels of rows 6 through 10 black. The venter is pale green. The head is leaf green dorsally and dorsolaterally. Pre- and postocular stripes are black and do not reach the tip of the snout or extend onto the neck. The supralabials are pale green, save for a suffusion of yellow below the eye. The eye is bright yellow. A single juvenile specimen from the Mosquitia (Caobita, Olancho) differs from the above color description in that the dorsal surfaces were olive green with a bronze middorsal stripe.
**Similar species:** *Leptophis mexicanus* has a loreal scale and a dorsal pattern of a bronze middorsal area flanked by a yellow and then a metallic green stripe below which is a mottled yellow, green, and black stripe. *Leptophis nebulosus* has a golden bronze middorsum flanked by a greenish blue lateral stripe. *Drymobius melanotropis* has 17–17–15 dorsal scale rows and a loreal scale. *Oxybelis brevirostris* has a very elongate, pointed head, a single cloacal scute, and 15–15–13 dorsal scale rows. *Oxybelis fulgidus* has a very elongate, pointed head and 17–17–13 dorsal scale rows.
**General geographic distribution:** *Leptophis ahaetulla* is found at low, moderate, and occasionally intermediate elevations on the Atlantic versant from central Veracruz, Mexico, to northeastern Argentina and southern Brazil and on the Pacific versant in Oaxaca, Mexico, and from northwestern Costa Rica to west-central Ecuador. It also occurs on Trinidad and Tobago and several small islands off the coast of Venezuela.
**Distribution in Honduras:** This species occurs in the northern, eastern, and south-central portions of the country and is known from near sea level to 1680 m elevation.
**Distribution in the Mosquitia:** Colón—Anzuelo Bridge (BMNH). El Paraíso—Arenales (LACM). Gracias a Dios—Río Coco (USNM); Karasangkan (UF); Kaska Tingni (USNM); Mocorón (CF); Palacios (BMNH); Rus Rus (UF; USNM); Tikiraya (UF). Olancho—confluence of Ríos Aner and Wampú (USNM); Caobita (SMF).
**Natural history comments:** *Leptophis ahaetulla* is a diurnal, arboreal and terrestrial inhabitant of disturbed and undisturbed evergreen broadleaf forest and disturbed broadleaf swamp forest in the Mosquitia. Five snakes were collected on the morning of 28 July 2001 while actively preying on frogs, especially *Smilisca baudinii*, that were sleeping on understory vegetation in and around a shallow pond at Kaska Tingni, Gracias a Dios. Several others were seen around this pond at the same time, but were not collected. Another was crawling in understory vegetation next to a river and yet another was crawling on the forest floor.

*Leptophis mexicanus* **A.M.C. Duméril, Bibron, and Duméril, 1854a**
**Common name(s):** Tamagás Verde (Spanish); Aubana (Garífuna)
**Description (Plate 135):** This snake is medium large (to about 1270 mm TL) with a long tail (0.38 to 0.43 of TL). The head is distinctly set off from the neck. Two scales (a loreal and a preocular) are present between the postnasal and the eye. Supralabials number 8 or 9, usually 8, with the fourth and fifth bordering the eye. Infralabials number 9 to 11, usually 10. The enlarged chinshields are paired, a mental groove is present, and the pupil is circular. Ventrals range from 145 to 161 (145 to 183) and subcaudals from 141 to 166 (140 to 181). The cloacal scute is divided. Dorsal scales are keeled (except for the outer row), with a single apical pit, in 15–15–11 rows. The dorsum of the head is iridescent emerald green grading to bronze on the middorsum of the body. The middorsal stripe is edged with iridescent blue-green. Scales of rows 3 to 5 are dull gold with black tips and blue-green bases, creating the impression of an irregular stripe. The black markings of this stripe coalesce on the neck to form a solid black stripe, which continues onto the temporal and preocular regions of the head.

**Plate 135.** *Leptophis mexicanus*. Photograph by McCranie.

Scales of rows 1 and 2 are pale orange, although the upper edge of the scales of row 2 is black. The venter is pale bronze grading to white on the chin. The underside of the tail is pale golden bronze. The iris is yellow dorsally, black ventrally, the latter portion continuous with the preocular and temporal stripes.

**Similar species:** *Leptophis ahaetulla* lacks a loreal scale and usually has a green dorsum with the keels of a variable number of the middorsal scales black. *Leptophis nebulosus* lacks a loreal and has a narrow pre- and postocular dark stripe that does not reach the tip of the snout nor continue beyond the neck. *Drymobius melanotropis* has 17–17–15 dorsal scale rows and a green dorsum with black keels on the three median dorsal scale rows. *Oxybelis brevirostris* has an elongate, pointed head, a single cloacal scute, 15–15–13 dorsal scale rows, and a uniformly green dorsum. *Oxybelis fulgidus* has an elongate, pointed head, 17–17–13 dorsal scale rows, and a uniformly green dorsum.

**General geographic distribution:** *Leptophis mexicanus* occurs at low and moderate elevations on the Atlantic versant from southern Tamaulipas, Mexico, to north-central Costa Rica and discontinuously on the Pacific versant from eastern Oaxaca, Mexico, to northwestern Costa Rica. It also occurs on Isla de Utila, Honduras, Islas del Maíz Grande, Nicaragua, and on several islands off the coast of Belize.

**Distribution in Honduras:** This species is widespread through much of the country (known from near sea level to 1600 m elevation), save for the extreme southern and southwestern portions. It also occurs on Isla de Utila.

**Distribution in the Mosquitia:** Gracias a Dios—Barra Patuca (USNM); Canco (UF); Crique Canco (USNM); Cauquira (UF); Kokotá (LSUMZ); Krahkra (USNM); Mocorón (UTA); Puerto Lempira (UTA); Rus Rus (UF; USNM); Tikiraya (UF); Walpatá (LSUMZ); Wampusirpe (LSUMZ).

**Natural history comments:** *Leptophis mexicanus* is an arboreal, diurnal inhabitant of disturbed evergreen broadleaf forest, disturbed broadleaf swamp forest, pine savanna, freshwater marshes, and coastal strand in the Mosquitia. Most individuals we have seen were active in low vegetation, although one was on the ground in a marshy area and had a *Leptodactylus fragilis* in its mouth. Another was in a rotten coconut palm stump.

*Leptophis nebulosus* **Oliver, 1942**

**Common name(s):** Tamagás Verde (Spanish); Aubana (Garífuna)

**Description (Plate 136):** This snake is medium-sized (to 854 mm TL) with a long tail (0.39 to 0.40 of TL). The head is distinctly set off from the neck. Two scales (a preocular and a lateral extension of each prefrontal) are present between the postnasal and the eye. Supralabials number 8 or 9, usually 8, with the fourth and fifth bordering the eye. Infralabials number 10 or 11, usually 10. The enlarged chinshields are paired, a mental groove is present, and the pupil is circular. Ventrals range from 146 to 151 (146 to 160) and subcaudals from 134 to 146 (134 to 151). The cloacal scute is divided. Dorsal scales are keeled (except for outer row), with a single apical pit, and in 15–15–11 rows. The top of the head is dull golden bronze mottled with emerald green, more predominantly so on the temporal region. A thin black postocular stripe begins on the lower postocular and continues along the junction of the temporals and supralabials to the anterior portion of the neck. The middorsum of the body is dull golden bronze with turquoise blue at the scale bases anteriorly, the turquoise blue becoming less prominent posteriorly. Scales of dorsal rows 1 and 2 and the venter are pale copper, grading to silver white on the chin. The iris is mustard yellow, with gray smudges antero- and posteromedially, in line with the dark postocular stripe.

**Similar species:** *Leptophis ahaetulla* usually has a green dorsum with the keels of a variable number of the middorsal scales black. *Leptophis mexicanus* has a loreal scale and a dorsal pattern of a bronze middorsal area flanked by a yellow and then a

**Plate 136.** *Leptophis nebulosus*. Photograph by McCranie.

metallic green stripe below which is a mottled yellow, green, and black stripe. *Drymobius melanotropis* has 17–17–15 dorsal scale rows, a loreal scale, and a green dorsum with black keels on the three median dorsal scale rows. *Oxybelis brevirostris* has an elongate, pointed head, a single cloacal scute, and 15–15–13 dorsal scale rows. *Oxybelis fulgidus* has a very elongate, pointed head, 17–17–13 dorsal scale rows, and a uniformly green dorsum.
**General geographic distribution:** *Leptophis nebulosus* occurs at low and moderate elevations on the Atlantic versant from northeastern Honduras to north-central Panama.
**Distribution in Honduras:** This species is known from two localities near sea level along the northeastern coastline.
**Distribution in the Mosquitia:** Gracias a Dios—Barra Patuca (USNM); Krahkra (USNM).
**Natural history comments:** We collected a single specimen of *Leptophis nebulosus* at night as it was sleeping in a thorn palm in an area of heavily disturbed broadleaf swamp forest. The other Mosquitia specimen was apparently taken in coastal strand. This species is diurnal.
**Remarks:** This species was known from Honduras from a single specimen collected in 1891 until Wilson et al. (2003) reported a second specimen from the Río Kruta Biological Reserve.

*Masticophis mentovarius* **(A.M.C. Duméril, Bibron, and Duméril, 1854a)**
**Common name(s):** Zumbadora (Spanish); Makchikcha, Siakwani* (Miskito)
**Description (Plate 137):** This is a large snake (to 2527 mm TL) with a long tail (0.25 to 0.26 of TL). The head is distinctly set off from the neck. Two scales (a loreal and a preocular) are present between the postnasal and the eye. Supralabials number 6 to 8, usually 7 or 8, with the fourth or the fourth and fifth bordering the eye. Infralabials number 8 to 11, usually 10. The enlarged chinshields are paired, a mental groove is present, and the pupil is circular. Ventrals range from 184 to 201 (166 to 205) and subcaudals from 104 to 126 (95 to 126). The cloacal scute is divided. Dorsal scales are smooth, with paired apical pits, and in 19–17–13 rows. The dorsum of the body is grayish brown to brown. The venter is pale yellow anteriorly, grading to pinkish orange on the posterior third of the body. The head is pale brown dorsally. Supralabials are pale brown on the upper portion,

**Plate 137.** *Masticophis mentovarius.* Photograph by McCranie.

cream below with black flecking on the lower portion. The chin is cream. and the iris bronze with a gold ring around the pupil.
**Similar species:** *Chironius grandisquamis* has 10 dorsal scale rows at midbody. Adult *Clelia clelia* have a uniformly shiny dark gray to bluish black dorsum, a vertically elliptical pupil, and 57 to 93 subcaudals. *Drymarchon melanurus* has a single cloacal scute, 55 to 88 subcaudals, and an oblique dark stripe on the neck. *Mastigodryas melanolomus* has usually 9 supralabials and the dorsal scales in 17–17–15 rows. *Oxybelis aeneus* has an elongate, pointed head, a very slender body and 158 to 203 subcaudals. *Pseustes poecilonotus* has a single cloacal scute and 19 or more dorsal scale rows at midbody.
**General geographic distribution:** *Masticophis mentovarius* occurs at low and moderate elevations on the Atlantic versant from southern San Luis Potosí and northern Veracruz, Mexico, to north-central Belize and on the Pacific versant from southern Sonora, Mexico, to west-central Costa Rica. Disjunct populations occur on the Atlantic versant in Guatemala, Honduras, Nicaragua, northeastern Colombia and adjacent Venezuela, and north-central Venezuela and on the Pacific versant in west-central Panama. It also occurs on the Islas Tres Marías, Mexico, and Isla Margarita, Venezuela, and an isolated record is reported from eastern Chihuahua, Mexico.
**Distribution in Honduras:** This species is known from open habitats (from 40 to 1320 m elevation) in the eastern three-quarters of the country.
**Distribution in the Mosquitia:** Gracias a Dios—Mocorón (USNM; UTA); Cabeceras de Río Rus Rus (USNM); Suhi (USNM).

**Natural history comments:** *Masticophis mentovarius* is a diurnal, terrestrial inhabitant of pine savanna in the Mosquitia. One was crawling on the ground near the beginning of the transition zone from pine savanna to evergreen broadleaf forest and another was active in open pine savanna.

*Mastigodryas melanolomus* **(Cope, 1868)**
**Common name(s):** Siakwani* (Miskito)
**Description (Plate 138):** This snake is medium large (to about 1500 mm TL) with a long tail (0.25 to 0.30 of TL). The head is moderately set off from the neck. Two scales (a loreal and a preocular) are present between the postnasal and the eye. Supralabials number 8 to 10, usually 9, with the fourth, fifth, and sixth bordering the eye. Infralabials number 8 to 11, usually 10. The enlarged chinshields are paired, a mental groove is present, and the pupil is circular. Ventrals range from 177 to 193 (160 to 195) and subcaudals from 91 to 114 (85 to 136). The cloacal scute is divided. Dorsal scales are smooth, with paired apical pits, and in 17–17–15 rows. The dorsum of the adults is brown. The venter is peach colored, with the chin slightly paler, closer to salmon in color. Supralabials are cream with salmon smudging. The iris is rust red. Coloration of juveniles consists of alternating dark brown-edged brown dorsal and lateral blotches on a pale brown background. The pale interspaces decrease in length and intensity posteriorly. The head is brown above with dark brown pre- and postocular stripes. Supralabials are pale cream with brown edging. The venter is salmon pink, with a pair of smudged brown lines on the throat, grading to pale salmon pink on the underside of the tail. The chin is white with brown spotting.

**Plate 138.** *Mastigodryas melanolomus.* Photograph by McCranie.

**Similar species:** A number of slender, rapidly moving, terrestrial racer-like snakes occur in the Mosquitia. Members of the genus *Dendrophidion* (*percarinatum* and *vinitor*) have keeled dorsal scales; in addition, *D. vinitor* has a single cloacal scute. *Drymarchon melanurus* is a larger snake with a single cloacal scute, a diagonal black mark on the neck, and a dorsal ground color grading from gray, brown, or gray to dark gray to black posteriorly. Members of the genus *Drymobius* (*margaritiferus* and *melanotropis*) have keeled dorsal scales. In addition, *D. margaritiferus* has a dorsal pattern of pale spots on each of the otherwise dark dorsal scales, and *D. melanotropis* adults have a bright green dorsum and lemon yellow venter. *Masticophis mentovarius* usually has 7 supralabial scales, with a single one bordering the eye, and dorsal scales in 19–17–13 rows.
**General geographic distribution:** *Mastigodryas melanolomus* is found at low and moderate elevations from southern Tamaulipas, Mexico, on the Atlantic versant and from southern Sinaloa, Mexico, on the Pacific versant to central Panama. It also occurs on the Cayos Cochinos and Isla de Utila off the north coast of Honduras and several Pacific islands off the coast of Costa Rica and Panama.
**Distribution in Honduras:** This species is widespread (from near sea level to 930 m elevation) in the northern and south-central portions of the country. It is also found on the Islas de la Bahía.
**Distribution in the Mosquitia:** Colón—Río Guaraska (BMNH). Gracias a Dios—Caño Awalwás (sight record); Awasbila (USNM); Río Coco (USNM); Karasangkan (UF); Rus Rus (UF; USNM); Tánsin (LSUMZ); Bodega de Río Tapalwás (USNM); Warunta Tingni Kiamp (USNM). Olancho—Quebrada El Mono (USNM); Quebrada El Robalo (USNM).
**Natural history comments:** *Mastigodryas melanolomus* occurs in primary and lightly to heavily disturbed evergreen broadleaf forest in the Mosquitia (including gallery forest through pine savanna), where it is diurnal and terrestrial. This species can be seen crawling on the forest floor on sunny days. It also can be found sleeping at night and on rainy days on understory vegetation in the forest. A snake near Caño Awalwás was observed preying on a small *Corytophanes cristatus*.
**Remarks:** A controversy has existed over the valid

generic name for this snake. However, Dixon and Tipton (2004) demonstrated that *Mastigodryas* is the correct name, not *Dryadophis* as used by some previous workers.

*Ninia maculata* **(W. Peters, 1861)**
**Common name(s):** None
**Description (Plate 139):** This snake is small (to 352 mm TL) with a moderately long tail (0.24 of TOL in single Honduran specimen). The head is distinctly set off from the neck. There are 1 or 2 scales, usually 1, between the postnasal and the eye (an elongated loreal present in the single Honduran specimen). Supralabials number 7, with the third and fourth bordering the eye. Infralabials number 7. The enlarged chinshields are paired and a mental groove is present. The pupil is vertically subelliptical. Ventrals number 127 (125 to 155) and subcaudals 52 (34 to 63) in the single Honduran specimen. The cloacal scute is single. Dorsal scales are keeled and strongly striated, without apical pits, and in 19 rows throughout the body. The dorsum is brownish orange with dark gray crossbands. The venter is pale cream with dark brown checkering. The dorsum of the head is dark grayish brown. Supralabials are marked with pale cream and dark brown. The iris is gray with dark flecking.
**Similar species:** *Ninia sebae* has an immaculate venter and a distinct pale nuchal band bordered posteriorly by a black neckband. *Adelphicos quadrivirgatum* has a lineate dorsal pattern, a pair of greatly enlarged chinshields, with the third infralabial reduced or absent, 15 smooth dorsal scale rows throughout the body, and a circular pupil. *Enuliophis sclateri* has a uniform dark gray dorsum with a white headband, a divided cloacal scute, 15–15–15 rows of smooth scales, and a circular pupil. *Geophis hoffmanni* has a uniform dorsal coloration, usually 5 supralabials, 24 to 37 subcaudals, 15 smooth dorsal scale rows (except a few scales are keeled above the vent in males) throughout the body, and a circular pupil. *Tantilla taeniata* has a lineate dorsal pattern, 15–15–15 smooth dorsal scale rows, and a circular pupil. *Tantillita lintoni* has a uniform dorsal coloration, an immaculate venter, 103 to 116 ventrals, 15 smooth dorsal scale rows throughout the body, and a circular pupil. *Urotheca decipiens* has a prominent zigzag white stripe on the lower body, an unmarked venter, 17–17–17 smooth dorsal scale rows, and a circular pupil. *Urotheca guentheri* has a lineate dorsal pattern, 17–17–17 smooth dorsal scale rows, and a circular pupil.
**General geographic distribution:** *Ninia maculata* occurs at low, moderate, and intermediate elevations from northeastern Honduras to central Panama on the Atlantic versant and from west-central Costa Rica to eastern Panama on the Pacific versant.
**Distribution in Honduras:** This species is known from a single low elevation (540 m) locality in Colón in the Mosquitia.
**Distribution in the Mosquitia:** Colón—Quebrada Machín (USNM).
**Natural history comments:** *Ninia maculata* is a diurnal, semifossorial species that is known from lightly disturbed evergreen broadleaf forest in the Mosquitia. The single Mosquitia specimen was under a small log on a steep hillside above a stream.
**Remarks:** This species was recently reported from Honduras by McCranie et al. (2001).

**Plate 139.** *Ninia maculata*. Photograph by McCranie.

*Ninia sebae* **(A.M.C. Duméril, Bibron, and Duméril, 1854a)**
**Common name(s):** Coral (Spanish)
**Description (Plate 140):** This snake is small (to 386 mm TL) with a moderately long tail (0.18 to 0.26 of TL). The head is distinctly set off from the neck. A single scale (an elongate loreal) is usually present between the postnasal and the eye. Supralabials number 6 to 8, usually 7, with the third and fourth bordering the eye. Infralabials number 5 to 8, usually 7. The enlarged chinshields are paired and a mental groove is present. The pupil is vertically subelliptical. Ventrals range from

**Plate 140.** *Ninia sebae*. Photograph by McCranie.

130 to 152 (130 to 156) and subcaudals from 48 to 73 (37 to 74). The cloacal scute is usually single. Dorsal scales are keeled and strongly striated, without apical pits, and in 19 rows throughout the body. The dorsum is dark red, with a series of yellow-orange-bordered dark brown dorsolateral blotches, which decrease in size posteriorly. The venter is cream, with the dorsal ground color encroaching onto the lateral portion of the ventral scales. The dorsum of the head is dark brown. A dull orange-yellow nuchal band follows, in turn followed by a dark brown nape band. The iris is black.

**Similar species:** *Ninia maculata* has a series of black markings on an otherwise immaculate venter and lacks a pale nuchal band. *Adelphicos quadrivirgatum* has a lineate dorsal pattern, a pair of greatly enlarged chinshields, with the third infralabial reduced or absent, 15–15–15 smooth dorsal scale rows, and a circular pupil. *Enuliophis sclateri* has a uniform dark gray dorsum, a divided cloacal scute, 15 rows of smooth scales throughout the body, and a circular pupil. *Geophis hoffmanni* has a uniform dorsal coloration, usually 5 supralabials, 24 to 37 subcaudals, 15–15–15 smooth dorsal scale rows (except a few scales are keeled above the vent in males), and a circular pupil. *Tantilla taeniata* has a lineate dorsal pattern, 15 smooth dorsal scale rows throughout the body, and a circular pupil. *Tantillita lintoni* has a uniform dorsal coloration, an immaculate venter, 103 to 116 ventrals, 15–15–15 smooth dorsal scale rows, and a circular pupil. *Urotheca decipiens* has a prominent zigzag white stripe on the lower body, 17–17–17 smooth dorsal scale rows, and a circular pupil. *Rhadinaea decorata* and *Urotheca guentheri* have a lineate dorsal pattern, 17–17–17 smooth dorsal scale rows (except faintly keeled posteriorly in the *Rhadinaea*), and a circular pupil.

**General geographic distribution:** *Ninia sebae* occurs at low, moderate, and intermediate elevations on the Atlantic versant from southern Veracruz, Mexico, to eastern Costa Rica and on the Pacific versant from southern Guatemala to northwestern Costa Rica.

**Distribution in Honduras:** This species is widespread throughout much of the country and is known from near sea level to 1650 m elevation.

**Distribution in the Mosquitia:** Colón—near Las Champas (BMNH); Quebrada Machín (USNM). Gracias a Dios—Caño Awalwás (USNM); Kokotá (LSUMZ); Mocorón (CF); Puerto Lempira (UTA); Rus Rus (UF; USNM); Tánsin (LSUMZ); Bodega de Río Tapalwás (USNM); Warunta Tingni Kiamp (USNM).

**Natural history comments:** *Ninia sebae* is a diurnal and nocturnal, semifossorial inhabitant of disturbed and undisturbed evergreen broadleaf forest and pine savanna in the Mosquitia. It is usually found under logs, leaf litter, and other debris on the ground. It is occasionally seen crawling on the ground at night.

*Nothopsis rugosus* **Cope, 1871**

**Common name(s):** None

**Description (Plate 141):** This snake is small (to 433 mm TL) and slender with a long tail (0.28 to 0. 33 of TL). The head is distinctly set off from the neck. The dorsal surface of the head is covered with numerous small, smooth to keeled scales. Numerous scales are present between the nasal

**Plate 141.** *Nothopsis rugosus*. Photograph by McCranie.

and the eye. Supralabials number 11 or 12 and are separated from the eye by 1 or 2 rows of small scales. Infralabials number 12 to 14. The enlarged chinshields are paired, a mental groove is present, and the pupil is circular. Ventrals number 147 to 156 (151 to 162) and subcaudals 85 to 93 (81 to 112). Most ventral scales do not extend the width of the ventral surface of the body. The cloacal scute is entire. Dorsal scales are heavily keeled, without apical pits, and in 26(27)–26(27)–22(24) rows. In Mosquitia specimens, the dorsa were cinnamon brown with a pattern of paired dark brown paramiddorsal blotches, usually offset from one another along the dorsal midline, and a series of beige-outlined dark brown lateral blotches located opposite the paramiddorsal series, in turn outlined by a rufous brown zigzag line, which contacts each paramiddorsal blotch. The dorsal and upper lateral portions of the head were dark brown. Supralabials were beige, edged dorsally with dark brown. The ventral surfaces of the body were cream with paired dark brown smudges that become increasingly fragmented posteriorly. The subcaudal surfaces were cream with a well-defined pair of dark brown blotches.

**Similar species:** *Boa constrictor* and *Corallus annulatus* are larger snakes with smooth dorsal scales and vertically elliptical pupils. All viperid snakes have a loreal pit between the nostril and the eye. All other colubrid snakes have a regular pattern of enlarged plates on the dorsum of the head and the ventral scales extending the width of the body.

**General geographic distribution:** *Nothopsis rugosus* occurs at low and moderate elevations from northeastern Honduras to northwestern Colombia on the Atlantic versant and on the Pacific versant from southeastern Costa Rica to western Ecuador.

**Distribution in Honduras:** This species is known from three low elevation (100 to 180 m) localities in the Mosquitia.

**Distribution in the Mosquitia:** Colón—4 km ESE of Tulito (BMNH). Gracias a Dios—Bodega de Río Tapalwás (UF); Urus Tingni Kiamp (USNM).

**Natural history comments:** *Nothopsis rugosus* is a nocturnal, semifossorial leaf litter inhabitant of undisturbed evergreen broadleaf forest in the Mosquitia. Two specimens were crawling in leaf litter at about 2100 to 2300 h and two others were found by day by raking through leaf litter on a steep hillside.

**Remarks:** This species was first recorded from Honduras by O'Shea (1986b), on the basis of a single specimen from near Tulito, a village at the confluence of the ríos Tulito and Paulaya. A second specimen was collected in June 2003 and three more were collected in May 2004. A recent paper by Dowling and Pinou (2003) placed this snake in their family Xenodermatidae. Divergent opinions exist about the content of this family and, for the present and for our purposes, we keep it in the unwieldy family Colubridae.

*Oxybelis aeneus* **(Wagler, 1824)**

**Common name(s):** Bejuquillo (Spanish); Andris Taya*, Lipyutang* (Miskito)

**Description (Plate 142):** This snake is medium large (to 1700 mm TL) and slender, with an extremely long, attenuate tail (0.39 to 0.43 of TL). The head is elongate, pointed, and distinctly set off from the neck. Two scales (a preocular and a lateral extension of each prefrontal) are present between the nasal and the eye. Supralabials number 6 to 10, usually 8 or 9, with the fourth, fifth, and sixth bordering the eye. Infralabials number 6 to 11, usually 8 or 9. The enlarged chinshields are paired, a mental groove is present, and the pupil is circular. Ventrals range from 176 to 198 (173 to 205) and subcaudals from 166 to 198 (158 to 203). The cloacal scute is usually divided. Dorsal scales are smooth to weakly keeled, without apical pits, and usually in 17–17–13 rows. The dorsum of the body is pale brown, flecked with dark brown. The dorsum of the head is reddish brown. Supralabials are pale yellow, edged dorsally by a thin dark grayish brown stripe. The venter is pale pinkish

**Plate 142.** *Oxybelis aeneus*. Photograph by McCranie.

tan, with mahogany red smudging on the middle of the white chin and neck. The iris is pale iridescent bronze dorsally and olive green ventrally.

**Similar species:** *Oxybelis brevirostris* has a single cloacal scute, 15 scale rows at midbody, usually 7 supralabials, a mostly green dorsum, and a thin dark stripe from the nostril across the eye to the neck. *Oxybelis fulgidus* is a larger snake with a uniformly bright green dorsum and a pair of white to pale yellow stripes on the pale green to chartreuse venter.

**General geographic distribution:** *Oxybelis aeneus* occurs at low, moderate, and occasionally intermediate elevations from south-central Nuevo León, Mexico, on the Atlantic versant and extreme southern Arizona, USA, on the Pacific versant to southern Brazil east of the Andes and northwestern Peru west of the Andes. It also occurs on numerous islands, as follows: Islas Tres Marías, Nayarit, and Isla Mujeres, Quintana Roo, Mexico; Islas de la Bahía and Zacate Grande, Honduras; Islas del Maíz, Nicaragua; Islas de Coiba and Perlas, Panama; Trinidad and Tobago; and several islands off the coast of Venezuela.

**Distribution in Honduras:** This species occurs at low and moderate elevations (near sea level to 1500 m) throughout much of the country, including the Bay Islands and Zacate Grande.

**Distribution in the Mosquitia:** Colón—Anzuelo Bridge (BMNH). Gracias a Dios—Barra Patuca (USNM); Crique Canco (USNM); Karasangkan (USNM); Mocorón (CF); Palacios (BMNH); Puerto Lempira (CAS); Rus Rus (UF; USNM); Tánsin (LSUMZ). Olancho—between La Llorona and confluence of Ríos Lagarto and Wampú (USNM).

**Natural history comments:** *Oxybelis aeneus* is a diurnal, arboreal species that is found in understory vegetation in primary to disturbed evergreen broadleaf forest, pine savanna, and freshwater marshes.

*Oxybelis brevirostris* **(Cope, "1860" [1861])**

**Common name(s):** Bejuquillo (Spanish); Lipyutang* (Miskito)

**Description (Plate 143):** This snake is medium-sized (to 1200 mm TL) and slender, with an extremely long, attenuate tail (0.38 to 0.42 of TL). The head is moderately elongate, bluntly acuminate, and distinctly set off from the neck. Two scales (a preocular and a lateral extension of each prefrontal) are present between the nasal and the eye. Supralabials number 6 or 7 (usually 6),

**Plate 143.** *Oxybelis brevirostris.* Photograph by McCranie.

usually with the third and fourth bordering the eye. Infralabials number 7 or 8, usually 7. The enlarged chinshields are paired, a mental groove is present, and the pupil is circular. Ventrals range from 168 to 181 (166 to 186) and subcaudals from 151 to 172 (151 to 179). The cloacal scute is entire. Dorsal scales are smooth to faintly keeled, without apical pits, and in 15–15–13 rows. The dorsum of the head and body is dark green, with the color of the body grading to leaf green on the sides. The skin between the dorsal scales is alternately white and gray, producing a checkerboard effect. The venter is yellowish green anteriorly, grading to leaf green posteriorly. Supralabials are yellowish green, this color separated from that of the dorsum of the head by a gray line, which passes across the eye. The remainder of the iris is gold.

**Similar species:** *Oxybelis aeneus* has a pale brown to gray dorsum, 17 dorsal scale rows at midbody, usually 8 or 9 supralabials, and a divided cloacal scute. *Oxybelis fulgidus* is a larger snake, with a pair of white to pale yellow stripes on the venter, 17 dorsal scale rows at midbody, usually 9 or 10 supralabials, and a divided cloacal scute. *Drymobius melanotropis* has a blunter head, 15 dorsal scale rows at the cloaca, a yellow venter, and a divided cloacal scute. Members of the genus *Leptophis* (*ahaetulla*, *mexicanus*, and *nebulosus*) have a blunter head, most dorsal scales heavily keeled, and a divided cloacal scute.

**General geographic distribution:** *Oxybelis brevirostris* occurs at low and moderate elevations on the Atlantic versant from northeastern Honduras to central Panama and on the Pacific versant from eastern Panama to northwestern Ecuador. The species also occurs marginally on the

Pacific versant in northwestern Costa Rica.
**Distribution in Honduras:** This species is known only from the Mosquitia at elevations ranging from 140 to 800 m.
**Distribution in the Mosquitia:** Colón—Quebrada Machín (USNM). Gracias a Dios—Bodega de Río Tapalwás (UF); Urus Tingni Kiamp (USNM); Cerro El Viejo (KU); between Wakling Kiamp and Río Rus Rus (USNM). Olancho—Quebrada El Guásimo (USNM); Quebrada de Las Marías (USNM).
**Natural history comments:** *Oxybelis brevirostris* is a diurnal, arboreal inhabitant of primary and relatively undisturbed evergreen broadleaf forest in the Mosquitia. Most individuals were found sleeping at night on palm leaves, usually in the vicinity of streams. An occasional specimen was seen at dusk, apparently searching for a nighttime sleeping place. A few were crawling on the ground or in vegetation during the day.

*Oxybelis fulgidus* **(Daudin, 1803)**
**Common name(s):** Bejuquillo (Spanish); Lipyutang* (Miskito)
**Description (Plate 144):** This snake is large (to 2000 mm TL) and slender, with an extremely long, attenuate tail (0.32 to 0.35 of TL). The head is distinctly set off from the neck. Two scales (a preocular and a lateral extension of each prefrontal) are present between the nasal and the eye. Supralabials number 9 to 12, usually 9 or 10, with the fourth, fifth, and sixth or fifth, sixth, and seventh bordering the eye. Infralabials number 9 to 12, usually 10. The enlarged chinshields are paired, a mental groove is present, and the pupil is circular. Ventrals range from 201 to 216 (198 to 215) and subcaudals from 153 to 166 (143 to 171). The cloacal scute is usually divided. The median dorsal scale rows are lightly keeled, without apical pits, and in 17–17–13 rows. The dorsal coloration is bright green. The venter is yellowish green with yellowish white lines coursing ventrolaterally the length of the body, each line extending onto the subcaudal surface. The head is green above with a dark green or black eye stripe. Supralabials and lower jaw are yellowish green.

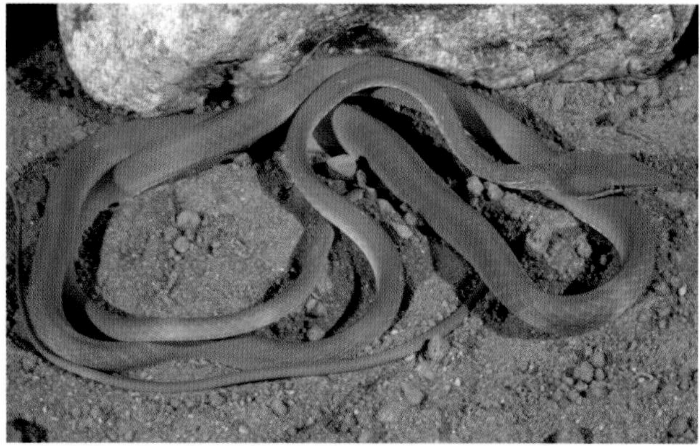
**Plate 144.** *Oxybelis fulgidus.* Photograph by McCranie.

**Similar species:** *Oxybelis aeneus* has a pale brown to gray dorsum. *Oxybelis brevirostris* is a smaller snake lacking pale stripes on the venter and has 15 dorsal scale rows at midbody, a single cloacal scute, usually 6 supralabials. *Drymobius melanotropis* has a blunter head, 15 dorsal scale rows at the vent, and a yellow venter, and lacks pale stripes on the venter. Members of the genus *Leptophis* (*ahaetulla*, *mexicanus*, and *nebulosus*) have a blunter head and most dorsal scales heavily keeled, and lack pale ventral stripes.
**General geographic distribution:** *Oxybelis fulgidus* occurs at low and moderate elevations on the Atlantic versant from the Yucatán Peninsula, Mexico, to the Amazonian Basin of southeastern Peru and central Brazil and on the Pacific versant from southeastern Oaxaca, Mexico, to north-central Costa Rica and eastern Panama. An apparently isolated population also occurs in southern Veracruz, Mexico. It also occurs on Isla de Utila, Honduras, and Isla de Patos, Venezuela.
**Distribution in Honduras:** This species occurs across northern Honduras; it is also known from a single locality in the south-central portion of the country and on Isla de Utila in the Bay Islands. Its known elevational range is from near sea level to 800 m.
**Distribution in the Mosquitia:** Gracias a Dios—Palacios (BMNH); near Rus Rus (USNM).
**Natural history comments:** *Oxybelis fulgidus* is a diurnal, terrestrial or arboreal species that is known from lightly disturbed evergreen broadleaf forest in the Mosquitia. One Mosquitia specimen was crossing a dirt road through gallery forest near Rus Rus.

*Oxyrhopus petola* **(Linnaeus, 1758)**
**Common name(s):** Coral (Spanish); Silbiera* (Miskito)
**Description (Plate 145):** This snake is moderate-sized (to 1200 mm TL) with a moderately long tail

**Plate 145.** *Oxyrhopus petola*. Photograph by McCranie.

(0.22 to 0.40 of TL). The head is distinctly set off from the neck. Two scales (a loreal and a preocular) are present between the postnasal and the eye. Supralabials number 7 to 9, usually 8, with the fourth and fifth bordering the eye. Infralabials number 9 to 11, usually 10. The enlarged chinshields are paired and a mental groove is present. The pupil is vertically elliptical. Ventrals range from 198 to 203 (189 to 244) and subcaudals from 88 to 101 (79 to 123). The cloacal scute is single. Dorsal scales are smooth, with paired apical pits, and usually in 19–19–17 rows. The dorsal coloration consists of alternating bands of dark brown to black (extending onto the lateral edges of the ventrals) and pale yellow-outlined red on the middle and posterior portions of the body (occasional individuals lack yellow pigment). On the anterior portion of the body, the pale bands grade anteriorly from red to orange or cream. The pale headband is cream to orange. The anterior portion of the head to the posterior portion of the parietals is dark brown to black. The venter is white to pale cream. The dark markings on the dorsum of the tail continue onto the venter to form rings.

**Similar species:** Most other bicolored (red and black) or tricolored (red, black, and yellow or white) snakes in the Mosquitia have the black components of the pattern in the form of rings (i.e., black markings that completely encircle the body). Such is the case with *Dipsas bicolor, Erythrolamprus mimus, Lampropeltis triangulum, Micrurus alleni, M. nigrocinctus, Pliocercus elapoides, P. euryzonus,* and *Rhinobothryum bovallii*. Only *Scaphiodontophis annulatus* and some *Ninia sebae* otherwise have dorsal black bands (i.e., transverse markings restricted to the dorsum of the body). *Ninia sebae* is a smaller snake with keeled and heavily striated dorsal scales in 19 rows throughout the body. *Scaphiodontophis annulatus* has tricolor banding usually restricted to some portion of the anterior body and a pattern of three narrow, longitudinal dark dotted lines on a brown to gray background on some portion of the posterior body. Occasional *S. annulatus* have the tricolor banding extending the length of the body, but those specimens have fewer than 170 ventrals, a divided cloacal scute, 17 or 15 scale rows at midbody, and a circular pupil.

**General geographic distribution:** *Oxyrhopus petola* occurs at low and moderate elevations on the Atlantic versant from central Veracruz, Mexico, to Bolivia and northeastern Argentina. It also occurs on the Pacific versant from west-central Costa Rica to northwestern Ecuador. The species also occurs on Trinidad and Tobago.

**Distribution in Honduras:** This species is known from widely scattered localities in the northern portion of the country at elevations ranging from near sea level to 635 m.

**Distribution in the Mosquitia:** Gracias a Dios—Caño Awalwás (USNM); Awasbila (USNM); Río Coco (USNM); Krahkra (USNM); Rus Rus (UF; USNM).

**Natural history comments:** *Oxyrhopus petola* is a nocturnal, terrestrial species that has been found in primary to heavily disturbed evergreen broadleaf forest and denuded broadleaf swamp forest in the Mosquitia. One specimen was in a hollow tree stump by day and another was sleeping at night on low vegetation. A clutch of 10 eggs was found in primary evergreen broadleaf forest alongside a tributary of the Caño Awalwás on 2 August 2002. The eggs were exposed on the bank above a river that had recently flooded because of heavy rains. Six of the eggs had already hatched. The remaining four contained living embryos. A subadult from the Mosquitia contained an adult *Mabuya unimarginata* in its stomach.

*Pliocercus elapoides* **Cope, 1860**

**Common name(s):** Coral (Spanish); Silbiera* (Miskito)

**Description (Plate 146):** This snake is medium small (to about 670 mm TL) with an extremely long, thick tail (0.40 to 0.45 of TL). The head is set off slightly from the neck. Two scales (a loreal and a preocular) are present between the postnasal and

**Plate 146.** *Pliocercus elapoides*. Photograph by McCranie.

the eye. Supralabials number 7 to 9, usually 8, with the fourth and fifth bordering the eye. Infralabials number 8 to 10, usually 9 or 10. The enlarged chinshields are paired, a mental groove is present, and the pupil is circular. Ventrals range from 123 to 136 (122 to 144) and subcaudals from 102 to 111 (85 to 115). The cloacal scute is divided. Dorsal scales are smooth, without apical pits, and in 17 rows throughout the body. The pattern of the body consists of red, black, and usually pale (yellow or cream) rings, with the scales of the dorsal portion of the red rings smudged with brown, except at their base. The iris is very dark gray.

**Similar species:** Three species of snakes in the Mosquitia, *Oxyrhopus petola*, *Scaphiodontophis annulatus*, and some *Ninia sebae* have bicolored or tricolored patterns in which the black components are transverse bands that do not cross the venter. The remainder of the bicolor and tricolored snakes in the Mosquitia have the black markings in the form of rings that completely encircle the body. *Pliocercus euryzonus* has a pattern in which the pale bands are red dorsally and cream to pale yellow ventrally and the black body rings are longer than the red body rings. The venomous coral snakes, *Micrurus alleni* and *M. nigrocinctus*, have only a single scale between the postnasal and the eye and 15 dorsal scale rows throughout the body. *Dipsas bicolor* is an arboreal snake with a strongly compressed body, a head distinctly set off from the neck, 15 dorsal scale rows throughout the body, and a vertically elliptical pupil. *Erythrolamprus mimus* is a larger snake with fewer subcaudals (42 to 56) and 15 dorsal scale rows throughout the body. *Lampropeltis triangulum* is a larger snake with fewer subcaudals (31 to 63), a single cloacal scute, and dorsal scales in 19 or more rows (usually 21 or 23) at midbody. *Rhinobothryum bovallii* is a larger snake with an enlarged nostril, a vertically elliptical pupil, and 21–19–17 dorsal scale rows, of which rows 9 to 13 are keeled on the posterior portion of the body. *Tropidodipsas sartorii* has 165 to 197 ventrals, 52 to 77 subcaudals, and a single cloacal scute.

**General geographic distribution:** *Pliocercus elapoides* occurs at low, moderate, and intermediate elevations from central Tamaulipas, Mexico, to northeastern Honduras on the Atlantic versant and from western Oaxaca, Mexico, to western El Salvador on the Pacific versant.

**Distribution in Honduras:** This species is known from across the northern portion of the country at elevations ranging from 30 to 1670 m.

**Distribution in the Mosquitia:** Colón—Quebrada Machín (USNM).

**Natural history comments:** *Pliocercus elapoides* is a diurnal and nocturnal species that has been taken in lightly disturbed evergreen broadleaf forest in the Mosquitia. It is both terrestrial and semifossorial. The single Mosquitia specimen was crawling during the late afternoon next to a large log under which it retreated.

**Remarks:** This species of false coral snake is an apparent mimic of *Micrurus nigrocinctus* in the Mosquitia and has a pattern essentially identical to that of the venomous coral snake (down to precise color shades).

*Pliocercus euryzonus* **Cope, 1862a**

**Common name(s):** Coral (Spanish); Silbiera* (Miskito)

**Description (Plate 147):** This snake is medium small (to 795 mm TL) with an extremely long, thick tail (about 0.45 of TL). The head is set off slightly from the neck. Two scales (a loreal and a preocular) are present between the postnasal and the eye. Supralabials number 8 or 9, usually 8, with the fourth and fifth bordering the eye. Infralabials number 9 to 11, usually 9 or 10. The enlarged chinshields are paired, a mental groove is present, and the pupil is circular. Ventrals number 128 to 134 (118 to 142) and subcaudals 119 in the single Honduran specimen with a complete tail (90 to 122). The cloacal scute is divided. Dorsal scales are smooth, without apical pits, and in 17 rows throughout the body. The body is crossed by a

**Plate 147.** *Pliocercus euryzonus.* Photograph by McCranie.

series of broad black rings. Interspaces between the black rings are red to dorsal row 4, thence grading to pale cream anteriorly, with the red color gradually descending to cover all dorsal scale rows posteriorly. The black body rings include a nuchal band and a band around the vent. The tail is ringed with black, with the interspaces red with black speckling dorsally. The head is black to the anterior portion of the parietals, save for a pale cream spot on supralabial 1, supralabial 2 (save for the posterodorsal corner), and the anteroventral corner of supralabial 3. The chin is white, except for the mental, anterior portion of the anterior chinshields, and infralabials 1, 2, 3, and most of 4, which are black. The iris is black.

**Similar species:** Three species of snakes in the Mosquitia, *Ninia sebae*, *Oxyrhopus petola*, and *Scaphiodontophis annulatus* have bicolored or tricolored patterns (at least somewhere on the body) in which the black components are transverse bands that do not cross the venter. The remainder of the bicolor and tricolored snakes in the Mosquitia has the black markings in the form of rings that completely encircle the body. *Pliocercus elapoides* has a body pattern of black, red, and (usually) yellow rings and the red body rings longer than, or equal in length to the black body rings. The venomous coral snakes, *Micrurus alleni* and *M. nigrocinctus* have only a single scale between the postnasal and the eye, 15 dorsal scale rows throughout the body, and have the red areas completely encircling the body. *Dipsas bicolor* is an arboreal snake with a strongly compressed body, a head distinctly set off from the neck, 15 dorsal scale rows throughout the body, and a vertically elliptical pupil. *Erythrolamprus mimus* is a larger snake with fewer subcaudals (42 to 56), 15 dorsal scale rows throughout the body, and red areas completely encircling the body. *Lampropeltis triangulum* is a larger snake with fewer subcaudals (31 to 63), a single cloacal scute, dorsal scales in 19 or more rows (usually 21 or 23) at midbody, and red areas completely encircling the body. *Rhinobothryum bovallii* is a larger snake with an enlarged nostril, a vertically elliptical pupil, 21–19–17 dorsal scale rows, of which rows 9 to 13 are keeled on the posterior portion of the body, and red areas completely encircling the body. *Tropidodipsas sartorii* has 165 to 197 ventrals, 52 to 77 subcaudals, and a single cloacal scute.

**General geographic distribution:** *Pliocercus euryzonus* occurs at low and moderate elevations on the Atlantic versant from near the Río Coco along the Honduran-Nicaraguan border to northwestern Colombia and on the Pacific versant from central Panama to western Ecuador. The species also occurs marginally on the Pacific versant of west-central Costa Rica.

**Distribution in Honduras:** This species is known from a single locality (100 m elevation) from Caño Awalwás, a tributary of the Río Coco upriver from Awasbila.

**Distribution in the Mosquitia:** Gracias a Dios—Caño Awalwás (USNM).

**Natural history comments:** *Pliocercus euryzonus* is a diurnal and nocturnal species that has been taken in undisturbed evergreen broadleaf forest in the Mosquitia. It is both terrestrial and semifossorial. The single Honduran specimen was crawling at night on the bank of a small river.

**Remarks:** This species recently has been reported in Honduras by Wilson et al. (2003). This false coral snake is an apparent mimic of *Micrurus multifasciatus* (Jan) closely resembling that venomous coral snake in its various guises (see Savage, 2002, for a detailed discussion of this resemblance; as *M. mipartitus*). The presence of *P. euryzonus* in the Tawahka-Asangni Biosphere Reserve raises the suspicion that *M. multifasciatus*, which has not been recorded in Honduras (Wilson and McCranie, 2002), may occur in the same area.

*Pseustes poecilonotus* **(Günther, 1858)**

**Common name(s):** Mica (Spanish); Matsiksa* (Miskito); Clampasaya (Garífuna)

**Description (Plate 148):** This is a large snake (to 2400 mm TL) with a moderately long tail (0.28 to

**Plate 148.** *Pseustes poecilonotus.* Photograph by McCranie.

0.31 of TL). The head is distinctly set off from the neck. Two scales (a loreal and a preocular) are present between the nasal and the eye. Supralabials number 6 to 10, usually 8 or 9, with the third, fourth, and fifth or fourth, fifth and sixth bordering the eye. Infralabials number 11 to 14, usually 12 or 13. The enlarged chinshields are paired, a mental groove is present, and the pupil is circular. Ventrals range from 199 to 213 (181 to 220) and subcaudals from 131 to 144 (95 to 147). The cloacal scute is usually single. Dorsal scales are keeled on the middorsal 3 to 4 rows in females and on the median 7 to 13 rows in males, have paired apical pits, and are in 19 to 27 (usually 21) rows at midbody. Dorsal coloration varies from individual to individual. In some individuals, the dorsum of the body is brown with narrow bright orange crossbands. The ventrolateral scale rows and the lateral portion of the ventrals are yellow-orange anteriorly grading to brown at midbody. The underside of the tail is brownish olive. The head is brown above and the supralabials yellowish tan. The chin is pale yellow. The iris is pale brown above, brown below. In other individuals, the dorsum is grayish olive with a yellow spot at the anteroventral corner of each scale. The chin and anterior venter are bright yellow, grading to dark gray posteriorly and the supralabials bright yellow.
**Similar species:** *Chironius grandisquamis* has 10 midbody dorsal scale rows and a divided cloacal scute. *Clelia clelia* has a shiny uniform dark gray to black dorsum, 57 to 93 subcaudals, and a vertically elliptical pupil. *Drymarchon melanurus* has 55 to 88 subcaudals, 17 dorsal scale rows at midbody, and an oblique black stripe on the side of the neck. *Masticophis mentovarius* has a divided cloacal scute, 95 to 126 subcaudals, and smooth dorsal scales in 19–17–13 rows. *Mastigodryas melanolomus* is a smaller snake with 17 midbody dorsal scale rows and a divided cloacal scute. *Spilotes pullatus* has 14 to 18 midbody dorsal scale rows and a vivid black and yellow anterior body pattern grading to solid black posteriorly.
**General geographic distribution:** *Pseustes poecilonotus* occurs at low and moderate elevations on the Atlantic versant from southeastern San Luis Potosí, Mexico, to Brazil. It also occurs on the Pacific versant in Oaxaca, Mexico, and from northwestern Costa Rica to northwestern Ecuador.
**Distribution in Honduras:** This species occurs at low elevations in the northern portion of the country and is known from near sea level to 540 m elevation.
**Distribution in the Mosquitia:** Colón—2 km W of Anzuelo Bridge (BMNH); Las Champas (BMNH); Empalme Río Chilmeca (was in UNAH, now lost); Quebrada Machín (USNM). Gracias a Dios—near Auka Kiamp (UF); Caño Awalwás (UF; USNM); about 30 km S of Mocorón (UTA); Mocorón (CF); Rus Rus (USNM); Bodega de Río Tapalwás (USNM).
**Natural history comments:** *Pseustes poecilonotus* is a diurnal, terrestrial or arboreal inhabitant of primary to lightly disturbed evergreen broadleaf forest (including gallery forest through pine savanna) in the Mosquitia. We have found this species in the Mosquitia both on the forest floor and up to about 10 m high in trees. One adult contained a recently swallowed tinamou egg (*Tinamus major* Gmelin).

*Rhadinaea decorata* **(Günther, 1858)**
**Common name(s):** None
**Description (Plate 149):** This is a small snake (to 470 mm TL) with a long tail (0.40 of TL in single Honduran specimen). The head is slightly set off from the neck. Two scales (a loreal and a preocular) are present between the nasal or postnasal (nasal usually undivided) and the eye. Supralabials number 7 to 9, usually 8, with usually the fourth and fifth bordering the eye. Infralabials number 8 to 11, usually 10. The enlarged chinshields are paired, a mental groove is present, and the pupil is circular. Ventrals number 117 (110 to 134) and subcaudals 101 (85 to 124) in the single Honduran specimen. The cloacal scute is divided. Dorsal scales are mostly smooth (a few middorsal scales weakly keeled posteriorly on body in the Honduran

**Plate 149.** *Rhadinaea decorata.* Photograph by McCranie.

specimen), with or without apical pits (apical pits lacking in the Honduran specimen), and in 17 rows throughout the body. The middorsum is brown with a pale brown dorsolateral stripe on the upper two-thirds of scale row 5 and lower two-thirds of scale row 6 on the neck, the pale stripe gradually fading into the middorsal color until barely evident at about the midlength of the body. A very dark brown lateral stripe is present on the lower one-third of scale row 5 and discontinuously on the upper one-third of scale row 4 on the body, the dark stripe extends onto the lower two-thirds of scale row 2 on the tail with the dark stripe becoming indistinct at about the midlength of the tail. The lateral field below the lateral dark stripe is dark brown. The dorsum of the head is brown. A dark brown outlined pale brown postorbital stripe that extends to the upper posterior temporal is present. A similarly colored nuchal spot is also present on each side. Supralabials are white with a narrow dark brown stripe along the upper edges. Ventral surfaces are white on the head and neck, grading to pale orange anteriorly on the body and dark orange on the posterior two-thirds of the body and all of the tail. A dark brown spot is present near the upper edge of each ventral scale. The iris is pale brown on the upper half and dark brown on the lower half.
**Similar species:** *Adelphicos quadrivirgatum* has 15 dorsal scale rows throughout the body and 29 to 50 subcaudal scales and lacks pale postorbital and nuchal markings. Members of the genus *Coniophanes* have 19 to 21 (sometimes 23) dorsal scales at midbody. *Tantilla taeniata* has a single scale between the postnasal and the eye, 63 to 70 subcaudal scales, and 15 dorsal scale rows throughout the body. The species of *Urotheca* have disproportionally thick tails for most of their length and paired pale lateral stripes. *Urotheca decipiens* also lacks postorbital and nuchal pale markings and has a white venter in life.
**General geographic distribution:** *Rhadinaea decorata* occurs at low and moderate elevations from southeastern San Luis Potosí, Mexico, to eastern Panama on the Atlantic versant and from southeastern Costa Rica to northwestern Ecuador on the Pacific versant. The species also occurs marginally on the Pacific versant in northwestern Costa Rica.
**Distribution in Honduras:** This species is known only from a single low elevation locality (180 m) in the Mosquitia.
**Distribution in the Mosquitia:** Gracias a Dios—Urus Tingni Kiamp (USNM).
**Natural history comments:** *Rhadinaea decorata* is a diurnal, semifossorial inhabitant of undisturbed evergreen broadleaf forest in the Mosquitia. The single Mosquitia specimen was crawling among leaf litter on the forest floor at 1000 h.
**Remarks:** This species was recently reported from Honduras by McCranie (2004a).

*Rhinobothryum bovallii* **Andersson, 1916**
**Common name(s):** None
**Description (Plate 150):** This snake is large (to 1760 mm TL) with a moderately long tail (0.22 to 0.27 of TOL; Savage, 2002). The head is very distinctly set off from the neck. Two scales (a loreal

**Plate 150.** *Rhinobothryum bovallii.* Photograph by Carl J. Franklin.

and a preocular) are present between the postnasal and the eye. Supralabials number 8, with the fourth and fifth bordering the eye. Infralabials number 10. The enlarged chinshields are paired and a mental groove is present. The pupil is vertically elliptical. Ventrals number 242 (239 to 246) and subcaudals 121 (115 to 125) in the single Honduran specimen. The cloacal scute is divided. All dorsal scales are smooth on the anterior portion of the body with rows 9 to 13 keeled posteriorly on the body. The dorsal body scales have paired apical pits and are in 21–19–17 or 21–21–17 rows. Dorsal coloration consists of tricolor rings, with each of 11 to 16 rings separated from the red ones by a narrow white to yellow ring. Red rings are heavily tipped with black. The dorsum of the head is black with the enlarged head scales outlined in white, cream, or yellow; the temporal area is red with black spots.

**Similar species:** The other tricolored or ringed snakes in the Mosquitia are terrestrial, with the exception of *Dipsas bicolor*. Tricolored *Ninia sebae*, *Oxyrhopus petola*, and *Scaphiodontophis annulatus* have patterns (at least somewhere on the body) in which the black components are transverse bands that do not cross the venter. The venomous coral snakes, *Micrurus alleni* and *M. nigrocinctus*, have only a single scale between the postnasal and the eye and 15 smooth (except, perhaps, for supracloacal tubercles in males) dorsal scale rows throughout the body. *Dipsas bicolor* is a much smaller snake without a mental groove and with undivided chinshields. *Erythrolamprus mimus* is a smaller snake with fewer subcaudals (42 to 56), 15 smooth dorsal scale rows throughout the body, and a circular pupil. *Lampropeltis triangulum* has fewer subcaudals (31 to 63), a single cloacal scute, a circular pupil, and smooth scales throughout the dorsum. Species of the genus *Pliocercus* (*elapoides* and *euryzonus*) have 17 rows of entirely smooth dorsal scales throughout the body and a circular pupil. *Tropidodipsas sartorii* has a normal-sized nostril, 17 weakly keeled dorsal scale rows throughout the body, 165 to 197 ventrals, 52 to 77 subcaudals, a bicolor pattern, and a single cloacal scute.

**General geographic distribution:** *Rhinobothryum bovallii* occurs at low elevations on the Atlantic versant from eastern Honduras to northwestern Venezuela and on the Pacific versant from central Panama to northwestern Ecuador.

**Distribution in Honduras:** This species is known from only a single low elevation locality (380) in the Mosquitia.

**Distribution in the Mosquitia:** El Paraíso—near Arenales (LACM).

**Natural history comments:** *Rhinobothryum bovallii* is an apparent tree canopy resident (Savage, 2002) in undisturbed broadleaf forest in other portions of its range. It is known from Honduras from a single specimen collected at an evergreen broadleaf forest locality that is now badly degraded. We have not encountered this species in the Mosquitia.

*Scaphiodontophis annulatus* **(A.M.C. Duméril, Bibron, and Duméril, 1854a)**

**Common name(s):** None

**Description (Plate 151):** This snake is moderately sized (to 795 mm TL) with a long, thick tail (0.40 to 0.49 of TL). The head is slightly set off from the neck. Two scales (a loreal and a preocular) are present between the postnasal and the eye. Supralabials number 8 to 10, usually 9, usually with the fourth, fifth, and sixth bordering the eye. Infralabials number 9 to 12, usually 10. The enlarged chinshields are paired, a mental groove is present, and the pupil is circular. Ventrals range from 132 to 160 (127 to 166) and subcaudals from 121 to 149 (93 to 149). The cloacal scute is divided. Dorsal scales are smooth, without apical pits, and usually in 17 rows throughout the body (occasionally other patterns prevail, such as 15–17–13 and 15–15–15). A varying portion of the anterior dorsum of the body is covered with a pattern of

**Plate 151.** *Scaphiodontophis annulatus.* Photograph by Louis Porras.

tricolor bands. The long red bands are bounded by narrower black bands that are separated by white, cream, or pale gray bands. The posterior portion of the body and the entire tail is usually gray to brown with three dark gray or dark brown interrupted stripes. However, occasional specimens have the entire dorsum of the body and tail with tricolor bands. The venter is cream to yellow with black flecking. The head is dark gray to black dorsally, with or without a pale snout or interocular band, followed by a red nuchal band.

**Similar species:** Most of the bicolored or tricolored snakes in the Mosquitia have black markings, if not red and yellow or white markings, in the form of rings (i.e., crossing the venter). Otherwise, *Ninia sebae* has a red dorsum the length of the body and tail, some portion of which is crossed by yellow-outlined black bands; in addition, the dorsal scales are keeled and heavily striated and the pupil is vertically subelliptical. *Oxyrhopus petola* always has black crossbands the length of the body and tail; in addition, the cloacal scute is single and the pupil is vertically elliptical.

**General geographic distribution:** *Scaphiodontophis annulatus* occurs at low and moderate elevations from southern Tamaulipas, Mexico, to north-central Colombia on the Atlantic versant and on the Pacific versant from southwestern Oaxaca, Mexico, to western El Salvador and from south-central Costa Rica to eastern Panama.

**Distribution in Honduras:** This species is known from the Atlantic versant in northern Honduras and from a single locality in southwestern Honduras. Known elevational range is from near sea level to 1400 m.

**Distribution in the Mosquitia:** Gracias a Dios—Mocorón (UTA); Rus Rus (UF; USNM).

**Natural history comments:** *Scaphiodontophis annulatus* is a diurnal, semifossorial and terrestrial species that has been taken in evergreen broadleaf gallery forest and in pine savanna in the Mosquitia. One specimen was under debris on the ground.

**Remarks:** A recent revision of the genus *Scaphiodontophis* (Savage and Slowinski, 1996) recognizes a single, highly variable snake, which is part of the coral snake mimic guild in Mexico, Central America, and Colombia (see discussion in Savage, 2002).

*Sibon annulatus* **(Günther, 1872)**
**Common name(s):** None

**Description (Plate 152):** This snake is small (to 557 mm) with a long tail (0.32 of TL in single Honduran specimen). The head is distinctly set off from the neck. There is usually a single scale (a loreal) between the postnasal and the eye; however, the single Honduran specimen also has a preocular. Supralabials number 7 to 9, with the fifth and sixth or sixth and seventh, but not the enlarged penultimate one, bordering the eye. Infralabials number 7 to 10, with the first pair separated behind the mental by a divided or single (though small) postmental scale (paired postmentals in Honduran specimen). The enlarged chinshields are paired and a mental groove is present. The pupil is vertically elliptical. Ventrals number 184 (161 to 192) and subcaudals 116 (108 to 135). The cloacal scute is single. Dorsal scales are smooth, without apical pits, and in 15 rows throughout the body. The vertebral scale row is scarcely or moderately enlarged. The dorsal components of the rings are brown with dark brown edging, the ventral components of these rings are dark brown and cross the venter. The dorsal components of the interspaces between these rings are pinkish orange medially, grading to gray laterally with white on the lowermost dorsal scales, the ventral components of these interspaces are white. The head is rust colored above with dark brown blotching; the lateral portion is variegated with rust, dark brown, and white. The chin is white with dark brown blotching. The iris is grayish brown.

**Similar species:** *Sibon longifrenis* has the dorsal crossbands extending only to the lateral edges of the ventral scales and the enlarged penultimate supralabial in contact with the eye. *Sibon nebulatus*

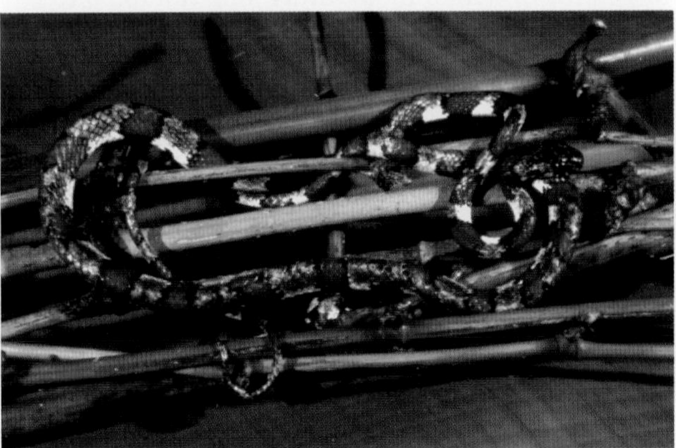

**Plate 152.** *Sibon annulatus*. Photograph by McCranie.

has the first pair of infralabials in contact posterior to the mental. *Sibon* sp. has a single, large postmental and about 95 subcaudals. *Dipsas bicolor* lacks a mental groove and has unpaired chinshields and a pattern of black rings separated by pale interspaces. *Imantodes cenchoa* is a longer snake with a very slender body, has dark crossbands on a pale ground color, 17 dorsal scale rows at midbody with the vertebral row greatly enlarged, and a divided cloacal scute. *Leptodeira septentrionalis* is a larger snake with dark crossbands on a pale ground color, usually 21 to 23 dorsal scale rows at midbody, and a divided cloacal scute. *Tropidodipsas sartorii* has 17 weakly keeled dorsal scale rows throughout the body and 52 to 77 subcaudals.
**General geographic distribution:** *Sibon annulatus* occurs at low and moderate elevations on the Atlantic versant from eastern Honduras to western Panama and on the Pacific versant in eastern Panama (a single record is also available from this versant in western Panama).
**Distribution in Honduras:** This species is known from a single locality (5 m elevation) in the extreme eastern portion of the Mosquitia.
**Distribution in the Mosquitia:** Gracias a Dios—Swabila (UF).
**Natural history comments:** The single Mosquitia specimen of *Sibon annulatus* was found a night in the top of an understory tree in slightly disturbed broadleaf swamp forest.
**Remarks:** This snail eater was recently reported from Honduras by McCranie et al. (2003b).

*Sibon longifrenis* **(Stejneger, 1909)**
**Common name(s):** None
**Description (Plate 153):** This snake is small (to 624 mm TL) with a moderately long tail (0.30 to 0.35 of TOL). The head is very distinctly set off from the narrow neck. There is usually a single scale (a loreal) between the postnasal and the eye. Supralabials number 7 to 9, usually 7, with the fourth and fifth and the large penultimate one (sixth in all Honduran specimens) bordering the eye. Infralabials number 6 to 9 with the first pair separated from each other by a single small postmental scale. The enlarged chinshields are paired and a mental groove is present. The pupil is vertically elliptical. Ventrals range from 159 to 169 (151 to 173) and subcaudals from 91 to 106 (82 to 106). The cloacal scute is single. Dorsal scales are smooth, without apical pits, and in 15 rows throughout the body. The vertebral scale row is not enlarged. The dorsum is olive green with a series of black-outlined pinkish tan crossbands, many of which are broken into middorsal and lateral portions; ivory blotches separate the lateral portions. The venter is bright yellow with black blotching and streaking. The head is olive green with black-outlined pinkish tan blotches. The iris is pale olive green with black and rust red speckling.

**Plate 153.** *Sibon longifrenis*. Photograph by McCranie.

**Similar species:** *Sibon annulatus* and *Sibon* sp. have the large penultimate supralabial separated from the eye and the bands or rings of the dorsal pattern extending across or well onto the venter. *Sibon nebulatus* has the bands or rings of the dorsal pattern continuing well onto the venter, the large penultimate supralabial separated from the eye, and the first pair of infralabials in contact posterior to the mental. *Dipsas bicolor* lacks a mental groove and has unpaired chinshields and a pattern of black rings separated by pale interspaces. *Imantodes cenchoa* is a longer snake with a very slender body, has dark crossbands on a pale ground color, 17 dorsal scale rows at midbody with the vertebral row greatly enlarged, and a divided cloacal scute. *Leptodeira septentrionalis* is a larger snake with dark crossbands on a pale ground color, usually 21 to 23 dorsal scale rows at midbody, and a divided cloacal scute.
**General geographic distribution:** *Sibon longifrenis* occurs at low and moderate elevations from northeastern Honduras to western Panama on the Atlantic versant.
**Distribution in Honduras:** This species is known from two nearby localities (540 to 700 m elevation) in the Mosquitia.
**Distribution in the Mosquitia:** Colón—Quebrada Machín (USNM). Olancho—Quebrada de Las Marías (USNM).

**Natural history comments:** *Sibon longifrenis* is a nocturnal, arboreal species that is known from lightly disturbed evergreen broadleaf forest in the Mosquitia. All Mosquitia specimens were found active at night in understory vegetation along streams.
**Remarks:** This snail eater was recently reported from Honduras by McCranie et al. (2001).

*Sibon nebulatus* **(Linnaeus, 1758)**
**Common name(s):** None
**Description (Plate 154):** This snake is medium-sized (to about 830 mm TL) with a long tail (0.21 to 0.29 of TL). The head is very distinctly set off from the narrow neck. There is usually a single scale (a loreal) between the postnasal and the eye. Supralabials number 5 to 9, usually 7 or 8, with the fourth and fifth or fifth and sixth bordering the eye, and the large penultimate one separated from the eye. Infralabials number 6 to 10, usually 8 or 9, with the first pair contacting each other behind the mental. The enlarged chinshields are paired and a mental groove is present. The pupil is vertically elliptical. Ventrals range from 170 to 185 (159 to 200) and subcaudals from 77 to 97 (64 to 114). The cloacal scute is usually single. Dorsal scales are smooth, without apical pits, and in 15 rows throughout the body. The vertebral scale row is moderately enlarged. The dorsum has a series of dark brownish gray bands or rings, irregularly outlined with pale pink. Dorsal interspaces are pinkish gray with dark brownish gray speckling. The head is dark brownish gray with cream speckling. The venter is cream with a salmon pink wash and a dark brownish gray continuation of the dorsal bands or rings. The iris is dark chocolate brown with gray flecking.

**Plate 154.** *Sibon nebulatus.* Photograph by McCranie.

**Similar species:** *Sibon annulatus, S. longifrenis,* and *Sibon* sp. have the first pair of infralabials separated from each other behind the mental. *Dipsas bicolor* lacks a mental groove and has unpaired chinshields and a pattern of black rings separated by pale interspaces. *Imantodes cenchoa* is a longer snake with a very slender body, has dark crossbands on a pale ground color, 17 dorsal scale rows at midbody, and a divided cloacal scute. *Leptodeira septentrionalis* is a larger snake with dark crossbands on a pale ground color, usually 21 to 23 dorsal scale rows at midbody, and a divided cloacal scute.
**General geographic distribution:** *Sibon nebulatus* occurs at low, moderate, and intermediate elevations of the Atlantic versant from northern Veracruz, Mexico, to northern Brazil and on the Pacific versant from southern Nayarit to southwestern Michoacán, Mexico, from southeastern Chiapas, Mexico, to south-central Guatemala, west-central Nicaragua, and from southeastern Costa Rica to western Ecuador. It also occurs on Trinidad and Tobago.
**Distribution in Honduras:** This snail-eater occurs across the northern portion of the country and is known from near seal level to 1690 m elevation.
**Distribution in the Mosquitia:** Gracias a Dios—Caño Awalwás (USNM); Karasangkan (USNM); Rus Rus (USNM); Bodega de Río Tapalwás (UF); Wampusirpe (LSUMZ); Warunta Tingni Kiamp (USNM). Olancho—Yapuwás (LSUMZ).
**Natural history comments:** *Sibon nebulatus* is a nocturnal, arboreal species known to occur in primary to lightly disturbed evergreen broadleaf forest in the Mosquitia. It has been found in understory vegetation and in trees up to about 8 m above the ground, both along rivers and in the forest well away from rivers and streams.

*Sibon* sp.
**Common name(s):** None
**Description (Plate 155):** This snake is small (477 mm TL in single known specimen) with a moderately long tail (0.31 of TL). The head is very distinctly set off from the narrow neck. A single scale (a loreal) is present between the postnasal and the eye. Supralabials number 8 (plus a small sub-supralabial between sutures of fourth and fifth supralabials), with the fifth and sixth (but not the

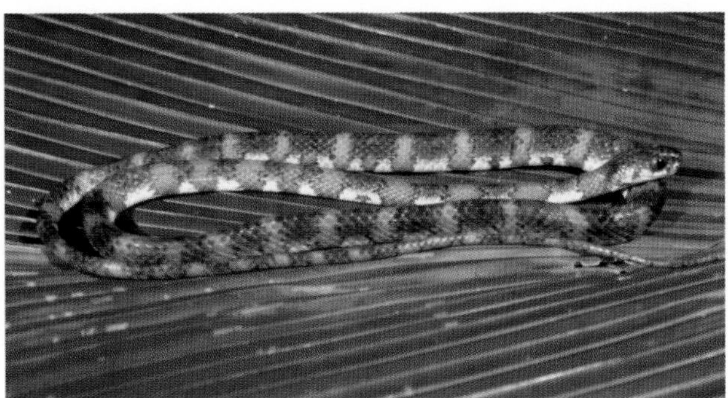

**Plate 155.** *Sibon* sp. Photograph by McCranie.

large penultimate one) bordering the eye. Infralabials number 8 with the first pair separated from each other by a single, large postmental scale. The enlarged chinshields are paired and a mental groove is present. The pupil is vertically elliptical. Ventrals number 168 and subcaudals 95. The cloacal scute is single. Dorsal scales are smooth, without apical pits, and in 15 rows throughout the body. The vertebral scale row is not enlarged anteriorly, barely enlarged posteriorly. The dorsum has tan bands or rings that become slightly darker brown ventrally, these bands or rings can be complete, divided medially, or alternating on each side ventrally. Dorsal interspaces between these bands or rings are dark brown with pale brown mottling, the ventral components of these interspaces are cream. The iris is dark brown.
**Similar species:** *Sibon annulatus* usually has paired postmental scales (occasionally a single, small postmental present) and has the dorsal components of the rings or bands darker than the dorsal components of the interspaces and 108 to 133 subcaudals. *Sibon longifrenis* has the enlarged penultimate supralabial in contact with the eye and the dorsal crossbands only reaching the lateral edges of the ventrals. *Sibon nebulatus* has the first pair of infralabials in contact posterior to the mental. *Dipsas bicolor* lacks a mental groove and has unpaired chinshields and a pattern of black rings separated by pale interspaces. *Imantodes cenchoa* is a longer snake with a very slender body, has dark crossbands on a pale ground color, 17 dorsal scale rows at midbody with the vertebral row greatly enlarged, and a divided cloacal scute. *Leptodeira septentrionalis* is a larger snake with dark crossbands on a pale ground color, usually 21 to 23 dorsal scale rows at midbody, and a divided cloacal scute.
**General geographic distribution:** *Sibon* sp. occurs at low elevations in southern Gracias a Dios, Honduras, in the Mosquitia.
**Distribution in Honduras:** This undescribed species is known only from the single locality in Gracias a Dios at 150 m elevation.
**Distribution in the Mosquitia:** Gracias a Dios—Warunta Tingni Kiamp (UF).
**Natural history comments:** *Sibon* sp. is a nocturnal, arboreal species that is known only from primary evergreen broadleaf forest in the Mosquitia. The single known specimen was active at night in a small tree in a karst limestone area.
**Remarks:** The single Mosquitia specimen represents an undescribed species (McCranie, 2006).

*Spilotes pullatus* **(Linnaeus, 1758)**
**Common name(s):** Mica (Spanish); Matsiksa* (Miskito); Clampasaya (Garífuna)
**Description (Plate 156):** This snake is large (to 2650 mm TL) with a moderately long tail (0.24 to 0.28 of TL). The head is distinctly set off from the neck. Two scales (a loreal and a preocular) are present between the nasal and the eye. Supralabials number 6 to 9, usually 7 or 8, with the third and fourth, fourth and fifth, or fifth and sixth bordering the eye. Infralabials number 6 to 10, usually 8. The enlarged chinshields are paired, a mental groove is present, and the pupil is circular. Ventrals range from 200 to 223 (198 to 241) and subcaudals from 116 to 139 (100 to 142). The cloacal scute is single. Dorsal scales are keeled, with paired apical pits, and in 14 to 18 rows at midbody. The dorsum is black with pale yellow markings on

**Plate 156.** *Spilotes pullatus.* Photograph by Gunther Köhler.

the head and anterior two-thirds of the body. The venter is pale yellow with black triangular markings on either side, which meet in the middle, increasing in size and amount of coverage posteriorly, until the posterior portion of the venter is completely black, as is the underside of the tail.
**Similar species:** *Chironius grandisquamis* is only one of two other snake species in the Mosquitia with an even number of dorsal scale rows; these rows number 10 at midbody. In addition, this snake has a uniform shiny black dorsum or black dorsum with salmon pink crossbands in adults; juveniles have a brown dorsum with pale crossbands. *Nothopsis rugosus* has 26 to 30 dorsal scale rows at midbody and the upper head surface broken up into many, small, smooth to keeled scales.
**General geographic distribution:** *Spilotes pullatus* occurs at low and moderate elevations on the Atlantic versant from southern Tamaulipas, Mexico, to northeastern Argentina and on the Pacific versant from southeastern Oaxaca, Mexico, to northwestern Ecuador. It also occurs on Trinidad and Tobago.
**Distribution in Honduras:** This species occurs throughout much of the country with a known elevational range of from near sea level to 900 m.
**Distribution in the Mosquitia:** Colón—Quebrada Machín (USNM); near Río Negro (BMNH). El Paraíso—Arenales (LACM). Gracias a Dios—Awasbila (USNM); Palacios (BMNH); Barra Patuca (USNM); Prumnitara (UF); Rus Rus (USNM); Sin Sin Warra (was in UNAH, now lost); Tikiraya (UF); near Crique Yulpruan (USNM). Olancho—Río Patuca between Quebrada El Guásimo and Río Cuyamel (USNM); confluence of Ríos Sausa and Wampú (USNM).
**Natural history comments:** *Spilotes pullatus* is a diurnal, arboreal and terrestrial species known to occur in lightly disturbed to primary evergreen broadleaf forest, denuded broadleaf swamp forest, and coastal strand in the Mosquitia. We have found this snake crawling on the forest floor, on a stream bank with its head inside a root cavity, swimming across a river, and under a stilt house.

**Plate 157.** *Tantilla taeniata*. Photograph by Eric N. Smith.

*Tantilla taeniata* **(Bocourt, 1833, *in* A.H.A. Duméril, Bocourt, and Mocquard, 1870–1909)**
**Common name(s):** None
**Description (Plate 157):** This snake is small (to 415 mm TL) with a moderately long tail (0.23 to 0.26 of TL). The head is moderately distinctly set off from the neck. There is a single scale (a preocular) between the postnasal and the eye. Supralabials number 7, with the third and fourth bordering the eye. Infralabials number 6. The enlarged chinshields are paired, a mental groove is present, and the pupil is circular. Ventrals range from 147 to 178 (143 to 178) and subcaudals from 63 to 70 (63 to 70). The cloacal scute is divided. Dorsal scales are smooth, without apical pits, and in 15 rows throughout the body. The dorsum is brown with middorsal and lateral (on adjacent halves of dorsal rows 3 and 4) very dark brown outlined gold stripes. These pale stripes commence about five scales posterior to the parietals and continue the length of the body and tail. The lower portion of the lowermost dorsal scale row is reddish orange; its upper portion is very dark brown. The venter is reddish orange, save for the chin and neck, which are cream. Some dark markings are present on infralabials 3 and 4. The head is brown above and the rostral scale is outlined with yellow. A yellow preocular spot is present on the nasal scale. A yellow postocular spot is located on the posterior half of supralabial 4, all of 5, and the anterior half of 6, the lower postocular, and the anteroventral corner of the anterior temporal. A yellow collar, about one to one and one-half scales long is present, commencing on the posterior edge of the parietals and laterally extending onto the posteroventral corner of the ultimate supralabial. The collar is divided middorsally by a single scale.
**Similar species:** *Adelphicos quadrivirgatum* has a pair of greatly enlarged chinshields, the third infralabial scale greatly reduced or absent, no preocular scale, and 29 to 50 subcaudals. Mosquitia members of the genus *Coniophanes* (*bipunctatus*,

*fissidens*, and *imperialis*) are larger snakes with two scales between the postnasal and eye and 146 or fewer ventrals. *Conophis lineatus* is a larger snake with two scales between the postnasal and eye and 19 dorsal scale rows at midbody. *Enuliophis sclateri* has a uniform dark gray dorsum with a white headband and 96 to 103 subcaudals on an extremely thick tail. *Geophis hoffmanni* has a uniformly dark dorsum, 5 supralabials, 115 to 135 ventrals, 24 to 37 subcaudals, and a single cloacal scute. *Ninia maculata* and *Ninia sebae* have keeled and heavily striated dorsal scales, a single cloacal scute, and a vertically subelliptical pupil. *Rhadinaea decorata* has 17 dorsal scale rows throughout the body, 85 to 124 subcaudals, and two scales between the nasal or postnasal and the eye. *Tantillita lintoni* has a uniform dorsal color, 103 to 116 ventrals, and 40 to 56 subcaudals. *Urotheca decipiens* and *U. guentheri* have 17 dorsal scale rows throughout the body.

**General geographic distribution:** *Tantilla taeniata* occurs at low and moderate elevations on the Atlantic versant from eastern Guatemala to north-central Nicaragua and on the Pacific versant in El Salvador and south-central Honduras.

**Distribution in Honduras:** This species is known from widely disjunct populations in the northwestern, northeastern, and south-central portions of the country. Its known elevational range is from near sea level to 1280 m.

**Distribution in the Mosquitia:** Gracias a Dios—Rus Rus (USNM); Tánsin (LSUMZ).

**Natural history comments:** *Tantilla taeniata* is a diurnal, semifossorial inhabitant of pine savanna in the Mosquitia. One specimen was crawling on the ground in the morning and another was beneath a tree stump.

*Tantillita lintoni* **(H. Smith, 1940)**

**Common name(s):** None

**Description (Plate 158):** This snake is small (to about 200 mm TL) with a relatively short tail (0.23 to 0.30 of TL). The head is slightly set off from the neck. There is a single scale (a preocular) between the postnasal and the eye. Supralabials number 6 or 7, usually 7, with the third and fourth bordering the eye. Infralabials number 6. The enlarged chinshields are paired, a mental groove is present, and the pupil is circular. Ventrals range from 103 to 116 (103 to 116) and subcaudals from 40 to 56 (40 to 56). The cloacal scute is usually divided. Dorsal scales are smooth, without apical pits, and in 15 rows throughout the body. The dorsal body coloration is uniform cinnamon brown. The dorsum of the head is dark brown with tiny tan flecks. The venter is uniform cream. The iris is very dark brown.

**Plate 158.** *Tantillita lintoni.* Photograph by McCranie.

**Similar species:** *Adelphicos quadrivirgatum* has a pair of greatly enlarged chinshields, the third infralabial scale greatly reduced or absent, no preocular scale, and a lineate dorsal pattern. Members of the genus *Coniophanes* are larger snakes with two scales between the postnasal and eye and a lineate dorsal pattern. *Enuliophis sclateri* has a uniform dark gray dorsum, a white headband, and 96 to 103 subcaudals on an extremely thick tail. *Geophis hoffmanni* has 5 supralabials, 115 to 135 ventrals, 24 to 37 subcaudals, and a single cloacal scute. *Ninia maculata* and *Ninia sebae* have keeled and heavily striated dorsal scales, a single cloacal scute, a vertically subelliptical pupil, and a dorsal pattern of dark crossbands on a paler ground color. *Rhadinaea decorata* has 17 dorsal scale rows throughout the body, 85 to 124 subcaudals, a lineate dorsal pattern, and pale postorbital and nuchal markings. *Tantilla taeniata* has a lineate pattern, 143 to 178 ventrals, and 63 to 70 subcaudals. *Urotheca decipiens* has a prominent zigzag white stripe on the lower body and 17 dorsal scale rows throughout the body. *Urotheca guentheri* has paired lateral pale stripes and 17 dorsal scale rows.

**General geographic distribution:** *Tantillita lintoni* occurs at low elevations on the Atlantic versant from southern Veracruz, Mexico, to northern Nicaragua.

**Distribution in Honduras:** This species is known

from low elevations (near sea level to 200 m) in the northern portion of the country.
**Distribution in the Mosquitia:** Gracias a Dios—Caño Awalwás (UF); Loma Pinto Quiath (USNM).
**Natural history comments:** *Tantillita lintoni* is a diurnal, semifossorial species known in the Mosquitia from two specimens taken in primary evergreen broadleaf forest. One was inside a rotten log on a hillside above a small stream and another was under leaf litter in a tree buttress on a hillside.

*Thamnophis proximus* **(Say, *in* James, 1823)**
**Common name(s):** None
**Description (Plate 159):** This snake is moderately large (to about 1250 mm TL) with a moderately long tail (0.27 to 0.30 of TL). The head is distinctly set off from the neck. Two scales (a loreal and a preocular) are present between the postnasal and the eye. Supralabials number 6 to 9, with the fourth and fifth bordering the eye. Infralabials number 8 to 11, usually 10. The enlarged chinshields are paired, a mental groove is present, and the pupil is circular. Ventrals range from 146 to 152 (141 to 181) and subcaudals from 85 to 96 (82 to 131). The cloacal scute is usually single. Dorsal scales are keeled, without apical pits, and usually in 19–19–17 rows. The dorsum is brown. The vertebral stripe is gold, narrowly outlined with black. The lateral stripe is gold. The venter is pale orange-tan laterally, cream medially. Supralabials are pale orange. The chin is white, save for pale orange pigment on the lateral portion of the infralabials.
**Similar species:** Members of the genus *Coniophanes* have smooth dorsal body scales.

**Plate 159.** *Thamnophis proximus*. Photograph by McCranie.

*Leptophis mexicanus* has a divided cloacal scute and 140 to 181 subcaudals. *Leptophis nebulosus* lacks a loreal scale and has a divided cloacal scute, and 134 to 151 subcaudals. *Tantilla taeniata* is a smaller snake with a single scale between the postnasal and the eye, a divided cloacal scute, and the dorsal scales in 15 rows throughout the body. *Urotheca decipiens* is a smaller snake with 17 smooth dorsal scale rows throughout the body. *Urotheca guentheri* is a smaller snake with smooth dorsal scales in 17 rows throughout the body and a bright orange venter.
**General geographic distribution:** *Thamnophis proximus* occurs at low and moderate elevations on the Atlantic versant from southern Wisconsin, USA, southward through the central United States (westward to eastern New Mexico) and eastern Mexico southward to central Costa Rica. It also occurs on the Pacific versant from south-central Guerrero to southeastern Oaxaca, Mexico, and from El Salvador to north-central Costa Rica.
**Distribution in Honduras:** This species is known from open habitats in about the eastern two-thirds of the country. Its known elevational range is from near sea level to 1000 m.
**Distribution in the Mosquitia:** Gracias a Dios—Barra Patuca (USNM); Mavita (USNM); Mocorón (UTA); Puerto Lempira (CAS); Rus Rus (USNM); Tánsin (LSUMZ).
**Natural history comments:** *Thamnophis proximus* is a diurnal and nocturnal, semiaquatic inhabitant of pine savanna in the Mosquitia. One specimen was crawling on the ground next to a drainage ditch, one was in a swampy area, and two were in inundated areas. One specimen regurgitated a subadult *Bufo coccifer* when captured.

*Tretanorhinus nigroluteus* **Cope, "1861" (1862)**
**Common name(s):** Li-pyutka* (Miskito)
**Description (Plate 160):** This snake is medium-sized (to about 885 mm TL) with a moderately long tail (0.23 to 0.33 of TL). The head is distinctly set off from the neck. The nostrils are dorsolaterally placed and separated by paired internasals. Two scales (a loreal and a preocular) are present between the postnasal (or nasal when that scale is only partially divided) and the eye. Supralabials number 7 to 9, usually 8, with the fourth (infrequently the fourth and fifth) bordering the eye. Infralabials number 9 to 11, usually 10. The enlarged chinshields are paired and a mental

**Plate 160.** *Tretanorhinus nigroluteus.* Photograph by McCranie.

groove is present. The pupil is vertically elliptical. Ventrals range from 130 to 152 (127 to 152) and subcaudals from 57 to 82 (56 to 82). The cloacal scute is divided. Dorsal scales are keeled, without apical pits, and usually in 21–21–19 or 21–21–17 rows (but also showing considerable departure from these basic schemata; anterior count either 21 or 23; midbody count 19, 21, or 23; posterior count 15, 17, or 19). The dorsum of the body is pale brown to black to the third scale row or the lateral edge of the ventrals with paired series of paravertebral and dorsolateral dark brown to black blotches. The venter is cream to reddish orange, with dark ventral tips and a varying amount of dark brown to black pigment midventrally. The head is pale brown to black.

**Similar species:** *Hydromorphus concolor* has smooth dorsal scales in 15 or 17 rows at midbody and the internasal scales are usually fused. All other colubrids in the Mosquitia have the nostrils laterally placed.

**General geographic distribution:** *Tretanorhinus nigroluteus* occurs at low and moderate elevations on the Atlantic versant from central Veracruz, Mexico, to northern Colombia and on the Pacific versant in south-central Honduras and western Nicaragua. It also occurs on the Islas de la Bahía, Honduras, and Isla del Maíz Grande, Nicaragua.

**Distribution in Honduras:** On the mainland of Honduras, this species occurs in the eastern two-thirds of the country, save for the southeastern and extreme southern portions. On the Bay Islands, the species occurs on Islas de Guanaja, Roatán, and Utila. Its known elevational range is from near sea level to 750 m.

**Distribution in the Mosquitia:** Colón—Anzuelo Bridge (BMNH). Gracias a Dios—Caño Awalwás (USNM); Brus Laguna (UNAH); Mocorón (CF); near Palacios (BMNH).

**Natural history comments:** *Tretanorhinus nigroluteus* is a nocturnal, aquatic inhabitant of streams in primary evergreen broadleaf forest and freshwater marshes in the Mosquitia. The single Mosquitia specimen we collected was sleeping in a coiled position among rocks in the morning beside a river.

*Tropidodipsas sartorii* **Cope, 1863**

**Common name(s):** None

**Description (Plate 161):** This is a medium-sized snake (to 857 mm TL) with a relatively short tail (0.19 to 0.23 of TL). The head is distinctly set off from the neck. Two scales (a loreal and a preocular; loreal occasionally absent) are usually present between the nasal and the eye. Supralabials number 6 to 9, usually 7, with usually the fourth and fifth bordering the eye. Infralabials number 7 to 11, usually 9. The enlarged chinshields are paired, a mental groove is present, and the pupil is vertically elliptical. Ventrals range from 176 to 189 (165 to 197) and subcaudals from 61 to 73 (52 to 77). The cloacal scute is single. Dorsal scales are weakly keeled, with or without apical pits, and in 17 rows throughout the body. The body is patterned with alternating dark brown and ivory white to dirty white rings in the Mosquitia specimens (pale rings red, orange, yellow, or beige in adults outside of the Mosquitia). Scales of the white rings are 4 to 5 and 1/2 scales long along the vertebral row and lack black tips in the Mosquitia specimens (pale

**Plate 161.** *Tropidodipsas sartorii.* Photograph by McCranie.

rings 1 to 5 scales long and usually black tipped in specimens outside of the Mosquitia). The anterior portion of the head is dark brown; this dark head cap is followed by a white to dirty white nuchal collar. The iris is dark brown.

**Similar species:** Several other species with a ringed body pattern occur in the Mosquitia. *Dipsas bicolor* has 15 smooth dorsal scale rows throughout the body and unpaired chinshields and lacks a mental groove. *Erythrolamprus mimus* has 15 smooth dorsal scale rows throughout the body, a circular pupil, a divided cloacal scute, and a tricolor pattern. *Lampropeltis triangulum* usually has 19 to 23 smooth dorsal scale rows at midbody and 17 or 19 at the vent and a tricolor pattern. The species of *Pliocercus* have 118 to 144 ventral scales, 85 to 122 subcaudal scales, and a divided cloacal scute. *Rhinobothryum bovallii* has a very large nostril, 21–19–17 or 21–21–17 dorsal scale rows that are smooth anteriorly and keeled on rows 9 to 13 posteriorly, 239 to 246 ventral scales, 115 to 125 subcaudal scales, a tricolor pattern, and a divided cloacal scute. *Sibon annulatus* has 15 smooth dorsal scale rows throughout the body and 108 to 135 subcaudals. *Sibon* sp. has 15 smooth dorsal scale rows throughout the body and 95 subcaudals. The species of *Micrurus* have 15 smooth dorsal scale rows throughout the body, a fixed fang on the anterior portion of each maxilla, and a divided cloacal scute.

**General geographic distribution:** *Tropidodipsas sartorii* occurs at low and moderate elevations on the Atlantic versant from central Nuevo León, Mexico, to eastern Honduras and on the Pacific versant from eastern Oaxaca, Mexico, to western El Salvador, and in western Nicaragua and northwestern Costa Rica.

**Distribution in Honduras:** This species is known from near sea level to 700 m elevation in the northwestern and eastern portions of the country.

**Distribution in the Mosquitia:** Gracias a Dios—Warunta Tingni Kiamp (USNM).

**Natural history comments:** *Tropidodipsas sartorii* is a nocturnal, terrestrial inhabitant of undisturbed evergreen broadleaf forest in the Mosquitia. The two Mosquitia specimens were active on the lower slopes of a mountain covered with karst limestone.

*Urotheca decipiens* **(Günther, 1893)**

**Common name(s):** None

**Description (Plate 162):** This snake is small (to about 570 mm TL) with an extremely long (0.43 of TL in single Honduran specimen), thick tail. The head is slightly distinct from the neck. Two scales (a loreal and a preocular, the latter sometimes divided into two or three scales) are present between the postnasal and the eye. Supralabials number 8 or 9, usually 8, with the fourth and fifth bordering the eye. Infralabials number 9 or 10. The enlarged chinshields are paired, a mental groove is present, and the pupil is circular. Ventrals number 143 (122 to 143) and subcaudals 110 (90 to 121). The cloacal scute is divided. Dorsal scales are smooth, without apical pits, and in 17 rows throughout the body. The middorsum of the body is dark brown and the lateral portion brown, the two areas separated by a pale yellow stripe on the middle of dorsal scale row 5. The lateral area of the dorsum is bounded ventrally by a zigzag white stripe on the adjacent portions of rows 1 and 2. The area below this stripe is brown, which is confluent with a similarly colored blotch on the lateral edge of the ventrals. The remainder of the venter is white. The dorsum of the head is rust colored to the mid-parietal level, followed by a bright orange nuchal band extending onto the first 1 or 2 postparietal scales. Supralabials are pinkish white, bounded above by a very dark brown line. The iris is brown.

**Plate 162.** *Urotheca decipiens*. Photograph by McCranie.

**Similar species:** *Adelphicos quadrivirgatum* has a pattern of dark stripes on a paler ground color, a pair of enlarged chinshields, with the third infralabial reduced or absent, and 15 dorsal scale rows throughout the body. Mosquitia members of the genus *Coniophanes* have 19 to 21 (sometimes 23) dorsal scales at midbody. *Rhadinaea decorata* has a thin tail, pale postorbital and nuchal markings, and orange ventral and subcaudal surfaces and lacks a pale lateral stripe. *Tantilla taeniata* has a single scale between the postnasal and the eye, 63 to 70 subcaudal scales and 15 dorsal scale rows throughout the body. *Urotheca guentheri* has a pair of parietal and nuchal pale spots and an orange or yellow venter in life.

**General geographic distribution:** *Urotheca decipiens* occurs at low, moderate, and intermediate elevations on the Atlantic versant from northeastern Honduras to western Panama and on the Pacific versant in southern Costa Rica, southeastern Panama, and northern Colombia.

**Distribution in Honduras:** The species is known from a single low elevation (190 m) locality in the eastern portion of the Mosquitia.

**Distribution in the Mosquitia:** Gracias a Dios—Bodega de Río Tapalwás (UF).

**Natural history comments:** The single Honduran specimen was collected at dusk in evergreen broadleaf forest as it was crawling on a bank above a small river.

**Remarks:** *Urotheca decipiens* was recently reported from Honduras by McCranie et al. (2003b).

*Urotheca guentheri* **(Dunn, 1938)**

**Common name(s):** None

**Description (Plate 163):** This snake is small to moderate-sized (to about 670 mm TL) with an extremely long (0.40 to 0.43 of TL), thick tail. The head is slightly set off from the neck. Two scales (a loreal and a preocular) are present between the postnasal (nasal sometimes only partially divided) and the eye. Supralabials number 6 to 8, usually 7, with the third and fourth bordering the eye (fourth and fifth when supralabial number is 8). Infralabials number 8. The enlarged chinshields are paired, a mental groove is present, and the pupil is circular. Ventrals range from 138 to 148 (135 to 176) and subcaudals from 95 to 109 (82 to 110). The cloacal scute is divided. Dorsal scales are smooth, without apical pits, and in 17 rows throughout the body. The middorsum is dark brown, except for the median row and portions of the paravertebral rows, which are tinted with olive. The dorsolateral stripe is cinnamon brown. The lateral field is brown, heavily flecked with dark brown and bounded by dark brown. The lateral stripe is gray. The lower half of row 1 and the lateral edges of the ventrals are dark brown. The venter is brownish orange. The dorsum of the head is brown. A cream colored pale marking is present behind the eye. A cinnamon brown spot is present posterior to the head. The lower portions of the supralabials are pale cream, save for brownish orange color along the lip line on supralabials 4, 5, and 6. The iris is rust red.

**Plate 163.** *Urotheca guentheri*. Photograph by McCranie.

**Similar species:** *Adelphicos quadrivirgatum* has a pattern of dark stripes on a paler ground color, a pair of greatly enlarged chinshields with the third infralabial reduced or absent, and 15 dorsal scale rows throughout the body. Mosquitia members of the genus *Coniophanes* have 19 to 21 (sometimes 23) dorsal scales at midbody. *Rhadinaea decorata* has a thin tail and lacks a pale lateral stripe. *Tantilla taeniata* has a single scale between the postnasal and the eye, 63 to 70 subcaudal scales, and 15 dorsal scale rows throughout the body. *Urotheca decipiens* lacks parietal and nuchal pale spots and has a white venter in life.

**General geographic distribution:** *Urotheca guentheri* occurs at low, moderate, and intermediate elevations from northeastern Honduras to western Panama on the Atlantic versant and from southeastern Costa Rica to central Panama on the Pacific versant. The species also occurs marginally on the Pacific versant in northwestern Costa Rica.

**Distribution in Honduras:** This species is known only from three low elevation localities (160 to 540 m) in the Mosquitia.

**Distribution in the Mosquitia:** Colón—Quebrada Machín (USNM). Gracias a Dios—Loma Pinto Quiath (USNM); Urus Tingni Kiamp (USNM).

**Natural history comments:** *Urotheca guentheri* is a diurnal, semifossorial inhabitant of lightly

disturbed and undisturbed evergreen broadleaf forest in the Mosquitia. All four specimens were collected inside rotten logs on steep slopes above streams.
**Remarks:** This species was recently reported from Honduras by McCranie et al. (2001).

*Xenodon rabdocephalus* **(Wied-Neuwied, 1824)**
**Common name(s):** Barba Amarilla (Spanish); Lal Pauni* (Miskito)
**Description (Plate 164):** This snake is medium-sized (to 800 mm TL) with a relatively short tail (0.14 to 0.18 of TL). The triangular head is distinctly set off from the neck. Two scales (a loreal and a preocular) are present between the postnasal and the eye. Supralabials number 7 to 9, usually 8, with the fourth and fifth bordering the eye. Infralabials number 9 to 12, usually 10 or 11. The enlarged chinshields are paired, a mental groove is present, and the pupil is circular. Ventrals range from 127 to 144 (124 to 153) and subcaudals from 39 to 52 (35 to 52). The cloacal scute is single. Dorsal scales are smooth, with a single apical pit, and in 19–19–17 rows. Dorsal coloration consists of a series of dark X-shaped blotches on a paler ground color, each blotch separated by an oval middorsal spot. The X-shaped blotches are brown peripherally and grayish brown centrally and are outlined by dark brown edging. Interspaces are pale brown to rust red with a central dark brown spot. The venter is brownish gray, increasingly mottled posteriorly with brown punctuations and washed with pale yellow. The chin is pale yellow. The head is brown above, bounded laterally by an oblique postocular tan stripe. The iris is brown.

**Plate 164.** *Xenodon rabdocephalus.* Photograph by McCranie.

**Similar species:** *Bothrops asper*, *Porthidium nasutum*, and *P. ophryomegas* have a vertically elliptical pupil, a loreal pit, and keeled dorsal scales. *Leptodeira nigrofasciata* has solid dark dorsal bands, a divided cloacal scute, and a vertically elliptical pupil.
**General geographic distribution:** *Xenodon rabdocephalus* occurs at low and moderate elevations on the Atlantic versant from central Veracruz, Mexico, to Bolivia and Brazil and on the Pacific versant from southern Guerrero, Mexico to northwestern Ecuador. Its distribution on the Pacific versant is discontinuous.
**Distribution in Honduras:** This species is known from the northern and eastern portions of the country at elevations ranging from near sea level to 1300 m.
**Distribution in the Mosquitia:** Colón—Río Guaraska (BMNH). El Paraíso—Arenales (LACM). Gracias a Dios—Awasbila (USNM); Rus Rus (USNM); Bodega de Río Tapalwás (UF); Tikiraya (UF); Cerro Wahatingni (USNM).
**Natural history comments:** *Xenodon rabdocephalus* is a diurnal, terrestrial inhabitant of evergreen broadleaf forest and broadleaf swamp forest in the Mosquitia. It can be encountered in the vicinity of human habitation carved from evergreen broadleaf forests, as well as in primary forest. In July and August of two consecutive years, we collected several specimens of this snake while we were resting on the porch of a house in Awasbila, Gracias a Dios. We were alerted to the nearby presence of these snakes either by shouts of local people or by chickens attacking the snakes. Apparently, the snakes are lured to this urban setting because of the abundance of small *Bufo marinus*.
**Remarks:** This snake is an apparent mimic of *Bothrops asper*. The patterns of the apparent mimic and model are similar to one another. Most people in the Mosquitia to whom we have shown this snake remain unconvinced that there are two species involved, even when we have the mimic in our hands. They are easily distinguished, however, because of the presence of a loreal pit, elliptical pupil, and heavily keeled scales in *B. asper*.

## Family Elapidae

Elapids are all venomous and have proteroglyph dentition on a relatively non-rotating maxilla. The members of this family of snakes range in the Western Hemisphere from the southern United States through Mexico and Central America, and into South America as far south as Peru (both west and east of the Andes), central Argentina, southeastern Brazil, and Uruguay. Members also are broadly distributed in the Eastern Hemisphere, occurring throughout Africa, the Arabian Peninsula, the southern Middle East, the Near East, the Indian subcontinent, southeastern Asia, China, Malaysia, Indonesia, Papua New Guinea, Taiwan, Japan, Australia, and the Solomon Islands. Sea snakes are found in the waters of the Indian and Pacific Oceans. Sixty genera containing 298 species were included in this family by David and Ineich (1999) and approximately 62 genera containing 300 species by Pough et al. (2003). Two genera comprising six species are known to occur in Honduras. Two species in one genus are known to range into the Mosquitia (but see Species of Probable Occurrence).

*Micrurus alleni* **K. Schmidt, 1936**
**Common name(s):** Coral, Coralillo (Spanish); Limlim*, Silbiera* (Miskito)
**Description (Plate 165):** This snake is moderate-sized (to 1340 mm TL) with a relatively short tail (0.08 to 0.10 of TL). The head is not set off from the neck. There is a single scale between the postnasal scale and the eye. Supralabials number 7, with the third and fourth bordering the eye. Infralabials number 7. The enlarged chinshields are paired, a mental groove is present, and the pupil is subcircular. Ventrals range from 228 to 231 (209 to 244) and subcaudals number 34 to 38 (32 to 59). The cloacal scute is divided. Dorsal scales are smooth,

**Plate 165.** *Micrurus alleni*. Photograph by McCranie.

without apical pits, and in 15 rows throughout the body. The dorsum is tricolor monad, with black rings surrounded by pale yellow rings separated by red rings. The yellow and red rings are marked with black dorsally. The tail is ringed with black and yellow. The pale headband is pale yellow with a tan patina. The area anterior to the eyes is black with a posterior extension along the interparietal suture to the posterior ends of the parietal scales.
**Similar species:** *Micrurus nigrocinctus* has the black head cap not or barely reaching the parietals scales and never extending posteriorly along the interparietal suture. *Erythrolamprus mimus* has white spotting in the black bands and 2 scales between the postnasal and the eye. *Lampropeltis triangulum* has 19 to 23 dorsal scale rows at midbody and a single cloacal scute. *Ninia sebae* has keeled scales and dark dorsal bands instead of rings. *Oxyrhopus petola* is banded, not ringed, and has a single cloacal scute and 19 dorsal scale rows at midbody. *Pliocercus elapoides* has 2 scales between the postnasal and the eye, a long, thick tail with 85 to 115 subcaudals, and 17 dorsal scale rows at midbody. *Pliocercus euryzonus* has the spaces between the black rings colored red dorsally and yellow ventrolaterally and ventrally, a long, thick tail with 90 to 122 subcaudals, 2 scales between the postnasal and eye, and 17 dorsal scale rows at midbody. *Rhinobothryum bovallii* has 19 or 21 dorsal scale rows at midbody and the dorsal head scales bordered with white pigment. *Scaphiodontophis annulatus* usually has a tricolored pattern only on the dorsum of the anterior portion of the body; the posterior portion of the dorsum of the body is usually brown to gray with three dotted stripes. The occasional *S. annulatus* with a tricolor dorsum throughout the body and tail have fewer than 170 ventrals, 8 to 10 supralabials, 9 to 12 infralabials, the dark dorsal bands not crossing the venter, and usually 17 dorsal scale rows at midbody. *Tropidodipsas sartorii* has 17 weakly keeled dorsal scale rows throughout the body, a bicolor pattern, and a single cloacal scute.
**General geographic distribution:** *Micrurus alleni* occurs at low and moderate elevations from northeastern Honduras to western Panama on the Atlantic versant and from west-central Costa Rica to western Panama on the Pacific versant.
**Distribution in Honduras:** This dangerously venomous coral snake is known from three low elevation localities (70 to 150 m) in the Mosquitia.
**Distribution in the Mosquitia:** Gracias a Dios—

Kaska Tingni (USNM); Warunta Tingni Kiamp (USNM); confluence of Quebrada Waskista and Río Wampú (USNM).

**Natural history comments:** *Micrurus alleni* is a nocturnal, semifossorial inhabitant of undisturbed evergreen broadleaf forest in the Mosquitia. One specimen was collected as it was active in leaf litter, another with its forebody emerging from a hole in a stream bank at dusk, another submerged in water in a swamp, and another crawling on a river bank.

*Micrurus nigrocinctus* **(Girard, 1854)**

Common name(s): Coral (Spanish); Limlim*, Silbiera* (Miskito)

**Description (Plate 166):** This snake is medium-sized (to 1150 mm TL) with a relatively short tail (0.09 to 0.17 of TL). The head is not set off from the neck. There is a single scale between the postnasal scale and the eye. Supralabials number 7, with the third and fourth bordering the eye. Infralabials number 7. The enlarged chinshields are paired, a mental groove is present, and the pupil is subcircular. Ventrals range from 190 to 224 (180 to 230) and subcaudals from 32 to 56 (31 to 56). The cloacal scute is divided. Dorsal scales are smooth, without apical pits, and in 15 rows throughout the body. Dorsal coloration often consists of tricolor monad rings of red, pale yellow, and black, with the black rings separated from the red rings by yellow on each side. Colors of the rings are slightly paler ventrally than dorsally. The head has a black snout to the level of the eyes followed by a pale yellow parietal band with a pale brown dusting, in turn followed by a black nuchal band. The iris is dark gray. Other pattern variations are seen, including one in which the black rings are reduced to a pair of ventrolateral blotches and a single midventral blotch and another in which no yellow rings are present.

**Plate 166.** *Micrurus nigrocinctus.* Photograph by McCranie.

**Similar species:** *Micrurus alleni* has the black head cap reaching the parietals scales and extending posteriorly along the interparietal suture. *Erythrolamprus mimus* has white spotting in the black bands and 2 scales between the postnasal and the eye. *Lampropeltis triangulum* has 19 to 23 dorsal scale rows at midbody and a single cloacal scute. *Ninia sebae* has keeled scales and dark dorsal bands instead of rings. *Oxyrhopus petola* is banded, not ringed, and has a single cloacal scute and 19 dorsal scale rows at midbody. *Pliocercus elapoides* has 2 scales between the postnasal and the eye, a long, thick tail with 85 to 115 subcaudals, and 17 dorsal scale rows at midbody. *Pliocercus euryzonus* has the spaces between the black rings colored red dorsally and yellow ventrolaterally and ventrally, a long, thick tail with 90 to 122 subcaudals, 2 scales between the postnasal and eye, and 17 dorsal scale rows at midbody. *Rhinobothryum bovallii* has 19 or 21 dorsal scale rows at midbody and the dorsal head scales bordered with white pigment. *Scaphiodontophis annulatus* usually has a tricolored pattern only on the dorsum of the anterior portion of the body; the posterior portion of the dorsum of the body is usually brown to gray with three dotted stripes. The occasional *S. annulatus* with a tricolor dorsum throughout the body and tail have fewer than 170 ventrals, 8 to 10 supralabials, 9 to 12 infralabials, the dark dorsal bands not crossing the venter, and usually 17 dorsal scale rows at midbody. *Tropidodipsas sartorii* has 17–17–17 weakly keeled dorsal scales and a single cloacal scute.

**General geographic distribution:** *Micrurus nigrocinctus* occurs at low, moderate, and occasionally intermediate elevations from Chiapas, Mexico, to central Panama on the Pacific versant and from northwestern Honduras to northern Colombia on the Atlantic versant. The species also occurs on Isla del Maíz Grande, Nicaragua, and the Panamanian islands of Coiba, Taboga, San José, and San Miguel.

**Distribution in Honduras:** This dangerously venomous coral snake occurs throughout much of the country, save for the southwestern portion (its known elevational range is from near sea level to 1600 m).

**Distribution in the Mosquitia:** Colón—Empalme Río Chilmeca (was in UNAH, now lost); Quebrada Machín (USNM). Gracias a Dios—Caño Awalwás (USNM); Barra Patuca (USNM); Buena Vista (BMNH); Dursuna (USNM); Mavita (USNM); Mocorón (CF); Rus Rus (USNM); Tánsin (LSUMZ); Bodega de Río Tapalwás (UF); Tikiraya (photograph).
**Natural history comments:** *Micrurus nigrocinctus* is a diurnal and nocturnal, semifossorial and ground level inhabitant of primary to lightly disturbed evergreen broadleaf forest (including gallery forest), disturbed broadleaf swamp forest, and pine savanna in the Mosquitia. This species is most often seen crawling on the forest floor in the daytime and occasionally at night. One was found inside a rotten tree stump.
**Remarks:** This coral snake is an apparent model for several members of the coral snake mimic guild (Greene and McDiarmid, 1981), including, most obviously, *Pliocercus elapoides* (see discussion in that species' account).

## Family Viperidae

Viperids are all venomous, having solenoglyph maxillary dentition (Pough et al., 2003). The members of this family of snakes occur in the Western Hemisphere from southern Canada through the United States, Mexico, Central America, and most of South America to southern Argentina. In the Eastern Hemisphere, they are distributed in Europe, Africa, and the Arabian Peninsula, then eastward through India, the Malay Peninsula and Archipelago. All Western Hemisphere members have a loreal sensory pit between the eye and nostril; thus, they are called pitvipers (subfamily Crotalinae). Thirty-two (McDiarmid et al., 1999) or 33 genera (David and Ineich, 1999) and 224 (McDiarmid et al., 1999) or 236 species (David and Ineich, 1999) were recognized in this family in the most recent worldwide summaries. David and Ineich (1999) did not recognize *Bothriopsis* Peters, but did recognize *Ermia* Zhang, and *Protobothrops* Hoge and Romano Hoge; the reverse position was taken by McDiarmid et al. (1999). Subsequently, new genera, new generic arrangements, new species, or new specific arrangements have been proposed and the exact number of genera and species in the Viperidae remains controversial (see J. Campbell and Lamar, 2004, for a recent review of the Western Hemisphere forms). Seven genera containing ten species are known to occur in Honduras. Three genera comprising four species are known to range into the Mosquitia.

*Bothriechis schlegelii* **(Berthold, 1845)**
**Common name(s):** Cornuda, Pestaña (Spanish); Waha Pyutka*, Dus Pyuatka* (Miskito)
**Description (Plate 167):** This pitviper is medium-sized (to 979 mm TL) with a relatively short, prehensile tail (0.14 to 0.19 of TL). The head is distinctly set off from the neck. One to 3, usually 2, flattened hornlike scales are present on the outer margin of the supraocular scale. Supralabials number 8 to 10, usually 8. Infralabials number 10 to 13. The pupil is vertically elliptical. Ventrals range from 144 to 162 (137 to 169) and the undivided subcaudals from 47 to 59 (42 to 64). The cloacal scute is single. Dorsal scales are keeled (except for outer row), without apical pits, and in 25 to 27 rows anteriorly, 21 to 25 at midbody, and 17 to 21 posteriorly. Dorsal coloration in this species is highly variable. One Mosquitia specimen had an olive gray dorsum, with a series of olive green-edged olive gray blotches, each successive pair of blotches separated by salmon crossbands. The venter of the body and tail was gray medially and pale reddish purple with scattered ivory white spots laterally. The head was olive green dorsally with dark olive blotches and a very dark brown postocular stripe. The chin was pale pink with gray flecking. The iris was pale grayish tan with dark brown flecking.
**Similar species:** Only the other pitvipers in the Mosquitia (*Bothrops asper*, *Porthidium nasutum*, and *P. ophryomegas)* have a loreal pit between the nostril and the eye. The three other pitvipers have

**Plate 167.** *Bothriechis schlegelii.* Photograph by McCranie.

non-prehensile tails and lack the flattened hornlike scales above the eye.
**General geographic distribution:** *Bothriechis schlegelii* is found at low and moderate elevations on the Atlantic versant from northwestern Chiapas, Mexico, to south-central Colombia and extreme southwestern Venezuela. It also occurs on the Pacific versant marginally in northwestern Costa Rica, and in southeastern Costa Rica, in central Panama, and from eastern Panama to northwestern Ecuador.
**Distribution in Honduras:** This dangerously venomous species occurs across the northern portion of the country with a known elevational range of from near sea level to 1300 m.
**Distribution in the Mosquitia:** Colón—Empalme Río Chilmeca (was in UNAH, now lost); Río Guaraska (BMNH); Subterráneo del Río Plátano (was in UNAH, now lost). Gracias a Dios—near Auka Kiamp (USNM); Caño Awalwás (sight record); Mocorón (UTA color slide); Rus Rus (UF); Bodega de Río Tapalwás (COHDEFOR); Cerro Wahatingni (UF). Olancho—Quebrada de Las Marías (USNM); Nueva Esperanza (USNM); confluence of Ríos Sausa and Wampú (USNM).
**Natural history comments:** *Bothriechis schlegelii* is a nocturnal, arboreal inhabitant of primary to disturbed evergreen broadleaf forest in the Mosquitia. This species is usually seen at night on low vegetation near streams, although it can also be found in the forest well away from streams. They are also sometimes found during the day sleeping on vegetation. A young adult contained an adult *Norops dariense* in its stomach.

*Bothrops asper* **(Garman, "1883" [1884])**
**Common name(s):** Barba Amarilla (Spanish); Lal Pauni*, Taningap (Miskito)
**Description (Plate 168):** This pitviper is large (to about 2500 mm TL) with a relatively short, non-prehensile tail (0.12 to 0.16 of TL). The triangular head is distinctly set off from the neck. Supralabials number 7 or 8, usually 7. Infralabials number 8 to 12, usually 10. The pupil is vertically elliptical. Ventrals range from 192 to 215 (161 to 249) and the divided subcaudals from 57 to 70 (46 to 86). The cloacal scute is single. Dorsal scales are keeled, without apical pits, and in 25 to 29 rows anteriorly, 23 to 33 (usually 25 to 29) at midbody, and 19 to 21 (usually 21) posteriorly. The dorsum of the body is a pale to dark gray or brown ground color with a series of dorsolateral dark brown triangular markings (apex dorsad) outlined laterally with cream to yellow bars, which markings may join middorsally to form an X-shaped blotch. Opposite each corner of the base of the triangular markings is a dark gray to brown blotch. The venter is cream with diffuse pale brown to brown blotching medially and dark brown blotching laterally. The head is brown to dark brown dorsally. Laterally, a dark postocular stripe extends from eye to the corner of the mouth, bounded above by a pale gray to brown line. The chin is immaculate cream.

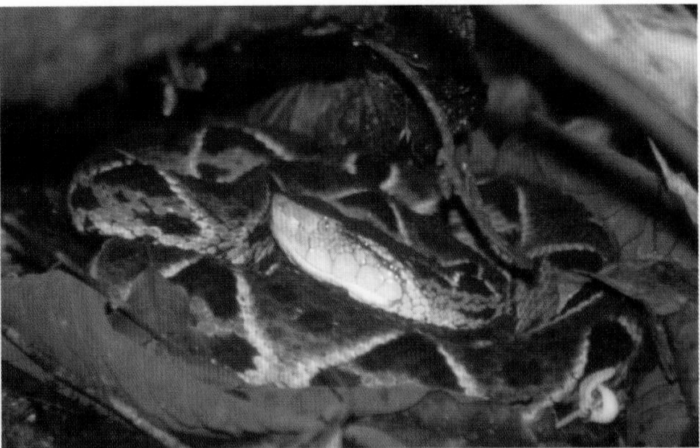
**Plate 168.** *Bothrops asper.* Photograph by Townsend.

**Similar species:** Only the other pitvipers in the Mosquitia (*Bothriechis schlegelii*, *Porthidium nasutum*, and *P. ophryomegas*) have a loreal pit between the nostril and the eye. The three other pitvipers have undivided subcaudals.
**General geographic distribution:** *Bothrops asper* occurs at low and moderate elevations on the Atlantic versant from southern Tamaulipas, Mexico, to northern Colombia and northern Venezuela. It also occurs in disjunct Pacific versant populations in southern Chiapas, Mexico, to southwestern Guatemala, and in more-or-less continuous Pacific versant populations from northwestern Costa Rica to southwestern Ecuador.
**Distribution in Honduras:** This dangerously venomous snake occurs across the northern portion of the country and has a known elevational range of from near sea level to 1300 m.
**Distribution in the Mosquitia:** Colón—Amarillo (BMNH); Las Champas (BMNH); Empalme Río Chilmeca (was in UNAH, now lost); Tulito (BMNH). Gracias a Dios—Caño Awalwás (UF); Awasbila (sight record); Río Coco (USNM); Crique Curamaira (sight record); Kalila Plapan Tingni (sight record); Karasangkan (sight record); Loma Pinto Quiath

(USNM); Mavita (sight record); Mocorón (CF); Rus Rus (UF); Swabila (UF); Bodega de Río Tapalwás (photograph); Tikiraya (UF); near Urus Tingni Kiamp (USNM); Urus Tingni Kiamp (USNM); Warunta Tingni Kiamp (USNM); Wausira (LSUMZ). Olancho—Caobita (SMF); Quebrada El Guásimo (USNM); Quebrada de Las Marías (USNM); Matamoros (USNM); Río Seco (FMNH); confluence of Quebrada Siksatara with Río Wampú (USNM).

**Natural history comments:** *Bothrops asper* is a nocturnal and diurnal, terrestrial to understory level inhabitant of primary to heavily disturbed evergreen broadleaf forest, broadleaf swamp forest, and pine savanna/evergreen broadleaf forest ecotone in the Mosquitia. This species is usually found coiled on the forest floor, but we have also found it coiled in vegetation nearly 3 m above the ground (including juveniles and adults). It also frequents stream and riverbanks and, on several occasions, we have seen it swimming in streams or half submerged in slow-moving backwater areas of streams or rivers. One crawled into our campsite during the middle of the night and another was under some gear during the daytime. One was coiled in the same spot near a tree buttress for at least 8 hours before we decided to kill it, as it was alongside a trail we were working. The species appears to be active throughout the year.

**Remarks:** This is the largest and most dangerous venomous snake in the Mosquitia. It is fairly common where it occurs; we generally encounter at least one a day while working in its habitat. It possesses an extremely effective cryptic pattern and is easily overlooked as it lies among the litter on the forest floor. Given that it is most often found on the forest floor, where it is a sit-and-wait predator, one's search pattern is not accustomed to expect this snake to be found above the level of the lower body. We have found this pitviper, however, at head level on the banks of streams and, even more surprisingly, on vines hanging from trees. We must caution people who work out-of-doors that these snakes can be in unexpected places. In our experience, medical clinics in remote areas usually do not have viable antivenin to treat the bites of venomous snakes. In some instances, people who are bitten turn to local *curanderos* for treatment. Although we have been told of individuals who have been successfully treated by such practitioners, we have also been witness to a case in which a Nicaraguan bitten 3 days prior to being brought by our camp on the Río Coco and treated by a local *curandero* died the next day in a clinic on the Nicaraguan side of the river. Ironically, a *curandero* living in Awasbila died after being bitten by an adult *B. asper* in 2004. In another instance, a woman was bitten by a snake said to be *B. asper*. We saw her in Rus Rus 6 hours after the bite took place and it appeared that she had not been bitten by a snake of this species. Nevertheless, the clinic in Rus Rus had no antivenin, having previously dumped a small supply of expired serum. The woman had to be transported to Puerto Lempira, 6 hours away, where she proved to have no serious consequences from the bite.

*Porthidium nasutum* **(Bocourt, 1868)**
**Common name(s):** Naríz de Chanco (Spanish); Pyuta Aingwa* (Miskito)
**Description (Plates 169 and 170):** This pitviper is small to moderate-sized (to 635 mm TL) with a relatively short, non-prehensile tail (0.09 to 0.13 of TL). The triangular head is distinctly set off from the neck. The rostral scale projects above the snout (a proboscis) and is bordered laterally by the anterior edge of the nasal and first supralabial. Supralabials number 8 to 11, usually 9 or 10. Infralabials number 9 to 13, usually 12. The pupil is vertically elliptical. Ventrals range from 133 to 141 (123 to 145) and the undivided subcaudals from 26 to 35 (24 to 41). The cloacal scute is single. Dorsal scales are keeled, without apical pits, and in 23 to 29 (usually 25) rows anteriorly, 21 to 27 (usually 23) at midbody, and 17 to 21 (usually 19) posteriorly. The dorsum is purplish gray to brownish gray with a series of dark gray blotches bisected by a maroon

**Plate 169.** *Porthidium nasutum* (blue phase). Photograph by McCranie.

**Plate 170.** *Porthidium nasutum* (brown phase). Photograph by McCranie.

middorsal stripe. The head is dark gray above with a maroon patina. The venter grades from grayish white on the chin to purplish gray posteriorly. The underside of the tail is yellowish tan with gray speckling. The iris is pale gray.

**Similar species:** Only the other pitvipers in the Mosquitia (*Bothriechis schlegelii*, *Bothrops asper*, and *P. ophryomegas*) have a loreal pit between the nostril and the eye. *Bothriechis schlegelii* has a prehensile tail and flattened hornlike scales projecting from the outer margin of the supraocular scale. *Bothrops asper* is a larger snake with divided subcaudals. *Porthidium ophryomegas* has the tip of the snout rounded and lacks a proboscis.

**General geographic distribution:** *Porthidium nasutum* occurs at low and moderate elevations on the Atlantic versant from northwestern Chiapas, Mexico, to northwestern Colombia. It also occurs on the Pacific versant in central and southern Panama, then southwards to western Ecuador. It also occurs marginally on the Pacific versant in northwestern Costa Rica.

**Distribution in Honduras:** This venomous snake occurs at low and the lower limits of moderate elevations (from near sea level to 660 m) in the northern portion of the country.

**Distribution in the Mosquitia:** Colón—Las Champas (BMNH); Río Guaraska (BMNH); Subterráneo del Río Plátano (was in UNAH, now lost). Gracias a Dios—Caño Awalwás (UF); Awasbila (sight record); Bodega de Río Tapalwás (USNM); Urus Tingni Kiamp (USNM); near Wakling Kiamp (USNM); Warunta Tingni Kiamp (USNM). Olancho—Quebrada de Las Marías (USNM).

**Natural history comments:** *Porthidium nasutum* is a nocturnal and diurnal, terrestrial to semifossorial inhabitant of lightly disturbed and undisturbed evergreen broadleaf forest in the Mosquitia. We have found this species coiled on trails, in leaf litter, and on top of logs, and crawling on the forest floor. One was crawling next to a tent in a McCranie campsite at about 650 h and another was coiled near midday between two tents.

*Porthidium ophryomegas* **(Bocourt, 1868)**

**Common name(s):** Sulkat* (Miskito)

**Description (Plate 171):** This pitviper is moderately small (to about 770 mm TL) with a relatively short, non-prehensile tail (0.10 to 0.15 of TL). The triangular head is distinctly set off from the neck. Supralabials number 8 to 10, usually 9 or 10. Infralabials number 9 to 13, usually 10 or 11. The pupil is vertically elliptical. Ventrals range from 156 to 171 (156 to 176) and the undivided subcaudals from 33 to 46 (32 to 46). The cloacal scute is single. Dorsal scales are keeled, with paired apical pits, and in 21 to 27 rows anteriorly, 23 to 27 (usually 25) at midbody, and 19 rows posteriorly. The median portion of the dorsum is pale gray, the lateral portion gray, with a series (33–53) of dark gray dorsal blotches on either side of the middorsum, separated by a narrow pale tan middorsal line. The venter is white and heavily blotched with black, which blotching increases in intensity posteriorly. The underside of the tail is blotched with black and white grading to uniform gray posteriorly. The dorsum of the head is dark gray with a black postocular stripe. The chin is

**Plate 171.** *Porthidium ophryomegas*. Photograph by McCranie.

white with black blotching. The iris is gray.
**Similar species:** Only the other pitvipers in the Mosquitia (*Bothriechis schlegelii*, *Bothrops asper*, and *P. nasutum*) have a loreal pit between the nostril and the eye. *Bothriechis schlegelii* has a prehensile tail and flattened hornlike scales projecting from the outer margin of the supraocular scale. *Bothrops asper* is a larger snake with divided subcaudals. *Porthidium nasutum* has the tip of the snout strongly upturned, usually with a fleshy proboscis.
**General geographic distribution:** *Porthidium ophryomegas* is found at low and moderate elevations on the Pacific versant from southwestern Guatemala to west-central Costa Rica. It also occurs on the Atlantic versant in interior valleys in Guatemala and Honduras. The species is also known from several Atlantic coastal localities in Honduras.
**Distribution in Honduras:** This venomous snake occurs in open habitats in the southern, south-central, north-central, and northeastern portions of the country. It is known from near sea level to 1400 m elevation.
**Distribution in the Mosquitia:** Gracias a Dios—Mavita (USNM); Mocorón (CF); Rus Rus (UF; USNM); Suhi (USNM); Tánsin (LSUMZ).
**Natural history comments:** *Porthidium ophryomegas* is a nocturnal, terrestrial inhabitant of pine savanna (including swamps in pine savanna) in the Mosquitia. A favorite resting place of this species appears to be at the base of heavy clumps of grass on the perimeter of swampy areas. This species is commonly found in the village of Rus Rus. The oldest son of Tomás Manzanares (see Dedication) has been bitten on the foot twice by *P. ophryomegas* while playing in his yard.
**Remarks:** Snakes of this species from the Mosquitia differ in color and number of dorsal blotches from those elsewhere in the range. However, a DNA sample from a Mocorón specimen shows it to be closely related to Guanacaste, Costa Rican specimens (Carl Franklin, pers. comm.).

# Ecological Distribution and Relationships of the Mosquitia Herpetofauna

The Mosquitia is a large, ecologically diverse area of Honduras (see Vegetation Zones and Environments in the chapter entitled Description of the Honduran Mosquita) and it is inhabited by a significantly large segment of the Honduran herpetofauna. Given the size and diversity of both the area and the herpetofauna, it is not surprising that individual species do not occur in all the habitats of the Mosquitia. On the contrary, various patterns of ecological distribution of the herpetofauna exist. Given the existence of these patterns and the diversity of lifestyles practiced by the herpetofauna, it is also the case that various patterns of ecological relationships also exist. It is the purpose of this section to examine these patterns.

Eight major vegetation zones or environments are recognized herein in the Mosquitia, i.e., lowland pine savanna, evergreen broadleaf forest, mangrove forest, freshwater marshes, coastal strand and *cocotales*, broadleaf swamp forest, estuaries, and marine environs. The distribution of 155 of the 156 Mosquitia herpetological species (*Hemidactylus frenatus* is strictly edificarian; thus it is not included in these vegetation zones) in these eight vegetation zones is indicated in Table 3. The largest number of species (132, or 85.2%) is found in evergreen broadleaf forest. This is to be expected, given the relative hospitability of this vegetation zone for amphibians and reptiles. The respective numbers found in the other seven

**Table 3.** Distribution of the herpetofauna in the vegetation zones and environments of the Mosquitia.

| Species[1] | Lowland Pine Savanna | Evergreen Broadleaf Forest | Mangrove Forest | Freshwater Marshes | Coastal Strand and Cocotales | Broadleaf Swamp Forest | Estuaries | Marine Environs | Totals |
|---|---|---|---|---|---|---|---|---|---|
| *Gymnopis multiplicata* | — | X | — | — | — | — | — | — | 1 |
| *Bolitoglossa mexicana* | — | X | — | — | — | — | — | — | 1 |
| *Bolitoglossa striatula* | — | X | — | — | — | — | — | — | 1 |
| *Oedipina cyclocauda* | — | X | — | — | — | — | — | — | 1 |
| *Bufo coccifer* | X | X | — | — | — | — | — | — | 2 |
| *Bufo haematiticus* | — | X | — | — | — | — | — | — | 1 |
| *Bufo marinus* | X | X | — | X | X | X | — | — | 5 |
| *Bufo valliceps* | X | X | — | X | — | X | — | — | 4 |
| *Centrolene prosoblepon* | — | X | — | — | — | — | — | — | 1 |

Table 3 (continued)

| Species[1] | Lowland Pine Savanna | Evergreen Broadleaf Forest | Mangrove Forest | Freshwater Marshes | Coastal Strand and Cocotales | Broadleaf Swamp Forest | Estuaries | Marine Environs | Totals |
|---|---|---|---|---|---|---|---|---|---|
| *Cochranella albomaculata* | — | X | — | — | — | — | — | — | 1 |
| *Cochranella granulosa* | — | X | — | — | — | — | — | — | 1 |
| *Cochranella spinosa* | — | X | — | — | — | — | — | — | 1 |
| *Hyalinobatrachium cardiacalyptum* | — | X | — | — | — | — | — | — | 1 |
| *Hyalinobatrachium fleischmanni* | — | X | — | — | — | — | — | — | 1 |
| *Hyalinobatrachium pulveratum* | — | X | — | — | — | — | — | — | 1 |
| *Agalychnis calcarifer* | — | X | — | — | — | — | — | — | 1 |
| *Agalychnis callidryas* | — | X | — | — | — | X | — | — | 2 |
| *Agalychnis saltator* | — | X | — | — | — | X | — | — | 2 |
| *Anotheca spinosa* | — | X | — | — | — | — | — | — | 1 |
| *Hyla ebraccata* | — | X | — | — | — | X | — | — | 2 |
| *Hyla loquax* | — | X | — | — | — | X | — | — | 2 |
| *Hyla microcephala* | X | X | — | — | X | X | — | — | 4 |
| *Hyla miliaria* | — | X | — | — | — | — | — | — | 1 |
| *Hyla picta* | — | — | — | — | X | — | — | — | 1 |
| *Phrynohyas venulosa* | X | X | — | — | X | X | — | — | 4 |
| *Ptychohyla hypomykter* | — | X | — | — | — | — | — | — | 1 |
| *Scinax boulengeri* | — | X | — | — | — | X | — | — | 2 |
| *Scinax staufferi* | X | X | — | X | X | X | — | — | 5 |

Table 3 (continued)

| Species[1] | Lowland Pine Savanna | Evergreen Broadleaf Forest | Mangrove Forest | Freshwater Marshes | Coastal Strand and Cocotales | Broadleaf Swamp Forest | Estuaries | Marine Environs | Totals |
|---|---|---|---|---|---|---|---|---|---|
| *Smilisca baudinii* | X | X | — | — | — | X | — | — | 3 |
| *Smilisca phaeota* | — | X | — | — | — | — | — | — | 1 |
| *Smilisca sordida* | — | X | — | — | — | — | — | — | 1 |
| *Craugastor epochthidius* | — | X | — | — | — | — | — | — | 1 |
| *Craugastor fitzingeri* | — | X | — | — | — | X | — | — | 2 |
| *Craugastor lauraster* | — | X | — | — | — | — | — | — | 1 |
| *Craugastor megacephalus* | — | X | — | — | — | — | — | — | 1 |
| *Craugastor mimus* | — | X | — | — | — | — | — | — | 1 |
| *Craugastor noblei* | — | X | — | — | — | — | — | — | 1 |
| *Craugastor pechorum* | — | X | — | — | — | — | — | — | 1 |
| *Eleutherodactylus cerasinus* | — | X | — | — | — | — | — | — | 1 |
| *Eleutherodactylus diastema* | — | X | — | — | — | — | — | — | 1 |
| *Eleutherodactylus ridens* | — | X | — | — | — | — | — | — | 1 |
| *Leptodactylus fragilis* | X | X | — | X | X | X | — | — | 5 |
| *Leptodactylus melanonotus* | — | X | — | — | — | — | — | — | 1 |
| *Leptodactylus pentadactylus* | — | X | — | — | — | X | — | — | 2 |
| *Rana brownorum* | X | X | — | X | X | X | — | — | 5 |
| *Rana maculata* | — | X | — | — | — | — | — | — | 1 |
| *Rana vaillanti* | X | X | — | — | — | X | — | — | 3 |

Table 3 (continued)

| Species[1] | Lowland Pine Savanna | Evergreen Broadleaf Forest | Mangrove Forest | Freshwater Marshes | Coastal Strand and Cocotales | Broadleaf Swamp Forest | Estuaries | Marine Environs | Totals |
|---|---|---|---|---|---|---|---|---|---|
| *Rana warszewitschii* | — | X | — | — | — | — | — | — | 1 |
| *Caiman crocodilus* | — | X | — | X | — | — | X | — | 3 |
| *Crocodylus acutus* | — | X | X | — | — | — | X | — | 3 |
| *Caretta caretta* | — | — | — | — | — | — | — | X | 1 |
| *Chelonia mydas* | — | — | — | — | — | — | — | X | 1 |
| *Eretmochelys imbricata* | — | — | — | — | — | — | — | X | 1 |
| *Chelydra serpentina* | — | X | — | — | — | X | — | — | 2 |
| *Dermochelys coriacea* | — | — | — | — | — | — | — | X | 1 |
| *Trachemys venusta* | X | X | — | X | — | X | X | — | 5 |
| *Rhinoclemmys annulata* | — | X | — | — | — | — | — | — | 1 |
| *Rhinoclemmys areolata* | X | — | — | — | — | — | — | — | 1 |
| *Rhinoclemmys funerea* | — | X | — | — | — | — | — | — | 1 |
| *Rhinoclemmys pulcherrima* | — | X | — | — | — | — | — | — | 1 |
| *Kinosternon leucostomum* | — | X | — | — | X | X | — | — | 3 |
| *Kinosternon scorpioides* | X | — | — | X | — | X | — | — | 3 |
| *Gonatodes albogularis* | X | — | — | — | — | — | — | — | 1 |
| *Sphaerodactylus millepunctatus* | X | X | — | — | X | — | — | — | 3 |
| *Thecadactylus rapicauda* | — | X | — | — | — | — | — | — | 1 |
| *Basiliscus plumifrons* | — | X | — | — | — | — | — | — | 1 |

Table 3 (continued)

| Species[1] | Lowland Pine Savanna | Evergreen Broadleaf Forest | Mangrove Forest | Freshwater Marshes | Coastal Strand and Cocotales | Broadleaf Swamp Forest | Estuaries | Marine Environs | Totals |
|---|---|---|---|---|---|---|---|---|---|
| *Basiliscus vittatus* | X | X | — | X | X | X | — | — | 5 |
| *Corytophanes cristatus* | — | X | — | — | — | — | — | — | 1 |
| *Ctenosaura similis* | — | — | — | X | X | — | — | — | 2 |
| *Iguana iguana* | — | X | — | — | — | — | — | — | 1 |
| *Sceloporus malachiticus* | — | X | — | — | — | — | — | — | 1 |
| *Sceloporus variabilis* | X | — | — | — | — | — | — | — | 1 |
| *Norops biporcatus* | — | X | — | — | — | X | — | — | 2 |
| *Norops capito* | — | X | — | — | — | — | — | — | 1 |
| *Norops dariense* | — | X | — | — | — | X | — | — | 2 |
| *Norops lemurinus* | — | X | — | — | — | — | — | — | 1 |
| *Norops limifrons* | — | X | — | — | — | X | — | — | 2 |
| *Norops lionotus* | — | X | — | — | — | — | — | — | 1 |
| *Norops pentaprion* | — | X | — | — | — | — | — | — | 1 |
| *Norops quaggulus* | — | X | — | — | — | — | — | — | 1 |
| *Norops sericeus* | X | — | — | — | — | X | — | — | 2 |
| *Norops tropidonotus* | — | X | — | — | — | — | — | — | 1 |
| *Norops wampuensis* | — | X | — | — | — | — | — | — | 1 |
| *Polychrus gutturosus* | — | X | — | — | — | — | — | — | 1 |
| *Mabuya unimarginata* | X | X | — | — | X | X | — | — | 4 |

Table 3 (continued)

| Species[1] | Lowland Pine Savanna | Evergreen Broadleaf Forest | Mangrove Forest | Freshwater Marshes | Coastal Strand and Cocotales | Broadleaf Swamp Forest | Estuaries | Marine Environs | Totals |
|---|---|---|---|---|---|---|---|---|---|
| *Sphenomorphus cherriei* | X | X | — | — | — | — | — | — | 2 |
| *Gymnophthalmus speciosus* | X | — | — | — | — | — | — | — | 1 |
| *Ameiva festiva* | — | X | — | — | — | — | — | — | 1 |
| *Ameiva undulata* | X | X | — | — | — | — | — | — | 2 |
| *Aspidoscelis deppii* | X | X | — | — | X | — | — | — | 3 |
| *Cnemidophorus lemniscatus* | — | — | — | — | X | — | — | — | 1 |
| *Lepidophyma flavimaculatum* | — | X | — | — | — | — | — | — | 1 |
| *Anomalepis mexicanus* | — | X | — | — | — | — | — | — | 1 |
| *Typhlops costaricensis* | — | X | — | — | — | — | — | — | 1 |
| *Boa constrictor* | X | X | — | — | — | X | — | — | 3 |
| *Corallus annulatus* | — | X | — | — | — | — | — | — | 1 |
| *Adelphicos quadrivirgatum* | — | X | — | — | — | — | — | — | 1 |
| *Chironius grandisquamis* | — | X | — | — | — | — | — | — | 1 |
| *Clelia clelia* | — | X | — | — | — | — | — | — | 1 |
| *Coniophanes bipunctatus* | X | — | — | — | — | — | — | — | 1 |
| *Coniophanes fissidens* | — | X | — | — | — | — | — | — | 1 |
| *Coniophanes imperialis* | — | — | — | — | — | X | — | — | 1 |
| *Conophis lineatus* | X | — | — | — | — | — | — | — | 1 |
| *Dendrophidion percarinatum* | — | X | — | — | — | — | — | — | 1 |

Table 3 (continued)

| Species[1] | Lowland Pine Savanna | Evergreen Broadleaf Forest | Mangrove Forest | Freshwater Marshes | Coastal Strand and Cocotales | Broadleaf Swamp Forest | Estuaries | Marine Environs | Totals |
|---|---|---|---|---|---|---|---|---|---|
| *Dendrophidion vinitor* | — | X | — | — | — | — | — | — | 1 |
| *Dipsas bicolor* | — | X | — | — | — | — | — | — | 1 |
| *Drymarchon melanurus* | X | X | — | — | — | — | — | — | 2 |
| *Drymobius margaritiferus* | X | X | — | — | — | X | — | — | 3 |
| *Drymobius melanotropis* | — | X | — | — | — | — | — | — | 1 |
| *Enuliophis sclateri* | — | X | — | — | — | — | — | — | 1 |
| *Erythrolamprus mimus* | — | X | — | — | — | — | — | — | 1 |
| *Geophis hoffmanni* | — | X | — | — | — | — | — | — | 1 |
| *Hydromorphus concolor* | — | X | — | — | — | — | — | — | 1 |
| *Imantodes cenchoa* | — | X | — | — | — | X | — | — | 2 |
| *Lampropeltis triangulum* | — | X | — | — | — | — | — | — | 1 |
| *Leptodeira annulata* | X | — | — | X | — | — | — | — | 2 |
| *Leptodeira nigrofasciata* | — | X | — | — | — | — | — | — | 1 |
| *Leptodeira septentrionalis* | — | X | — | — | — | — | — | — | 1 |
| *Leptophis ahaetulla* | — | X | — | — | — | X | — | — | 2 |
| *Leptophis mexicanus* | X | X | — | X | X | X | — | — | 5 |
| *Leptophis nebulosus* | — | — | — | — | X | X | — | — | 2 |
| *Masticophis mentovarius* | X | — | — | — | — | — | — | — | 1 |
| *Mastigodryas melanolomus* | — | X | — | — | — | — | — | — | 1 |

Table 3 (continued)

| Species[1] | Lowland Pine Savanna | Evergreen Broadleaf Forest | Mangrove Forest | Freshwater Marshes | Coastal Strand and Cocotales | Broadleaf Swamp Forest | Estuaries | Marine Environs | Totals |
|---|---|---|---|---|---|---|---|---|---|
| *Ninia maculata* | — | X | — | — | — | — | — | — | 1 |
| *Ninia sebae* | X | X | — | — | — | — | — | — | 2 |
| *Nothopsis rugosus* | — | X | — | — | — | — | — | — | 1 |
| *Oxybelis aeneus* | X | X | — | X | — | — | — | — | 3 |
| *Oxybelis brevirostris* | — | X | — | — | — | — | — | — | 1 |
| *Oxybelis fulgidus* | — | X | — | — | — | — | — | — | 1 |
| *Oxyrhopus petola* | — | X | — | — | — | X | — | — | 2 |
| *Pliocercus elapoides* | — | X | — | — | — | — | — | — | 1 |
| *Pliocercus euryzonus* | — | X | — | — | — | — | — | — | 1 |
| *Pseustes poecilonotus* | — | X | — | — | — | — | — | — | 1 |
| *Rhadinaea decorata* | — | X | — | — | — | — | — | — | 1 |
| *Rhinobothryum bovallii* | — | X | — | — | — | — | — | — | 1 |
| *Scaphiodontophis annulatus* | X | X | — | — | — | — | — | — | 2 |
| *Sibon annulatus* | — | — | — | — | — | X | — | — | 1 |
| *Sibon longifrenis* | — | X | — | — | — | — | — | — | 1 |
| *Sibon nebulatus* | — | X | — | — | — | — | — | — | 1 |
| *Sibon* sp. | — | X | — | — | — | — | — | — | 1 |
| *Spilotes pullatus* | — | X | — | — | X | X | — | — | 3 |
| *Tantilla taeniata* | X | — | — | — | — | — | — | — | 1 |

Table 3 (continued)

| Species[1] | Lowland Pine Savanna | Evergreen Broadleaf Forest | Mangrove Forest | Freshwater Marshes | Coastal Strand and Cocotales | Broadleaf Swamp Forest | Estuaries | Marine Environs | Totals |
|---|---|---|---|---|---|---|---|---|---|
| *Tantillita lintoni* | — | X | — | — | — | — | — | — | 1 |
| *Thamnophis proximus* | X | — | — | — | — | — | — | — | 1 |
| *Tretanorhinus nigroluteus* | X | X | — | X | — | — | — | — | 3 |
| *Tropidodipsas sartorii* | — | X | — | — | — | — | — | — | 1 |
| *Urotheca decipiens* | — | X | — | — | — | — | — | — | 1 |
| *Urotheca guentheri* | — | X | — | — | — | — | — | — | 1 |
| *Xenodon rabdocephalus* | — | X | — | — | — | X | — | — | 2 |
| *Micrurus alleni* | — | X | — | — | — | — | — | — | 1 |
| *Micrurus nigrocinctus* | X | X | — | — | — | X | — | — | 3 |
| *Bothriechis schlegelii* | — | X | — | — | — | — | — | — | 1 |
| *Bothrops asper* | X | X | — | — | — | X | — | — | 3 |
| *Porthidium nasutum* | — | X | — | — | — | — | — | — | 1 |
| *Porthidium ophryomegas* | X | — | — | — | — | — | — | — | 1 |
| Totals (155) | 40 | 132 | 1 | 14 | 17 | 39 | 3 | 4 | — |

[1]*Hemidactylus frenatus* is not included in this table, because in the Mosquitia it is found only in edificarian situations.

vegetation zones are as follows: pine savanna—40 (25.8%); mangrove forest—1 (0.6%); freshwater marshes—14 (9.0%); coastal strand and *cocotales* —17 (11.0%); broadleaf swamp forest—39 (25.2%); estuaries—3 (1.9%); and marine environs—4 (2.6%).

Community ecologists recognize guild structures based on a variety of ecological criteria. Heyer et al. (1990) recognized a set of adult amphibian guilds, based on the criteria of microhabitat occurrence, diel activity, and feeding behavior, which were adapted for use in defining guild structure for Honduran amphibians (McCranie and Wilson, 2002). We have further adapted this structure for use in identifying the guilds for the Mosquitia amphibian species adults (Table 4). Ten such guilds are recognized. The

**Table 4.** Adult guilds for the amphibian species of the Mosquitia. This listing is adapted from that in McCranie and Wilson (2002). Species in each category are arranged in the same order as they appear in the text.

| | | |
|---|---|---|
| 1. | Fossorial predators | |
| | *Gymnopis multiplicata* | *Oedipina cyclocauda* |
| 2. | Ground level, sit-and-wait, diurnal/nocturnal predators | |
| | *Bufo haematiticus* | *Craugastor mimus* |
| | *Craugastor lauraster* | *Craugastor noblei* |
| 3. | Pond, marshside, or streamside, sit-and-wait, diurnal/nocturnal predators | |
| | *Rana brownorum* | *Rana warszewitschii* |
| 4. | Ground level, sit-and-wait, nocturnal predators | |
| | *Bufo coccifer* | *Craugastor megacephalus* |
| | *Bufo marinus* | *Leptodactylus pentadactylus* |
| | *Bufo valliceps* | |
| 5. | Ground level/understory, sit-and-wait, nocturnal predators | |
| | *Craugastor fitzingeri* | |
| 6. | Understory level, sit-and-wait, nocturnal predators | |
| | *Hyla ebraccata* | *Scinax boulengeri* |
| | *Hyla loquax* | *Scinax staufferi* |
| | *Hyla microcephala* | *Smilisca baudinii* |
| | *Hyla picta* | *Smilisca phaeota* |
| | *Phrynohyas venulosa* | *Smilisca sordida* |
| | *Ptychohyla hypomykter* | |
| 7. | Understory/canopy level, sit-and-wait, nocturnal predators | |
| | *Bolitoglossa mexicana* | *Hyalinobatrachium fleischmanni* |
| | *Bolitoglossa striatula* | *Hyalinobatrachium pulveratum* |
| | *Centrolene prosoblepon* | *Agalychnis callidryas* |
| | *Cochranella albomaculata* | *Agalychnis saltator* |
| | *Cochranella granulosa* | *Eleutherodactylus cerasinus* |
| | *Cochranella spinosa* | *Eleutherodactylus diastema* |
| | *Hyalinobatrachium cardiacalyptum* | *Eleutherodactylus ridens* |
| 8. | Canopy level, sit-and-wait, nocturnal predators | |
| | *Agalychnis calcarifer* | *Hyla miliaria* |
| | *Anotheca spinosa* | |
| 9. | Seep or streamside, sit-and-wait, nocturnal predators | |
| | *Craugastor epochthidius* | *Rana maculata* |
| | *Craugastor pechorum* | |
| 10. | Pond or marshside, sit-and-wait, nocturnal predators | |
| | *Leptodactylus fragilis* | *Rana vaillanti* |
| | *Leptodactylus melanonotus* | |

greatest number of species (14) consists of understory-canopy level, sit-and-wait, nocturnal predators (guild 7). These species include the two salamanders of the genus *Bolitoglossa*, all of the centrolenid frogs, two species of *Agalychnis*, and the three species of *Eleutherodactylus*. The next largest group of species (11) contains understory level, sit-and-wait, nocturnal predators (guild 6). This group includes four of the five species of *Hyla*, plus those of the hylid genera *Phrynohyas*, *Ptychohyla*, *Scinax*, and *Smilisca*. Ground level, sit-and-wait, nocturnal predators (guild 4) make up the next largest group, with five species, including three species of toads (*Bufo*), one large rain frog (*Craugastor megacephalus*), and the very large *Leptodactylus pentadactylus*. The remaining seven groups (guilds 1, 2, 3, 5, 8, 9, and 10) contain from one to four species.

In general, adult amphibians in the Mosquitia are all animal predators (most likely on hard-bodied and soft-bodied terrestrial and fossorial invertebrates). Almost all amphibian species are sit-and-wait species, save for the two fossorial species (*Gymnopis multiplicata* and *Oedipina cyclocauda*). Presumably, these two fossorial predators encounter their prey opportunistically, in connection with their burrowing activities. Most species hunt at night, with no species hunting exclusively during the day and just six species hunting both during the day and night.

McDiarmid and Altig (1999) identified the range of guilds (ecomorphological categories of their terminology) seen among anuran tadpoles. McCranie and Wilson (2002) adapted this classification for use with 60 species of anurans in Honduras with free-living larvae. We have further adapted this classification for the 33 species of Mosquitia anurans known to have free-living larvae (Table 5). The larva of *Hyla miliaria* is not known (Duellman, 2001; Savage, 2002). These 33 species fall into 10 guilds. The largest number of species (nine) belongs to the benthic lentic and lotic guild, which species have exotrophic larvae that occur in both lentic (standing) and lotic (moving) water and rasp food from submerged surfaces. These species, according to McDiarmid and Altig (1999), are found mostly at or near the bottom in pools and backwaters in lotic environments. This guild includes all of the toad species (members of the genus *Bufo*), two species of *Smilisca*, the two smaller species of *Leptodactylus*, and one species of *Rana*. The next largest group consists of the fossorial lotic species, which contains all seven species of centrolenid frogs, whose larvae are vermiform and inhabit leaf mats in slow water areas (McDiarmid and Altig, 1999). The remaining eight guilds contain from one to five species.

In general, the free-living larvae of Mosquitia anurans are either lentic only (seven species), lotic only (12 species), or both lentic and lotic (14 species). In lentic/lotic habitats, the larvae are either benthic; i.e., feeding at or near the bottom (nine species), or nektonic; i.e., feeding somewhere in the water column (five species). The solely lentic species occur in arboreal "ponds" (tank bromeliads or tree holes; two species) or in terrestrial ponds (five species). The twelve lotic species are either clasping species (three species of *Rana*), adherent species (*Ptychohyla hypomykter* and *Smilisca sordida*), or are fossorial (seven species of centrolenids; see paragraph above).

In identifying the reptile guilds in the Mosquitia, we have used microhabitat, food capture strategy, and diel activity, as did Heyer et al. (1990) for the anurans of Boracéia. The results are indicated in Table 6. Based on the data in this table, we identified 39 guilds. These guilds are based on the activities of adults. The substantially larger number of reptile than amphibian guilds is due to the broader array of lifestyles possessed by reptiles. This is especially evident in the range of food capture strategies and food sources used by reptiles compared to amphibians. Thus, a limited number of reptile species prey on plants, a few prey on both plants and animals, and most prey on animals. Some species use a sit-and-wait strategy, but most actively pursue their prey; some use both strategies. As a consequence, we had to establish a relatively large number of food capture strategy categories.

The largest number of species of reptiles (18) are ground level, active (on animals), diurnal predators (guild 20). These species include seven lizards (of the genera *Sceloporus*, *Norops*, *Ameiva*, *Aspidoscelis*, and *Cnemidophorus*) and eleven snakes (of the genera *Conophis*, *Dendrophidion*, *Drymarchon*, *Drymobius*, *Erythrolamprus*, *Lampropeltis*, *Masticophis*, *Mastigodryas*, and *Xenodon*). Thirteen species are in a group of semifossorial, active (on animals), diurnal predators (guild 13), including five lizards (of the genera *Sphaerodactylus*, *Mabuya*, *Sphenomorphus*, *Gymnophthalmus*, and *Lepidophyma*) and eight

**Table 5.** Tadpole guilds for the 33 Mosquitia anurans with known free-living larvae. Guilds follow those of McDiarmid and Altig (1999). Species in each category are arranged in the same order in which they appear in the text. Larvae of *Hyla miliaria* is unknown.

| | |
|---|---|
| Lentic and Lotic: Benthic | |
| *Bufo coccifer* | *Smilisca phaeota* |
| *Bufo haematiticus* | *Leptodactylus fragilis* |
| *Bufo marinus* | *Leptodactylus melanonotus* |
| *Bufo valliceps* | *Rana brownorum* |
| *Smilisca baudinii* | |
| Lentic and Lotic: Nektonic | |
| *Hyla loquax* | *Scinax boulengeri* |
| *Hyla picta* | *Scinax staufferi* |
| *Phrynohyas venulosa* | |
| Lentic only: Arboreal. Type 2 | |
| *Anotheca spinosa* | |
| Lentic only: Arboreal. Type 5 | |
| *Agalychnis calcarifer* | |
| Lentic only: Carnivorous | |
| *Leptodactylus pentadactylus* | |
| Lentic only: Macrophagous | |
| *Hyla ebraccata* | *Hyla microcephala* |
| Lentic only: Suspension-Rasper | |
| *Agalychnis callidryas* | *Agalychnis saltator* |
| Lotic only: Clasping | |
| *Rana maculata* | *Rana warszewitschii* |
| *Rana vaillanti* | |
| Lotic only: Adherent | |
| *Ptychohyla hypomykter* | *Smilisca sordida* |
| Lotic only: Fossorial | |
| *Centrolene prosoblepon* | *Hyalinobatrachium cardiacalyptum* |
| *Cochranella albomaculata* | *Hyalinobatrachium fleischmanni* |
| *Cochranella granulosa* | *Hyalinobatrachium pulveratum* |
| *Cochranella spinosa* | |

snakes (of the genera *Coniophanes*, *Ninia*, *Rhadinaea*, *Tantilla*, *Tantillita*, and *Urotheca*). Twelve species are understory tree-trunk, active (on animals), diurnal predators (guild 30) and include eight lizards (of the genera *Basiliscus*, *Sceloporus*, and *Norops*) and four snakes (of the genera *Leptophis* and *Oxybelis*). The remaining 36 guilds contain from one to six species.

Most reptiles are predators on animals, including all snakes and crocodilians. Some lizards and turtles, however, prey on plants, at least partially. Most reptiles actively pursue prey, but

**Table 6.** Adult guilds for the reptile species of the Mosquitia. Species in each category are arranged in the same order as they appear in the text. Food capture strategies are as follows: sit-and-wait—SAW; active on animals (A); active on plants (P); active on both plants and animals (P+A).

| | | | |
|---|---|---|---|
| 1. | Marine, active (A), diurnal predators | | |
| | | *Caretta caretta* | *Eretmochelys imbricata* |
| | | *Chelonia mydas* | *Dermochelys coriacea* |
| 2. | Freshwater, SAW/active (A), nocturnal predators | | |
| | | *Caiman crocodilus* | *Hydromorphus concolor* |
| | | *Crocodylus acutus* | *Tretanorhinus nigroluteus* |
| 3. | Freshwater, active (P+A), diurnal/nocturnal predators | | |
| | | *Rhinoclemmys funerea* | *Trachemys venusta* |
| 4. | Freshwater, SAW/active (P), diurnal/nocturnal predators | | |
| | | *Chelydra serpentina* | |
| 5. | Semiaquatic, SAW/active (P), diurnal/nocturnal predators | | |
| | | *Kinosternon leucostomum* | *Kinosternon scorpioides* |
| 6. | Semiaquatic, active (A), diurnal predators | | |
| | | *Norops lionotus* | |
| 7. | Semiaquatic, active (A), diurnal/nocturnal predators | | |
| | | *Coniophanes bipunctatus* | *Thamnophis proximus* |
| 8. | Semiaquatic, active (P), diurnal predators | | |
| | | *Rhinoclemmys areolata* | |
| 9. | Semiaquatic, active (P+A), diurnal predators | | |
| | | *Rhinoclemmys pulcherrima* | |
| 10. | Edificarian, active (A), nocturnal predators | | |
| | | *Hemidactylus frenatus* | |
| 11. | Edificarian/tree trunk, active (A), diurnal predators | | |
| | | *Gonatodes albogularis* | |
| 12. | Fossorial predators | | |
| | | *Anomalepis mexicanus* | *Typhlops costaricensis* |
| 13. | Semifossorial, active (A), diurnal predators | | |
| | | *Sphaerodactylus millepunctatus* | *Ninia maculata* |
| | | *Mabuya unimarginata* | *Rhadinaea decorata* |
| | | *Sphenomorphus cherriei* | *Tantilla taeniata* |
| | | *Gymnophthalmus speciosus* | *Tantillita lintoni* |
| | | *Lepidophyma flavimaculatum* | *Urotheca decipiens* |
| | | *Coniophanes fissidens* | *Urotheca guentheri* |
| | | *Coniophanes imperialis* | |

Table 6 (continued)

14. Semifossorial, active (A), diurnal/nocturnal predators
*Adelphicos quadrivirgatum* | *Geophis hoffmanni*

15. Semifossorial/ground level, active (A), diurnal/nocturnal predators
*Enuliophis sclateri*
*Ninia sebae*
*Nothopsis rugosus*
*Pliocercus elapoides*
*Pliocercus euryzonus*
*Micrurus nigrocinctus*

16. Semifossorial/ground level, SAW/active (A), diurnal predators
*Scaphiodontophis annulatus*

17. Semifossorial/ground level, active (A), nocturnal predators
*Micrurus alleni*

18. Semifossorial/ground level, SAW/active (A), diurnal/nocturnal predators
*Porthidium nasutum*

19. Ground level, active (P), diurnal predators
*Rhinoclemmys annulata*

20. Ground level, active (A), diurnal predators
*Sceloporus variabilis*
*Norops quaggulus*
*Norops tropidonotus*
*Ameiva festiva*
*Ameiva undulata*
*Aspidoscelis deppii*
*Cnemidophorus lemniscatus*
*Conophis lineatus*
*Dendrophidion percarinatum*
*Dendrophidion vinitor*
*Drymarchon melanurus*
*Drymobius margaritiferus*
*Drymobius melanotropis*
*Erythrolamprus mimus*
*Lampropeltis triangulum*
*Masticophis mentovarius*
*Mastigodryas melanolomus*
*Xenodon rabdocephalus*

21. Ground level, active (A), nocturnal predators
*Clelia clelia*
*Tropidodipsas sartorii*

22. Ground level, active (A), diurnal/nocturnal predators
*Oxyrhopus petola*

23. Ground level, SAW/active (A), nocturnal predators
*Porthidium ophryomegas*

24. Ground level/understory, active (A), nocturnal predators
*Leptodeira annulata*
*Leptodeira nigrofasciata*

25. Ground level/understory, SAW/active (A), diurnal/nocturnal predators
*Bothrops asper*

26. Ground level/understory/tree trunk, active (P+A), diurnal predators
*Basiliscus plumifrons*
*Ctenosaura similis*

Table 6 (continued)

27. Ground level/understory/tree trunk/canopy, active (A), diurnal predators
*Chironius grandisquamis*
*Leptophis ahaetulla*
*Oxybelis fulgidus*
*Pseustes poecilonotus*
*Spilotes pullatus*

28. Ground level/understory/tree trunk/canopy, active (P), diurnal predators
*Iguana iguana*

29. Ground level/tree trunk, SAW/active (A), diurnal/nocturnal predators
*Boa constrictor*

30. Understory/tree trunk, active (A), diurnal predators
*Basiliscus vittatus*
*Sceloporus malachiticus*
*Norops capito*
*Norops dariense*
*Norops lemurinus*
*Norops limifrons*
*Norops sericeus*
*Norops wampuensis*
*Leptophis mexicanus*
*Leptophis nebulosus*
*Oxybelis aeneus*
*Oxybelis brevirostris*

31. Understory, active (A), nocturnal predators
*Dipsas bicolor*
*Sibon longifrenis*

32. Understory, SAW/active (A), nocturnal predators
*Bothriechis schlegelii*

33. Understory/tree trunk, active (A), nocturnal predators
*Imantodes cenchoa*
*Leptodeira septentrionalis*
*Sibon annulatus*
*Sibon nebulatus*
*Sibon sp.*

34. Understory/tree trunk/canopy, active (A), diurnal predators
*Norops biporcatus*
*Norops pentaprion*

35. Tree trunk, active (A), nocturnal predators
*Thecadactylus rapicauda*

36. Tree trunk, SAW, diurnal predators
*Corytophanes cristatus*

37. Tree trunk/canopy, SAW, diurnal predator
*Polychrus gutturosus*

38. Tree trunk/canopy, SAW/active (A), nocturnal predators
*Corallus annulatus*

39. Tree trunk/canopy, active (A), nocturnal predators
*Rhinobothryum bovallii*

some use a sit-and-wait strategy and some use both strategies. Most species hunt during the day, but a sizable number hunt at night or during both day and night.

Using the ecological guilds established for amphibians and reptiles of the Mosquitia of Honduras, it is possible to create a rough picture of their involvement in the community structure of the most complex of vegetation zones in this region; i.e., evergreen broadleaf forest. We have chosen for this analysis, a pair of closely approximated localities (about 7 airline km apart at their nearest points) in this vegetation zone near the Río Coco. Both localities are adjacent to rivers that flow into the Río Coco and are named for those rivers. One is Caño Awalwás, near the border of the department of Gracias a Dios and Olancho, and the other is Caño Awawás, between the former tributary and Awasbila (see Gazetteer). Collections were made from 70 to 100 m elevation at Caño Awalwás and from 60 m elevation at Caño Awawás. At both localities, we camped along the river and worked in the surrounding forest and along tributary rivers and streams. The forest at Caño Awalwás is more intact than that at Caño Awawás, inasmuch as a group of squatters has taken up residence alongside the confluence of the latter river and the Río Coco, which is within the Tawahka-Asangni Biosphere Reserve, and has cleared a substantial amount of forest on both sides of the river for farming and ranching. The following discussion will proceed upstream from the rivers' mouths and into the forest, beginning during the day and extending on into the night.

The Caños Awalwás and Awawás are relatively clear (especially during the dry season), tannin-stained, narrow, meandering, relatively shallow-water rivers flowing out of the forest and into the large Río Coco. During the day, *Crocodylus acutus* basks on the banks of the lower ends of the rivers and hunts at night, using both sit-and-wait and active pursuit tactics. *Trachemys venusta* also basks during the day, however, on exposed logs and tree branches in the rivers. *Rhinoclemmys funerea* also basks in these situations, but is seen much less commonly out of the water than the former turtle. Both these turtles actively prey on plants and animals and search for these foods during the day and night. The only other turtle known at these localities is *Kinosternon leucostomum*, which occurs in small rivers and streams feeding into the *caños* as well as on land, where, in the former location, it feeds as a sit-and-wait predator and, in the latter location as a plant predator, both during the day and night. The snake *Tretanorhinus nigroluteus* is also found in such rivers, remaining hidden during the day and emerging at night to forage using both sit-and-wait and active pursuit feeding strategies.

Moving up into the forest, one encounters the classic stratified evergreen broadleaf forest, which presents a multitude of microhabitats for occupancy by amphibians and reptiles, including those active during the day, at night, and at both times. Several fossorial, semifossorial, and semifossorial/ground level amphibians and reptiles occur in the forest. The single fossorial predator at this locality is *Gymnopis multiplicata*, usually encountered under or within logs. Also found under logs and other forest floor debris are the diurnal lizards *Sphaerodactylus millepunctatus* and *Sphenomorphus cherriei* and the diurnal snake *Tantillita lintoni*. In addition, the diurnal/nocturnal semifossorial and semifossorial/ground level snakes *Adelphicos quadrivirgatum*, *Enuliophis sclateri*, *Ninia sebae*, *Pliocercus euryzonus*, *Micrurus nigrocinctus*, and *Porthidium nasutum* are found in these environs, as well as out in the open in the case of *Enuliophis sclateri* and the last three snakes.

Also at the ground level, the diurnal/nocturnal, sit-and-wait frogs *Craugastor mimus* and *C. noblei* are infrequently seen leaping about. Much more commonly found, *Craugastor lauraster* is another ground level species. The ground level microhabitat is shared during the day by the active predators *Ameiva festiva*, *Dendrophidion vinitor*, *Mastigodryas melanolomus*, and *Oxyrhopus petola*. The last-named snake is also active at night. Ground level nocturnal species that can be found at these two localities are *Bufo marinus*, *B. valliceps*, and *Leptodactylus pentadactylus*.

Occasional ponds and marshes are seen in these evergreen broadleaf forests (especially in deforested areas) where the sit-and-wait anuran predators *Leptodactylus fragilis*, and *Rana vaillanti*, can be found at night. The streamside *Rana warszewitschii* can be found active during the day and at night.

At and above ground level, several anurans, lizards, and snakes can be found active during the day (*Basiliscus plumifrons*, *Iguana iguana*, *Chironius grandisquamis*, and *Pseustes poecilonotus*), active at night (*Craugastor fitzingeri*), and active during the day and at night (*Bothrops asper*).

Several anurans can be found at night in the understory level, most abundantly in disturbed areas, such as active and fallow crop fields. These anurans are *Hyla ebraccata*, *H. loquax*, *H. microcephala*, *Scinax boulengeri*, *S. staufferi*, *Smilisca baudinii*, and *S. phaeota*. The sit-and-wait/active snake *Bothriechis schlegelii* is also found at night in this microhabitat.

Several anoles (*Norops capito*, *N. dariense*, and *N. pentaprion*) are found in the understory and on tree trunks hunting during the day; at night they can be replaced by the snakes *Leptodeira septentrionalis* and *Sibon nebulatus*.

From the understory to the canopy, the diurnal anoles *Norops biporcatus* and *N. pentaprion* are found. At night, the amphibians *Bolitoglossa striatula*, *Centrolene prosoblepon*, *Agalychnis callidryas*, *Eleutherodactylus diastema*, and *E. ridens* emerge.

On tree trunks during the day, the sit-and-wait lizard *Corytophanes cristatus* is encountered and at night the boid snake *Corallus annulatus* occurs on both tree trunks and in the canopy.

In summary, at these two evergreen broadleaf forest localities, members of 8 of the 10 amphibian guilds and 19 of 39 reptile guilds make up the known herpetofauna. The best-represented amphibian guild is the understory level, sit-and-wait, nocturnal predator group, with seven members at these localities; for reptiles, it is the semifossorial, active (on animals), diurnal predator and semifossorial/group level, active (on animals) diurnal/nocturnal predator groups, each with five members.

# Biogeographic Relationships and Significance of the Mosquitia Herpetofauna

The Honduran Mosquitia, as recognized herein, is largely comprised of ecophysiographic area 21 (the Eastern Caribbean Lowlands of McCranie and Wilson, 2002), but also includes, as noted in the Physiography section of the third chapter, Description of the Honduran Mosquitia, the extreme eastern portion of area 22 (the East-Central Caribbean Lowlands), and the northeastern portion of area 15 (the Eastern Caribbean Slope). Thus, nine species not known from area 21 are included in this book because they occur in those portions of areas 15 (*Ptychohyla hypomykter*, *Craugastor epochthidius*, *C. pechorum*, *Ninia maculata*, *Pliocercus elapoides*, and *Sibon longifrenis*) and 22 (*Craugastor epochthidius*, *Sceloporus malachiticus*, and *Drymobius melanotropis*) herein included in the Honduran Mosquitia.

One of the biogeographic questions of interest to ask, because the answer is also of importance to conservation biology (see the next chapter), is to what extent the entire Caribbean lowland and windward slope herpetofauna of Honduras is represented in the Mosquitia of the country. There are 238 species occurring in the Atlantic lowlands and windward slope areas of Honduras (Table 7). The 156 Mosquitia species comprise 65.5% of these 238 species. Thus, two-thirds of the Atlantic lowland and windward slope species occur in the Honduran Mosquitia. Given this relatively large percentage and that the Mosquitia is a "refuge of last resort" for the lowland herpetofauna of Honduras, because of the higher human population densities and concomitant degradation of the vegetation of the lowland and windward slope regions to the west, it is clear that the Honduran Mosquitia has important significance with respect to this segment of the herpetofauna of Honduras and efforts being made to conserve it (see following chapter).

Also of biogeographic interest is the degree of resemblance of the lowland component of the Mosquitia herpetofauna (the 148 species of area 21, the Eastern Caribbean Lowlands) to those of the other lowland areas along the Atlantic coast of the country. The data in Table 7 indicate that area 21 contains the highest number of species (148) of any of the Atlantic lowland regions. The next largest number of species (110) occurs in area 26 (West-Central Caribbean Lowlands). The number and percentages of species shared between area 21 and each of the other lowland regions is as follows: area 22—82 (90.1% of 91 species); area 26—82 (74.5% of 110 species); area 27—58 (72.5% of 80 species); area 28—20 (87.0% of 23 species). As expected, the percentage of resemblance decreases towards the west (from 90.1% to 75.0% to 72.5%) until area 28 is reached. The increase in percentage resemblance to area 28 is an artifact of the relatively few, but widespread, species known from this relatively small region. The importance of the Honduran Mosquitia as a refuge for the Atlantic lowland herpetofauna of Honduras is again emphasized by these data.

Use of Duellman's (1990) Coefficient of Biogeographic Resemblance algorithm (see Materials and Methods chapter for a description of this algorithm) provides a better assessment of the degree of resemblance among these ecophysiographic areas, inasmuch as it acts to smooth out the distortions caused by faunas of widely differing sizes. The CBR figures for area 21 are as follows: (area 22—67.8; area 26—63.6; area 27—50.9; area 28—22.2). These figures illustrate the expected decline in resemblance from east to west.

The Honduran Mosquitia, as herein defined, also includes a small portion of the Eastern Caribbean Slope (area 15), a Caribbean slope area. It is of interest, therefore, to determine the degree of resemblance of the Honduran Mosquitia lowland herpetofauna (area 21) to each of the three Caribbean slope areas. The other two Caribbean slope areas are the Central Caribbean Slope (area 16) and the Western Caribbean Slope (area 30). There are six species that occur in the portion of area 15 included within our concept of the Honduran Mosquitia, but are not reported for area 21. It is expected that the herpetofauna of area 21

**Table 7.** Herpetofaunas of Caribbean lowland and windward slope areas of Honduras.

| Species | Eastern Caribbean Lowlands (Area 21) | East-Central Caribbean Lowlands (Area 22) | Eastern Caribbean Slope (Area 15) | Central Caribbean Slope (Area 16) | West-Central Caribbean Lowlands (Area 26) | Western Caribbean Lowlands (Area 27) | Lower Motagua Valley (Area 28) | Western Caribbean Slope (Area 30) | Totals |
|---|---|---|---|---|---|---|---|---|---|
| *Dermophis mexicanus* | — | — | — | — | X | X | — | — | 2 |
| *Gymnopis multiplicata* | X | — | — | — | X | — | — | — | 2 |
| *Bolitoglossa conanti* | — | — | — | — | — | — | — | X | 1 |
| *Bolitoglossa dofleini* | — | — | — | X | — | — | — | X | 2 |
| *Bolitoglossa dunni* | — | — | — | — | — | — | — | X | 1 |
| *Bolitoglossa mexicana* | X | X | X | X | X | — | — | — | 5 |
| *Bolitoglossa porrasorum* | — | — | — | X | — | — | — | — | 1 |
| *Bolitoglossa rufescens* | — | — | — | X | X | X | — | X | 4 |
| *Bolitoglossa striatula* | X | — | — | — | — | — | — | — | 1 |
| *Cryptotriton nasalis* | — | — | — | — | — | — | — | X | 1 |
| *Nototriton barbouri* | — | — | — | X | — | — | — | — | 1 |
| *Oedipina cyclocauda* | X | X | X | X | X | — | — | — | 5 |
| *Atelophryniscus chrysophorus* | — | — | — | X | — | — | — | — | 1 |
| *Bufo campbelli* | — | — | — | — | — | — | — | X | 1 |
| *Bufo coccifer* | X | — | — | — | — | — | — | — | 1 |
| *Bufo haematiticus* | X | X | — | — | — | — | — | — | 2 |
| *Bufo leucomyos* | — | — | X | X | X | — | — | — | 3 |
| *Bufo marinus* | X | X | X | X | X | X | X | X | 8 |
| *Bufo valliceps* | X | X | X | X | X | X | X | X | 8 |

Table 7 (continued)

| Species | Eastern Caribbean Lowlands (Area 21) | East-Central Caribbean Lowlands (Area 22) | Eastern Caribbean Slope (Area 15) | Central Caribbean Slope (Area 16) | West-Central Caribbean Lowlands (Area 26) | Western Caribbean Lowlands (Area 27) | Lower Motagua Valley (Area 28) | Western Caribbean Slope (Area 30) | Totals |
|---|---|---|---|---|---|---|---|---|---|
| *Centrolene prosoblepon* | X | X | X | — | — | — | — | — | 3 |
| *Cochranella albomaculata* | X | X | X | — | — | — | — | — | 3 |
| *Cochranella granulosa* | X | — | X | — | — | — | — | — | 2 |
| *Cochranella spinosa* | X | — | — | — | — | — | — | — | 1 |
| *Hyalinobatrachium cardiacalyptum* | X | — | X | — | — | — | — | — | 2 |
| *Hyalinobatrachium crybetes* | — | — | X | — | — | — | — | — | 1 |
| *Hyalinobatrachium fleischmanni* | X | — | X | X | X | X | — | X | 6 |
| *Hyalinobatrachium pulveratum* | X | X | X | — | — | — | — | — | 3 |
| *Agalychnis calcarifer* | X | — | — | — | — | — | — | — | 1 |
| *Agalychnis callidryas* | X | X | X | — | X | X | — | X | 6 |
| *Agalychnis moreletii* | — | — | — | X | — | — | — | X | 2 |
| *Agalychnis saltator* | X | — | — | — | — | — | — | — | 1 |
| *Anotheca spinosa* | X | — | — | — | — | — | — | — | 1 |
| *Duellmanohyla salvavida* | — | — | — | X | X | — | — | — | 2 |
| *Duellmanohyla soralia* | — | — | — | — | — | X | — | X | 2 |
| *Hyla bromeliacia* | — | — | — | — | — | — | — | X | 1 |
| *Hyla ebraccata* | X | — | X | — | — | — | — | — | 2 |
| *Hyla loquax* | X | — | — | X | X | — | X | X | 5 |
| *Hyla microcephala* | X | X | X | X | X | — | X | X | 7 |

Table 7 (continued)

| Species | Eastern Caribbean Lowlands (Area 21) | East-Central Caribbean Lowlands (Area 22) | Eastern Caribbean Slope (Area 15) | Central Caribbean Slope (Area 16) | West-Central Caribbean Lowlands (Area 26) | Western Caribbean Lowlands (Area 27) | Lower Motagua Valley (Area 28) | Western Caribbean Slope (Area 30) | Totals |
|---|---|---|---|---|---|---|---|---|---|
| *Hyla miliaria* | X | — | — | — | — | — | — | — | 1 |
| *Hyla picta* | X | X | — | — | X | X | — | X | 5 |
| *Phrynohyas venulosa* | X | X | — | — | X | X | — | — | 4 |
| *Plectrohyla chrysopleura* | — | — | — | X | — | — | — | — | 1 |
| *Plectrohyla guatemalensis* | — | — | X | X | — | — | — | X | 3 |
| *Plectrohyla matudai* | — | — | — | — | — | — | — | X | 1 |
| *Ptychohyla hypomykter* | — | — | X | X | — | — | — | X | 3 |
| *Ptychohyla spinipollex* | — | — | — | X | X | — | — | — | 2 |
| *Scinax boulengeri* | X | — | — | — | — | — | — | — | 1 |
| *Scinax staufferi* | X | X | X | — | X | X | X | X | 7 |
| *Smilisca baudinii* | X | X | X | X | X | X | X | X | 8 |
| *Smilisca phaeota* | X | X | X | — | — | — | — | — | 3 |
| *Smilisca sordida* | X | — | — | — | — | — | — | — | 1 |
| *Craugastor aurilegulus* | — | — | X | X | X | — | — | — | 3 |
| *Craugastor chac* | — | — | — | X | X | X | — | — | 3 |
| *Craugastor charadra* | — | — | — | — | — | X | — | X | 2 |
| *Craugastor chrysozetetes* | — | — | — | X | — | — | — | — | 1 |
| *Craugastor coffeus* | — | — | — | — | — | — | — | X | 1 |
| *Craugastor epochthidius* | — | X | X | — | — | — | — | — | 2 |

Table 7 (continued)

| Species | Eastern Caribbean Lowlands (Area 21) | East-Central Caribbean Lowlands (Area 22) | Eastern Caribbean Slope (Area 15) | Central Caribbean Slope (Area 16) | West-Central Caribbean Lowlands (Area 26) | Western Caribbean Lowlands (Area 27) | Lower Motagua Valley (Area 28) | Western Caribbean Slope (Area 30) | Totals |
|---|---|---|---|---|---|---|---|---|---|
| *Craugastor fecundus* | — | — | — | X | X | — | — | — | 2 |
| *Craugastor fitzingeri* | X | X | X | — | — | — | — | — | 3 |
| *Craugastor laevissimus* | — | — | X | — | — | — | — | X | 2 |
| *Craugastor laticeps* | — | — | — | X | — | — | — | X | 2 |
| *Craugastor lauraster* | X | — | X | — | — | — | — | — | 2 |
| *Craugastor megacephalus* | X | — | — | — | — | — | — | — | 1 |
| *Craugastor merendonensis* | — | — | — | — | — | X | — | — | 1 |
| *Craugastor milesi* | — | — | — | — | — | — | — | X | 1 |
| *Craugastor mimus* | X | — | X | — | — | — | — | — | 2 |
| *Craugastor noblei* | X | X | X | — | X | — | — | — | 4 |
| *Craugastor olanchano* | — | — | X | — | — | — | — | — | 1 |
| *Craugastor omoaensis* | — | — | — | — | — | — | — | X | 1 |
| *Craugastor pechorum* | — | X | X | — | — | — | — | — | 2 |
| *Craugastor rostralis* | — | — | — | X | — | — | — | X | 2 |
| *Craugastor stadelmani* | — | — | X | X | — | — | — | — | 2 |
| *Craugastor* sp. (*alfredi* group) | — | — | — | — | — | — | — | X | 1 |
| *Eleutherodactylus cerasinus* | X | X | X | — | — | — | — | — | 3 |
| *Eleutherodactylus diastema* | X | — | — | — | — | — | — | — | 1 |
| *Eleutherodactylus ridens* | X | X | X | X | X | — | — | — | 5 |

Table 7 (continued)

| Species | Eastern Caribbean Lowlands (Area 21) | East-Central Caribbean Lowlands (Area 22) | Eastern Caribbean Slope (Area 15) | Central Caribbean Slope (Area 16) | West-Central Caribbean Lowlands (Area 26) | Western Caribbean Lowlands (Area 27) | Lower Motagua Valley (Area 28) | Western Caribbean Slope (Area 30) | Totals |
|---|---|---|---|---|---|---|---|---|---|
| *Leptodactylus fragilis* | X | — | X | X | — | — | — | — | 3 |
| *Leptodactylus melanonotus* | X | — | — | — | X | — | X | — | 3 |
| *Leptodactylus pentadactylus* | X | X | X | — | X | — | — | — | 4 |
| *Physalaemus pustulosus* | — | — | X | — | — | X | — | X | 3 |
| *Gastrophryne elegans* | — | — | — | — | X | X | — | — | 2 |
| *Hypopachus variolosus* | — | — | — | X | X | — | — | — | 2 |
| *Rana brownorum* | X | X | X | X | X | X | X | X | 8 |
| *Rana maculata* | X | X | X | X | X | X | — | X | 7 |
| *Rana vaillanti* | X | X | — | X | X | X | X | X | 7 |
| *Rana warszewitschii* | X | — | — | — | — | — | — | — | 1 |
| *Rhinophrynus dorsalis* | — | — | — | — | — | — | X | — | 1 |
| *Caiman crocodilus* | X | X | — | — | X | X | — | — | 4 |
| *Crocodylus acutus* | X | X | — | — | X | X | — | — | 4 |
| *Caretta caretta* | X | — | — | — | — | — | — | — | 1 |
| *Chelonia mydas* | X | — | — | — | — | — | — | — | 1 |
| *Eretmochelys imbricata* | X | — | — | — | X | — | — | — | 2 |
| *Chelydra serpentina* | X | — | — | — | X | X | — | — | 3 |
| *Dermochelys coriacea* | X | — | — | — | X | — | — | — | 2 |
| *Trachemys venusta* | X | X | — | — | X | — | X | — | 4 |

Table 7 (continued)

| Species | Eastern Caribbean Lowlands (Area 21) | East-Central Caribbean Lowlands (Area 22) | Eastern Caribbean Slope (Area 15) | Central Caribbean Slope (Area 16) | West-Central Caribbean Lowlands (Area 26) | Western Caribbean Lowlands (Area 27) | Lower Motagua Valley (Area 28) | Western Caribbean Slope (Area 30) | Totals |
|---|---|---|---|---|---|---|---|---|---|
| *Rhinoclemmys annulata* | X | X | — | — | X | — | — | — | 3 |
| *Rhinoclemmys areolata* | X | — | — | — | — | — | — | — | 1 |
| *Rhinoclemmys funerea* | X | — | — | — | — | — | — | — | 1 |
| *Rhinoclemmys pulcherrima* | X | — | — | X | — | — | — | — | 2 |
| *Kinosternon leucostomum* | X | X | X | — | X | X | X | X | 7 |
| *Kinosternon scorpioides* | X | — | — | — | — | — | — | — | 1 |
| *Staurotypus triporcatus* | — | — | — | — | X | — | — | — | 1 |
| *Coleonyx mitratus* | — | — | X | — | X | X | — | — | 3 |
| *Gonatodes albogularis* | X | — | — | — | X | — | — | — | 2 |
| *Hemidactylus frenatus* | X | — | — | — | X | — | — | — | 2 |
| *Hemidactylus mabouia* | — | — | — | — | X | — | — | — | 1 |
| *Sphaerodactylus dunni* | — | X | — | — | X | X | — | — | 3 |
| *Sphaerodactylus millepunctatus* | X | X | — | X | X | X | — | — | 5 |
| *Thecadactylus rapicauda* | X | X | X | — | X | X | — | — | 5 |
| *Basiliscus plumifrons* | X | X | — | — | — | — | — | — | 2 |
| *Basiliscus vittatus* | X | X | X | X | X | X | X | X | 8 |
| *Corytophanes cristatus* | X | X | X | X | X | X | — | — | 6 |
| *Corytophanes hernandesii* | — | — | — | — | — | X | — | X | 2 |
| *Laemanctus longipes* | — | — | X | — | X | X | — | X | 4 |

Table 7 (continued)

| Species | Eastern Caribbean Lowlands (Area 21) | East-Central Caribbean Lowlands (Area 22) | Eastern Caribbean Slope (Area 15) | Central Caribbean Slope (Area 16) | West-Central Caribbean Lowlands (Area 26) | Western Caribbean Lowlands (Area 27) | Lower Motagua Valley (Area 28) | Western Caribbean Slope (Area 30) | Totals |
|---|---|---|---|---|---|---|---|---|---|
| *Ctenosaura similis* | X | X | — | — | X | X | — | — | 4 |
| *Iguana iguana* | X | X | — | — | X | — | — | — | 3 |
| *Sceloporus malachiticus* | — | X | X | X | — | — | — | X | 4 |
| *Sceloporus variabilis* | X | — | X | X | — | X | — | X | 5 |
| *Norops biporcatus* | X | X | X | — | X | X | — | X | 6 |
| *Norops capito* | X | X | X | — | — | X | — | X | 5 |
| *Norops dariense* | X | X | X | — | X | — | — | — | 4 |
| *Norops laeviventris* | — | — | X | X | — | — | — | X | 3 |
| *Norops lemurinus* | X | X | — | X | X | X | X | — | 6 |
| *Norops limifrons* | X | X | — | — | — | — | — | — | 2 |
| *Norops lionotus* | X | — | — | — | — | — | — | — | 1 |
| *Norops loveridgei* | — | — | — | X | X | — | — | — | 2 |
| *Norops ocelloscapularis* | — | — | — | — | — | — | — | X | 1 |
| *Norops pentaprion* | X | X | X | — | X | — | — | — | 4 |
| *Norops pijolensis* | — | — | — | X | — | — | — | — | 1 |
| *Norops quaggulus* | X | X | X | — | — | — | — | — | 3 |
| *Norops rodriguezii* | — | — | — | X | — | X | X | X | 4 |
| *Norops sagrei* | — | — | — | — | X | X | — | — | 2 |
| *Norops sericeus* | X | X | — | X | X | X | X | — | 6 |

Table 7 (continued)

| Species | Eastern Caribbean Lowlands (Area 21) | East-Central Caribbean Lowlands (Area 22) | Eastern Caribbean Slope (Area 15) | Central Caribbean Slope (Area 16) | West-Central Caribbean Lowlands (Area 26) | Western Caribbean Lowlands (Area 27) | Lower Motagua Valley (Area 28) | Western Caribbean Slope (Area 30) | Totals |
|---|---|---|---|---|---|---|---|---|---|
| *Norops tropidonotus* | X | X | X | X | X | X | — | X | 7 |
| *Norops uniformis* | — | — | — | — | — | X | X | X | 3 |
| *Norops wampuensis* | X | — | — | — | — | — | — | — | 1 |
| *Norops yoroensis* | — | — | — | X | — | — | — | — | 1 |
| *Norops zeus* | — | — | — | X | X | — | — | — | 2 |
| *Polychrus gutturosus* | X | — | — | — | — | X | — | — | 2 |
| *Eumeces sumichrasti* | — | — | — | X | X | — | — | — | 2 |
| *Mabuya unimarginata* | X | — | X | X | X | — | — | — | 4 |
| *Sphenomorphus cherriei* | X | X | X | X | X | X | X | X | 8 |
| *Sphenomorphus incertus* | — | — | — | X | — | — | — | — | 1 |
| *Gymnophthalmus speciosus* | X | X | — | — | X | — | — | — | 3 |
| *Ameiva festiva* | X | X | X | X | X | X | — | X | 7 |
| *Ameiva undulata* | X | X | X | X | X | X | X | — | 7 |
| *Aspidoscelis deppii* | X | X | — | — | X | X | — | — | 4 |
| *Cnemidophorus lemniscatus* | X | X | — | — | X | X | X | — | 5 |
| *Lepidophyma flavimaculatum* | X | X | X | X | X | X | X | X | 8 |
| *Lepidophyma mayae* | — | — | — | — | — | — | — | X | 1 |
| *Anomalepis mexicanus* | X | — | — | — | — | — | — | — | 1 |
| *Typhlops costaricensis* | X | — | — | — | — | — | — | — | 1 |

Table 7 (continued)

| Species | Eastern Caribbean Lowlands (Area 21) | East-Central Caribbean Lowlands (Area 22) | Eastern Caribbean Slope (Area 15) | Central Caribbean Slope (Area 16) | West-Central Caribbean Lowlands (Area 26) | Western Caribbean Lowlands (Area 27) | Lower Motagua Valley (Area 28) | Western Caribbean Slope (Area 30) | Totals |
|---|---|---|---|---|---|---|---|---|---|
| *Typhlops stadelmani* | — | — | — | X | X | — | — | X | 3 |
| *Boa constrictor* | X | X | — | X | X | X | — | — | 5 |
| *Corallus annulatus* | X | — | — | — | — | — | — | — | 1 |
| *Ungaliophis continentalis* | — | — | — | X | — | — | — | — | 1 |
| *Adelphicos quadrivirgatum* | X | X | X | X | X | — | — | X | 6 |
| *Chironius grandisquamis* | X | X | X | X | X | — | — | — | 5 |
| *Clelia clelia* | X | — | X | — | X | X | — | X | 5 |
| *Coniophanes bipunctatus* | X | X | — | — | X | X | X | — | 5 |
| *Coniophanes fissidens* | X | X | X | X | X | X | — | X | 7 |
| *Coniophanes imperialis* | X | X | — | — | X | X | — | X | 5 |
| *Conophis lineatus* | X | X | — | — | X | — | — | — | 3 |
| *Dendrophidion nuchale* | — | — | X | X | X | — | — | — | 3 |
| *Dendrophidion percarinatum* | X | X | — | — | X | — | — | — | 3 |
| *Dendrophidion vinitor* | X | — | — | — | — | — | — | — | 1 |
| *Dipsas bicolor* | X | — | X | — | — | — | — | — | 1 |
| *Drymarchon melanurus* | X | — | — | — | X | X | — | — | 3 |
| *Drymobius chloroticus* | — | — | X | X | — | — | — | X | 3 |
| *Drymobius margaritiferus* | X | X | X | X | X | X | — | X | 7 |
| *Drymobius melanotropis* | — | X | — | — | — | — | — | — | 1 |

Table 7 (continued)

| Species | Eastern Caribbean Lowlands (Area 21) | East-Central Caribbean Lowlands (Area 22) | Eastern Caribbean Slope (Area 15) | Central Caribbean Slope (Area 16) | West-Central Caribbean Lowlands (Area 26) | Western Caribbean Lowlands (Area 27) | Lower Motagua Valley (Area 28) | Western Caribbean Slope (Area 30) | Totals |
|---|---|---|---|---|---|---|---|---|---|
| *Enuliophis sclateri* | X | — | — | — | — | — | — | — | 1 |
| *Enulius flavitorques* | — | — | — | X | X | X | — | — | 3 |
| *Erythrolamprus mimus* | X | — | X | X | — | — | — | — | 3 |
| *Ficimia publia* | — | — | — | — | X | X | — | — | 2 |
| *Geophis hoffmanni* | X | X | X | — | — | — | — | — | 3 |
| *Hydromorphus concolor* | X | — | — | X | — | — | — | X | 3 |
| *Imantodes cenchoa* | X | X | — | X | X | X | X | X | 7 |
| *Imantodes inornatus* | — | — | X | — | — | — | — | — | 1 |
| *Lampropeltis triangulum* | X | X | — | X | X | X | — | X | 6 |
| *Leptodeira annulata* | X | — | X | X | — | — | — | — | 3 |
| *Leptodeira nigrofasciata* | X | — | — | X | — | — | — | — | 2 |
| *Leptodeira septentrionalis* | X | X | X | X | X | X | — | X | 7 |
| *Leptodrymus pulcherrimus* | — | — | — | X | — | X | — | — | 2 |
| *Leptophis ahaetulla* | X | X | — | X | X | X | — | — | 5 |
| *Leptophis mexicanus* | X | X | — | X | X | X | — | X | 6 |
| *Leptophis nebulosus* | X | — | — | — | — | — | — | — | 1 |
| *Masticophis mentovarius* | X | — | — | — | — | — | — | — | 1 |
| *Mastigodryas dorsalis* | — | — | X | X | — | — | — | — | 2 |
| *Mastigodryas melanolomus* | X | X | — | X | X | X | — | X | 6 |

Table 7 (continued)

| Species | Eastern Caribbean Lowlands (Area 21) | East-Central Caribbean Lowlands (Area 22) | Eastern Caribbean Slope (Area 15) | Central Caribbean Slope (Area 16) | West-Central Caribbean Lowlands (Area 26) | Western Caribbean Lowlands (Area 27) | Lower Motagua Valley (Area 28) | Western Caribbean Slope (Area 30) | Totals |
|---|---|---|---|---|---|---|---|---|---|
| *Ninia diademata* | — | — | — | X | — | X | — | X | 3 |
| *Ninia espinali* | — | — | — | — | — | — | — | X | 1 |
| *Ninia maculata* | — | X | — | — | — | — | — | — | 1 |
| *Ninia sebae* | X | X | X | X | X | X | — | X | 7 |
| *Nothopsis rugosus* | X | X | — | — | — | — | — | — | 2 |
| *Omoadiphas aurula* | — | — | — | — | — | — | — | X | 1 |
| *Oxybelis aeneus* | X | X | — | X | X | X | — | — | 5 |
| *Oxybelis brevirostris* | X | X | X | — | — | — | — | — | 3 |
| *Oxybelis fulgidus* | X | X | — | — | X | X | — | — | 4 |
| *Oxyrhopus petola* | X | — | — | — | X | — | — | — | 2 |
| *Pliocercus elapoides* | — | X | X | X | X | — | — | X | 5 |
| *Pliocercus euryzonus* | X | — | — | — | — | — | — | — | 1 |
| *Pseudelaphe flavirufa* | — | X | — | — | X | X | — | — | 3 |
| *Pseustes poecilonotus* | X | X | — | — | X | — | — | — | 3 |
| *Rhadinaea decorata* | X | — | — | — | — | — | — | — | 1 |
| *Rhadinaea kinkelini* | — | — | — | — | — | — | — | X | 1 |
| *Rhinobothryum bovallii* | X | — | — | — | — | — | — | — | 1 |
| *Scaphiodontophis annulatus* | X | — | X | X | X | X | — | X | 6 |
| *Senticolis triaspis* | — | — | — | X | X | — | — | — | 2 |

Table 7 (continued)

| Species | Eastern Caribbean Lowlands (Area 21) | East-Central Caribbean Lowlands (Area 22) | Eastern Caribbean Slope (Area 15) | Central Caribbean Slope (Area 16) | West-Central Caribbean Lowlands (Area 26) | Western Caribbean Lowlands (Area 27) | Lower Motagua Valley (Area 28) | Western Caribbean Slope (Area 30) | Totals |
|---|---|---|---|---|---|---|---|---|---|
| *Sibon annulatus* | X | — | — | — | — | — | — | — | 1 |
| *Sibon dimidiatus* | — | — | X | X | — | — | — | X | 3 |
| *Sibon longifrenis* | — | X | X | — | — | — | — | — | 2 |
| *Sibon nebulatus* | X | — | — | X | X | X | — | X | 5 |
| *Sibon* sp. | X | — | — | — | — | — | — | — | 1 |
| *Spilotes pullatus* | X | X | X | — | X | X | — | — | 5 |
| *Stenorrhina degenhardtii* | — | — | X | X | — | — | — | X | 3 |
| *Storeria dekayi* | — | — | — | X | — | — | — | — | 1 |
| *Tantilla schistosa* | — | — | X | X | — | — | — | X | 3 |
| *Tantilla taeniata* | X | — | — | — | — | — | — | — | 1 |
| *Tantillita lintoni* | X | — | — | — | X | — | — | — | 2 |
| *Thamnophis proximus* | X | X | — | — | — | — | — | — | 2 |
| *Tretanorhinus nigroluteus* | X | X | — | — | X | X | — | — | 4 |
| *Tropidodipsas sartorii* | X | — | — | — | X | X | — | — | 3 |
| *Urotheca decipiens* | X | — | — | — | — | — | — | — | 1 |
| *Urotheca guentheri* | X | X | — | — | — | — | — | — | 2 |
| *Xenodon rabdocephalus* | X | X | — | X | X | X | — | — | 5 |
| *Micrurus alleni* | X | — | — | — | — | — | — | — | 1 |
| *Micrurus diastema* | — | — | — | — | — | — | — | X | 1 |

Table 7 (continued)

| Species | Eastern Caribbean Lowlands (Area 21) | East-Central Caribbean Lowlands (Area 22) | Eastern Caribbean Slope (Area 15) | Central Caribbean Slope (Area 16) | West-Central Caribbean Lowlands (Area 26) | Western Caribbean Lowlands (Area 27) | Lower Motagua Valley (Area 28) | Western Caribbean Slope (Area 30) | Totals |
|---|---|---|---|---|---|---|---|---|---|
| *Micrurus nigrocinctus* | X | X | X | X | X | X | — | — | 6 |
| *Atropoides mexicanus* | — | — | X | X | X | X | — | X | 5 |
| *Bothriechis marchi* | — | — | — | X | — | — | — | X | 2 |
| *Bothriechis schlegelii* | X | X | X | X | X | X | — | X | 7 |
| *Bothriechis thalassinus* | — | — | — | — | — | — | — | X | 1 |
| *Bothrops asper* | X | X | X | X | X | X | — | X | 7 |
| *Cerrophidion godmani* | — | — | — | — | — | — | — | X | 1 |
| *Crotalus simus* | — | — | — | X | — | — | — | — | 1 |
| *Porthidium nasutum* | X | X | X | — | X | X | — | X | 6 |
| *Porthidium ophryomegas* | X | — | — | X | — | — | — | — | 2 |
| Totals (238) | 148 | 91 | 85 | 96 | 110 | 80 | 23 | 82 | — |

(the majority of the Honduran Mosquitia) would most closely resemble that of area 15 because it lies adjacent to area 21. Area 16 is next closest geographically to area 21 and area 30 most remote, so their herpetofaunas should be of intermediate and least resemblance, respectively. The percentages of resemblance are as follows: area 15—59 (69.4% of 85 species); area 16—50 (52.1% of 96 species); area 30—39 (47.6% of 82 species); thus, on this basis, the contention is basically upheld. The CBR values also support this contention, as follows: area 15—51.5; area 16—41.0; area 30—33.9.

It is evident from a comparison of the figures for percentage of resemblance between area 21 and the other Atlantic lowland regions, on the one hand, and between area 21 and the Atlantic windward slope areas, that the lowlands of the Honduran Mosquitia are more important as a reserve for lowland species in general (average percentage resemblance of 81.0 for lowland areas vs. 57.4 for slope areas). The CBR values also support this conclusion (average CBR of 51.5 for lowland areas vs. 42.2 for slope areas).

Given the relatively high number of species known from the Honduran Mosquitia compared to other Atlantic lowland and windward slope areas of the country, it is expected that the Mosquitia may harbor species known otherwise only from areas to the south in lower Central America (Nicaragua, Costa Rica, and Panama). Thus, we divided the nonmarine, non-introduced Honduran Mosquitia herpetofauna into four groups, viz., species occurring only in the Honduran Mosquitia (i.e., endemics); species occurring in the Honduran Mosquitia and points west; species occurring in the Honduran Mosquitia and points south; and species occurring in the Honduran Mosquitia and to both the west and the south. The species included in these four groups are indicated below.

---

Species endemic to the Honduran Mosquitia:

*Hyalinobatrachium cardiacalyptum*
*Craugastor pechorum*
*Norops wampuensis*
*Sibon* sp.

Species occurring in the Honduran Mosquitia and points west:

*Bolitoglossa mexicana*
*Hyla picta*
*Craugastor epochthidius*
*Rhinoclemmys areolata*
*Adelphicos quadrivirgatum*
*Coniophanes imperialis*
*Pliocercus elapoides*
*Tropidodipsas sartorii*

Species occurring in the Honduran Mosquitia and points south:

*Bolitoglossa striatula*
*Bufo haematiticus*
*Cochranella granulosa*
*Cochranella spinosa*
*Agalychnis calcarifer*
*Agalychnis saltator*
*Hyla miliaria*
*Scinax boulengeri*
*Smilisca sordida*
*Craugastor fitzingeri*
*Craugastor megacephalus*
*Craugastor mimus*
*Eleutherodactylus cerasinus*
*Eleutherodactylus diastema*
*Rana warszewitschii*
*Rhinoclemmys funerea*
*Basiliscus plumifrons*
*Norops limifrons*
*Norops lionotus*
*Norops quaggulus*
*Anomalepis mexicanus*
*Enuliophis sclateri*
*Leptophis nebulosus*
*Ninia maculata*
*Nothopsis rugosus*
*Oxybelis brevirostris*
*Pliocercus euryzonus*
*Rhinobothryum bovallii*
*Sibon annulatus*
*Sibon longifrenis*
*Urotheca decipiens*
*Urotheca guentheri*
*Micrurus alleni*

Species occurring in the Honduran Mosquitia and to both the west and south:

*Gymnopis multiplicata*
*Oedipina cyclocauda*
*Bufo coccifer*
*Bufo marinus*
*Bufo valliceps*
*Centrolene prosoblepon*
*Cochranella albomaculata*
*Hyalinobatrachium fleischmanni*
*Hyalinobatrachium pulveratum*
*Agalychnis callidryas*
*Anotheca spinosa*
*Mabuya unimarginata*
*Sphenomorphus cherriei*
*Gymnophthalmus speciosus*
*Ameiva festiva*
*Ameiva undulata*
*Aspidoscelis deppii*
*Cnemidophorus lemniscatus*
*Lepidophyma flavimaculatum*
*Typhlops costaricensis*
*Boa constrictor*
*Corallus annulatus*

*Hyla ebraccata*
*Hyla loquax*
*Hyla microcephala*
*Phrynohyas venulosa*
*Ptychohyla hypomykter*
*Scinax staufferi*
*Smilisca baudinii*
*Smilisca phaeota*
*Craugastor lauraster*
*Craugastor noblei*
*Eleutherodactylus ridens*
*Leptodactylus fragilis*
*Leptodactylus melanonotus*
*Leptodactylus pentadactylus*
*Rana brownorum*
*Rana maculata*
*Rana vaillanti*
*Caiman crocodilus*
*Crocodylus acutus*
*Chelydra serpentina*
*Rhinoclemmys annulata*
*Rhinoclemmys pulcherrima*
*Trachemys venusta*
*Kinosternon leucostomum*
*Kinosternon scorpioides*
*Gonatodes albogularis*
*Sphaerodactylus millepunctatus*
*Thecadactylus rapicauda*
*Basiliscus vittatus*
*Corytophanes cristatus*
*Ctenosaura similis*
*Iguana iguana*
*Sceloporus malachiticus*
*Sceloporus variabilis*
*Norops biporcatus*
*Norops capito*
*Norops dariense*
*Norops lemurinus*
*Norops pentaprion*
*Norops sericeus*
*Norops tropidonotus*
*Polychrus gutturosus*
*Chironius grandisquamis*
*Clelia clelia*
*Coniophanes bipunctatus*
*Coniophanes fissidens*
*Conophis lineatus*
*Dendrophidion percarinatum*
*Dendrophidion vinitor*
*Dipsas bicolor*
*Drymarchon melanurus*
*Drymobius margaritiferus*
*Drymobius melanotropis*
*Erythrolamprus mimus*
*Geophis hoffmanni*
*Hydromorphus concolor*
*Imantodes cenchoa*
*Lampropeltis triangulum*
*Leptodeira annulata*
*Leptodeira nigrofasciata*
*Leptodeira septentrionalis*
*Leptophis ahaetulla*
*Leptophis mexicanus*
*Masticophis mentovarius*
*Mastigodryas melanolomus*
*Ninia sebae*
*Oxybelis aeneus*
*Oxybelis fulgidus*
*Oxyrhopus petola*
*Pseustes poecilonotus*
*Rhadinaea decorata*
*Scaphiodontophis annulatus*
*Sibon nebulatus*
*Spilotes pullatus*
*Tantilla taeniata*
*Tantillita lintoni*
*Thamnophis proximus*
*Tretanorhinus nigroluteus*
*Xenodon rabdocephalus*
*Micrurus nigrocinctus*
*Bothriechis schlegelii*
*Bothrops asper*
*Porthidium nasutum*
*Porthidium ophryomegas*

---

The distributional group allocations above indicate that four species, or 2.6% of the 151 nonmarine, non-introduced species, are endemic to the Honduran Mosquitia. Eight species, or 5.3%, occur in the Mosquitia and points west. Thirty-three species, or 21.9%, occur in the Mosquitia and points south. Finally, 106 species, or 70.2%, occur in the Mosquitia and both points west and south. Thus, the large majority of the Mosquitia species fall into the fourth category, but a significant number are distributed in the Mosquitia and only points south.

This discussion indicates that the Mosquitia is a repository of a significant amount of the Atlantic lowland and windward slope herpetofaunal component in Honduras. In addition, a sizable number of species occurs in the Mosquitia (37, including 4 Honduran Mosquitia endemics) that range no farther west into the country.

A more detailed examination of the broad pattern of geographical distribution is possible using the categories established by Wilson and Meyer (1985) and expanded upon by Wilson et al. (2001) and McCranie and Wilson (2002). McCranie, in a book on the reptiles of Honduras (in preparation), uses the most extensive number of such patterns. That author recognizes 13 broad patterns of geographical distribution for elements of the Honduran herpetofauna. These 13 patterns are as follows:

A. Northern terminus of range in United States (or Canada) and southern terminus in South America;
B. Northern terminus of range in United States and southern terminus in Central America south of the Nicaraguan Depression;
C. Northern terminus of range in United States and southern terminus in Nuclear Middle America;
D. Northern terminus of range in Mexico north of Isthmus of Tehuantepec and southern terminus in South America;
E. Northern terminus of range in Mexico north of Isthmus of Tehuantepec and southern terminus in Central America south of Nicaraguan Depression;
F. Northern terminus of range in Mexico north of Isthmus of Tehuantepec and southern terminus in Nuclear Middle America;
G. Northern terminus of range in Nuclear Middle America and southern terminus in South America;
H. Northern terminus of range in Nuclear Middle America and southern terminus in Central America south of Nicaraguan Depression;
I. Restricted to Nuclear Middle America (exclusive of Honduran endemics);
J. Endemic to Honduras;
K. Marine species;
L. Insular species;
M. Introduced species.

The allocation of Mosquitia species to these categories is as follows (species listed in the same order as they appear in the text; category L does not apply to the Mosquitia herpetofauna):

A—*Bufo marinus*, *Leptodactylus fragilis*, *Chelydra serpentina*, *Drymarchon melanurus*, *Drymobius margaritiferus*, *Lampropeltis triangulum*, *Leptodeira septentrionalis*, and *Oxybelis aeneus*;

B—*Smilisca baudinii*, *Sceloporus variabilis*, and *Thamnophis proximus*;

C—*Coniophanes imperialis*;

D—*Hyalinobatrachium fleischmanni*, *Hyla ebraccata*, *H. microcephala*, *Phrynohyas venulosa*, *Leptodactylus melanonotus*, *Rana vaillanti*, *Crocodylus acutus* (isolated populations also occur in extreme southern Florida and the West Indies), *Trachemys venusta*, *Kinosternon leucostomum*, *K. scorpioides*, *Basiliscus vittatus*, *Corytophanes cristatus*, *Iguana iguana*, *Norops biporcatus*, *Mabuya unimarginata*, *Boa constrictor*, *Coniophanes fissidens*, *Dendrophidion vinitor*, *Imantodes cenchoa*, *Leptodeira annulata*, *Leptophis ahaetulla*, *Masticophis mentovarius*, *Oxybelis fulgidus*, *Oxyrhopus petola*, *Pseustes poecilonotus*, *Rhadinaea decorata*, *Scaphiodontophis annulatus*, *Sibon nebulatus*, *Spilotes pullatus*, *Tretanorhinus nigroluteus*, *Xenodon rabdocephalus*, and *Bothrops asper*;

E—*Bufo coccifer*, *B. valliceps*, *Agalychnis callidryas*, *Anotheca spinosa*, *Hyla loquax*, *Scinax staufferi*, *Rhinoclemmys pulcherrima*, *Norops lemurinus*, *N. sericeus*, *Sphenomorphus cherriei*, *Ameiva undulata*, *Aspidoscelis deppii*, *Lepidophyma flavimaculatum*, *Coniophanes bipunctatus*, *Conophis lineatus*, *Leptodeira nigrofasciata*, *Leptophis mexicanus*, *Mastigodryas melanolomus*, and *Ninia sebae*;

F—*Bolitoglossa mexicana*, *Hyla picta*, *Rana brownorum*, *Rhinoclemmys areolata*, *Norops tropidonotus*, *Adelphicos quadrivirgatum*, *Pliocercus elapoides*, *Tantillita lintoni*, and *Tropidodipsas sartorii*;

G—*Bufo haematiticus*, *Centrolene prosoblepon*, *Cochranella albomaculata*, *C. spinosa*, *Agalychnis calcarifer*, *Scinax boulengeri*, *Smilisca phaeota*, *Craugastor fitzingeri*, *C. megacephalus*, *Eleutherodactylus diastema*, *E. ridens*, *Leptodactylus pentadactylus*, *Caiman crocodilus*, *Rhinoclemmys annulata*, *Gonatodes albogularis*, *Thecadactylus rapicauda*, *Norops pentaprion, Polychrus gutturosus, Gymnophthalmus speciosus, Ameiva festiva, Cnemidophorus lemniscatus, Anomalepis mexicanus, Corallus annulatus, Chironius grandisquamis, Clelia clelia, Dendrophidion percarinatum, Enuliophis sclateri, Erythrolamprus mimus, Nothopsis rugosus, Oxybelis brevirostris, Pliocercus euryzonus, Rhinobothryum bovallii, Urotheca decipiens, Micrurus nigrocinctus, Bothriechis schlegelii,* and *Porthidium nasutum*;

H—*Gymnopis multiplicata, Bolitoglossa striatula, Oedipina cyclocauda, Cochranella granulosa, Hyalinobatrachium pulveratum, Agalychnis saltator, Hyla miliaria, Smilisca sordida, Craugastor mimus, C. noblei, Eleutherodactylus cerasinus, Rana warszewitschii, Rhinoclemmys funerea, Sphaerodactylus millepunctatus, Basiliscus plumifrons, Ctenosaura similis, Sceloporus malachiticus, Norops capito, N. limifrons, N. lionotus, N. quaggulus, Typhlops costaricensis, Dipsas bicolor, Drymobius melanotropis, Geophis hoffmanni, Hydromorphus concolor, Leptophis nebulosus, Ninia maculata, Sibon annulatus, S. longifrenis, Urotheca guentheri, Micrurus alleni,* and *Porthidium ophryomegas*;

I— *Ptychohyla hypomykter, Craugastor lauraster, Rana maculata, Norops dariense,* and *Tantilla taeniata*;

J— *Hyalinobatrachium cardiacalyptum, Craugastor epochthidius, C. pechorum, Norops wampuensis,* and *Sibon* sp.;

K—*Caretta caretta, Chelonia mydas, Eretmochelys imbricata, Dermochelys coriacea*;

M—*Hemidactylus frenatus.*

The number of species in each distribution category is as follows (highest to lowest):

G—36 species (23.1% of total herpetofauna);
H—33 species (21.2%);
D—32 species (20.5%);
E—19 species (12.2%);
F—9 species (5.8%);
A—8 species (5.1%);
I— 5 species (3.2%);
J— 5 species (3.2%);
K—4 species (2.6%);
B—3 species (1.9%);
C—1 species (0.6%);
M—1 species (0.6%).

This summary indicates that about two-thirds of the species (101 or 64.7%) of the Mosquitia amphibians and reptiles fall into categories D, G, and H, including species whose distributions are relatively broad; i.e., having a northern terminus in either Mexico or Nuclear Middle America and a southern terminus in either Central America south of the Nicaraguan Depression or South America. The next largest group of species (19) belongs to category E, with a northern terminus of the range in Mexico north of the Isthmus of Tehuantepec and the southern terminus in Central America south of the Nicaraguan Depression; if these are added to those for categories D, G, and H, the resulting figure is 120 species or 76.9% of the known Mosquitia herpetofauna. Thus, in contrast to the pattern demonstrated by Wilson et al. (2001) and McCranie and Wilson (2002) for the country as a whole, in which the largest percentage of species fell into category J (endemic species), most of the Mosquitia species (151 or 96.8%) are not endemic to Honduras; rather, they have distributions extending either to the west and north or south of Honduras or both.

In summary, the herpetofauna of the Mosquitia contains few species endemic to Honduras, but it is extremely significant because it contains a large number of species whose distributions in Honduras are restricted to the Atlantic coastal lowlands and the windward slopes of the mountain ranges that back those lowlands. Nonetheless, as indicated above, the total distributions of these species are relatively broad. It remains to assess the conservation status of this herpetofauna and the degree to which recognized protected areas act as refuges for this herpetofauna. In addition, we also wish to make some predictions about the future for this important herpetofauna.

# Conservation Status of the Mosquitia Herpetofauna

Considerable interest in the Mosquitia is building among conservation biologists, especially as it is being viewed as one of the centers of biodiversity in Mesoamerica (Boza, 1999) and as a major component of the Paseo Pantera or Mesoamerican Biological Corridor (Illueca, 1997). This corridor consists of a series of forest fragments more-or-less separated from one another intended or already designated for legal protection through which it is envisioned wide-ranging animals, such as the jaguar (*Panthera onca*), might be provided the means to move through at least a portion of the historical range of these animals, with the ultimate goal of allowing the maintenance of viable populations or at least the best approximation thereto of the animals in question. In Honduras, the largest and most closely approximated components of the Paseo Pantera exist in the Mosquitia.

One might believe there is reason for hope that other faunal elements whose home ranges are much more limited in scope might be afforded protection in such a corridor. There is, however, a considerable gap between the genesis of a concept such as the Paseo Pantera and its realization in fact. This is also the case with any of the components of such a biological corridor. Several such components exist within the Honduran Mosquitia; they are discussed in some detail in the following section.

Wilson and McCranie (2004) identified as the principal threat to efforts to conserve the herpetofauna of Honduras in general is uncontrolled human population growth. This factor is at work in the Mosquitia of Honduras as well (Dodds, 1994; pers. observ.). In addition to the greater-than-replacement-level growth rate among Hondurans native to the Mosquitia, the human population of the region is being augmented by the transmigration of people from the more western areas of Honduras, due to the failure of agricultural activities in heavily degraded areas that have been subjected to unsustainable methods of raising food and other agricultural products.

It is expected that such uncontrolled growth will act to degrade the remaining pristine habitats in the Mosquitia until they will come to resemble the areas to the west that were abandoned by the transmigrants. The existence of extensive protected areas, perhaps, will slow the rate of degradation, but evidence is available from our work in the Mosquitia that the boundaries of these protected areas are not respected. However, the currently low population density in the Mosquitia, coupled with the fact that most residents of the Mosquitia are indigenous peoples that practice less destructive and more sustainable resource management practices, lends to the potential for successful conservation efforts that rely as much on community-based resource management as they do outside intervention. But without the wholehearted support of the Honduran government in securing the region from the threat posed by illegal migration and settlement in protected areas, the residents of the Mosquitia will have an uphill battle in maintaining their livelihoods and, in turn, protecting the forests and other natural areas of the region.

In light of these social concerns, Wilson and McCranie (2004) examined the conservation status of the entire herpetofauna, concluding that no Honduran amphibians or reptiles are entirely free of human impact. These authors used a so-called environmental vulnerability gauge to generate environmental vulnerability scores (EVS) to create a theoretical means of assessing the conservation status of the country's herpetofauna. Based on the analysis of these EVS, Wilson and McCranie (2004) divided the country's species of amphibians and reptiles into three categories of low, medium, and high vulnerability. We have used these same categories to allocate the members of the Mosquitia herpetofauna (save for the marine *Caretta caretta*, *Chelonia mydas*, *Eretmochelys imbricata*, and *Dermochelys coriacea*). The results are indicated below.

Low Vulnerability Species (57)

*Bolitoglossa mexicana*
*Bufo coccifer*
*Bufo marinus*
*Bufo valliceps*
*Hyalinobatrachium fleischmanni*
*Hyla loquax*
*Hyla microcephala*
*Hyla picta*
*Phrynohyas venulosa*
*Ptychohyla hypomykter*
*Scinax staufferi*
*Smilisca baudinii*
*Leptodactylus fragilis*
*Leptodactylus melanonotus*
*Rana brownorum*
*Rana maculata*
*Rana vaillanti*
*Rhinoclemmys pulcherrima*
*Kinosternon leucostomum*
*Kinosternon scorpioides*
*Hemidactylus frenatus*
*Sphaerodactylus millepunctatus*
*Basiliscus vittatus*
*Sceloporus malachiticus*
*Sceloporus variabilis*
*Norops dariense*
*Norops lemurinus*
*Norops sericeus*
*Norops tropidonotus*
*Mabuya unimarginata*
*Sphenomorphus cherriei*
*Gymnophthalmus speciosus*
*Ameiva undulata*
*Aspidoscelis deppii*
*Typhlops costaricensis*
*Boa constrictor*
*Adelphicos quadrivirgatum*
*Coniophanes fissidens*
*Conophis lineatus*
*Drymarchon melanurus*
*Drymobius margaritiferus*
*Hydromorphus concolor*
*Imantodes cenchoa*
*Lampropeltis triangulum*
*Leptodeira annulata*
*Leptodeira septentrionalis*
*Leptophis ahaetulla*
*Leptophis mexicanus*
*Mastigodryas melanolomus*
*Ninia sebae*
*Oxybelis aeneus*
*Sibon nebulatus*
*Spilotes pullatus*
*Thamnophis proximus*
*Tretanorhinus nigroluteus*
*Micrurus nigrocinctus*
*Porthidium ophryomegas*

Medium Vulnerability Species (75)

*Gymnopis multiplicata*
*Oedipina cyclocauda*
*Bufo haematiticus*
*Centrolene prosoblepon*
*Cochranella albomaculata*
*Cochranella granulosa*
*Cochranella spinosa*
*Hyalinobatrachium pulveratum*
*Agalychnis calcarifer*
*Agalychnis callidryas*
*Agalychnis saltator*
*Hyla ebraccata*
*Scinax boulengeri*
*Smilisca phaeota*
*Smilisca sordida*
*Craugastor fitzingeri*
*Craugastor mimus*
*Craugastor noblei*
*Polychrus gutturosus*
*Ameiva festiva*
*Cnemidophorus lemniscatus*
*Lepidophyma flavimaculatum*
*Anomalepis mexicanus*
*Corallus annulatus*
*Chironius grandisquamis*
*Clelia clelia*
*Coniophanes bipunctatus*
*Coniophanes imperialis*
*Dendrophidion percarinatum*
*Dipsas bicolor*
*Enuliophis sclateri*
*Erythrolamprus mimus*
*Geophis hoffmanni*
*Leptodeira nigrofasciata*
*Masticophis mentovarius*
*Ninia maculata*

*Eleutherodactylus ridens*
*Leptodactylus pentadactylus*
*Rana warszewitschii*
*Crocodylus acutus*
*Chelydra serpentina*
*Rhinoclemmys annulata*
*Rhinoclemmys areolata*
*Trachemys venusta*
*Gonatodes albogularis*
*Thecadactylus rapicauda*
*Basiliscus plumifrons*
*Corytophanes cristatus*
*Ctenosaura similis*
*Iguana iguana*
*Norops biporcatus*
*Norops capito*
*Norops limifrons*
*Norops lionotus*
*Norops pentaprion*
*Norops quaggulus*
*Nothopsis rugosus*
*Oxybelis brevirostris*
*Oxybelis fulgidus*
*Oxyrhopus petola*
*Pliocercus elapoides*
*Pseustes poecilonotus*
*Rhadinaea decorata*
*Scaphiodontophis annulatus*
*Sibon annulatus*
*Sibon longifrenis*
*Tantilla taeniata*
*Tantillita lintoni*
*Tropidodipsas sartorii*
*Urotheca decipiens*
*Urotheca guentheri*
*Xenodon rabdocephalus*
*Bothriechis schlegelii*
*Bothrops asper*
*Porthidium nasutum*

High Vulnerability Species (20)

*Bolitoglossa striatula*
*Hyalinobatrachium cardiacalyptum*
*Anotheca spinosa*
*Hyla miliaria*
*Craugastor epochthidius*
*Craugastor lauraster*
*Craugastor megacephalus*
*Craugastor pechorum*
*Eleutherodactylus cerasinus*
*Eleutherodactylus diastema*
*Caiman crocodilus*
*Rhinoclemmys funerea*
*Norops wampuensis*
*Dendrophidion vinitor*
*Drymobius melanotropis*
*Leptophis nebulosus*
*Pliocercus euryzonus*
*Rhinobothryum bovallii*
*Sibon* sp.
*Micrurus alleni*

Fifty-seven of 152 species (37.5%) fall into the low vulnerability category, 75 (49.3%) into the medium vulnerability category, and 20 (13.2%) into the high vulnerability category. The percentage values differ from those provided by Wilson and McCranie (2004) for the entire nonmarine Honduran herpetofauna in that a smaller percentage of Mosquitia species falls into the high vulnerability category than with the total herpetofauna (13.2%, as opposed to 31.4%, respectively) and a larger percentage of Mosquitia species falls into the low vulnerability category than with the total herpetofauna (37.5%, as opposed to 21.6%, respectively). The percentage figures for the medium vulnerability category, however, are almost the same for the two groups (49.3%, as opposed to 47.0%, respectively). This distinction is largely due to the presence of very few endemic and Nuclear Middle American species in the Mosquitia.

The categorization above represents only an initial step in attempting to determine the conservation status of the Mosquitia herpetofauna. Assessments of population status of the constituent species need to be undertaken as well. In addition, an assessment of the degree to which the existing protected areas will provide perpetual protection for the members of the herpetofauna needs to be undertaken. An initial step in this direction is taken in the following section.

# Protected Areas of the Mosquitia

A far larger percentage of the Mosquitia has been designated as protected than any other comparably sized area of Honduras. In terms of the interest in conservation of natural resources, this situation is highly desirable. Legal designation of given areas of Honduras as protected, however, does not guarantee, by itself, the conservation of the natural resources located within such areas, as will be discussed below. Nonetheless, these protected areas do exist, at least on paper, and it is the purpose of this chapter to discuss these areas, in terms of their size, location, biological features, legal status, and current condition.

## Laguna de Caratasca Wildlife Refuge

**Size:** 120,000 ha (http://www.cohdefor.hn/areas_protegidas/; most recently viewed 23 December 2004).

**Location:** Northeastern portion of Depto. Gracias a Dios. Laguna de Caratasca is the largest of a group of lagoons located along the Caribbean coast of Honduras between the mouths of the Río Patuca to the west and Río Coco to the east. Puerto Lempira, the capital of the department of Gracias a Dios, is located on the southeastern shore of the lagoon. The lagoon is narrowly separated from the ocean by a strip of land, which is narrowly broken by a channel at Barra de Caratasca.

**Biological features:** This proposed wildlife refuge consists mostly of estuarine and open water habitat, plus some surrounding mangrove, denuded evergreen broadleaf, and pine forests, open *llanos* (freshwater marshes), as well as coastal strand.

**Legal status:** Proposed.

**Current condition:** There are a series of small settlements and villages, as well as the town of Puerto Lempira along the shores of the lagunas within this reserve. Puerto Lempira was established in 1960 as a military outpost for the Honduran Army (Dodds, 1994), and quickly grew to become the capital of Depto. Gracias a Dios and the primary transit point for people and goods in the Mosquitia. The town has experienced a great deal of growth in recent years, as settlers migrate from the crowded towns and cities of much of Honduras to the relatively unspoiled Mosquitia. As the human population increases and expands beyond Puerto Lempira, pressure on the resources of the proposed wildlife refuge will likewise increase.

**Known herpetofauna:** 41 species (see Table 8).

## Patuca National Park

**Size:** 375,584 ha (http://www.cohdefor.hn/areas_protegidas/; most recently viewed 23 December 2004).

**Location:** Much of the southeastern portion of the Department of Olancho, bordered to the north by the Tawahka-Asangni Biosphere Reserve, to the west and south by the heavily developed farms of east-central and southeastern Olancho, and to the east by the Río Coco. The park protects forest on both sides of the middle portion of the Río Patuca.

**Biological features:** This national park is located within the Lowland Moist Forest and Premontane Wet Forest formations of Holdridge (1967). The park contains portions of three mountain ranges: Montañas de Patuca to the west of the Río Patuca; Cordillera Entre Ríos located between the ríos Patuca and Coco in the southern part of the park; and Montañas de Colón between the ríos Patuca and Coco to the north of Cordillera Entre Ríos. The terrain is typified by rugged, steep hills shaped by numerous tributary streams. The habitat is evergreen broadleaf rainforest. The steep banks of the Río Patuca, and to a lesser extent the Río Coco, were reshaped by the heavy floods associated with Hurricane Mitch in 1998, which left them scoured and bare sometimes as far as 15 m from the normal river level.

**Legal status:** Established 20 October 1999 (Nicholson et al., 2000).

**Table 8.** Distribution of the Herpetofauna in the Protected Areas of the Mosquitia.

| Species | Laguna de Caratasca Wildlife Refuge | Patuca National Park | Río Kruta Biological Reserve | Mocorón Multiple Use Zone | Río Plátano Biosphere Reserve | Río Warunta National Park | Rus Rus Biological Reserve | Tawahka-Asangni Biosphere Reserve | Totals |
|---|---|---|---|---|---|---|---|---|---|
| *Gymnopis multiplicata* | — | X | — | — | X | — | X | X | 4 |
| *Bolitoglossa mexicana* | — | — | — | X | X | X | X | X | 5 |
| *Bolitoglossa striatula* | — | X | — | — | — | X | X | X | 4 |
| *Oedipina cyclocauda* | — | — | — | — | X | X | X | X | 4 |
| *Bufo coccifer* | — | — | — | X | — | — | X | — | 2 |
| *Bufo haematiticus* | — | X | — | X | X | X | X | X | 6 |
| *Bufo marinus* | X | X | X | X | X | X | X | X | 8 |
| *Bufo valliceps* | X | X | X | X | X | X | X | X | 8 |
| *Centrolene prosoblepon* | — | — | — | — | X | X | — | X | 3 |
| *Cochranella albomaculata* | — | X | — | — | X | — | — | — | 2 |
| *Cochranella granulosa* | — | X | — | — | X | X | X | X | 5 |
| *Cochranella spinosa* | — | X | — | — | — | — | X | X | 3 |
| *Hyalinobatrachium cardiacalyptum* | — | X | — | X | X | X | X | — | 5 |
| *Hyalinobatrachium fleischmanni* | — | — | — | X | X | — | X | — | 3 |
| *Hyalinobatrachium pulveratum* | — | X | — | — | X | — | X | — | 3 |
| *Agalychnis calcarifer* | — | X | — | — | X | X | X | — | 4 |
| *Agalychnis callidryas* | — | X | X | X | X | X | X | X | 7 |
| *Agalychnis saltator* | — | — | X | — | X | — | — | X | 3 |
| *Anotheca spinosa* | — | — | — | — | X | — | X | — | 2 |

Table 8 (continued)

| Species | Laguna de Caratasca Wildlife Refuge | Patuca National Park | Río Kruta Biological Reserve | Mocorón Multiple Use Zone | Río Plátano Biosphere Reserve | Río Warunta National Park | Rus Rus Biological Reserve | Tawahka-Asangni Biosphere Reserve | Totals |
|---|---|---|---|---|---|---|---|---|---|
| *Hyla ebraccata* | — | X | X | X | X | — | X | X | 6 |
| *Hyla loquax* | — | — | X | — | X | — | — | X | 3 |
| *Hyla microcephala* | — | X | X | X | X | — | X | X | 6 |
| *Hyla miliaria* | — | — | — | — | — | X | X | — | 2 |
| *Hyla picta* | — | — | — | — | X | — | — | — | 1 |
| *Phrynohyas venulosa* | X | — | X | X | X | — | X | X | 6 |
| *Ptychohyla hypomykter* | — | — | — | — | X | — | — | — | 1 |
| *Scinax boulengeri* | — | — | X | X | — | — | X | X | 4 |
| *Scinax staufferi* | X | — | X | X | X | — | X | X | 6 |
| *Smilisca baudinii* | X | X | X | X | X | — | X | X | 7 |
| *Smilisca phaeota* | — | X | — | X | X | X | X | X | 6 |
| *Smilisca sordida* | — | — | — | — | X | — | — | — | 1 |
| *Craugastor epochthidius* | — | — | — | — | X | — | — | — | 1 |
| *Craugastor fitzingeri* | — | X | X | X | X | X | X | X | 7 |
| *Craugastor lauraster* | — | X | — | X | — | X | X | X | 5 |
| *Craugastor megacephalus* | — | — | — | — | — | — | X | X | 2 |
| *Craugastor mimus* | — | — | — | — | X | X | X | X | 4 |
| *Craugastor noblei* | — | X | — | X | X | X | X | X | 6 |
| *Craugastor pechorum* | — | — | — | — | X | — | — | — | 1 |

Table 8 (continued)

| Species | Laguna de Caratasca Wildlife Refuge | Patuca National Park | Río Kruta Biological Reserve | Mocorón Multiple Use Zone | Río Plátano Biosphere Reserve | Río Warunta National Park | Rus Rus Biological Reserve | Tawahka-Asangni Biosphere Reserve | Totals |
|---|---|---|---|---|---|---|---|---|---|
| *Eleutherodactylus cerasinus* | — | — | — | — | X | X | X | — | 3 |
| *Eleutherodactylus diastema* | — | — | — | — | — | X | X | X | 3 |
| *Eleutherodactylus ridens* | — | X | — | X | X | X | X | X | 6 |
| *Leptodactylus fragilis* | X | X | X | X | — | — | X | X | 6 |
| *Leptodactylus melanonotus* | — | — | — | — | — | — | — | — | 0 |
| *Leptodactylus pentadactylus* | — | X | X | X | X | X | X | X | 7 |
| *Rana brownorum* | X | X | X | X | X | — | X | — | 6 |
| *Rana maculata* | — | X | — | — | X | — | — | — | 2 |
| *Rana vaillanti* | X | X | X | X | X | X | X | X | 8 |
| *Rana warszewitschii* | — | X | — | — | X | X | X | X | 5 |
| *Caiman crocodilus* | X | — | — | X | X | — | X | — | 4 |
| *Crocodylus acutus* | X | X | — | — | X | — | X[1] | X | 5 |
| *Caretta caretta* | X | — | X | — | X | — | — | — | 3 |
| *Chelonia mydas* | — | — | X | — | X | — | — | — | 2 |
| *Eretmochelys imbricata* | — | — | X | — | X | — | — | — | 2 |
| *Chelydra serpentina* | — | X | X | — | — | X | — | — | 3 |
| *Dermochelys coriacea* | — | — | X | — | X | — | — | — | 2 |
| *Trachemys venusta* | X | X | X | X | X | — | X | X | 7 |
| *Rhinoclemmys annulata* | — | X | — | X | X | X | X | — | 5 |

Table 8 (continued)

| Species | Laguna de Caratasca Wildlife Refuge | Patuca National Park | Río Kruta Biological Reserve | Mocorón Multiple Use Zone | Río Plátano Biosphere Reserve | Río Warunta National Park | Rus Rus Biological Reserve | Tawahka-Asangni Biosphere Reserve | Totals |
|---|---|---|---|---|---|---|---|---|---|
| *Rhinoclemmys areolata* | — | — | X | — | — | — | — | — | 1 |
| *Rhinoclemmys funerea* | — | — | — | — | X | — | X | X | 3 |
| *Rhinoclemmys pulcherrima* | — | X | — | — | — | — | — | — | 1 |
| *Kinosternon leucostomum* | X | X | X | X | X | X | X | X | 8 |
| *Kinosternon scorpioides* | X | — | X | X | — | — | X | — | 4 |
| *Gonatodes albogularis* | — | — | — | — | X | — | X | — | 2 |
| *Hemidactylus frenatus* | X | — | — | — | — | — | — | — | 1 |
| *Sphaerodactylus millepunctatus* | X | X | — | — | X | — | X | X | 5 |
| *Thecadactylus rapicauda* | — | X | — | — | X | X | X | — | 4 |
| *Basiliscus plumifrons* | — | X | X | X | X | X | X | X | 7 |
| *Basiliscus vittatus* | X | X | X | X | X | — | X | X | 7 |
| *Corytophanes cristatus* | — | X | X | X | X | X | X | X | 7 |
| *Ctenosaura similis* | X | — | — | — | X | — | — | — | 2 |
| *Iguana iguana* | X | X | X | X | X | X | X[1] | X | 8 |
| *Sceloporus malachiticus* | — | — | — | — | X | — | — | — | 1 |
| *Sceloporus variabilis* | X | — | — | X | — | — | X | X | 4 |
| *Norops biporcatus* | — | — | X | X | X | X | X | X | 6 |
| *Norops capito* | — | X | — | X | X | X | X | X | 6 |
| *Norops dariense* | — | X | X | — | X | X | X | X | 6 |

Table 8 (continued)

| Species | Laguna de Caratasca Wildlife Refuge | Patuca National Park | Río Kruta Biological Reserve | Mocorón Multiple Use Zone | Río Plátano Biosphere Reserve | Río Warunta National Park | Rus Rus Biological Reserve | Tawahka-Asangni Biosphere Reserve | Totals |
|---|---|---|---|---|---|---|---|---|---|
| *Norops lemurinus* | — | X | — | X | X | X | X | X | 6 |
| *Norops limifrons* | — | X | X | X | X | X | X | X | 7 |
| *Norops lionotus* | — | X | — | — | X | — | — | X | 3 |
| *Norops pentaprion* | — | — | — | — | X | — | — | X | 2 |
| *Norops quaggulus* | — | X | — | — | X | X | X | X | 5 |
| *Norops sericeus* | X | — | X | X | X | — | X | X | 6 |
| *Norops tropidonotus* | — | — | — | — | X | — | — | X | 2 |
| *Norops wampuensis* | — | — | — | — | X | — | — | — | 1 |
| *Polychrus gutturosus* | — | — | — | — | X | — | X | — | 2 |
| *Mabuya unimarginata* | X | — | X | X | X | — | X | — | 5 |
| *Sphenomorphus cherriei* | — | X | — | — | X | X | X | X | 5 |
| *Gymnophthalmus speciosus* | X | — | — | — | X | — | X | — | 3 |
| *Ameiva festiva* | — | X | X | X | X | X | X | X | 7 |
| *Ameiva undulata* | X | X[1] | — | X | X | — | X | X | 6 |
| *Aspidoscelis deppii* | X | X[1] | — | X | — | — | — | — | 3 |
| *Cnemidophorus lemniscatus* | X | — | — | — | X | — | — | — | 2 |
| *Lepidophyma flavimaculatum* | — | — | — | — | X | — | X | X | 3 |
| *Anomalepis mexicanus* | — | — | — | — | — | X | — | — | 1 |
| *Typhlops costaricensis* | — | — | — | — | — | X | — | — | 1 |

Table 8 (continued)

| Species | Laguna de Caratasca Wildlife Refuge | Patuca National Park | Río Kruta Biological Reserve | Mocorón Multiple Use Zone | Río Plátano Biosphere Reserve | Río Warunta National Park | Rus Rus Biological Reserve | Tawahka-Asangni Biosphere Reserve | Totals |
|---|---|---|---|---|---|---|---|---|---|
| *Boa constrictor* | X | X | X | X | X | X[1] | X | — | 7 |
| *Corallus annulatus* | — | — | — | — | — | X | X | X | 3 |
| *Adelphicos quadrivirgatum* | — | — | — | — | X | — | — | X | 2 |
| *Chironius grandisquamis* | — | — | — | X | X | X | X | X | 5 |
| *Clelia clelia* | — | X | — | X | X | X | X | X | 6 |
| *Coniophanes bipunctatus* | — | — | — | — | — | — | — | — | 0 |
| *Coniophanes fissidens* | — | — | — | — | X | — | X | — | 2 |
| *Coniophanes imperialis* | — | — | X | — | — | — | — | — | 1 |
| *Conophis lineatus* | X | — | — | — | X | — | X | — | 3 |
| *Dendrophidion percarinatum* | — | X | — | — | X | X | X | — | 4 |
| *Dendrophidion vinitor* | — | — | — | — | — | X | X | X | 3 |
| *Dipsas bicolor* | — | — | — | — | X | X | X | — | 3 |
| *Drymarchon melanurus* | X | — | — | — | — | — | — | — | 1 |
| *Drymobius margaritiferus* | X | — | X | X | X | — | X | — | 5 |
| *Drymobius melanotropis* | — | — | — | — | X | — | — | — | 1 |
| *Enuliophis sclateri* | — | — | — | — | — | — | X | X | 2 |
| *Erythrolamprus mimus* | — | — | — | X | X | — | X | — | 3 |
| *Geophis hoffmanni* | — | — | — | — | X | X | X | — | 3 |
| *Hydromorphus concolor* | — | X | — | — | — | X | — | — | 2 |

Table 8 (continued)

| Species | Laguna de Caratasca Wildlife Refuge | Patuca National Park | Río Kruta Biological Reserve | Mocorón Multiple Use Zone | Río Plátano Biosphere Reserve | Río Warunta National Park | Rus Rus Biological Reserve | Tawahka-Asangni Biosphere Reserve | Totals |
|---|---|---|---|---|---|---|---|---|---|
| *Imantodes cenchoa* | X | X | X | — | X | X | X | — | 6 |
| *Lampropeltis triangulum* | — | X | — | — | — | — | — | — | 1 |
| *Leptodeira annulata* | X | — | — | X | X | — | X | — | 4 |
| *Leptodeira nigrofasciata* | — | — | — | — | — | — | — | — | 0 |
| *Leptodeira septentrionalis* | — | — | — | X | X | X | X | X | 5 |
| *Leptophis ahaetulla* | — | X | X | X | X | — | X | X | 6 |
| *Leptophis mexicanus* | X | — | X | X | X | — | X | — | 5 |
| *Leptophis nebulosus* | — | — | X | — | X | — | — | — | 2 |
| *Masticophis mentovarius* | — | — | — | X | — | — | X | — | 2 |
| *Mastigodryas melanolomus* | X | X | X | — | X | X | X | X[1] | 7 |
| *Ninia maculata* | — | — | — | — | X | — | — | — | 1 |
| *Ninia sebae* | X | — | — | X | X | X | X | X | 6 |
| *Nothopsis rugosus* | — | — | — | — | X | X | X | — | 3 |
| *Oxybelis aeneus* | X | — | — | X | X | — | X | — | 4 |
| *Oxybelis brevirostris* | — | X | — | — | X | X | X | — | 4 |
| *Oxybelis fulgidus* | — | — | — | — | X | — | X | — | 2 |
| *Oxyrhopus petola* | — | — | X | — | — | — | X | X | 3 |
| *Pliocercus elapoides* | — | — | — | — | X | — | — | — | 1 |
| *Pliocercus euryzonus* | — | — | — | — | — | — | — | X | 1 |

Table 8 (continued)

| Species | Laguna de Caratasca Wildlife Refuge | Patuca National Park | Río Kruta Biological Reserve | Mocorón Multiple Use Zone | Río Plátano Biosphere Reserve | Río Warunta National Park | Rus Rus Biological Reserve | Tawahka-Asangni Biosphere Reserve | Totals |
|---|---|---|---|---|---|---|---|---|---|
| *Pseustes poecilonotus* | — | — | — | X | X | X | X | X | 5 |
| *Rhadinaea decorata* | — | — | — | — | — | X | — | — | 1 |
| *Rhinobothryum bovallii* | — | — | — | — | — | — | — | — | 0 |
| *Scaphiodontophis annulatus* | — | — | — | X | — | — | X | — | 2 |
| *Sibon annulatus* | — | — | X | — | — | — | — | — | 1 |
| *Sibon longifrenis* | — | — | — | — | X | — | — | — | 1 |
| *Sibon nebulatus* | — | X | — | — | — | X | X | X | 4 |
| *Sibon* sp. | — | — | — | — | — | X | — | — | 1 |
| *Spilotes pullatus* | X | X | X | — | X | — | X | — | 5 |
| *Tantilla taeniata* | X | — | — | — | — | — | X | — | 2 |
| *Tantillita lintoni* | — | — | — | — | — | — | X | X | 2 |
| *Thamnophis proximus* | X | — | — | X | X | — | X | — | 4 |
| *Tretanorhinus nigroluteus* | — | — | — | X | X | — | — | X | 3 |
| *Tropidodipsas sartorii* | — | — | — | — | — | X | — | — | 1 |
| *Urotheca decipiens* | — | — | — | — | — | — | X | — | 1 |
| *Urotheca guentheri* | — | — | — | — | X | X | X | — | 3 |
| *Xenodon rabdocephalus* | — | — | X | — | X | — | X | — | 3 |
| *Micrurus alleni* | — | — | — | — | — | X | — | X | 2 |
| *Micrurus nigrocinctus* | X | — | X | X | X | — | X | X | 6 |

Table 8 (continued)

| Species | Laguna de Caratasca Wildlife Refuge | Patuca National Park | Río Kruta Biological Reserve | Mocorón Multiple Use Zone | Río Plátano Biosphere Reserve | Río Warunta National Park | Rus Rus Biological Reserve | Tawahka-Asangni Biosphere Reserve | Totals |
|---|---|---|---|---|---|---|---|---|---|
| *Bothriechis schlegelii* | — | — | — | X | X | X | X | X | 5 |
| *Bothrops asper* | — | X | X | X | X | X | X | X | 7 |
| *Porthidium nasutum* | — | — | — | — | X | X | X | X | 4 |
| *Porthidium ophryomegas* | X | — | — | X | — | — | X | — | 3 |
| Totals (156) | 41 | 60 | 49 | 62 | 113 | 65 | 107 | 76 | — |

X[1] = Sight record.

**Current condition:** There is strong deforestation pressure along all sides of Patuca National Park, and settlement along the Río Patuca has continued subsequent to the establishment of the park. The majority of intact evergreen broadleaf forest lies in hilly terrain between the ríos Patuca and Coco. Over the past few years, at least two proposals to build hydroelectric dams along the Patuca have been thwarted by pressure from a combination of local indigenous organizations and outside environmental groups.

**Remarks:** Fundación Patuca has established a pilot project to teach sustainable agricultural practices to residents of the park at Matamoros, along the Río Cuyamel (pers. observ.). Buitrago (2001) reported on a collection of reptiles and amphibians from Patuca National Park, including four species we have not included in our list from the park. Buitrago's (2001) report contains a nonexistent species (*Smilisca bromeliacia*), two species that do not occur in Honduras (*Craugastor bransfordii* and *C. gollmeri*), and numerous unidentified species (e.g., *Norops* sp. a-f). Thus, we consider Buitrago's (2001) report to be unreliable; additionally, apparently no voucher specimens were collected.

**Known herpetofauna:** 60 species (see Table 8).

## Río Kruta Biological Reserve

**Size:** 50,000 ha (http://www.cohdefor.hn/areas_protegidas/; most recently viewed 23 December 2004).

**Location:** The easternmost corner of the department of Gracias a Dios. This reserve is located between the ríos Kruta and Coco, from the Caribbean coast to the Llanos de Auka. The lower Río Kruta is accessed by a dredged canal from Laguna Sirpi on the eastern side of Laguna de Caratasca.

**Biological features:** Much of the Río Kruta is a tidally influenced black water river that rises out of the vast wetlands between the Laguna de Caratasca and Río Coco. The Río Kruta takes on its characteristic dark color downriver of its confluence with Crique Krahkratingni. The lowermost part of the river is lined with mangroves. Most of the reserve is below 5 m elevation and the majority of available habitat is either temporarily or permanently flooded. Flooded broadleaf forest (broadleaf swamp forest), mangroves, and grassy marshes dotted with tree islands are the typical habitats in this reserve. Laguna de Apalca (also spelled Apalka) and a smaller lagoon northwest of Laguna de Apalca are important wading bird rookeries, with 1520 Wood Stork (*Mycteria americana*) nests, 155 Roseate Spoonbill (*Ajaia ajaja*) nests, and about 150 Great Egret (*Ardea alba*) nests recorded in the smaller lagoon in February 1994 (Frederick et al., 1997). Frederick et al. (1997) also reported that the large wetland expanses of the Río Kruta Biological Reserve and surrounding areas are important breeding habitat for Jabiru Storks (*Jabiru mycteria*). Coastal beaches also offer important nesting sites for four species of marine turtles (Wilber, 1996).

**Legal status:** Proposed.

**Current condition:** Human activity in the Río Kruta Biological Reserve is largely restricted to the vicinities of the ríos Kruta and Coco. As one travels up the Río Kruta, the human population along its banks gradually increases. Since most of the reserve is poorly drained, insect infested swamps that lack local sources of potable water, most territory within the reserve should escape exploitation for at least the near future. However, a slight rise in sea level associated with global warming will likely cause salt-water intrusion over a large portion of the reserve. The primary areas of human habitation in the reserve are between the towns of Siakwalaya and Kuri along the Río Kruta and, to a lesser extent, along the coast, particularly around the town of Raya.

**Known herpetofauna:** 49 species (see Table 8).

## Mocorón Multiple Use Zone

**Size:** 50,000 ha (http://www.cohdefor.hn/areas_protegidas/; most recently viewed 23 December 2004).

**Location:** South-central portion of the department of Gracias a Dios. This proposed reserve encompasses the watershed of the Río Mocorón. The Río Mocorón is a tributary of the Río Ibantara, which empties into Laguna de Tánsin to the west of Puerto Lempira.

**Biological features:** This proposed reserve lies entirely within the Lowland Moist Forest formation of Holdridge (1967). However, two distinctive types of forest occur in this region. These are evergreen broadleaf forest and pine savanna.

**Legal status:** Proposed.

**Current condition:** Much of this proposed reserve has been degraded by the human population living in and around the village of Mocorón. Undisturbed evergreen broadleaf forest apparently still occurs in the upper reaches of the Río Mocorón. We have had no experience in this proposed reserve.

**Known herpetofauna:** 62 species (see Table 8).

## Río Plátano Biosphere Reserve

**Size:** 815,000 ha (http://www.cohdefor.hn/areas_protegidas/; most recently viewed 23 December 2004).

**Location:** Eastern portion of the department of Colón (about 45% of area; figures based on Cruz, 1986), northwestern portion of the department of Gracias a Dios (about 50%), and northeastern portion of the department of Olancho (about 5%). It comprises the entirety of the Río Plátano watershed, extending approximately 115 km from the highlands of northeastern Olancho to the river's mouth between Laguna Ébano to the west and Laguna Brus to the east. The reserve also includes portions of neighboring watersheds, such as those of the Río Paulaya, Río Wampú, and Río Sigre (Cruz, 1986). This park is bounded on the north by the Caribbean Sea, on the west by the ríos Paulaya and Wampú, on the south by the Río Wampú, and on the east by the ríos Pao, Tuscruwás, and Patuca.

**Biological features:** Dodds (1994:90) presented an overview of the biological resources under protection in this reserve. He noted the presence of "broadleaf [vegetation] areas, such as gallery forests, swamps, mangroves, and beach forest" and pine covered areas "of which the largest are the lowland Mosquitia pine savanna, and at the southern tip, the subtropical highland pine areas of Olancho." Dodds (1994:90) stated "for the northern Rio Plátano Biosphere Reserve, terrestrial ecozones include the coastal strip (now mostly secondary growth, houses, and fields); low-lying tique palm savanna; pine savanna; gallery forest along streams in the pine savanna; and broadleaf tropical rainforest, to the south and west sides of the Laguna de Ibans [Laguna de Ébano]. Riparian ecozones of the northern Rio Plátano Biosphere Reserve include freshwater streams, freshwater lagoons, inland channels (fresh or brackish, depending on the season), brackish mangrove swamps, beaches, and the shelf saltwater of the Caribbean Sea." Froehlich et al. (1983) conducted preliminary mammalian and botanical surveys at two sites along tributaries of the Río Plátano, and reported 48 species of mammals and around 300 plant species, of which 118 were trees. Poorly drained marshes were typically inhabited by Suita Palms (*Caluptrogyne sarapiquensis*), gallery forest commonly contained *Calophyllum* cf. *chiapense*, *Cedrela odorata*, *Ceiba pentandra*, *Ficus* spp., *Luehea seemanii*, and *Virola* sp., and along slopes and ridges *Didymopanax morotoni*, *Ficus insipida*, *Quararibea* sp., and *Spondius mombin* (Froehlich et al., 1983). Dodds (1994:91) quoted Cruz (1986:35–36) as follows (Dodds' translation): "With reference to fauna, the species in danger of extinction, and identified within the Rio Plátano Reserve, are: manatee [*Trichechus manatus*], jaguar [*Panthera onca*], puma [*Felis concolor*], ocelot [*Felis pardalis*], collared peccary [*Tayassu tajacu*], white-lipped peccary [*Tayassu pecari*], wild turkey [*Meleagris gallopavo*], alligator [*Crocodylus acutus*], caiman [*Caiman crocodilus*], pajuil [*Crax rubra*], tapir [*Tapirus bairdii*], giant anteater [*Myrmecophaga tridactyla*], cuyamel [*Joturus picardi*], harpy eagle [*Harpia harpyja*], and various tufted eagles [*Harpyhalietus*, *Morphnus*, *Spizaetus*, *Spizastur*], red macaws [*Ara macao*], and green macaws [*Ara ambigua*]. Several marine turtles lay their eggs on its beaches, including the giant sea tortoise [*Dermochelys coriacea*], the green turtle [*Chelonia mydas*], the caguama [*Caretta caretta*], and hawksbill [*Eretmochelys imbricata*]." McCain (2001) also documented the presence in the reserve of the Silky Anteater (*Cyclopes didactylus*), as well as the Giant Anteater (*Myrmecophaga tridactyla*).

**Legal status:** Legally established in December 1980 by Decreed Law No. 977 of the Honduran Congress, also recognized the same year as a World Heritage Site under the 1972 Convention for the Protection of the World Cultural and Natural Heritage (Dodds, 1994). This area had previously been set aside as a Parque Antropológico Nacional by the Honduran president in 1969, in an effort to protect the poorly known pre-Columbian ruins and artifacts from removal (Froehlich and Schwerin, 1983).

**Current condition:** Areas in the southwestern portion of the nuclear zone have been invaded by sizable numbers of *campesinos*, ranchers, and illegal loggers, the activities of the last listed prompting the threat of the removal of World Heritage Site status by the United Nations Educational, Scientific, and Cultural Organization (D. Meyer, 2000). Based on our observations made in 1999, some of these activities had already been in place for several years. In 1998 the Nature Conservancy "added the 2-million-acre reserve to its list of Latin American Parks in Peril" (D. Meyer, 2000:6).

**Remarks:** A stronghold for the last Pech villages. Miskitos and some Garífunas live along the coast. The Biosphere protects pre-Columbian ruins and petroglyphs as well as the wildlands needed by indigenous Pech to survive using sustainable hunting and agricultural practices. Although discussion of these resources is outside of the scope of this book, the reader is directed to Dodds' doctoral dissertation (1994) for an interesting treatment of them. The park also protects numerous pre-Columbian ruins and petroglyphs, including the ruins of Las Crucitas.

**Known herpetofauna:** 113 species (see Table 8).

## Río Warunta National Park

**Size:** 41,200 ha (http://www.cohdefor.hn/areas_protegidas/; most recently viewed 23 December 2004).

**Location:** Southwestern portion of the department of Gracias a Dios. This proposed national park encompasses the upper portion of the Río Warunta and its tributaries. The Río Warunta's headwaters are in the Montañas de Colón north of Awasbila. The Río Warunta empties into the Laguna Warunta just west of Laguna de Caratasca.

**Biological features:** This proposed national park is located entirely within the Lowland Moist Forest formation of Holdridge (1967). Evergreen broadleaf forest covers the entire reserve. Much of the reserve also contains karsted slopes of the Montañas de Colón. This is the most primitive of all of the reserves in the Mosquitia, as there are no roads or even trails into the park, at least on the southern, western, and eastern sides as far into the reserve as the Río Warunta itself. McCranie spent 5 days in November 2003 and 16 days in May 2004 in this reserve and saw the following large mammals: Jaguar (*Panthera onca*),

White-lipped Peccary (*Tayassu pecari*), Red Brocket Deer (*Mazama americana*), Mantled Howler Monkey (*Alouatta palliata*), Central American Spider Monkey (*Ateles geoffroyi*), White-faced Capuchin Monkey (*Cebus capuchinus*), Paca (*Agouti paca*), and Central American Agouti (*Dasyprocta punctata*). Tracks of Baird's Tapir (*Tapirus bairdii*) were also seen. Conspicuous large birds seen were the Great Curassow (*Crax rubra*), the Tinamou (*Tinamus major*), Green Macaw (*Ara ambigua*), and the Scarlet Macaw (*Ara macao*).

**Legal status:** Proposed.

**Current condition:** The portions of this proposed reserve visited by McCranie is in a pristine, even "virgin" condition. In McCranie's 21 days there, he saw absolutely no sign of other humans ever having been there and people in the village of Rus Rus knew of nobody who had ever been there. Indeed, several species of mammals listed above showed no fear towards humans. One large group (ca. 100 individuals) of White Lipped Peccary nonchalantly walked into McCranie's campsite one morning even though a campfire was going and he and his crew were talking and in the process of breaking camp. Also, all three species of monkeys showed more curiosity towards the humans than the humans did towards them, with several individuals of the Spider and Howler monkeys even following the humans for the better part of an hour on several occasions. Spider Monkeys became such a nuisance in camp on one occasion that they had to be driven away by throwing rocks in their direction. Green Macaws were more numerous in this proposed reserve than McCranie has ever seen them elsewhere in the Mosquitia.

**Known herpetofauna:** 65 species (see Table 8).

## Rus Rus Biological Reserve

**Size:** 35,000 ha (http://www.cohdefor.hn/areas_protegidas/; most recently viewed 23 December 2004).

**Location:** South-central portion of the department of Gracias a Dios. This proposed reserve encompasses the watershed of the Río Rus Rus. The Río Rus Rus is a tributary of the Río Coco, emptying into the latter river between Waspuk and Suhi. The Río Rus Rus passes alongside the village of Rus Rus, the latter located at the point the road from Puerto Lempira to Awasbila crosses the river.

**Biological features:** This proposed reserve is located entirely within the Lowland Moist Forest formation of Holdridge (1967). However, as noted by McCranie, Castañeda, and Nicholson (2002:22), "two distinct types of forest occur in this region. Broadleaf [evergreen] forest occurs as gallery forest along the Río Rus Rus and its larger tributaries in the vicinity of the village of Rus Rus. The width of this gallery forest gradually increases as one proceeds northwest of the village towards the Río Tapalwás. At about the confluence of the Río Tapalwás with the Río Rus Rus (about 16 airline km NW of the village of Rus Rus), this broadleaf forest completely covers the landscape to the east, west, and north of that confluence. Thus, broadleaf forest entirely covers the northwestern portion of this projected reserve . . . The other forest type in the projected reserve is open pine savanna. This pine savanna occurs on either side of the gallery forest along the Río Rus Rus southward of its confluence with the Río Tapalwás. Nearly treeless swamps also occur to the east, southeast, and southwest of the village of Rus Rus." It has been subjected to some initial survey work, carried out under the auspices of COHDEFOR. In addition, more extensive herpetofaunal survey work has been conducted in 2000, 2001 (see McCranie, Castañeda, and Nicholson, 2002), 2002, and 2003. During work conducted in this reserve by the authors the evidence of the following large mammals were observed: Jaguar (*Panthera onca*), Ocelot (*Felis pardalis*), Baird's Tapir (*Tapirus bairdii*), White Lipped Peccary (*Tayassu pecari*), Collared Peccary (*Tayassu tajacu*), Red Brocket Deer (*Mazama americana*), and White-tailed Deer (*Odocoileus virginianus*). The work of McCranie, Castañeda, and Nicholson (2002) established the presence of 71 herpetofaunal species (69 of which were documented by voucher specimens). Fieldwork in 2002 and 2003 added another 36 species, bringing the total to 107 species of amphibians and reptiles.

**Legal status:** Proposed reserve (McCranie, Castañeda, and Nicholson, 2002).

**Current condition:** McCranie, Castañeda, and Nicholson (2002:22) noted that "Almost all of this broadleaf forest in the northwestern portion is in a pristine condition, transversed [traversed] only by several foot trails used by game hunters from the village, and occasionally dotted with small areas of secondary forest. These patches of secondary forest are the result of the establishment of Nicaraguan refugee camps in the area during the 1980s. About 4,000 refugees lived for almost eight years near the confluence of the ríos Rus Rus and Tapalwás." These same authors (2002:22–23) indicated that the "pine savannas are frequently burned during the dry season, although apparently not intentionally. People living in the village of Rus Rus claim that these fires are caused by lightning and lit cigarettes tossed from vehicles traveling the road connecting the village with Puerto Lempira to the northeast and Awasbila to the west. The abundant grasses and sedges that prevail in the pine savannas provide ample fuel for these fires. Thus, all of the pine trees and logs lying on the ground in the pine savanna are fire scarred." However, it seems likely that some of these fires, especially those near villages, are deliberately set. Arguedas-Negrini (2001) noted the Miskito peoples traditional fire practices of using fire to clear the pine savanna and provide fodder for cattle. This author also stated "Miskitos do not practice fire control but expect the fire to burn itself out, except when the winds drive it toward the village. Fires that spread into more distant areas are responsible for large tracts of burnt savanna . . ." (p. 706).

**Known herpetofauna:** 107 species (see Table 8).

## Tawahka-Asangni Biosphere Reserve

**Size:** 233,142 ha (http://www.cohdefor.hn/areas_protegidas/; most recently viewed 23 December 2004).

**Location:** The Tawahka-Asangni Biosphere Reserve is located in the northeastern part of the department of Olancho and the southwestern portion of the department of Gracias a Dios. The reserve is bordered by the Río Wampú (which also forms the boundary with the Río Plátano Biosphere Reserve) to the northwest, the Río Coco to the southeast, and Patuca National Park to the south.

**Biological features:** Much of the biosphere contains part of the Montañas de Colón, a rugged karstic range that extends roughly southwest to northeast between the middle courses of the ríos Patuca and Coco. Areas between the Montañas de Colón and Río Coco are flatter, and covered by evergreen broadleaf forest with meandering streams and some grassy ponds. A number of notable rivers drain into the Patuca and Coco in the biosphere, including the ríos Kosmako, Wampú, Wasparasni, Sutawala, and Caños Almukwás, Awawás, Awalwás, and Kamanán. The park contains vegetation in the Lowland Moist Forest and Premontane Wet Forest formations of Holdridge (1967). We have seen a number of large mammals within the confines of this reserve, including Jaguar (*Panthera onca*), Tapir (*Tapirus bairdii*), and White Lipped (*Tayassu pecari*) and Collared (*Tayassu tajacu*) peccaries.

**Legal status:** First proposed as the Tawahka Sumu Reserve in 1990, the idea of a protected area for the traditional lands of the Tawahka Sumu people has taken various forms in the subsequent years (Herlihy, 1993). Officially declared a Biosphere on 20 October 1999 by an act of the Honduran Congress (Zepeda, 1999).

**Current condition:** Much of the habitat in the biosphere remains intact, particularly the primary evergreen broadleaf forests between the ríos Coco and Patuca. Most areas along the lower Río Wampú are denuded, and a relatively large homestead has been established at the mouth of Caño Awawás on the Río Coco. In addition, much of the area along the Río Coco between Caño Awawás and Caño Awalwás was denuded between August 2002 and May 2003. Human movements between the Coco and Patuca are facilitated by a trail that goes from the mouth of the Río Sutawala at the Río Patuca through the Sutawala Pass in the Montañas de Colón to the Río Coco near the mouth of Caño Awawás. Unfortunately, human movements into this area have dramatically increased since 2003 (H. Portillo, pers. comm. to McCranie).

**Remarks:** This is the traditional home of the Tawahka group of Sumu Amerindians, who today number fewer than 1,500 (Herlihy, 1997). This park is designed to protect both the higher-use areas in the vicinity of the seven or eight Tawahka villages along the Río Patuca and the low and mid-elevation evergreen broadleaf forests that surround them, and to recognize this area as the ancestral homeland of the Tawahka.

**Known herpetofauna:** 76 species (see Table 8).

The data in Table 8 indicate that of the 156 species making up the known Mosquitia herpetofauna, all but one anuran and three snakes (*Leptodactylus melanonotus*, *Coniophanes bipunctatus*, *Leptodeira nigrofasciata*, and *Rhinobothryum bovallii*) have been found in at least one of the eight protected areas. This is a situation that differs considerably from that in other areas of the country (Wilson et al., 2001), in which a significant percentage of the herpetofauna is not included in the system of protected areas (see next chapter).

The largest number of species (113, or 72.4% of the total) is found within the Río Plátano Biosphere Reserve, which is to be expected, since this is the largest of the eight reserves. The smallest number (41, or 26.3% of the total) is known from the Laguna de Caratasca Wildlife Refuge, but that figure is an artifact of the area having been poorly collected. The next smallest number (49, or 31.4% of the total) occurs in the Río Kruta Biological Reserve, which is also expected, inasmuch as it is also one of the more poorly collected protected area. The figures for the other reserves are as follows: Rus Rus Biological Reserve—107 (68.6%); Tawahka-Asangni Biosphere Reserve—76 (48.7%); Río Warunta National Park—65 (41.7%); Patuca National Park—60 (38.5%); Mocorón Multiple Use Zone—62 (39.7%). A very few of the records (six) in Table 8 are based on sight records (about which, however, there is no doubt about the identity of the species involved).

Of the 152 species that are known from one to eight protected areas, 25 (16.4%) are known from a single area, 26 (17.1%) from two, 27 (17.8%) from three, 17 (11.2%) from four, 18 (11.8%) from five, 21 (13.8%) from six, 13 (8.6%) from seven, and 5 (3.3%) from eight. The mean occupancy figure for all 156 species is 3.7, signifying that the average Mosquitia species is found in reasonably close to four of the eight reserves. This redundancy is desirable to increase the chances of the survival of viable populations of the component species.

# The Future of the Mosquitia Herpetofauna

Assessment of the prospects of the members of the Honduran herpetofauna has been undertaken in several recent papers. The first such attempt was that of Wilson et al. (2001), which paper attempted to determine how well the existing system of protected areas offered refuge to the entire herpetofauna. Wilson et al. (2001:152) concluded that "All told, 75.4% of the Honduran herpetofauna is given some measure of protection in the existing system of biotic reserves." They (2001:152) indicated that "This is a significantly smaller percentage, however, than the 90.9% that would be protected under the system of 25 reserves suggested by [them]."

Wilson and McCranie (2004) examined the conservation status of the entire Honduran herpetofauna and concluded that the prospects for the Honduran herpetofauna are growing dimmer, primarily due to the lack of adequate control of human population growth and the impact such uncontrolled growth has on environmental stability. These authors (2004:31) documented a frightening trend by stating that "It is . . . evident that we have been idle too long, and that the study of the Honduran herpetofauna has turned a corner into a torturous maze from which there is no easy exit. It is already clear . . . that a new era has been breached—one in which advances in our cataloguing of the herpetodiversity of Honduras is being offset by documented losses of that same diversity over the last decade or so. We are, thus, fighting an uphill battle on very slippery slopes." Wilson and McCranie (2004:32) promulgated a set of recommendations for the protection of the Honduran herpetofauna, concluding with the following: "Our strongest recommendation is that the steps outlined . . . be taken with all dispatch possible. We have demonstrated that populations of a highly significant number of species of Honduran amphibians and reptiles are already in decline or have disappeared, especially of the most important segment containing the endemic species and those whose distribution is otherwise restricted to Nuclear Middle America. In addition, deforestation has been demonstrated to be increasing at an exponential rate, commensurate with the increase in human population. Deforestation is the principal type of habitat destruction in Honduras, which is, in turn, the major threat to the highly distinctive and important Honduran herpetofauna. There is, in the final analysis, no time to dawdle."

Wilson and McCranie (2003) devised a procedure for identifying herpetofaunal indicator species, the biological characteristics of which were used to establish a gauge of environmental stability for most of the ecophysiographic areas existing in Honduras. They pointed again to uncontrolled human population growth as the major culprit in the erosion of the quality of natural environments in Honduras. Their analysis of stability of herpetofaunal populations in the most vulnerable taxa in 26 ecophysiographic areas in the country indicated that 23 of these 26 areas are judged unstable. They (2003:67) concluded "The construction of a sustainable human society in Honduras is crucial for the long-term stability of its herpetofauna . . . Any change will have to occur soon because the Honduran herpetofauna is being subjected to destructive changes at a rate that threatens to overwhelm all efforts to reverse them."

In light of these dire predictions, one might wonder whether the same end awaits the herpetofauna of the Mosquitia. The answer to the question is that there are several aspects of the Mosquitia that have the potential to ameliorate the full impact of the type of damage occurring elsewhere in Honduras. The operative phrase in the last sentence, however, is "have the potential." In our opinion, whatever potential exists will only do so for a few years longer than elsewhere in the country. This is the case because of the nature of the exponential growth of the Honduran human population.

Exponential population growth is a difficult concept for many to grasp, especially with respect to the way in which population numbers increase in the final stage of such growth. It is defined by

Raven and Berg (2001:G-6) as, "The accelerating population growth that occurs when optimal conditions allow a constant rate of increase over a period of time." They further stated (2001:G-6), "When the increase in population number versus time is plotted on a graph, exponential population growth produces a characteristic J-shaped curve." This J-shaped or exponential growth curve indicates a large increase in population number over a relatively short period of time in the upper portion of the "J" or the final stage of this pattern of growth.

The degree of exponential growth depends on the rate of increase or the growth rate. This rate is the natural increase of a population, expressed as percent per year (Raven and Berg, 2001). The natural increase depends, in turn, on the relationship between the birth rate and the death rate of the population. Based on this relationship and the natural increase this relationship produces, then one can calculate the doubling time in years for a population. The formula for doubling time is: D. T. = 70/% increase. The demographic data for Honduras can be used as an example of how to determine doubling time for a population. The birth rate for Honduras is 33 per sample population of 1000; the death rate is 6 per 1000. The rate of natural increase, thus is 33–6/1000 x 100 = 2.7%. Inserting this figure into the doubling time formula gives the following: 70/2.7 = 25.9 years. Thus, the time it will take to double the current population size of Honduras of about 8.5 million (estimated from the mid-2001 figure given in Raven and Berg (2001:World Population Data Sheet) to 17.0 million is 25.9 years, *assuming the current trend remains the same over this period of time*. This population figure will be reached in early 2029. In early 2055, the Honduran population should have increased to 34 million. By mid-2081, the population of the country should be about 68 million. Finally, by about 2107, the population should grow to about 136 million. Thus, within about the next century, the population of Honduras is expected to increase by a factor of 16! This growth will also increase density by the same factor. The current density is about 196 people per square mile. By about 2107, this figure is projected to rise to 3136 people per square mile! This increase will give the entire country about a third of the current density of the District of Columbia, USA, 100% of which is urbanized (McGeveran, 2004).

The calculations indicated in the paragraph above portend extreme, likely insuperable difficulties for Honduras in the present century, again assuming that the current trend of population growth is maintained. The impact that this pattern of uncontrolled human population growth will have on the Mosquitia is reasonably easy to predict, because the beginnings of this trend for this region are already apparent—and they are frightening in the extreme.

For a country like Honduras, the third most rapidly growing country in Central America and in Latin America and the Caribbean as a whole (Raven and Berg, 2001), human population pressure in the more heavily populated areas, coupled with unsustainable agricultural practices produces the trend to transmigrate; i.e., for people in exhausted regions of a country to move to remaining productive areas. In the case of Honduras, the trend is to move from areas to the west to the still lightly populated Mosquitia. Manifestations of this trend have been made evident to us during our fieldwork in connection with this book. Puerto Lempira, the capital of Depto. Gracias a Dios and the gateway to the Mosquitia, is growing rapidly. New construction is abundantly evident. In the villages in the interior (e.g., Awasbila and Rus Rus), strangers from other parts of the country, especially the adjoining department of Olancho, have moved into these traditional Miskito settings to set up residence. This has created conflict between the native residents and the newcomers. In some cases, the conflict has led to violence, including murder.

The conflict resulting from this transmigration is not simply due to the movement of one group of Hondurans into the lands occupied by another group of Hondurans. It involves a clash of cultures, as has happened again and again in the history of the Western Hemisphere. The clash results from the movement of a group of people who see nature as humanity's servant into areas occupied by a group of people who have a more benign relationship with their natural surroundings. The indigenous peoples of the Mosquitia have a much more sustainable relationship with their environment than do those people who live to the west (Dodds, 1994). Nonetheless, the Miskitos do believe that the resources of the Mosquitia *belong* to them. As a consequence, there is resentment among them directed towards those who would come into their lands, essentially without the permission of the Miskitos, to exploit resources that have rested in the hands of the natives for generations. Given the reality of uncontrolled population growth in Honduras, however, the people of the Mosquitia undoubtedly are facing the prospect of being inundated with waves of transmigrants that will swell to tsunami strength.

Not only are we predicting a major change in the nature of human life in the Mosquitia, we also have to consider what effect this increasing transmigration will have on the herpetofauna of the Mosquitia, which is the subject of this book. We noted in a paragraph above that there are factors operating in this region that could act to make the Mosquitia more resilient to the trend in population declines of amphibians and reptiles seen elsewhere in the country and documented by Wilson and McCranie (2003, 2004). The major factors involved are the broader ranges of most of the members of the Mosquitia herpetofauna than is the case in many other parts of the country to the west, the greater representation of relatively pristine environments in the Mosquitia than elsewhere in Honduras, and the greater percentage of the land placed under protection.

Unlike much of Honduras, the Mosquitia is not an area of significant endemism. We have noted elsewhere that only five species occurring in the Mosquitia are endemic to Honduras. The total number of species of amphibians and reptiles endemic to Honduras is 80 (McCranie and Wilson, 2002; McCranie, unpubl. data), thus the Mosquitia endemics comprise only 6.3% of the total. In addition, as noted above, about two-thirds of the Mosquitia species have relatively broad geographic distributions, having a northern terminus in either Mexico or Nuclear Middle America and a southern terminus in either Central America south of the Nicaraguan Depression or South America.

As noted by Wilber (1996:1), "The Honduran Mosquitia comprises one of the last great wilderness regions of Central America . . . It contains both terrestrial and marine ecosystems that are of national, regional, and global importance. It encompasses a forest corridor which extends south into Nicaragua, forming the largest contiguous tract of tropical forest remaining in Central America." Thus, the biota of this region, including the amphibians and reptiles, are of major interest to conservation biologists working in Latin America.

Finally, a relatively large portion of the Mosquitia has been set aside or is proposed to be set aside in protected areas. There are eight such areas, as discussed above, each associated with one or more of the major rivers in the region. We have noted above that all but four of the 156 species comprising the known Mosquitia herpetofauna are known to occur in one or more of these eight areas.

Nonetheless, the efficacy of these factors in protecting the components of the Mosquitia herpetofauna will be tested by the continuing influx of people into the Mosquitia from elsewhere in Honduras. The question arises, therefore, as to what patterns of change in herpetofaunal composition will occur as the human population in this region continues to grow.

In the chapter on conservation status of the Mosquitia herpetofauna, we allocated each of the known herpetofaunal members (excluding the four marine species) to one of three categories of environmental vulnerability: low, medium, and high. As noted above, 57 species belong to the low vulnerability category, 75 to the medium vulnerability category, and 20 to the high vulnerability category. Those species in the high vulnerability category can be expected to face the greatest danger as habitat destruction and concomitant effects continue. This group includes the five Mosquitia species endemic to Honduras.

Moreover, habitat destruction (i.e., conversion of pristine forest to cattle pastures and crop fields) is expected to have the greatest effect on populations of those species that are restricted in distribution to evergreen broadleaf forest (Table 3), the vegetation zone that harbors the largest number of species in the Mosquitia. Of the 132 species occurring in evergreen broadleaf forest, 86 (65.2%) are restricted to this zone.

Within the structurally complex evergreen broadleaf forest, the species that are dependent on the canopy (see Tables 4 and 6) are especially vulnerable, since these canopy trees, once they are cut, take the longest to reach maturity and by reason of their dominant status in the ecosystem are required to reestablish the microhabitat conditions to which the constituent species are adapted. The species so dependent on canopy trees are listed below.

*Bolitoglossa mexicana*
*Bolitoglossa striatula*
*Centrolene prosoblepon*
*Cochranella albomaculata*

*Cochranella granulosa*
*Cochranella spinosa*
*Hyalinobatrachium cardiacalyptum*
*Hyalinobatrachium fleischmanni*
*Hyalinobatrachium pulveratum*
*Agalychnis calcarifer*
*Agalychnis callidryas*
*Agalychnis saltator*
*Anotheca spinosa*
*Hyla miliaria*
*Eleutherodactylus cerasinus*
*Eleutherodactylus diastema*
*Eleutherodactylus ridens*
*Iguana iguana*
*Norops biporcatus*
*Norops pentaprion*
*Polychrus gutturosus*
*Corallus annulatus*
*Chironius grandisquamis*
*Leptophis ahaetulla*
*Oxybelis fulgidus*
*Pseustes poecilonotus*
*Rhinobothryum bovallii*
*Spilotes pullatus*

It can be argued that all of the species resident in evergreen broadleaf forest depend on the intactness of the canopy vegetation; on the other hand, there are species that are more tolerant of anthropogenic abuse than are others. Some idea of which species are involved can be gained by examining the EVS (environmental vulnerability scores of McCranie and Wilson, 2002; Wilson and McCranie, 2004) of the least vulnerable species. Within this group of 57 species (see the chapter on conservation status), there are 15 species that have lower EVS (3–6). These species are (listed in order of increasing EVS):

*Rana brownorum* (3)
*Smilisca baudinii* (4)
*Ninia sebae* (4)
*Bufo marinus* (5)
*Bufo valliceps* (5)
*Hyla microcephala* (5)
*Phrynohyas venulosa* (5)
*Scinax staufferi* (5)
*Norops tropidonotus* (5)
*Bufo coccifer* (6)
*Hyla loquax* (6)
*Leptodactylus fragilis* (6)
*Leptodactylus melanonotus* (6)
*Rana maculata* (6)
*Imantodes cenchoa* (6)

These species all have relatively broad ecological tolerances. The anurans, for example, are opportunistic breeders that will use a wide variety of disturbed situations for laying their eggs, and all but *Rana maculata* are much more common in disturbed sites than they are in primary evergreen broadleaf forest. The reptiles are also found in disturbed settings. Nonetheless, the large majority of the species resident in evergreen broadleaf forest will undergo population decline and, perhaps, disappearance when such forest is clearcut and burned for pasture and croplands.

The next largest groups of species (39) are those found in pine savanna or broadleaf swamp forest, although this number is only about a third of that found in evergreen broadleaf forest. Of these 39 species found in pine savanna, 9 (23.1%) are restricted to pine savanna. As noted elsewhere, these species are subjected to the conditions of the annual burning of large expanses of the savanna. What the impact is on populations of these species is unstudied, but under the influence of increased human population density the dry, hot, fire-scarred pine savannas can be expected to become increasingly less hospitable to amphibian and reptile populations. Of the 39 species found in broadleaf swamp forest, only three (7.7%) are restricted to that habitat. The broadleaf swamp forest herpetofauna is largely a depauperate extension of the evergreen broadleaf forest herpetofauna. Thus, the same concerns alluded to above for the evergreen broadleaf forest apply to the broadleaf swamp forest.

In short, as the waves of transmigrants continue to sweep into the Mosquitia, the entire area, including the largest of the protected areas in Honduras, will be subjected increasingly to the major weapons of human domination of the natural environment, the machete and the match. These simple tools (as well as machines such as chainsaws) have transformed the face of Honduras, and even though the Mosquitia is essentially a last outpost lying on the frontier, it, too, will succumb to the same destruction occurring elsewhere in the country, since it is the nature of frontiers to be trampled by the very forces that made them frontiers for a time.

# Species of Probable Occurrence in the Honduran Mosquitia

Further collecting in the Honduran Mosquitia should reveal the presence of several species of amphibians and reptiles not presently recorded from the area. This list of species is considered conservative and each of these species almost certainly occurs within the Mosquitia. Evidence exists that the first two in fact do occur in the Mosquitia; however, voucher specimens are lacking, as are verifiable sight records. In anticipation of these species being eventually found in the Mosquitia, we have included them in our identification keys.

*Physalaemus pustulosus* **(Cope, 1864)**—A single male of this species was calling on the night of 5 August 1998 at Quebrada de Las Marías, Olancho, in the southwestern portion of the Río Plátano Biosphere Reserve. Unfortunately, no effort was made to collect this frequently common frog and we left the area the following morning. This locality was in the late stages of being cleared of its evergreen broadleaf forest by the expanding human population. As this destruction of the forest continues, this frog of open areas will probably expand its range farther into this reserve.

*Rhinophrynus dorsalis* **A.M.C. Duméril and Bibron (1841)**—A few males of this species were calling from a vegetation-filled pond at Kaska Tingni, Gracias a Dios, on the night of 27 July 2001. The frogs were extremely wary and would sink beneath vegetation in the pond when our lights were shone in the area. As a result, we were unable to collect any specimens. A single specimen of this species is also known from Waspam, Atlántico Norte, Nicaragua (Duellman, 1971). Waspam lies along the Río Coco in the Nicaraguan portion of the Mosquitia.

*Dendrophidion nuchale* **(W. Peters, 1863c)**—This infrequently collected snake is known from evergreen broadleaf forest in north-central Honduras to the west (specimen in USNM) and southern Nicaragua to the south (Stafford, 2002). Populations of this species are expected to occur in undisturbed to lightly disturbed evergreen broadleaf forest in the Mosquitia.

*Imantodes inornatus* **(Boulenger, 1896)**—This species is known from evergreen broadleaf forest in north-central Honduras (specimens in FMNH and USNM) and north-central Nicaragua to the south (Köhler, 2001). *Imantodes inornatus* likely occurs in undisturbed to lightly disturbed evergreen broadleaf forest in the Mosquitia.

*Leptophis depressirostris* **(Cope, "1860" [1861])**—This species has been reported from evergreen broadleaf forest along the Río Bocay in the vicinity of Pueblo Wiso, Jinotega, Nicaragua (Köhler, 2001). The Río Bocay is a tributary of the Río Coco and Pueblo Wiso lies only about 20 km from the Honduran border. *Leptophis depressirostris* should occur in the evergreen broadleaf forests of the Honduran Mosquitia.

*Trimorphodon biscutatus* **(A.M.C. Duméril, Bibron, and Duméril, 1854b)**—Campbell and Howell (1965) reported this species from a pine savanna locality in the northeastern portion of the Nicaraguan Mosquitia. Thus, it likely occurs in similar habitat in the Honduran Mosquitia.

*Micrurus multifasciatus* **(Jan, 1858)**—The probable occurrence of this species in the Honduran Mosquitia has already been alluded to in the account of its apparent mimic *Pliocercus euryzonus*. *Micrurus multifasciatus* is also known from north-central Nicaragua (Köhler, 2001) and likely occurs in evergreen broadleaf forest in the Río Coco drainage in the Mosquitia.

# Glossary

We have included in this glossary, the technical terms and their definitions that we believe will be unfamiliar to many readers. We have tried to err on the side of inclusiveness rather than exclusiveness so that some terms that will be readily familiar to most biologists have also been included, in the event that they may not be known to lay readers. Some terms included here do not appear in the text, but are used to define terms that do appear there and may themselves be unfamiliar to some readers. The glossaries in Peters (1964) *Dictionary of Herpetology*, Lee's (1996) *The Amphibians and Reptiles of the Yucatán Peninsula*, McCranie and Wilson's (2002) *The Amphibians of Honduras*, and Savage's (2002) *The Amphibians and Reptiles of Costa Rica* were especially helpful in the construction of this glossary.

**Adpressed limbs**—in salamanders, a means of positioning the limbs so that the forelimb is laid at full length backward along the body and the hind limb in the same manner forward so that the number of intervening costal folds (q.v.) (or spaces between costal grooves [q.v.]) can be counted.

**Algorithm**—any systematic method of solving a particular type of problem.

**Allopatric species**—two or more related species separated from one another by a geographical barrier.

**Alveolar surface**—in turtles, the masticatory or crushing surface of the jaw.

**Annular grooves**—in caecilians, the furrows that separate the annuli (q.v.) from one another.

**Annuli**—in caecilians, the body folds lying between the annular grooves (q.v.).

**Anterior**—towards the head; may be used in conjunction with other directional terms (e.g., anterodorsal).

**Anterodorsal**—a positional term referring to an area near both the head and upper ends of the body.

**Anthropogenic**—adjective used to describe conditions or circumstances brought about by the action of humans.

**Apical pit**—a small depression or pair of depressions on the dorsal surface of an epidermal scale, near the posterior end.

**Arboreal**—adjective referring to organisms that live in trees or bushes.

**Autotomy**—in some lizards, the autotomous separation of the tail, usually through intravertebral breakage, followed by tail regeneration.

**Axilla**—the posterior angle formed with the body by the insertion of the forelimb.

**Axillary membrane**—in anurans, a web of skin extending from the axillary region to the posterior margins of each upper arm.

**Axillary pocket**—in anole lizards, a scale-less pocket in the skin at the axilla (q.v.).

**Azygous**—an adjective meaning unpaired, refers to median head scale(s) between other scales.

**Barbel**—a thin, fleshy protuberance, usually located on the head (including the region around the mouth) or neck.

**Bilobed**—having two lobes.

**Biodiversity**—a shorthand term for the diversity of life characteristic of a particular area.

**Biogeography**—the scientific study of the distribution of organisms on Earth.

**Biphasic life cycle**—life cycle typical of amphibians, in which a larva hatches from the egg and later metamorphoses into the adult.

**Brackish**—pertaining to an aquatic habitat in which the water is intermediate in degree of salinity between fresh and salt water.

**Bridge**—in turtles, the portion of the shell that connects the carapace and plastron.

**Brille**—in snakes and some lizards, a transparent scale closely applied and covering the eye.

**Calcar**—in anurans, an elongate heel tubercle having a broad, flat base.

**Canthal scale**—any of a series of scales lying on the canthus (q.v.).

**Canthus**—the angle between the top of the head and the side of the snout that forms a ridge extending anteriorly from the eye to the nostrils.

**Carapace**—in turtles, the upper portion of the shell.

**Cartilage**—a translucent elastic tissue that can preform bone.

**Casque**—in corytophanid lizards, a posterior bony, helmetlike projection of the head.

**Caudal**—of or pertaining to the tail.

**Cephalic crest**—in corytophanid lizards, a flattened, fleshy lobe arising from the posterodorsal portion of the head, more prominent in males than in females.

**Cervical scute**—see Nuchal scute.

**Chest spines**—in anurans, the black cornified spines on the chest region in some adult male *Leptodactylus*.

**Chinshields**—in snakes, the enlarged plates, usually paired, between the mental scale (q.v.) and the smaller throat scales.

**Cladogram**—a repeatedly branching, dichotomously structured phylogenetic tree, used to illustrate the evolutionary relationships of a group of organisms, based on the time sequence in which the branches arose.

**Cloaca**—the posterior portion of the digestive tract into which dump the tubes of the excretory and reproductive systems.

**Cloacal gland**—in some turtles and crocodilians, the glands that open into the cloaca and produce a musk.

**Cloacal opening**—the vent (q.v.).

**Cloacal scute**—in snakes, the large scale overlying the vent, which may be single or divided (i.e., bisected by an oblique groove). Frequently called the anal plate in the literature.

**Cloacal spur**—in boid snakes, the external remnant of the hind limb.

**Coarsely areolate**—in anurans, a condition of the skin surface, especially of the ventral region and the area around the vent, in which closely set, raised, rounded areas are found.

**Commensal**—adjective used to describe the symbiotic relationship in which one species benefits from the association and the other is neither benefited nor harmed.

**Coni apicales**—in anurans, a thickened, usually blackened, cone-shaped tip, tip can be associated with apex of tubercles or not.

**Conical**—resembling or shaped like a cone.

**Co-ossified**—in anurans, the deposition of bone in the connective tissue of the lower dermis of the skin on the top of the head.

**Copulatory organ**—intromittant organ used for direct transfer of sperm from male to the interior of the body of the female.

**Cosmopolitan**—having a worldwide distribution.

**Costal folds**—in salamanders, the surface of the body wall lying between successive costal grooves (q.v.).

**Costal grooves**—in salamanders, the vertical furrows on the lateral portion of the body indicating the position of the ribs.

**Costal scute**—in turtles, one of the several epidermal lamina lying between the vertebrals and marginals (q.v.) that cover the ribs in the carapace.

**Cranial crests**—in anurans, raised crests or ridges on the top and sides of the head.

**Crepuscular**—active under conditions of dim illumination, such as at dawn and dusk.

**Crocodilian**—collective common name of the members of the Order Crocodylia.

**Cycloid**—in lizards and blind snakes, referring to a type of rounded scale.

**Dental formula**—in crocodiles, a notation for the number of maxillary teeth anterior to the gap into which the fourth tooth of the lower jaw fits plus the number posterior to this point over the number of teeth on the dentary.

**Dentary**—a tooth bearing bone in the lower jaw.

**Denticulate**—in anurans, tiny pointed projections on skin.

**Dermal glands**—organs of secretion derived from the ectoderm and embedded in the dermal portion of the skin.

**Dewlap**—in some iguanid and polychrotid lizards, a distensible (in polychrotids) or nondistensible (in some iguanids) midventral fold of skin found in the throat region.

**Digital groove**—in anurans, the circum-marginal groove above the disc pad (q.v.) forming the disc cover (q.v.).

**Disc**—in anurans, "refers to the entire expanded structure on the end of the digit" (Savage, 1987:4).

**Disc cover**—in anurans, "The dorsal area above the pad, which is bounded by the circummarginal groove anteriorly and to some extent laterally" (Savage, 1987:4).

**Disc pad**—in anurans, "The specialized ventral (subdigital) area of adhesive epithelium" (Savage, 1987:4).
**Distal**—away from the origin of an appendage.
**Distally**—adjectival form of distal.
**Distalmost**—the most distal of a series of structures located away from the midaxis of the body.
**Diurnal**—an adjective that refers to an animal that is active chiefly in the daytime.
**DNA molecule**—the chemical compound that stores information about structure and function of organisms in the form of strings of nitrogen bases (q.v.).
**Dorsal**—the upper surface of the body of a bilaterally symmetrical organism.
**Dorsal crest scales**—in ctenosaurs and iguanas, the series of enlarged, elongate scales coursing down the dorsal midline of the body.
**Dorsal scales**—the scales covering the dorsum of the body; in snakes, they are arranged in rows extending the length of the body; these rows are counted at one head length past the head, at midbody, and one head length in front of the vent; may be smooth or keeled (i.e., provided with a median ridge).
**Dorsolateral**—a positional term referring to an area located approximately midway between the dorsum and the lateral region of the body.
**Dorsolateral ridges**—in some anurans, paired longitudinal folds in the skin on the dorsolateral region of the body.
**Dorsum**—the dorsal portion of the body.
**Ear opening**—in some lizards, the external opening of the auditory meatus; used in lieu of tympanum, when the tympanum is recessed below the surface of the head.
**Ecosystem**—in ecological terminology, a community of organisms and the factors of the non-living environment that support it.
**Ectothermic**—an adjective describing the condition in which body temperature is determined largely by heat sources external to the organism.
**Edificarian**—an adjective meaning of or pertaining to human habitation; used in reference to an animal that lives around humans and their structures.
**Endemic**—restricted in distribution to a particular specified area.
**Endemism**—the relative amount of species restricted in distribution to a particular area (e.g., a country) compared to the total number of species occupying that same area.
**Endochondral bones**—bones preformed in cartilage (q.v.) that ossify during development.
**Epidermal**—relating to the epidermis (q.v.).
**Epidermis**—the superficial layer of the skin.
**Erectile**—in pit vipers, the condition of the fangs, which are capable of being raised to an upright position.
**Escutcheon**—in some geckos, a shieldlike structure on the venter and adjacent undersurfaces of the legs composed of a series of differentiated glandular scales.
**Estuary**—an inlet or arm of the sea, especially the lower portion of a river where the salty tide meets the freshwater current.
**Eye mask**—in anurans, a dark mark from the tip of the snout across the eye to the level of the axilla or beyond.
**Family**—term used for the taxonomic category (q.v.) between the order (q.v.) and the genus (q.v.).
**Fang**—a tooth modified for the conduct of venom.
**Femoral pore**—in some lizards, one of a series of exocrine gland openings on the posteroventral or ventral surface of the thigh.
**Finger disc**—in anurans, enlarged, adhesive surface on the tip of the finger.
**Flanks**—the lateral surface of the body between the forelimb and hind limb insertions.
**Flared**—spreading outward.
**Fossorial**—an adjective meaning pertaining to burrowing or digging; used in reference to an animal that lives underground.
**Frontal region**—used in reference to the dorsal surface of the head lying approximately between and just anterior to the eyes.
**Frontal scale**—in lizards and snakes, the large unpaired scale on the dorsal surface of the head lying between the orbits.
**Frontoparietal region**—used in reference to the dorsal surface of the head lying just posterior to the eyes.
**Frontoparietal scale**—in lizards, the scale(s) lying between the frontal (q.v.) and parietal (q.v.) scales.
**Generic name**—the first of the two names given to each organismic species recognized.

**Genus**—(pl., genera) term used for the taxonomic category (q.v.) between the family (q.v.) and the species (q.v.).

**Genetic variability**—the variation in the information content of the DNA molecule (q.v.) seen in populations of all organisms.

**Girdle**—one of two sets of bones that connect the limb bones to the vertebral column in vertebrate animals; either pectoral or pelvic.

**Granular**—in anurans, the skin surface texture having raised granules or pustules (can be visible in some cases only with the aid of a microscope [=weakly granular]); in lizards, used to describe small, rounded and elevated scales.

**Groin**—the angle formed with the body by the anterior surface of the hind limb at its point of insertion.

**Gular**—pertaining to the ventral surface of the throat or neck.

**Gular fold**—in some lizards, a transverse fold of skin found in the gular region.

**Gular scales**—in lizards, the scales found on the ventral surface of the throat.

**Gular scute**—in turtles, usually the anteriormost scute or pair of scutes on the plastron; in some turtles, an intergular scute (q.v.) is present.

**Head casque**—in corytophanid lizards, refers to a triangular shaped head casque that projects posteriorly past the head.

**Head crest**—in some iguanian lizards, refers to a laterally compressed lobe of skin (in *Basiliscus*) or enlarged, dorsally projecting scales.

**Heliothermic**—an adjective that described ectothermic (q.v.) organisms that rely on solar radiation to elevate the body temperature.

**Hemipenes**—paired copulatory organs (q.v.) found in squamate reptiles.

**Herbivorous**—adjective referring to animals that feed on plants.

**Herpetofauna**—the amphibians and reptiles of a particular area.

**Herpetology**—the scientific study of amphibians and reptiles.

**Heterogeneous**—in anole lizards, referring to the lateral body scales being of dissimilar sizes.

**Hexagonal**—in lizards, referring to a scale having six angles and six sides.

**Holocene Epoch**—the current epoch of the Quaternary Period (q.v.), extending from the close of the Pleistocene Epoch (q.v.; see also).

**Homogeneous**—in anole lizards, referring to the lateral body scales being of uniform size throughout.

**Humeral hook**—in centrolenid anurans, a hook-like process extending anteriorly from the deltoid ridge of the humerus (q.v.).

**Humerus**—an endochondral bone that forms the skeletal support of the upper portion of the forelimbs in tetrapods.

**Hyoid apparatus**—the skeletal elements and muscles supporting and moving the tongue.

**Hypertrophied arm**—in anurans, excessive development of a forelimb.

**Imbricate**—in some lizards and snakes, referring to scales that are overlapping.

**Infralabial scales**—in snakes and lizards, the scales lying ventral to the lip line and extending from the mental scale (q.v.) and the oral rictus.

**Infralabials**—see Infralabial scales.

**Infralingual plicae**—in some lizards, referring to having fleshy longitudinal folds on the lower surface of the tongue.

**Infranasal scale**—in scolecophidian snakes, the portion of the nasal scale (q.v.) anterior to the suture dividing the scale.

**Infrared-sensitive pits**—in some snakes, pits or pores in the skin leading to organs that are capable of sensing thermal radiation of wavelengths longer than those of visible light (see also Loreal pit).

**Inner metatarsal tubercle**—in anurans, the large raised projection on the ventral surface of the foot at the base of Toe I.

**Inner tarsal fold**—in anurans, a longitudinal fold of the skin located on the inner, or medial, side of the tarsus (q.v.) adjacent to, or connecting with the inner metatarsal tubercle (q.v.).

**Inner tarsal tubercle**—in anurans, a raised projection found on the inner, or medial, side of the tarsus (q.v.) near the mid-tarsus.

**Intercalary scales**—in ctenosaurs, the small scales lying between the enlarged, spinous whorls on the tail (see also Interwhorl).

**Intercalary space**—in ctenosaurs, the space between the enlarged, spinous whorls of scales occupied by the intercalary (q.v.) or interwhorl (q.v.) scales.

**Intergular scute**—in turtles, the single epidermal lamina lying between the gular scutes.

**Internasal scales**—in lizards and snakes, one of the usually two or more scales on the top of the head lying between the nasal scales (q.v.).
**Interorbital**—occurrence between the eyes.
**Interorbital bar**—a marking on the dorsal surface of the head between the orbits.
**Interparietal scale**—in some lizards, a scale on the dorsal midline of the head, lying between the parietals (q.v.).
**Interparietal suture**—in snakes, the suture of the paired parietal scales (q.v.).
**Interwhorl**—in ctenosaurs, a ring of small scales encircling the tail, alternating with whorls of enlarged, spinous scales (see also Intercalary scale).
**Iris**—the opaque contractile diaphragm perforated by the pupil that forms the pigmented portion of the eye.
**Ischium**—an endochondral bone (q.v.) forming the posterior portion of the pelvic girdle (q.v.).
**Isotherm**—an imaginary line on a map connecting points on the Earth's surface that have the same mean temperature or the same temperature at a particular time.
**Juxtaposed**—in some lizards (e.g., *Cnemidophorus lemniscatus*), referring to scales placed side by side.
**Keel**—a raised, ridgelike process.
**Keratin**—a durable, complex, water-impermeable protein found in vertebrate animals and making up the larger portion of the epidermal scales of reptiles and the thumb pads of anurans.
**Keratinous**—composed of keratin (q.v.).
**Kinetic**—capable of movement, as in the bones of the skull of squamate reptiles.
**Labial pits**—see infrared-sensitive pits.
**Lamellae**—in some lizards, a series of flat, overlapping scales found on the undersurface of the digits (see Subdigital lamellae).
**Larval stage**—in frogs and toads, a free-living developmental stage that on metamorphosis transforms into a juvenile resembling the adult.
**Lateral**—the portion of the body of a bilaterally symmetrical organism lying to one side or the other of the sagittal plane (q.v.).
**Lateral fleshy fringes**—in anurans, the fleshy, infolded (at least in preservative) fringes along the lateral margins of the toes distal to the webbing.
**Lateral keels**—in anurans, the flattened ridges along the lateral margins of some or all digits.
**Lateral vocal sacs**—in anurans, paired vocal sacs that lie behind the angle of the jaws.
**Lineage**—all of the evolutionary descendents of a common ancestor.
**Loreal pit**—the external opening to the infrared heat receptor in the loreal region (q.v.) of pitvipers.
**Loreal scale**—in lizards and snakes, one or more scales in the loreal region (q.v.); in some cases when a preocular scale (q.v.) is absent, this scale borders the eye.
**Loreal region**—pertaining to the side of the head between the eye and the nostril (q.v.).
**Lyre**—a stringed instrument of the harp family used as accompaniment by singers and poetry readers.
**Lyriform**—in the shape of a lyre (q.v.).
**Mandible**—collective term for the bones of the lower jaw.
**Mandibular teeth**—the teeth on the lower jaw.
**Marginal**—in turtles, one of several epidermal lamina comprising the outermost series on the carapace.
**Maxilla**—a dermal bone in the upper jaw.
**Maxillary teeth**—teeth located on the tooth-bearing bone (maxilla; q.v.) of the upper jaw.
**Mental groove**—in snakes, a groove on the midline of the chin.
**Mental scale**—the scale lying at the anteriormost point of the lower jaw.
**Mesoamerica**—the portion of the Western Hemisphere extending from Mexico through Central America to Panama.
**Mesoptychial scales**—in teiid lizards, the scale in the throat region lying immediately anterior to the gular fold (q.v.).
**Metacarpals**—elongate endochondral bones forming the base of the hand, lying between the wrist bones and the phalanges (q.v.).
**Metamorph**—recently metamorphosed amphibian.
**Metatarsal tubercle**—in anurans, an elevation, thickened protuberance on the skin of the metatarsus (q.v.).
**Metatarsus**—in anurans, the portion of the foot supported by the metatarsal bones, extending from the heel to the base of the digits.
**Microhabitat**—within a habitat, a particular zone or region in which a species is found (e.g., the canopy of a rainforest).

**Middorsal**—a positional term referring to occurrence along the midline of the upper portion of the body.
**Middorsal crest**—in some iguanian lizards, referring to enlarged, dorsally projecting, serrated scales on the vertebral row of the body or a large, flat fold of dorsally directed skin.
**Midgular**—the mid portion of the gular (q.v.) region.
**Modal**—pertaining to the number or value that occurs most frequently in a particular series.
**Monophyletic**—referring to a taxon (q.v.) derived from a single ancestral species.
**Monophyly**—condition of having arisen from a single ancestral species.
**Mucronate**—in lizards, scales bearing a projecting spine on the posterior margin.
**Naris**—see Nostril.
**Nasal scale**—one of the series of scales, or the single scale surrounding the nostril opening.
**Nasolabial groove**—in salamanders, a depression or shallow groove extending from each nostril (q.v.) to the lip.
**Nicaraguan Depression**—the low-lying area in Nicaragua south of the mountains of Nuclear Middle America (q.v.) and those of lower Central America.
**Nitrogen base**—one of four chemical components of the DNA molecule (q.v.) that allow for the storage of information about structure and function.
**Nocturnal**—an adjective referring to an animal that is active at night.
**Nostril**—the external opening of the nasal passage.
**Notched**—possessing a V-shaped excavation.
**Nuchal**—referring to the dorsal surface of the neck or neck region.
**Nuchal band**—a band of color in the nuchal (q.v.) region.
**Nuchal crest**—in some iguanian lizards, referring to enlarged, dorsally projecting scales on the vertebral row on the neck or nuchal region.
**Nuchal scales**—in crocodilians, used for greatly enlarged scales on the nape of the neck.
**Nuchal scute**—in turtles, the epidermal plate located at the anteriormost point of the carapace (q.v.).
**Nuclear Middle America**—the largely mountainous area between the Isthmus of Tehuantepec and the Nicaraguan Depression (q.v.).
**Nuptial excrescences**—in some male anurans, a horny or spinulate keratinized area found on, but not always restricted to the prepollex (q.v.), or minute or granular asperities usually centered on the thumb or nuptial thumb pad (q.v.).
**Nuptial thumb pad**—in some male anurans, a raised pad on the thumb; pad can also have minute or granular nuptial excrescences (q.v.).
**Occipital**—adjective used in reference to the posterior portion of the head.
**Ocellate**—patterned with ocelli.
**Ocellus (pl., ocelli)**—an eyelike structure of pattern element.
**Ocular groove**—the groove around the eye, separating it from the circumorbital scales.
**Order**—in taxonomy, a taxonomic level between class and family (e.g., the Order Anura).
**Organismic**—the adjectival form of the word "organism."
**Osteoderm**—in reptiles, a bony deposit in the form of a plate or scale found in the dermal skin layers.
**Outer metatarsal tubercle**—in anurans, a small raised projection on the ventral surface of the foot at the base of Toes IV or V.
**Outer tarsal tubercle**—in anurans, a small raised projection on the outer surface of the tarsus (q.v.).
**Palmar tubercle**—in anurans, the raised projection found on the palm of the hand at the base of Fingers III–IV.
**Palmate disc cover**—in anurans, a very slightly pointed disc cover (q.v.; see Fig. 4 in Savage, 1987, and Fig. 3 in Savage, 1997).
**Palpebral membrane**—in anurans, the transparent (or translucent in preservative) moveable eyelid.
**Pantropical**—in reference to distribution, occurrence in tropical regions around the world.
**Para-cloacal tubercles**—in coral snakes, protuberances on the surface of the lateral scales of the dorsum in the region of the vent.
**Paraphyletic**—referring to a taxon (q.v.) that excludes some members sharing a common ancestor with members included in the taxon.
**Parietal crest**—in corytophanine lizards, a crest in the parietal region (q.v.).

**Parietal pericardium**—the portion of the visceral peritoneum (q.v.) overlying the heart; visible in centrolenid frogs with a colorless parietal peritoneum (q.v.).

**Parietal peritoneum**—the portion of the coelomic lining located on the inside of the body wall.

**Parietal region**—used to refer to that part of the dorsal surface of the head occupied by the parietals when the large paired plates are replaced by numerous small scales.

**Parietal ridge**—in corytophanine lizards, a ridge in the parietal region (q.v.).

**Parietal scale**—in squamate reptiles, either of a pair or more of enlarged scales on the dorsum of the head, lying immediately posterior to the frontal scale (q.v.) in snakes and lying posterior to the frontoparietal scale(s) (q.v.) in lizards.

**Parotoid gland**—in anurans, the enlarged, swollen concentration of granular glands located on the head behind the eye above the level of the tympanum.

**Pech**—a group of people currently living on the north coast of Honduras.

**Pectoral girdle**—the bony or cartilaginous structures to which the forelimbs of a vertebrate animal are attached.

**Pelvic girdle**—the bony or cartilaginous structures to which the hind limbs of a vertebrate animal are attached.

**Pelvic vestiges**—a small or imperfectly developed part of the pelvic girdle (q.v.) that was more fully developed in ancestral forms.

**Pentagonal**—in lizards, referring to a scale having five angles and five sides.

**Pilose**—in geckos, referring to the condition of having many hairlike extensions located on the toe pads.

**Phalanges**—the bones distal to the metacarpals in the fingers or metatarsals in the toes.

**Plantar tubercles**—in anurans, the raised projections found on the sole of the foot, exclusive of the inner and outer metatarsal tubercles (q.v.); equals supernumerary metatarsal tubercles of some authors and supernumerary plantar tubercles of Lynch and Duellman (1980, 1997).

**Plastral scute**—in turtles, any of the epidermal plates covering the plastron.

**Plastron**—in turtles, the lower portion of the shell.

**Pleistocene Epoch**—the epoch of the Quaternary period (q.v.) prior to the Recent Epoch (q.v.) beginning about 1.8 million years before the present; geological time period when the ice ages occurred and humans appeared.

**Pleural scute**—see Costal scute.

**Polyphyletic**—referring to a taxon (q.v.) whose members were derived from more than one ancestral form not common to all members.

**Polytypic species**—a species of organism composed of two or more distinct subgroups.

**Postcloacal scale**—in some lizards, one of a pair of enlarged scales lying immediately posterior to the vent (q.v.).

**Posterior**—away from the head; may be used in combination with other directional terms (e.g., posterolateral).

**Postfemoral dermal pocket**—in sceloporine lizards, a scaleless pocket located just posterior to the proximal segment of the hind leg.

**Postnasal scale**—the scale lying immediately posterior to the nostril; in snakes, the posterior scale of the divided nasal scale (q.v.).

**Postoccipital**—occupying a position behind the occiput.

**Postoccipital scutes**—in crocodilians, a group of enlarged scales located posterior to the occiput.

**Postocular ridges**—in anurans, ridges extending posteriorly from the region of the upper eyelids.

**Postorbital**—adjective referring to the region behind the eye.

**Postparietal scales**—in snakes, the dorsal scales of the neck posterior to the parietal scales.

**Precloacal pores**—in lizards, the opening of an exocrine gland situated in the region immediately anterior to the cloaca (q.v.).

**Precloacal spur**—in teiid lizards of the genus *Cnemidophorus*, a laterally projecting scale extension located anterior to the cloaca (q.v.).

**Prefrontal scale**—in turtles, lizards, and snakes, one of a pair (or more) of epidermal scutes lying anterior to the frontal scale on the dorsal surface of the head.

**Prehensile**—adapted for seizing or wrapping around an object.

**Premaxillary teeth**—the teeth attached to the premaxillary bone, located in the anteromedial portion of the upper jaw.

**Preocular scale**—in snakes, one of one or more higher than long scales lying immediately in front of the eye forming its anterior border.

**Preorbital ridge**—in crocodilians, a transverse ridge located on the top of the head just in front of the orbits.
**Prepollex**—in anurans, a vestigial digit on the inner side of the first digit of the hand; usually barely indicated externally as a rounded or elliptical projection, although in some groups or species, the process can be distinctly enlarged, especially in males.
**Prepollical spine**—in anurans, the distal end of the prepollex (q.v.) in the form of a spine.
**Proteroglyph dentition**—in elapid snakes, a type of dentition in which the fangs are located in the anterior portion of the mouth cavity.
**Quaternary Period**—the most recent geological period, consisting of the Pleistocene (q.v.) and Recent (q.v.) Epochs, beginning about 1.8 million years before the present.
**Recent Epoch**—the most recent geological epoch, beginning about 10,000 years before the present; historical time (see also Holocene Epoch).
**Regenerated**—in lizards, referring to a lost portion of a tail that has been replaced by a new growth of tissue.
**Rostral scale**—the scale in snakes and lizard at the anteriormost portion of the snout, lying just above the lip line.
**Rounded disc cover**—in anurans, rounded disc covers (q.v.; see Fig. 4 in Savage, 1987).
**Sacral**—of or pertaining to the sacrum (q.v.) or the region of the body where the sacrum is located.
**Sacrum**—a vertebra or vertebrae articulating with the pelvic girdle (q.v.).
**Sagittal plane**—the imaginary plane of section that passes from the dorsal midline to the ventral midline of the body of a bilaterally symmetrical organism.
**Scientific name**—the two-part formal name (generic and specific) given to an organism, which is used to insure accuracy of communication among biologists.
**Scolecophidian**—the adjectival form of the proper noun Scolecophidia, referring to an infraorder of the suborder Serpentes, if the latter is recognized, containing the blind snakes, blind worm snakes, and thread snakes, all characterized by having vestigial eyes, blunt heads, and equally-sized dorsal and ventral cycloid body and tail scales.
**Seat patch**—in anurans of the Craugastor gollmeri group, "a discrete, dark brown to black seat patch mark that contrasts strikingly with the dark pigment covering the posterior thigh, subanal, and posteroventral thigh surfaces" (Savage, 1987:7; see Figure 11 in Savage, 1987).
**Secondary palate**—in crocodilians, the platform of bones roofing the mouth cavity that forms the floor of the nasal passages, the roof of which constitutes the primary palate.
**Serrate**—notched or toothed along the edge; resembling the toothed edge of a saw.
**Setae**—in gekkonid lizards, the microscopic hairlike structures lying on the surface of the lamellae (q.v.).
**Sexual dimorphism**—differences in structure related to gender.
**Shank**—used in reference to the hind limb segment between the knee and the ankle.
**Species**—term used for the taxonomic category (q.v.) connoting a group of organisms reproductively isolated from other such groups (biological definition) or a group of organisms occupying a distinct evolutionary trajectory (evolutionary definition).
**Specific name**—the second of the two names given to each organismic species recognized.
**Spiculate**—of or pertaining to the possession of spicules (q.v.).
**Spicules**—in anurans, tiny pointed projections on the skin or on the apices of tubercles.
**Subarticular tubercles**—in anurans, the enlarged raised projections below the articulations of the phalanges (q.v.).
**Subcaudal scales**—the scales lying on the underside of the tail; may be divided or single.
**Subcaudals**—see Subcaudal scales.
**Subdigital lamellae**—the series of overlapping, flat scales on the undersurface of some lizards (e.g., anoles and some geckos; see Lamellae).
**Subdigital pads**—in salamanders, elevated pad on the ventral surface of a digital tip.
**Subdigital toe pad**—in lizards, the dilated ventral portion of the digit, composed of a series of lamellae (q.v.).
**Subequal**—more or less equal, as in size.
**Subgular vocal sac**—in anurans, a vocal sac (q.v.) lying in the gular or throat region.
**Subimbricate**—scales that are nonoverlapping.
**Sublingual fold**—in salamanders, a fold of skin underlying the tongue.

**Subocular scales**—in lizards and snakes, the enlarged scales lying below the eye, forming its ventral border.

**Subterminal disc pad**—in anurans, the thick, fleshy area on the ventral surface of the tip of the digit.

**Sulcus**—in gekkonid lizards, a shallow fold into which the claw can be retracted.

**Supernumerary tubercle**—in anurans, the small, raised projections on the ventral surfaces of the digits (associated with the phalanges [q.v.] only), exclusive of the larger subarticular tubercles (q.v.), not to be confused with the tubercles on the fleshy part of the palm or soles called supernumerary palmar tubercles and supernumerary plantar tubercles, respectively, by Lynch and Duellman (1980), or supernumerary (palmar) tubercles and supernumerary plantar tubercles, respectively, by Lynch and Duellman (1997).

**Supraciliary scales**—in lizards, the small, usually elongate scales bordering the outer edge of the head above the eye.

**Supralabial scales**—the scales on the head of a snake or lizard that lie above the lip line and extend from the rostral scale (q.v.) to the oral rictus.

**Supralabial stripe**—a stripe located on the upper lip.

**Supralabials**—see Supralabial scales.

**Supranasal scales**—in scincid lizards, used for scales lying on the top of the head between the nasal scales (q.v.); in scolecophidian snakes, the portion of the nasal scale (q.v.) posterior to the suture dividing the scale.

**Supraocular scale**—in snakes, an enlarged scale lying immediately above each eye.

**Supraorbital scales**—in lizards, a group of scales occupying the region above the eye.

**Supraorbital semicircles**—in lizards, an arc of scales bordering the enlarged supraorbital scales (q.v.).

**Suprascapular fold**—in anurans, a weak fold of skin across the midsection of the back.

**Supratympanic**—position above the tympanum (q.v.).

**SVL**—abbreviation for snout-vent length, the length from the tip of the snout to the vent (q.v.).

**Swollen disc pads**—in anurans, disc pads (q.v.) with tips swollen beyond disc covers (q.v.; see Fig. 4 in Savage, 1987).

**Tarsus**—in anurans, the hind limb segment between the tibiofibula (q.v.) and metatarsus (q.v.).

**Taxon (pl., taxa)**—a named taxonomic unit of organisms at any given level of the taxonomic hierarchy (q.v.).

**Taxonomic hierarchy**—the nested set of categories used to classify organisms (e.g., species, genus, family, etc.).

**Temporal**—referring to the region on the side of the head lying posterior to the eye.

**Temporal scale**—in snakes, a scale or scales lying posterior to the eye lateral to the parietal region (q.v.).

**Tentacle**—in caecilians, a fleshy, protrusible structure located in a groove or canal in the maxillary bone.

**Tentacular aperture**—in caecilians, the opening between the eye and nostril through which the tentacle (q.v.) is protruded.

**Terminal**—an anatomical position pertaining to the distal (q.v.) end of a structure.

**Terrestrial**—adjective referring to organisms that live on the ground.

**Thenar tubercle**—in anurans, a raised projection located at the base of Finger I.

**Thigh**—the section of the hind limb between the knee and the point of insertion of the limb.

**Thumb pad**—in anurans, the thick, fleshy or cushiony area on the thumb.

**Thumb spine**—in anurans, the black cornified spines on the thumb of some adult male *Leptodactylus*.

**Tibiofibula**—a complex endochondral bone supporting the shank (q.v.) of anurans.

**TL**—abbreviation for total length, the length from the tip of the snout to the tip of the tail.

**Toe disc**—in anurans, enlarged, adhesive surface on the tip of the toe.

**Toe pad**—see Subdigital toe pad.

**Trachea**—the main trunk of the system of tubes by which air passes to and from the lungs.

**Tracheal lung**—a lung that lies craniad to the heart and lateral to the trachea (q.v.).

**Translucent**—transmitting and diffusing light so that objects beyond cannot be seen clearly.

**Transparent**—transmitting light without appreciable scattering so that objects beyond are entirely visible.

**Triangular disc pads**—in anurans, triangular-shaped disc pads (q.v.; see Fig. 4 in Savage, 1987).

**Tricarinate**—having three keels.
**Truncate disc covers**—in anurans, disc covers (q.v.) terminating in a square or even end (see Fig. 4 in Savage, 1987).
**Truncate disc pads**—in anurans, disc pads (q.v.) terminating in a square or even end (see Fig. 4 in Savage, 1987).
**Tubercles**—in anurans, raised knoblike projections in the skin, especially on the dorsal surfaces; also the variously shaped raised projections on the ventral surfaces of the hands and feet; in lizards, raised scales that are larger than the surrounding scales.
**Tuberculate**—of or having tubercles (q.v.).
**Tympanum**—the rounded or oval shaped, flat membrane covering the external opening of the middle ear and, in anurans, its raised rim (tympanic annulus) as well.
**Unicarinate**—having a single keel.
**Upper eyelids**—in salamanders and anurans, a raised portion of skin on the dorsal surface of the head above the eye.
**Vent**—the external opening of the cloaca (q.v.); also see Cloacal opening.
**Venter**—the lower surface of the body of a bilaterally symmetrical organism.
**Ventral**—of or pertaining to the venter (q.v.).
**Ventral scales**—in snakes and lizards, the scales lying on the underside of the body; in snakes they lie in a single row from the neck to the vent.
**Ventrals**—see Ventral scales.
**Ventrolateral**—referring to a position approximately midway between the bottom and lateral portion of an organism.
**Ventrolateral glands**—in anurans, large concentrations of mucous glands embedded in the dermis in the ventrolateral region of some male hylids.
**Vertebral**—of or pertaining to a vertebra or the vertebral column.
**Vertebral scutes**—in turtles, any of a series of unpaired epidermal lamina lying along the dorsal midline of the carapace.
**Visceral peritoneum**—the portion of the coelomic lining overlying the viscera, visible in centrolenid frogs with a colorless parietal peritoneum (q.v.).
**Vocal sac(s)**—in male anurans, the inflatable pouch(es) in the throat or on the sides of the neck.
**Vocal slits**—in male anurans, the paired openings in the floor of the mouth leading to the vocal sac(s) (q.v.).
**Vomerine teeth**—the teeth attached to the vomer bone in the palate.
**Voucher specimen**—a preserved biological specimen used to document distributional and other information.
**Webbing**—the membrane connecting adjacent digits.
**Webbing formula**—in anurans, Roman numerals represent fingers or toes and Arabic numerals represent the number of segments of the digits completely or partially free of webbing. The number zero (0) indicates the webbing extends to the tip of the digit; the number one (1) indicates the entire terminal segment is free of webbing. A plus ($^{+}$) sign indicates the webbing reaches the proximal end of a subarticular tubercle (q.v.) and a minus ($^{-}$) sign means the webbing reaches the distal end of a subarticular tubercle (q.v.).
**Whorl**—in ctenosaurs, a ring of enlarged, spinous scales encircling the tail.

# Gazetteer

The following is a list of the collecting localities and others of interest in the Mosquitia that are mentioned in the text. We follow the same conventions used in *The Amphibians of Honduras* (McCranie and Wilson, 2002). Selected localities are shown on Map 5. Each locality in the Gazetteer that appears on Map 5 has its corresponding numbered point in brackets (in boldface) at the end of its entry.

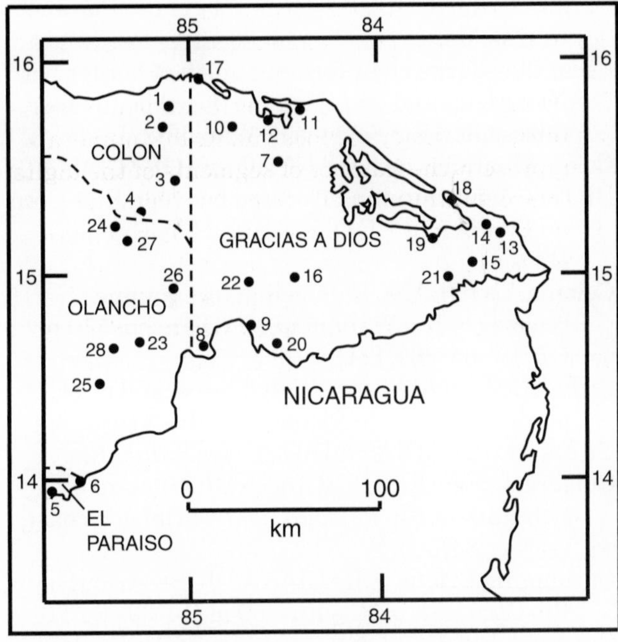


**Map 5.** Select localities in the Mosquitia. Localities mapped are: COLON—(1) Amarillo, (2) Barranco, (3) Empalme Río Chilmeca, (4) Quebrada Machín; EL PARAISO—(5) Arenales, (6) Boca Español; GRACIAS A DIOS—(7) Ahuás, (8) Caño Awalwás, (9) Awasbila, (10) Baltiltuk, (11) Barra Patuca, (12) Brus Laguna, (13) Calpo, (14) Canco, (15) Krahkra, (16) Mocorón, (17) Palacios, (18) Prumnitara, (19) Puerto Lempira, (20) Rus Rus, (21) Tikiraya, (22) Warunta Tingni Kiamp; OLANCHO—(23) Caobita, (24) La Colonia, (25) Quebrada El Guásimo, (26) Río Kosmako, (27) La Llorona, (28) Matamoros.

Ahuás (GRACIAS A DIOS)—large village beside Río Patuca about 37 airline km upstream from mouth; 20 m (15°29', 84°21'), **[7]**.

Amarillo (COLON)—village along Río Paulaya; 25 m (15°47', 85°06'), **[1]**.

Amatingni, Crique (GRACIAS A DIOS)—a small river that flows between the Río Patuca and Laguna de Brus.

Aner, Río (OLANCHO)—tributary of Río Wampú (sometimes spelled Río Amer); confluence of ríos Aner and Wampú at 110 m (15°03', 85°07').

Anzuelo Bridge (COLON)—locality on Río Paulaya about 3 airline km SW of confluence of Río Guaraska; 20 m (15°45', 85°08').

Arenales (EL PARAISO)—village ESE of Los Paredes near Río Poteca near confluence with Río Coco; 380 m (13°56', 85°49'), **[5]**.

Auka Kiamp (GRACIAS A DIOS)—campsite along an unnamed tributary of Río Warunta, located S of that river; 180 m (14°54', 84°40').

Awalwás, Caño (GRACIAS A DIOS)—tributary of Río Coco near border with Olancho; collections made from 70 to 100 m (14°49', 84°52', 14°49', 84°53'), **[8]**.

Awasbila (GRACIAS A DIOS)—village along Río Coco in SW Gracias a Dios (also spelled Auasbila on some maps); 60 m (14°47', 84°45'), **[9]**.

Awawás, Caño (GRACIAS A DIOS)—tributary of Río Coco between Caño Awalwás and Awasbila; 60 m (14°50', 84°49').

Bacalar, Laguna (GRACIAS A DIOS)—large lagoon on Caribbean coast near Palacios.

Baltiltuk (GRACIAS A DIOS)—village along Río Plátano; 20 m (15°51', 84°45'), **[10]**.

Baraya, Laguna (GRACIAS A DIOS)—lagoon near mouth of Río Plátano in NW Gracias a Dios; (15°53', 84°42').

Barranco (COLON)—village along Río Paulaya; 40 m (15°37', 85°14'), **[2]**.

Barra Patuca (GRACIAS A DIOS)—village on Caribbean coast at mouth of Río Patuca; (15°48', 84°18'), **[11]**.

Barra Río Plátano (GRACIAS A DIOS)—village on Caribbean coast at mouth of Río Plátano; (15°53', 84°42').

Belén (GRACIAS A DIOS)—village along NE shore of Laguna de Ébano; (15°54', 84°46').

Bil Almuk (GRACIAS A DIOS)—village along Río Patuca about 70 airline km upstream from mouth; 25 m (15°17', 84°36').

Biltamaira, Laguna (GRACIAS A DIOS)—small coastal lagoon at NW end of and connected to Laguna de Caratasca; (15°30', 84°06').

Blanco, Río (COLON)—tributary of Río Plátano in E Colón.

Blanco, Río (OLANCHO)—tributary of Río Cuyamel in E Olancho.

Blanquito, Río (COLON)—not located.

Boca Español (EL PARAISO)—small port for river travel on Río Coco at mouth of Caño Españolita; 220 m (13°59', 85°43'), **[6]**.

Brus Laguna (GRACIAS A DIOS)—town along Laguna de Brus in NW Gracias a Dios; (15°46', 84°33'), **[12]**.

Brus, Laguna de (GRACIAS A DIOS)—large coastal lagoon between mouths of Ríos Plátano and Patuca.

Cajón, Caño El (OLANCHO)—small river entering Río Patuca; mouth at 180 m (14°21', 85°29').

Caldera, Raudal La (OLANCHO)—rapids in Río Patuca; 80 m (14°49', 85°08').

Callejón (OLANCHO)—not located, but said to be a village along Río Coco by J. Meyer and Wilson (1971), although the coordinates given by these authors for this locality are erroneous.

Calpo (GRACIAS A DIOS)—village along Río Kruta; 2 m (15°12', 83°27'), **[13]**. Also spelled Kalpo or Kalpu.

Camalotál, Río (COLON)—tributary of Río Guarascá, in turn a tributary of Río Plátano in E Colón.

Canco (GRACIAS A DIOS)—village along Crique Canco; near sea level (15°15', 83°28'), **[14]**. Also spelled Kanko or Kanku.

Canco, Crique (GRACIAS A DIOS)—coastal small brackish river W of Río Kruta, dredged portion part of canal system connecting Laguna Sirpi with Río Kruta; collections made near sea level (15°15', 83°28').

Caobita (OLANCHO)—cattle farm on hillside above Río Patuca; collections made from 100 to 300 m (14°39', 85°18'), **[23]**.

Caratasca, Barra de (GRACIAS A DIOS)—N shore of Laguna de Caratasca at its outlet to Caribbean Sea N of Puerto Lempira; (15°23', 83°45').

Caratasca, Laguna de (GRACIAS A DIOS)—large lagoon on Caribbean coast N of Puerto Lempira.

Casamacoa (OLANCHO)—small village along Río Patuca; 100 m (14°46', 85°09').

Cauquira (GRACIAS A DIOS)—village on NE shore of Laguna Caratasca; near sea level (15°18', 83°35'). Also spelled Kaurkira.

Champas, Las (COLON)—village along Río Paulaya; 40 m (15°39', 85°12').

Chilmeca, Cañon del (COLON)—canyon along Río Chilmeca near confluence with Río Plátano; 280 m (15°26', 85°05').

Chilmeca, Empalme Río (COLON)—confluence of Río Chilmeca with Río Plátano; 220 m (15°27', 85°05), **[3]**.

Chilmeca, Río (COLON)—tributary of Río Plátano in E Colón.

Coco, Río—large river forming much of border with Nicaragua and emptying into Caribbean Sea (also called Río Segovia or Wangki).

Colón, Montañas de (OLANCHO and GRACIAS A DIOS)—mountain range located between Ríos Coco and Patuca in NE Olancho and SW Gracias a Dios.

Colonia, La (OLANCHO)—village near upper reaches of Río Wampú in NE Olancho; 570 m (15°12', 85°26'), **[24]**.

Criba, Río La (GRACIAS A DIOS)—coastal river joining Laguna de Ébano with Río Negro.

Cruta, Río (GRACIAS A DIOS)—see Kruta, Río.

Culebra, Crique La (GRACIAS A DIOS)—small tributary of Río Palacios near Caribbean coast; (15°56', 84°56').

Curamaira, Crique (GRACIAS A DIOS)—tributary of Río Coco SSE of Rus Rus; 50 m (14°39', 84°26').

Cuyamel, Río (COLON)—tributary of Río Paulaya, draining W flanks of Montaña de Río Plátano.

Cuyamel, Río (OLANCHO)—tributary of Río Patuca in E Olancho.

Dursuna (GRACIAS A DIOS)—COHDEFOR encampment along Puerto Lempira-Rus Rus road; 70 m (15°01', 84°13').

Ébano, Laguna de (GRACIAS A DIOS)—lagoon on Caribbean coast in W Gracias a Dios (also called Laguna de Ibans); (centered at 15°53', 84°49').

Españolita, Caño (EL PARAISO)—tributary of Río Coco; their confluence at 220 m (13°59', 85°43').

Esperanza, La (GRACIAS A DIOS)—village along Río Coco S of village of Rus Rus; 40 m (14°37', 84°25').

Flores, Crique Las (GRACIAS A DIOS)—small coastal tributary of Río Negro; (15°57', 84°54').

Gabú Dende, Crique (GRACIAS A DIOS)—small coastal tributary on N side of Laguna Bacalar near its E end; (15°57', 84°56').

Guarascá, Río (COLON)—tributary of Río Plátano in E Colón (also spelled Waraská on some maps).

Guaraska, Río (COLON)—tributary of Río Paulaya, draining N slopes of Montaña de Río Plátano.

Guásimo, Quebrada El (OLANCHO)—tributary of Río Patuca; confluence of Quebrada El Guásimo and Río Patuca at 140 m and collections made from 140 to 170 m (14°35', 85°18'), **[25]**.

Ibantara, Crique (GRACIAS A DIOS)—tributary of Río Rus Rus; their confluence at 70 m (14°47', 84°27').

Ibantara, Río (GRACIAS A DIOS)—large river between Ríos Warunta and Nakunta and flowing into Laguna de Tánsin.

Jolamaya, Laguna (GRACIAS A DIOS)—small coastal lagoon extending S from Laguna Bacalar (15°57', 84°57').

Kalila Plapan Tingni (GRACIAS A DIOS)—tributary stream of Río Coco; their confluence about 2 airline km WNW of Awasbila; 60 m (14°48', 84°47').

Kalpo (GRACIAS A DIOS)—see Calpo.

Kanko (GRACIAS A DIOS)—see Canco.

Karasangkan (GRACIAS A DIOS)—area along Río Karasangkan about 8 airline km SSW of Rus Rus; 70 m (14°42', 84°30').

Karasangkan, Río (GRACIAS A DIOS)—tributary of Río Coco SW of Rus Rus.

Kaska Tingni (GRACIAS A DIOS)—a small river about 1.5 airline km NW of Awasbila, tributary of Río Coco; 70 m (14°48', 84°46').

Kasunta (GRACIAS A DIOS)—scattered houses along Río Kruta about 6 airline km SW of Krahkra; 5 m (15°04', 83°36').

Kaurkira (GRACIAS A DIOS)—see Cauquira.

Kauroahuika (OLANCHO)—several houses along Río Coco; 120 m (14°34', 85°09').

Kinikisne, Río (COLON)—tributary of Río Paulaya in NE Colón.

Kiplatara, Raudal (GRACIAS A DIOS)—rapids in Río Plátano; 40 m (15°36', 84°57').

Klanea, Río (GRACIAS A DIOS)—tributary of Río Mocorón near village of Mocorón.

Kohunta, Laguna (GRACIAS A DIOS)—large lagoon on E end of Laguna Caratasca system.

Kokotá (GRACIAS A DIOS)—village along N shore of Laguna de Tánsin about 9 airline km NW of Puerto Lempira; (15°17', 83°52').

Kosmako, Río (OLANCHO)—tributary of Río Patuca in NE Olancho; collections made around two nearby campsites at 135 and 140 m (14°44', 85°10'), **[26]**.

Krahkra (GRACIAS A DIOS)—village along Río Kruta; 5 m (15°05', 83°33'), **[15]**.

Krasa—village on Nicaraguan side of Río Coco about 165 km upstream from mouth (also spelled Crasa); 50 m (14°42', 84°44').

Krausirpe (GRACIAS A DIOS)—village along Río Patuca in SW Gracias a Dios; 70 m (15°02', 84°53').

Kropunta (GRACIAS A DIOS)—village near Río Patuca about 4 km N of Ahuás (also spelled Cropunta); 20 m (15°31', 84°21').

Kruta, Río (GRACIAS A DIOS)—river in NE Gracias a Dios between Río Coco and Puerto Lempira (also spelled Río Cruta on some maps).

Kuilma Tingni, Quebrada (OLANCHO)—tributary of Río Coco near border with Gracias a Dios; 100 m (14°39', 85°03').

Kyras (NICARAGUA)—village on Nicaraguan side of Río Coco across from extreme SW part of Gracias a Dios (also called Anris Tara); 60 m (14°46', 84°56').

Lagarto, Río (OLANCHO)—tributary of Río Wampú; confluence of Ríos Lagarto and Wampú at 180 m (15°00', 85°17').

Laguntara (GRACIAS A DIOS)—moderate-sized coastal lagoon NW of Laguna de Caratasca (centered at about 15°36', 84°07').

Limaraya (GRACIAS A DIOS)—village along Río Plátano in NW Gracias A Dios; 20 m (15°47', 84°45').

Limoncito, Quebrada (COLON)—tributary of Río Paulaya in E Colón, draining W flanks of Montaña de Río Plátano.

Llorona, La (OLANCHO)—village E of Dulce Nombre de Culmí along Río Lagarto (also spelled La Yarona on some maps); 550 m (15°05', 85°21'), **[27]**.

Machín, Quebrada (COLON)—tributary of Río Guarascá in SE Colón near confluence of Ríos Guarascá and Blanco; collections made from 510 to 540 m (15°19', 85°17'), **[4]**.

Marías, Las (OLANCHO)—town in NE Olancho about 3.5 airline km NNE of La Colonia; 540 m (15°14', 85°25').

Marías, Montaña de Las (OLANCHO)—mountain range in NE Olancho near border with Colón; collections made from 660 to 810 m (15°18', 85°21').

Marías, Quebrada de Las (OLANCHO)—upper tributary of Río Wampú in NE Olancho near border with Colón; collections made from 660 to 700 m along a small tributary of the Quebrada de Las Marías about 12 airline km NNE of La Colonia (15°18', 85°21').

Mata de Guineo, Río (COLON)—tributary of Río Camalotál, in turn an upper tributary of Río Plátano.

Mata de Maíz (OLANCHO)—small village in NE Olancho (Wilson and Meyer, 1985, erroneously placed this locality in Departamento de Colón); 600 m (15°13', 85°20').

Matamoros (OLANCHO)—small village along Río Cuyamel; 150 m (14°40', 85°23'), **[28]**.

Mavita (GRACIAS A DIOS)—small village near Río Rus Rus about 4 km N of village of Rus Rus; 60 m (14°45', 84°27').

Mistruk (GRACIAS A DIOS)—village about 13 airline km WSW of Puerto Lempira along S shore of Laguna de Tánsin; (15°14', 83°53').

Mocorón (GRACIAS A DIOS)—village in south-central Gracias a Dios; 40 m (15°01', 84°17'), **[16]**.

Mocorón, Río (GRACIAS A DIOS)—river draining N flank of the Montañas de Colón and a confluence of Río Ibantara.

Mono, Quebrada El (OLANCHO)—tributary of Río Cuyamel near Río Cuyamel's confluence with Río Patuca; confluence of Quebrada El Mono and Río Cuyamel at 100 m (14°39', 85°20').

Nakunta, Río (GRACIAS A DIOS)—large river in E Gracias a Dios flowing into Laguna de Caratasca E of Puerto Lempira.

Negro, Río—large Caribbean versant river extending from north-central Olancho through E Colón and into NW Gracias a Dios (also called Río Sico, Río Sico Tinto, or Río Tinto).

Nueva Esperanza (OLANCHO)—village about 9 airline km NE of La Colonia near headwaters of Río Wampú; 710 m (15°16', 85°21').

Oscana (GRACIAS A DIOS)—small village along Río Rus Rus near village of Rus Rus; 60 m (14°42', 84°27').

Palacios (GRACIAS A DIOS)—village on Caribbean coast in extreme NW Gracias a Dios; (15°57', 84°56'), **[17]**.

Palacios, Río (GRACIAS A DIOS)—coastal river connecting Río Negro with Laguna Bacalar, village of Palacios located along this river.

Pao, Río (OLANCHO)—tributary of Río Wampú; confluence of Ríos Pao and Wampú at 95 m (15°05', 85°02').

Paptatingni, Laguna (GRACIAS A DIOS)—small coastal lagoon near W end of Laguna de Ébano; (15°55', 84°52').

Patuca, Río—major river of Caribbean drainage in departments of Olancho and Gracias a Dios.

Paulaya, Río (COLON)—tributary of Río Negro in E Colón.

Pinto Quiath, Loma (GRACIAS A DIOS)—hill in foothills of Montañas de Colón about 23 airline km NW of Rus Rus; collections made at 200 m (14°57', 84°32').

Plaplaya (GRACIAS A DIOS)—small coastal village along Río La Criba; (15°56', 84°52').

Plaplaya, Criques (GRACIAS A DIOS)—small coastal tributaries of Río La Criba near village of Plaplaya; (15°56', 84°52').

Plátano, Montaña de Río (COLON)—mountain range in E Colón and W Gracias a Dios; 1200 m (15°38', 85°02').

Plátano, Río—Caribbean drainage river in W Gracias a Dios and SE Colón.

Pomokir, Raudal (GRACIAS A DIOS)—rapids in Río Plátano; 100 m (15°29', 84°57').

Poteca, Río (EL PARAISO)—tributary of Río Coco, partially forming border with Nicaragua (also called Río Bodega).

Pranza (GRACIAS A DIOS)—small village along Río Coco S of Puerto Lempira-Rus Rus road; 30 m (14°46', 84°14').

Prumnitara (GRACIAS A DIOS)—village on NE shore of Laguna Caratasca; near sea level (15°20', 83°40'), **[18]**.

Puerto Lempira (GRACIAS A DIOS)—town on Caribbean coast about 40 km from Nicaraguan border; about sea level (15°16', 83°46'), **[19]**.

Quiguastara (GRACIAS A DIOS)—village along Río Coco about 65 km upstream from mouth; 10 m (14°52', 83°43').

Qururia (OLANCHO)—pig farm on hillside above Río Patuca; 100 m (14°47', 85°12').

Robalo, Quebrada El (OLANCHO)—tributary of Río Cuyamel about 3 km W of Matamoros; 160 m (14°40', 85°25').

Rus Rus (GRACIAS A DIOS)—small village N of Río Coco in S Gracias a Dios on road between Puerto Lempira and Awasbila; 60 m (14°43', 84°27'), **[20]**.

Rus Rus, Cabeceras de Río (GRACIAS A DIOS)—headwaters of Río Rus Rus; 180 to 200 m (14°52', 84°39' to 14°54', 84°40').

Rus Rus, Río (GRACIAS A DIOS)—tributary of Río Coco in S Gracias a Dios.

Saúpuka—village on Nicaraguan side of Río Coco; 30 m (14°45', 83°55').

Sausa, Río (OLANCHO)—tributary of Río Wampú; confluence of Ríos Sausa and Wampú at 100 m (15°04', 85°06').

Sico, Río—see Negro, Río.

Sikiatingni, Crique (GRACIAS A DIOS)—small tributary of Río Kruta; 5 m (15°03', 83°39').

Siksa, Laguna (GRACIAS A DIOS)—small coastal lagoon N of and connected to Laguna Biltamaira; (15°32', 84°07').

Siksatara, Quebrada (OLANCHO)—tributary of Río Wampú; confluence of Quebrada Siksatara with Río Wampú at 95 m (15°04, 85°02').

Sin Sin Warra (GRACIAS A DIOS)—village along Río Plátano; 70 m (15°34', 84°58').

Sirpi, Laguna (GRACIAS A DIOS)—small coastal lagoon about 26 airline km NNE of Puerto Lempira; (15°17', 83°32').

Subterráneo (OLANCHO)—small village on hill above Río Patuca; 190 m (14°32', 85°20').

Subterráneo del Río Plátano, Cañon (COLON)—canyon where Río Plátano goes underground in extreme E Colón; 150 m (15°27', 85°01').

Sucio, Caño (GRACIAS A DIOS)—tributary of Río Tapalwás; 190 m (14°56', 84°32').

Suhi (GRACIAS A DIOS)—village along Río Coco about 5 airline km NE of mouth of Río Rus Rus; 50 m (14°42', 84°20').

Sutawala, Río (GRACIAS A DIOS)—tributary of Río Patuca in SW Gracias a Dios; collections made at 90 m (14°56', 84°54').

Swabila (GRACIAS A DIOS)—village along Río Kruta; 5 m (15°05', 83°35').

Tampatingni, Laguna (GRACIAS A DIOS)—not located.

Tánsin (GRACIAS A DIOS)—coastal village about 13 airline km WNW of Puerto Lempira along N shore of Laguna de Tánsin (15°18', 83°53').

Tánsin, Laguna de (GRACIAS A DIOS)—large lagoon on Caribbean coast W of Puerto Lempira.

Tapalwás, Bodega de Río (GRACIAS A DIOS)—name for a campsite along Río Tapalwás used by game hunters from Rus Rus, about 20 airline km NW of Rus Rus; 180 m (14°56', 84°32').

Tapalwás, Río (GRACIAS A DIOS)—tributary of Río Rus Rus; their confluence at 110 m (14°51', 84°32').

Tata, Laguna (GRACIAS A DIOS)—see Laguntara.

Tikiraya (GRACIAS A DIOS)—village along Río Kruta; 7 m (15°01', 85°39'), **[21]**.

Tilbalacán, Laguna (GRACIAS A DIOS)—moderate-sized coastal lagoon NW of and connected to Laguna de Caratasca (15°30', 84°11').

Tinguitara, Laguna (GRACIAS A DIOS)—not located.

Torno, El (OLANCHO)—a single hut and small cultivated area (in 1992) above Río Wampú, 3.5 airline km ENE of Villa Linda; 180 m (15°01', 85°15').

Tulito (COLON)—village at confluence of Ríos Tulito and Paulaya; 50 m (15°33', 85°14').

Tulito, Río (COLON)—tributary of Río Paulaya in E Colón.

Turalka, Crique (GRACIAS A DIOS)—tributary of Río Rus Rus SSE of village of Rus Rus; 45 m (14°41', 84°25').

Urus Tingni Kiamp (GRACIAS A DIOS)—campsite along tributary of Río Warunta, located S of that river; 160 m (14°55', 84°41').

Viejo, Cerro El (GRACIAS A DIOS)—peak in Montaña de Río Plátano W of Río Plátano; 802 m (15°42', 84°55').

Villa Linda (OLANCHO)—small village at confluence of Ríos Lagarto and Wampú; 180 m (15°00', 85°17').

Wahatingni, Cerro (GRACIAS A DIOS)—small hilly area E of Río Tapalwás; collections made from 200 to 300 m (14°56', 84°32' to 14°56', 84°31').

Wahatingni, Crique (GRACIAS A DIOS)—tributary of Río Tapalwás; collections made from 200 to 220 m (14°57', 84°31' to their confluence at 14°57', 84°32').

Wakling Kiamp (GRACIAS A DIOS)—campsite along an unnamed upper tributary of Río Rus Rus, located between Ríos Rus Rus and Warunta; 190 m (14°54', 84°40').

Walpatá (GRACIAS A DIOS)—coastal village about 8 airline km W of Puerto Lempira along N shore of Laguna de Tánsin; (15°17', 83°51').

Walpatanta (GRACIAS A DIOS)—village along Río Coco, but not located.

Walpunpansilpi (GRACIAS A DIOS)—village along Río Plátano; 50 m (15°40', 84°54').

Wampú, Cerro (GRACIAS A DIOS)—mountain on E side of Río Patuca at its confluence with Río Wampú; collections made at 480 m (14°57', 84°59').

Wampú, Río (OLANCHO and GRACIAS A DIOS)—tributary of Río Patuca E of Dulce Nombre de Culmí; confluence of Ríos Wampú and Patuca at 60 m elevation just inside Gracias a Dios, collections made from 60 to 180 m (Río Wampú's confluence with Río Patuca at 14°58', 84°59').

Wampusirpe (GRACIAS A DIOS)—village along Río Patuca about 85 airline km from mouth; 50 m (15°10', 84°37').

Warunta, Laguna de (GRACIAS A DIOS)—lagoon just W of Lagunas de Caratasca and Tánsin (also spelled Laguna de Guarunta).

Warunta, Río (GRACIAS A DIOS)—river of Caribbean drainage that flows into Laguna de Warunta just W of Laguna de Caratasca NW of Puerto Lempira, its headwaters in the Montañas de Colón N of Awasbila (also spelled Río Guarunta).

Warunta Tingni Kiamp (GRACIAS A DIOS)—campsite along upper portion of Río Warunta; 150 m (14°55', 84°41'), **[22]**.

Waskista, Quebrada (GRACIAS A DIOS)—tributary of Río Wampú; confluence of Quebrada Waskista with Río Wampú at 85 m (15°00', 84°59').

Waspuk (GRACIAS A DIOS)—village along Río Coco, S of Rus Rus; 40 m (14°37' 84°26').

Wausira (GRACIAS A DIOS)—not located.

Yanguay, Río (OLANCHO)—tributary of Río Wampú; confluence of Ríos Yanguay and Wampú at 110 m (15°03', 85°08').

Yapuwás (OLANCHO)—village along Río Patuca about 3 km W of Río Patuca's confluence with Río Wampú; 60 m (14°58', 85°00').

Yapuwás, Río (OLANCHO)—small tributary of Río Patuca just upstream from mouth of Río Wampú in extreme E Olancho; confluence of Ríos Yapuwás and Patuca at 60 m (14°58', 85°00').

Yulpruan, Crique (GRACIAS A DIOS)—tributary of Río Tapalwás; 140 m (14°54', 84°31').

# Literature Cited


Andersson, L.G. 1916. Notes on the reptiles and batrachians in the Zoological Museum at Gothenburg with an account of some new species. Meddel. Göteborgs Mus. Zool. Afdelning 9:1–41.

Anonymous. 1983. Military road threatens Honduras virgin forest. Oryx 17(3):110.

Anonymous. 2002. Reserva del Hombre y la Biósfera del Río Plátano. Diagnóstico ambiental. AFE/COHDEFOR, Tegucigalpa. 176 pp.

Arguedas-Negrini, N. 2001. Distribution, habitat and behavior of grasshopper sparrows, *Ammodramus savannarum* (Passeriformes: Emberizidae) in northeastern Nicaragua. Rev. Biol. Trop. 49(2):703–708.

Austin, C.C. 2000. Molecular phylogeny and historical biogeography of Pacific Island boas (*Candoia*). Copeia 2000(2):341–352.

Azofeifa, J., E. Ruiz, and R. Barrantes. 1998. Genetic variation and racial admixture in the Miskito of the southern Mosquito Shore, Nicaragua. Rev. Biol. Trop. 46(1):157–165.

Baird, S.F. 1859. Reptiles of the boundary, with notes by the naturalists of the survey, pp. 1–35. *In* W.H. Emory. United States and Mexican Boundary Survey, Part II, Zoology of the Boundary. Dept. Interior, Washington.

Barbour, T., and E.R. Dunn. 1921. Herpetological novelties. Proc. Biol. Soc. Washington 34:157–162.

Begley, C.T. 1999. Elite power strategies and external connections in ancient eastern Honduras. Ph.D. Dissertation, University of Chicago. xx + 511 pp.

Berry, J.F., and J.B. Iverson. 2001a. *Kinosternon leucostomum*. Cat. Amer. Amphib. Reptiles 724.1–724.8.

Berry, J.F., and J.B. Iverson. 2001b. *Kinosternon scorpioides*. Cat. Amer. Amphib. Reptiles 725.1–725.11.

Berthold, A.A. 1845. Ueber verschiedene neue oder seltene Reptilien aus Neu-Granada und Crustaceen aus China. Nachr. Georg-Augusts Univ. und Königl. Gesellsch. Wissensch., Göttingen 3:37–48.

Bezy, R.L. 1989. Morphological differentiation in unisexual and bisexual xantusiid lizards of the genus *Lepidophyma* in Central America. Herpetol. Monographs 3:61– 80.

Bezy, R.L., and J.L. Camarillo R. 2002. Systematics of xantusiid lizards of the genus *Lepidophyma*. Nat. Hist. Mus. Los Angeles Co., Contrib. Sci. 493:1–41.

Bocourt, M.F. 1868. Descriptions de quelques crotaliens nouveaux appartenant au genre *Bothrops*, recueillis dans le Guatémala. Ann. Sci. Nat., Zool. Ser. (5)10:201–202.

Boettger, O. 1892. Katalog der Batrachier-Sammlung im Museum der Senckenbergischen Naturforschenden Gesellschaft in Frankfurt am Main. Gebrüder Knauer, Frankfurt am Main. x + 73 pp.

Boettger, O. 1893. Ein neuer Laubfrosch aus Costa Rica. Ber. Senckenberg. Naturforsch. Gesellsch. 1893:251–252.

Boulenger, G.A. 1894. Catalogue of the Snakes in the British Museum (Natural History). Volume II., Containing the Conclusion of the Colubridae Aglyphae. Printed by Order of Trustees of British Museum (Natural History), London. xi + 382 pp.

Boulenger, G.A. 1896. Catalogue of the Snakes in the British Museum (Natural History). Volume III., Containing the Colubridae (Opisthoglyphae and Proteroglyphae), Amblycephalidae, and Viperidae. Printed by Order of Trustees of British Museum (Natural History), London. xiv + 727 pp.

Boulenger, G.A. 1902. Descriptions of new batrachians and reptiles from north-western Ecuador. Ann. Mag. Nat. Hist., ser. 7, 9:51–57.

Bour, R., and A. Dubois. 1986. Nomenclature ordinale et familiale des tortues (Reptilia). Note complémentaire. Bull. Soc. Linn. Lyon 55(3):87–90.

Boza, M.A. 1999. Biodiversity conservation in Mesoamerica, pp. 51–60. *In* L.U. Hatch and M.E. Swisher (eds.). Managed Ecosystems: the Mesoamerican Response. Oxford Univ. Press, New York. x + 292 pp.

Brady, J.E., G. Hasemann, and J.H. Forarty. 1995. Buried secrets, luminous find: new archaeological discovery sheds light on the development of early Mesoamerican society. Americas 47(4):6–16.

Brocchi, P. 1877. Sur quelques batraciens raniformes et bufoniformes de l'Amérique Centrale. Bull. Soc. Philomath. Paris, ser. 7, 1:175–197.

Brooks, D.C. 1989. U.S. Marines, Miskitos and the hunt for Sandino: the Rio Coco Patrol of 1928. Jour. Latin American Studies 21(2):311–342.

Buitrago V.F. 2001. Muestreo preliminar de la herpetofauna de la microcuenca del Río Cuyamel, Parque Nacional Patuca, Olancho, Honduras, 16 pp. In La diversidad biológica de las microcuencas de los ríos Capapán-Cuyamel, y sus amenazas en el Parque Nacional Patuca-Carlos Luna, Honduras. Univer. Nac. Autón. Costa Rica, Heredia. Not continuously paginated.

Campbell, H.W., and T.R. Howell. 1965. Herpetological records from Nicaragua. Herpetologica 21(2):130–140.

Campbell, L. 1979. Middle American languages, pp. 902–1000. In L. Campbell and M. Mithun (eds.). The Languages of Native America: Historical and Comparative Assessment. Univ. Texas Press, Austin. 1034 pp.

Campbell, J.A., and W.W. Lamar. 2004. The Venomous Reptiles of the Western Hemisphere. Comstock. Publ. Assoc., Ithaca, New York. Vol. I:i–xviii, 1–476 [1–28], plates 1–751, Vol. II:i–xiv, 477–616, plates 752–1365.

Carr, A. 1953. High Jungles and Low. Univ. Florida Press, Gainesville. xvi + 226 pp.

Carr, A., M.H. Carr, and A.B. Meylan. 1978. The ecology and migrations of sea turtles, 7. The West Caribbean green turtle colony. Bull. Amer. Mus. Nat. Hist. 162(1):1–46.

Cayetano, E.R. (ed.). 1993. The People's Garifuna Dictionary. Dimureiágei Garifuna. National Garifuna Council of Belize, Dangriga. x + 170 pp.

Conaway, J. 2001. Lifelines leading from the river. Americas (English ed.) 53(6):24–30.

Conzemius, E. 1932. Ethnographical survey of the Miskito and Sumu Indians of Honduras and Nicaragua. Smithsonian Institution, Bureau of American Ethnology Bull. 106. United States Government Printing Office, Washington D.C. 191 pp.

Cope, E.D. 1860. Catalogue of the Colubridae in the Museum of the Academy of Natural Sciences of Philadelphia, with notes and descriptions of new species. Part 2. Proc. Acad. Nat. Sci. Philadelphia 12:241–266.

Cope, E.D. "1860" (1861). Catalogue of the Colubridae in the Museum of the Academy of Natural Sciences of Philadelphia. Part 3. Proc. Acad. Nat. Sci. Philadelphia 12:553–566.

Cope, E.D. 1861. Notes and descriptions of anoles. Proc. Acad. Nat. Sci. Philadelphia 13:208–215.

Cope, E.D. "1861" (1862). Contributions to the ophiology of Lower California, Mexico and Central America. Proc. Acad. Nat. Sci. Philadelphia 13:292–306.

Cope, E.D. 1862a. Synopsis of the species of *Holcosus* and *Ameiva*, with diagnoses of new West Indian and South American Colubridae. Proc. Acad. Nat. Sci. Philadelphia 14:60–82.

Cope, E.D. 1862b. On some new and little known American Anura. Proc. Acad. Nat. Sci. Philadelphia 14:151–159.

Cope, E.D. 1862c. Contributions to Neotropical saurology. Proc. Acad. Nat. Sci. Philadelphia 14:176–188.

Cope, E.D. 1862d. Catalogues of the reptiles obtained during the explorations of the Parana, Paraguay, Vermejo and Uraguay rivers, by Capt. Thos. J. Page, U.S.N.; and of those procured by Lieut. N. Michler, U.S. Top. Eng., Commander of the expedition conducting the survey of the Atrato River. Proc. Acad. Nat. Sci. Philadelphia 14:346–359.

Cope, E.D. 1863. Descriptions of new American Squamata, in the Museum of the Smithsonian Institution, Washington. Proc. Acad. Nat. Sci. Philadelphia 15:100–106.

Cope, E.D. 1864. Contributions to the herpetology of tropical America. Proc. Acad. Nat. Sci. Philadelphia 16:166–181.

Cope, E.D. 1865. Third contribution to the herpetology of tropical America. Proc. Acad. Nat. Sci. Philadelphia 17:185–198.

Cope, E.D. 1866. Fourth contribution to the herpetology of tropical America. Proc. Acad. Nat. Sci. Philadelphia 18:123–132.

Cope, E.D. 1868. An examination of the Reptilia and Batrachia obtained by the Orton Expedition to Equador and the upper Amazon, with notes on other species. Proc. Acad. Nat. Sci. Philadelphia 20:96–140.

Cope, E.D. "1868" (1869). Sixth contribution to the herpetology of tropical America. Proc. Acad. Nat. Sci. Philadelphia 20:305–313.

Cope, E.D. 1871. Ninth contribution to the herpetology of tropical America. Proc. Acad. Nat. Sci. Philadelphia 23:200–224.

Cope, E.D. 1874. Description of some species of reptiles obtained by Dr. John F. Bransford, assistant surgeon United States Navy, while attached to the Nicaraguan surveying expedition in 1873. Proc. Acad. Nat. Sci. Philadelphia 26:64–72.

Cope, E.D. 1875. On the Batrachia and Reptilia of Costa Rica. Jour. Acad. Nat. Sci. Philadelphia (2)8:93–154 (separates published in 1875 in advance of volume published in 1876).

Cope, E.D. 1885. A contribution to the herpetology of Mexico. Proc. Amer. Philos. Soc. 22:379–404.

Cope, E.D. "1885" (1886). Thirteenth contribution to the herpetology of tropical America. Proc. Amer. Philos. Soc. 23:271–287.

Cope, E.D. 1887. Catalogue of batrachians and reptiles of Central America and Mexico. Bull. U.S. Natl. Mus. 32:1–98.

Cope, E.D. 1893. Second addition to the knowledge of the Batrachia and Reptilia of Costa Rica. Proc. Amer. Philos. Soc. 31:333–347 (separates published in 1893, in advance of volume published in 1894).

Crawford, A.J., and E.N. Smith. 2005. Cenozoic biogeography and evolution in direct-developing frogs of Central America (Leptodactylidae: *Eleutherodactylus*) as inferred from a phylogenetic analysis of nuclear and mitochondrial genes. Mol. Phylog. Evol. 35:536–555.

Cruz, G.A. Herpetofauna del Río Plátano. Unpubl. Thesis Univ. Aut., Honduras, Tegucigalpa. iii + 61 pp.

Cruz, G.A. 1986. Guía de los Parques Nacionales, Refugios de Vida Silvestre, Reservas Biológicas y Monumentos Naturales de Honduras. Assoc. Hondureña de Ecol., Tegucigalpa. 49 pp.

Cuvier, G. 1807. Sur les différentes espèces de crocodiles vivans et sur leurs caractères distinctifs. Ann. Mus. Hist. Natl., Paris 10:8–66.

Daudin, F.M. 1803. Histoire Naturelle, Générale et Particulière des Reptiles; Ouvrage faisant suite aux Ouvres de Leclerc de Buffon, et partie du Cours complet d'Histoire naturelle rédigé par C.S. Sonnini, membre de plusieurs Sociétés savantes. Tome Sixième. F. Dufart, Paris. 447 pp.

David, P. 1994. Liste des reptiles actuels du Monde I. Chelonii. Dumerelia 1:7–127.

David, P., and I. Ineich. 1999. Les serpents venimeux du Monde: Systématique et repartition. Dumerilia 3:3–499.

Davidson, W.V. and F. Cruz S. 1995. Delimitación de la región habitada por los sumos taguacas de Honduras en el período de 1600 a 1990. Mesoamérica 29:159–165.

De Vries, G.W. 2000. Post-hurricane reconstruction in La Moskitia, Honduras. M.A. Thesis, University of Florida, Gainesville. xi + 149 pp.

Dixon, J.R., and B.L. Tipton. *Dryadophis* versus *Mastigodryas* (Ophidia: Colubridae): A proposed solution. Herpetol. Rev. 35(4):347–349.

Dixon, J.R., J.A. Wiest, Jr., and J.M. Cei. "1993" (1995). Revision of the Neotropical snake genus *Chironius* Fitzinger (Serpentes, Colubridae). Mus. Reg. Sci. Nat. Monogr. 13:1–279.

Dodd, C.K., Jr. 1988. Synopsis of the biological data on the loggerhead sea turtle *Caretta caretta* (Linnaeus 1758). U.S. Fish Wildl. Serv. Biol. Rep. 88(14). viii + 110 pp.

Dodd, C.K., Jr. 1990. *Caretta caretta*. Cat. Amer. Amphib. Reptiles 483.1–483.2.

Dodds, D.J. 1994. The Ecological and Social Sustainability of Miskito Subsistence in the Río Plátano Biosphere Reserve, Honduras: The Cultural Ecology of Swidden Horticulturalists in a Protected Area. Unpubl. Ph.D Dissertation, Univ. California, Los Angeles. xxxi + 568 pp.

Dodds, D.J. 1998. Lobster in the rainforest: The political ecology of Miskito wage labor and agricultural deforestation. Jour. Political Ecology 5:83–108.

Dowling, H.G., and T. Pinou. 2003. Xenodermatid snakes in America. Herpetol. Rev. 34(1):20–23.

Dubois, A. 1999. Miscellanea nomenclatorica batrachologica. 19. Notes on the nomenclature of Ranidae and related groups. Alytes 17(1–2):81–100.

Duellman, W.E. 1971. The burrowing toad, *Rhinophrynus dorsalis*, on the Caribbean lowlands of Central America. Herpetologica 27(1):55–56.

Duellman, W.E. 1990. Herpetofaunas in Neotropical rainforests: Comparative composition, history, and resource use, pp. 455–505. *In* A.H. Gentry (ed.). Four Neotropical Rainforests. Yale Univ. Press, New Haven. xiii + 627 pp.

Duellman, W.E. 2001. The hylid frogs of Middle America. Soc. Study Amphib. Reptiles, Contrib. Herpetol. 18:i–xvi, 1–694, i–x, 695–1159.

Duellman, W.E. 2003. An overview of anuran phylogeny, classification and reproductive modes, pp. 1–18. *In* B.G.M. Jamieson (ed.). Reproductive Biology and Phylogeny of Anura. Science Publ., Inc., Enfield, New Hampshire. vii + 452 pp.

Duellman, W.E., and J. Wellman. 1960. A systematic study of the lizards of the *deppei* group (Genus *Cnemidophorus*) in Mexico and Guatemala. Misc. Publ. Mus. Zool., Univ. Michigan 111:1–80.

Dueñas, C., L.D. Wilson, and J.R. McCranie. 2001. A list of the amphibians and reptiles of El Salvador, with notes on additions and deletions, pp. 93–99. *In* J.D. Johnson, R.G. Webb, and O.A. Flores-Villela (eds.). Mesoamerican Herpetology: Systematics, Zoogeography, and Conservation. Centennial Mus., Univ. Texas El Paso, Spec. Publ. 1:i–iv, 1–200.

Duméril, A.H.A., M.F. Bocourt, and F. Mocquard. 1870–1909. Études sur les Reptiles. Mission Scientifique au Mexique et dans l'Amérique Centrale. Recherches Zoologiques pour servir a l'Histoire de la Fauna de l'Amérique Centrale et du Mexique. Troisieme Partie.—1re Section. Imprimeire Nationale, Paris. xiv + 1012 pp.

Duméril, A.M.C., and G. Bibron. 1836. Erpétologie Générale ou Histoire Naturelle Complète des Reptiles, Tome Troisième. Contenant l'Histoire de Toutes les Espèces des Quatre Premières Familles de l'Ordre des Lézards ou Sauriens, Savoir: les Crocodiles, les Camèléons, les Geckos et les Varans. Libr. Encyclopédique Roret, Paris. iv + 517 pp.

Duméril, A.M.C., and G. Bibron. 1841. Erpétologie Générale ou Histoire Naturelle Complète des Reptiles. Tome Huitième. Librairie Encyclopédique de Roret, Paris. iii + 792 pp.

Duméril, A.M.C., G. Bibron, and A.H.A. Duméril. 1854a. Erpétologie Générale ou Histoire Naturelle Complète des Reptiles. Tome Septième.—Première Partie. Comprenant l'Histoire Naturelle des Serpents non Venimeux. Libr. Encyclopédique Roret, Paris. vii + 1–780 pp.

Duméril, A.M.C., G. Bibron, and A.H.A. Duméril. 1854b. Erpétologie Générale ou Histoire Naturelle Complète des Reptiles. Tome Septième.—Deuxième Partie. Comprenant l'Histoire Naturelle des Serpents Venimeux. Libr. Encyclopédique Roret, Paris. xii + 781–1536 pp.

Duméril, A.M.C., G. Bibron, and A.H A. Duméril. 1854c. Erpétologie Générale ou Histoire Naturelle Complète des Reptiles. Tome Neuvième. Librairie Encyclopédique de Roret, Paris. xx + 440 pp.

Duméril, A.M.C., and A.H.A. Duméril. 1851. Catalogue Méthodique de la Collection des Reptiles du Muséum d'Histoire Naturelle de Paris. Gide et Baudry, Paris. iv + 224 pp.

Dunn, E.R. 1938. A new *Rhadinaea* from Central America. Copeia 1938(4):197–198.

Echternacht, A.C. 1971. Middle American lizards of the genus *Ameiva* (Teiidae) with emphasis on geographic variation. Univ. Kansas Mus. Nat. Hist., Misc. Publ. 55:1–86.

Eckert, K.L. 2001. Status and distribution of the leatherback turtle, *Dermochelys coriacea*, in the wider Caribbean region, pp. 24-31. *In* Proceedings of the Regional Meeting: "Marine Turtle Conservation in the Wider Caribbean Region: A Dialogue for Effective Regional Management," Santo Domingo, Dominican Republic, 16–18 November 1999. WIDECAST, IUCN-MTSG, WWF, and UNEP-CEP. x + 154 pp.

Ernst, C.H. 1978. A revision of the neotropical turtle genus *Callopsis* (Testudines: Emydidae: Batagurinae). Herpetologica 34(2):113–134.

Ernst, C.H. 1980a. *Rhinoclemmys annulata*. Cat. Amer. Amphib. Reptiles 250.1–250.2.

Ernst, C.H. 1980b. *Rhinoclemmys areolata*. Cat. Amer. Amphib. Reptiles 251.1–251.2.

Ernst, C.H. 1981. *Rhinoclemmys funerea*. Cat. Amer. Amphib. Reptiles 263.1–263.2.

Ernst, C.H., and R.W. Barbour. 1989. Turtles of the World. Smithsonian Inst. Press, Washington D.C. xii + 313 pp.

Fitch, H.S., and R.A. Seigel. 1984. Ecological and taxonomic notes on Nicaraguan anoles. Milwaukee Publ. Mus., Publ. Contrib. Biol. Geol. 57:1–13.

Flores, G. 1985. A new *Centrolenella* (Anura) from Ecuador, with comments on nuptial pads and prepollical spines in *Centrolenella*. Jour. Herpetol. 19(3):313–320.

Floyd, T.S. 1967. The Anglo-Spanish Struggle for Mosquitia. Univ. New Mexico Press, Albuquerque. xiii + 235 pp.

Frederick, P.C., J. Correa Sandoval, C. Luthin, and M. Spalding. 1997. The importance of the Caribbean coastal wetlands of Nicaragua and Honduras to Central American populations of waterbirds and jabiru storks (*Jabiru mycteria*). Jour. Field Ornithol. 68(2):287–295.

Froehlich, J.W., L. Benshoof, J. Saunders, and T.R. Logan. 1983. Mammalian and floral survey: Initial documentation of Río Plátano Reserve, pp. 43–67. *In* J.W. Froehlich and K.H. Schwerin (eds.). Conservation and Indigenous Human Land Use in the Río Plátano Watershed, northeast Honduras. Latin Amer. Inst. Res. Pap. Ser. 12:1–94.

Froehlich, J.W., and K.H. Schwerin. 1983. Introduction: The Río Plátano Biosphere Reserve, pp. 1–12. *In* J.W. Froehlich and H.H. Schwerin (eds.). Conservation and Indigenous Human Land Use in the Río Plátano Watershed, northeast Honduras. Latin American Institute Research Papers Ser. 12:1–94.

Frost, D.R. 2004. Amphibian Species of the World: an online reference. Version 3.0 (22 August 2004). Electronic Database accessible at http://research.amnh.org/herpetology/amphibia/index.html. Amer. Mus. Nat. Hist., New York.

Frost, D.R., and R. Etheridge. 1989. A phylogenetic analysis and taxonomy of iguanian lizards (Reptilia: Squamata). Univ. Kansas Mus. Nat. Hist., Misc. Publ. 81:1–65.

Frost, D.R., R. Etheridge, D. Janies, and T.A. Titus. 2001. Total evidence, sequence alignment, evolution of polychrotid lizards, and a reclassification of the Iguania (Squamata: Iguania). Amer. Mus. Novitates 3343:1–38.

Gaige, H.T., and L.C. Stuart. 1934. A new *Hyla* from Guatemala. Occas. Pap. Mus. Zool., Univ. Michigan 281:1–3.

García-París, M., G. Parra-Olea, and D.B. Wake. 2000. Phylogenetic relationships within the lowland tropical salamanders of the *Bolitoglossa mexicana* complex (Amphibia: Plethodontidae), pp. 199–214. *In* R.C. Bruce, R.G. Jaeger, and L.D. Houck (eds.). The Biology of Plethodontid Salamanders. Kluwer Academic/Plenum Publ., New York. xiii + 485 pp.

García-París, M., G. Parra-Olea, A.H. Brame, Jr., II, and D.B. Wake. 2002. Systematic revision of the *Bolitoglossa mexicana* species group (Amphibia: Plethodontidae) with description of a new species from México. Rev. Esp. Herp. 16:43–71.

Garman, S. "1883" (1884). The reptiles and batrachians of North America. Part I Ophidia–Serpentes. Mem. Mus. Comp. Zoöl. 83(3):i–xxxi, 1–185.

Gibbons, J.W., S.S. Novak, and C.H. Ernst. 1988. *Chelydra serpentina*. Cat. Amer. Amphib. Reptiles 420.1–420.4.

Girard, C. 1854. Abstract of a report to Lieut. James M. Gilliss, U.S.N., upon the reptiles collected during the U.S.N. Astronomical Expedition to Chili. Proc. Acad. Sci. Philadelphia 7:226–227.

Godoy, R., N. Brokaw, D. Wilkie, G. Cruz, A. Cubas, J. Demmer, K. McSweeney, and H. Overman. 1996. Rates of return on investment in cattle among Amerindians of the rainforest of Honduras. Human Ecology 24(3):395–400.

Godoy, R., D. Wilkie, and J. Franks. 1997. The effects of markets on neotropical deforestation: a comparative study of four Amerindian societies. Current Anthropology 38(5):875–879.

González, N.L. 1997. La Historia del Pueble Garifuna: Pasado y Presente. Editorial Universitaria, Tegucigalpa. 80 pp.

Gray, J.E. 1831. A synopsis of the species of the class Reptilia, pp. 1–110. *In* E. Griffith and E. Pidgeon. The Class Reptilia Arranged by the Baron Cuvier, with Specific Descriptions. Whittaker, Treacher, and Co., London. 481 +110 pp.

Gray, J.E. 1855. Catalogue of Shield Reptiles in the Collection of the British Museum. Part I. Testudinata (Tortoises). Printed by Order of the Trustees, British Museum (Natural History), London. iv + 79 + ii pp.

Gray, J.E. 1860. Description of a new species of *Geoclemmys* from Ecuador. Proc. Zool. Soc. London 28:231–232.

Greene, H.W., and R.W. McDiarmid. 1981. Coral snake mimicry: Does it occur? Science 213:1207–1212.

Günther, A. 1858. Catalogue of Colubrine Snakes in the Collection of the British Museum. Printed by Order of the Trustees of British Museum, London. xvi + 281 pp.

Günther, A. 1868. Sixth account of new species of snakes in the collection of the British Museum. Ann. Mag. Nat. Hist., (4)1:413–429.

Günther, A. 1872. Seventh account of new species of snakes in the collection of the British Museum. Ann. Mag. Nat. Hist., (4)9:13–37.

Günther, A. 1885–1902. Reptilia and Batrachia. *In* O. Salvin and F.D. Godman (eds.). Biologia Centrali-Americana; or, Contributions to the Knowledge of the Fauna and Flora of Mexico and Central America. R.H. Porter and Dulau & Co., London. xx + 326 pp.

Hallowell, E. "1856" (1857). Notes on the reptiles in the collection of the Academy of Natural Sciences of Philad'a. Proc. Acad. Nat. Sci. Philadelphia 8:221–238.

Hallowell, E. "1860" (1861). Report upon the Reptilia of the North Pacific Exploring Expedition, under command of Capt. John Rogers [sic], U.S.N. Proc. Acad. Nat. Sci. Philadelphia 12:480–510.

Hasemann, G. 1991. Etnología y la Linguística en Honduras: Una Mirada Retrospectiva. Instituto Hondureño de Antropología e Historia. Tegucigalpa. 88 pp.

Helms, M.W. 1969. The cultural ecology of a colonial tribe. Ethnology 8(1):76–84.

Henderson, R.W., M. Höggren, W.W. Lamar, and L.W. Porras. 2001. Distribution and variation in the treeboa *Corallus annulatus* (Serpentes: Boidae). Stud. Neotrop. Fauna Environ. 36(1):39–47.

Herlihy, P.H. 1993. Securing a homeland: The Tawahka Sumu of Mosquitia's rain forest, pp. 55–62. *In* M.S. Miller (ed.). State of the Peoples. A Global Human Rights Report on Societies in Danger. Beacon Press, Boston. x + 262 pp.

Herlihy, P.H. 1997. Central American Indian peoples and lands today, pp. 215–240. *In* A.G. Coates (ed.). Central America. A Natural and Cultural History. Yale Univ. Press, New Haven. xvi + 277 pp.

Herlihy, P.H., and A.P. Leake. 1989. The Tawahka Sumu: A delicate balance in Mosquitia. Cultural Survival Quarterly 14(4):13–16.

Herrera-MacBryde, O. 2005. North-east Honduras and Rio Platano Biosphere Reserve. Centres of Plant Diversity Site MA15. Website: http://nmnhwww.si.edu/botany/projects/centres/platano.html.

Heyer, W.R. 1970. Studies on the frogs of the genus *Leptodactylus* (Amphibia: Leptodactylidae). VI. Biosystematics of the *melanonotus* group. Los Angeles Co. Mus. Nat. Hist., Contrib. Sci. 191:1–48.

Heyer, W.R. 1978. Systematics of the *fuscus* group of the frog genus *Leptodactylus* (Amphibia, Leptodactylidae). Nat. Hist. Mus. Los Angeles Co., Sci. Bull. 29:1–85.

Heyer, W.R. 1998. The relationships of *Leptodactylus diedrus* (Anura, Leptodactylidae). Alytes 16(1–2):1–24.

Heyer, W.R. 2002. *Leptodactylus fragilis*, the valid name for the Middle American and northern South American white-lipped frog (Amphibia: Leptodactylidae). Proc. Biol. Soc. Washington 115(2):321–322.

Heyer, W.R., A.S. Rand, C.A.G. da Cruz, O.L. Peixoto, and C.E. Nelson. 1990. Frogs of Boracéia. Arq. Zool., Mus. Zool., Univ. São Paulo 31(4):231–410.

Hillis, D.M., and R. de Sá. 1988. Phylogeny and taxonomy of the *Rana palmipes* group (Salientia: Ranidae). Herpetol. Monogr. 2:1–26.

Holdridge, L.R. 1967. Life zone ecology. Revised edition. Trop. Sci. Center, San José, Costa Rica. 206 pp.

Houttuyn, M. 1782. Het onderscheid der Salamanderen van de Haagdissen in 't algemeen, en van de Gekkoos in 't byzonder aangetoond. Verh. Zeeuwsch Gen. Wet. Vlissingen (1)9(2):305–336.

Humphrey, C. 2000. Moon Handbooks: Honduras. Including the Bay Islands and Copán. Second Edition. Avalon Travel Publ., Inc., Emeryville, California. 402 pp.

Illueca, J. 1997. The Paseo Pantera agenda for regional conservation, pp. 241–257. *In* A. G. Coates (ed.). Central America. A Natural and Cultural History. Yale Univ. Press, New Haven. xvi + 277 pp.

James, E. 1823. Account of an Expedition from Pittsburgh to the Rocky Mountains, Performed in the Years 1819 and '20, by Order of the Hon. J.C. Calhoun, Sec'y of War: Under the Command of Major Stephen H. Long. From the Notes of Major Long, Mr. T. Say, and other Gentlemen of the Exploring Party. H.C. Carey and I. Lea, Philadelphia. Vol. I. 503 pp.

Jan, G. 1858. Plan de 'une Iconographie descriptive des ophidians, et description sommaire de nouvelles espèces de serpents. Rev. Mag. Zool. (2)10:514–527.

Jan, G. 1862. Enumerazione sistematica delle specie d'ofidi del gruppo Calamaridae. Arch. Zool. Anat. Fisiol. 2(1):1–76.

Jan, G., and F. Sordelli. 1860–1881. Iconographie Générale des Ophidiens. Tome Premier (Livrais 1 à 17). J. B. Bailliére et Fils, Paris. 11 pp. + 17 livr., 9 pp. +17 livr., 19 pp. + 16 livr.

Jiménez, A., and J.M. Savage. 1962. A new blind snake (genus *Typhlops*) from Costa Rica. Rev. Biol. Trop. 10(2):199–203.

Johnson, F. 1948. Central American cultures: an introduction, pp. 43–68. *In* J. Steward (ed.). Handbook of South American Indians. Vol. 4. The Circum-Caribbean Tribes. Smithsonian Institution, Bureau of American Ethnology Bull. 143. United States Government Printing Office, Washington D.C. 609 pp.

Johnson, J.D., C A. Ely, and R.G. Webb. "1976" (1977). Biogeographical and taxonomic notes on some herpetozoa from the northern highlands of Chiapas, Mexico. Trans. Kansas Acad. Sci. 79(3–4):131–139.

Johnston-Dodds, K.A. and D.J. Dodds. 1999. El proyecto de la presa Patuca y el corridor de la Mosquitia Hondureña: a segurar un trato justo par alas generaciones futures. Mesoamérica 37:169–195.

Joyce, R. and J. Brady. 2001. Cuyamel caves (Colón, Honduras), p. 199. *In* S.T. Evans and D.L. Webster (eds.). Archaeology in Ancient Mexico and Central America: An Encyclopedia. Garland Publishers, New York. xliii + 948 pp.

Jukofsky, D. 1999. Unnatural disaster. Conservation lessons from Hurricane Mitch. Nature Conservancy 49(5):18–26.

King, F.W., M. Espinal, and C.A. Cerrato. 1990. Distribution and status of the crocodilians of Honduras. Results of a survey conducted for the Convention on International Trade in Endangered Species of Wild Fauna and Flora and the Honduras Secretaria de Recursos Naturales Renovables, pp. 313–354. *In* Crocodiles. Proceedings of the 10th Working Meeting of the Crocodile Specialist Group of the Species Survival Commission of IUCN-The World Conservation Union convened at Gainesville, Florida, U.S.A., 23 to 27 April 1990. Gainesville, Florida. Vol. 1. xvi + 354 pp.

Kizirian, D.A., and C.J. Cole. 1999. Origin of the unisexual lizard *Gymnophthalmus underwoodi* (Gymnophthalmidae) inferred from mitochondrial DNA nucleotide sequences. Molecular Phylog. Evol. 11(3):394–400.

Klein, E.H. 1979. Los cocodrilidos de Honduras: Su biología y estado actual con recomendaciones para su manejo. Unpubl. Rep., Dirección General de Recursos Naturales Renovables, Tegucigalpa. 33 pp.

Kluge, A.G. 1987. Cladistic relationships in the Gekkonoidea (Squamata, Sauria). Misc. Publ. Mus. Zool., Univ. Michigan 173:i–iv, 1–54.

Köhler, G. 2001. Anfibios y Reptiles de Nicaragua. Herpeton, Verlag Elke Köhler, Offenbach. 208 pp.

Köhler, G. 2003. Reptiles of Central America. Herpeton, Verlag Elke Köhler, Offenbach. 367 pp.

Köhler, G., and P. Heimes. 2002. Stachelleguane. Lebensweise • Pflege • Zucht. Herpeton, Verlag Elke Köhler, Offenbach. 174 pp.

Köhler, G., J.R. McCranie, and K.E. Nicholson. 2000. Eine Herpetologische Expedition in den Patuca-Nationalpark, Honduras. Natur und Mus. 130(12):421–425.

Köhler, G., J.R. McCranie, K.E. Nicholson, and J. Kreutz. 2003. Geographic variation in hemipenial morphology in *Norops humilis* (Peters 1863), and the systematic status of *Norops quaggulus* (Cope 1885) (Reptilia, Squamata, Polychrotidae). Senckenberg. Biol. 82(1/2):213–222.

Kolankiewicz, L. 1989. The Pesch of Honduras face uncertain prospects. Cultural Survival Quarterly 13(3):35–36.

Lacepède, B.G.E. 1789. Histoire Naturelle des Serpens. Tome Second. Hôtel de Thou, Paris. 19 + 8 + 144 + 527 pp.

Lagueux, C.J. 1998. Marine turtle fishery of Caribbean Nicaragua: Human use patterns and harvest trends. Unpubl. Ph.D Diss., Univ. Florida, Gainesville. xv + 214 pp.

Lagueux, C.J., C.L. Campbell, and W.A. McCoy. 2003. Nesting and conservation of the hawksbill turtle, *Eretmochelys imbricata*, in the Pearl Cays, Nicaragua. Chelonian Conserv. Biol. 4(3):588–602.

Lara Pinto, G. 1991. Change for survival: the case of the sixteenth-century indigenous populations of northeast and mideast Honduras, pp. 227–243. *In* D.H. Thomas (ed.), Columbian Consequences, Vol. 3: The Spanish Borderlands in Pan-American Perspective. Smithsonian Institution Press, Washington, D.C. xxii + 592 pp.

Lara Pinto, G., and G. Hasemann. 1988. La sociedad indígena del noreste de Honduras en el siglo XVI: son la etnohístoria y la arqueología contradictories? Yaxkin 11(2):5–28.

Laurenti, J.N. 1768. Specimen Medicum, Exhibens Synopsin Reptilium Emendatam cum Experimentis circa Venena et Antidota Reptilium Austriacorum, quod Authoritate et Consensu. Joan. Thomae Trattnern, Viennae. 214 pp.

Lee, J.C. 1996. The Amphibians and Reptiles of the Yucatán Peninsula. Comstock Publ. Assoc., Ithaca, New York. xii + 500 pp.

Leviton, A.E., R.H. Gibbs, Jr., E. Heal, and C.E. Dawson. 1985. Standards in herpetology and ichthyology: part I. Standard symbolic codes for institutional resource collections in herpetology and ichthyology. Copeia 1985(3): 802–832.

Lichtenstein, M.H.C., and E.C. von Martens. 1856. Nomenclator Reptilium et Amphibiorum Musei Zoologici Berolinensis. Namenverzeichniss der in der zoologischen Sammlung der Königlichen Universität zu Berlin aufgestellten Arten von Reptilien und Amphibien nach ihren. Ordnungen, Familien und Gattungen. Buchdruckerei Königlichen Akademie Wissenschaften, Berlin. iv + 48 pp.

Linnaeus, C. 1758. Systema Naturae per Regna Tria Naturae, Secundum Classes, Ordines, Genera, Species, cum Characteribus, Differentiis, Synonymis, Locis. Tomus I. Editio Decima, Reformata. Laurentii Salvii, Stockholm. 823 pp.

Linnaeus, C. 1766. Systema Naturae per Regna Tria Naturae, Secundum Classes, Ordines, Genera, Species, cum Characteribus, Differentiis, Synonymis. Locis. Tomus I. Editio Duodecima, Reformata. Laurentii Salvii, Stockholm. 532 pp.

López, A. 2001. Preserving the magic: a tangible debut. The UNESCO Courier. September 2001:43.

Lynch, J.D., and W.E. Duellman. 1980. The *Eleutherodactylus* of the Amazonian slopes of the Ecuadorian Andes (Anura: Leptodactylidae). Misc. Publ., Univ. Kansas Mus. Nat. Hist. 69:1–86.

Lynch, J.D., and W.E. Duellman. 1997. Frogs of the genus *Eleutherodactylus* (Leptodactylidae) in western Ecuador: Systematics, ecology, and biogeography. Univ. Kansas Nat. Hist. Mus. Spec. Publ. 23:i–iv, 1–236.

Lynch, J.D., and C.W. Myers. 1983. Frogs of the *fitzingeri* group of *Eleutherodactylus* in eastern Panama and Chocoan South America (Leptodactylidae). Bull. Amer. Mus. Nat. Hist. 175(5):481–572.

Malkin, B. 1956. Sumu ethnozoology: herpetological knowledge. Davidson Jour. Anthropology 2(2):165–180.

Manuel, A. (ed.). 1987. The Sumus in Nicaragua and Honduras: An Endangered People. America's Watch Committee, New York. iii + 43 pp.

Marin, M. 1984. El reporte nacional por el pais de Honduras, pp. 220–224. *In* P. Bacon et al. (eds.). Proceedings of the Western Atlantic Turtle Symposium. San José, Costa Rica, 17–22 July 1983. Vol. 3. Univ. Miami Press, Coral Gables. 514 pp.

Marx, W.G., and G.R. Heath. 1992. Diccionario Miskito-Español, Español-Miskito. The Moravian Church in America, Bethlehem, Pennsylvania. 232 pp.

Matson, G.A., H.E. Sutton, J. Swanson, and A.R. Robinson. 1963. Distribution of haptoglobin, transferring, and hemoglobin types among Indians of Middle America. Southern Mexico, Guatemala, Honduras, and Nicaragua. Human Biology 35:474–483.

Matson, G.A., and J. Swanson. 1963. Distribution of hereditary blood antigens among Indians in Middle America. V. In Nicaragua. American Jour. Physical Anthropology 21(4):545–559.

McCain, C.M. 2001. First evidence of the giant anteater (*Myrmecophaga tridactyla*) in Honduras. Southwest. Nat. 46(2):252–254.

McCranie, J.R. 1993. Additions to the herpetofauna of Honduras. Carib. Jour. Sci. 29(3–4):254–255.

McCranie, J.R. 2004a. Geographic distribution. *Rhadinaea decorata*. Herpetol. Rev. 35(3):294.

McCranie, J.R. 2004b. *Anomalepis mexicanus* Jan (Serpentes, Anomalepididae) in Honduras. Herpetol. Bull. 89:21.

McCranie, J.R. 2005. The herpetofauna of Parque Nacional Cerro Azul, Honduras (Amphibia, Reptilia). Herpetol. Bull. 90:10–21.

McCranie, J.R. 2006. New species of *Sibon* (Squamata: Colubridae) from northwestern Honduras. Jour. Herptol. 40: in press.

McCranie, J.R. In Preparation. The Reptiles of Honduras.

McCranie, J.R., and F.E. Castañeda. 2004. A new species of snake of the genus *Omoadiphas* (Reptilia: Squamata: Colubridae) from the Cordillera Nombre de Dios in northern Honduras. Proc. Biol. Soc. Washington. 117(3):311–316.

McCranie, J.R., F.E. Castañeda, and K.E. Nicholson. 2002. Preliminary results of herpetofaunal survey work in the Rus Rus region, Honduras: A proposed biological reserve. Herpetol. Bull. 81:22–29.

McCranie, J.R., M.R. Espinal, and L.D. Wilson. 2005. New species of montane salamander of the *Bolitoglossa dunni* group from northern Comayagua, Honduras (Urodela: Plethodontidae). Jour. Herpetol. 39(1):108–112.

McCranie, J.R., and G. Köhler. 2001. A new species of anole from eastern Honduras related to *Norops tropidonotus* (Reptilia, Squamata, Polychrotidae). Senckenberg. Biol. 81(1/2): 227–233.

McCranie, J.R., K.E. Nicholson, and F.E. Castañeda. 2002. Geographic distribution. *Eleutherodactylus diastema*. Herpetol. Rev. 33(3):220.

McCranie, J.R., J.H. Townsend, and L.D. Wilson. 2003a. *Hyla miliaria* (Anura: Hylidae) in Honduras, with notes on calling site. Carib. Jour. Sci. 39(3):398–399.

McCranie, J.R., J.H. Townsend, and L.D. Wilson. 2003b. Three snakes new to the herpetofauna of Honduras. Herpetol. Rev. 34(4):391–392.

McCranie, J.R., and L.D. Wilson. 1993. Taxonomic changes associated with the names *Hyla spinipollex* Schmidt and *Ptychohyla merazi* Wilson and McCranie (Anura: Hylidae). Southwest. Nat. 38(2):100–104.

McCranie, J.R., and L.D. Wilson. 1997a. A review of the *Eleutherodactylus milesi*-like frogs (Anura, Leptodactylidae) from Honduras with the description of four new species. Alytes 14(4):147–174.

McCranie, J.R., and L.D. Wilson. 1997b. Two new species of centrolenid frogs of the genus *Hyalinobatrachium* from eastern Honduras. Jour. Herpetol. 31(1):10–16.

McCranie, J.R., and L.D. Wilson. 1999. Two new species of the *Eleutherodactylus rugulosus* group (Amphibia: Anura: Leptodactylidae) from Honduras. Proc. Biol. Soc. Washington 112(3):515–522.

McCranie, J.R., and L.D. Wilson. 2002. The amphibians of Honduras. Soc. Study Amphib. Reptiles, Contrib. Herpetol. 19:i–x, 1–625.

McCranie, J.R., and L.D. Wilson. 2003. *Eleutherodactylus operosus* Savage, McCranie, and Wilson, 1999, a synonym of *Eleutherodactylus cerasinus* (Cope, "1876" [1875]). Jour. Herpetol. 37(2):408–409.

McCranie, J.R., L.D. Wilson, and S.W. Gotte. 2001. Three new country records for Honduran snakes. Herpetol. Rev. 32(1):62–63.

McCranie, J.R., L.D. Wilson, and J.H. Townsend. 2003. Natural history notes: *Agalychnis callidryas*. Reproduction. Herpetol. Rev. 34(1):49.

McDiarmid, R.W., and R. Altig. 1999. Research: Materials and techniques, pp. 7–23. *In* R.W. McDiarmid and R. Altig (eds.). Tadpoles. The Biology of Anuran Larvae. Univ. Chicago Press, Chicago. xiv + 444 pp.

McDiarmid, R.W., J.A. Campbell, and T.A. Touré. 1999. Snake Species of the World: A Taxonomic and Geographic Reference. Vol. 1. Herpetologist's League, Washington. xi + 511 pp.

McGeveran, W.A., Jr. (ed. dir.). 2004. The World Almanac and Book of Facts 2004. World Almanac Books, New York. 1008 pp.

Merrem, B. 1820. Versuch eines Systems der Amphibien. Tentamen Systematis Amphibiorum. J.C. Krieger, Marburg. xv + 188 pp (German text), xv + 191 pp (Latin text).

Meyer, D. 2000. Perils in Río Plátano: Rampant Deforestation Leads to U.N. Warning. Nature Conservancy 50(2):6.

Meyer, J.R., and L.D. Wilson. 1971. A distributional checklist of the amphibians of Honduras. Los Angeles Co. Mus. Nat. Hist., Contrib. Sci. 218:1–47.

Meylan, A. 1984. Feeding ecology of the hawksbill turtle (*Eretmochelys imbricata*): spongivory as a feeding niche in the coral reef community. Unpubl. Ph.D Diss., Univ. Florida, Gainesville. vi + 118 pp.

Moll, D. and E.O. Moll. 1990. The slider turtle in the Neotropics: Adaptation of a temperate species to a tropical environment, pp. 152–161. *In* J.W. Gibbons (ed.). Life History and Ecology of the Slider Turtle. Smithson. Inst. Press, Washington. xiv + 368 pp.

Monroe, B.L., Jr. 1968. A distributional survey of the birds of Honduras. Amer. Ornithol. Union, Ornithol. Monogr. 7:1–458.

Moreira, Y. 1986. Análisis lexicoestadístico de las relaciones entre el Cacaopera, Matagalpa, Sumo, Septentrional, Ulua, y Mosquito. Tesis de Licenciatura en Lingüística. Universidad de Costa Rica, San José. 45 pp

National Geographic Society. 2002. Map: Pueblos Indígenas y Ecosistemas Naturales en Centroamérica y el Sur de México. National Geographic Society, Washington, D.C.

Naylor, R.A. 1989. Penny Ante Imperialism: The Mosquito Shore and the Bay of Honduras, 1600–1914: A Case Study in British Informal Empire. Fairleigh Dickinson Univ. Press, Rutherford, New Jersey. 315 pp.

Nicholson, K.E., J.R. McCranie, and G. Köhler. 2000. Herpetofaunal expedition to Parque Nacional Patuca: A newly established park in Honduras. Herpetol. Bull. 72:26–31.

Nietschmann, B. 1973. Between Land and Water: The Subsistence Ecology of the Miskito Indians, Eastern Nicaragua. Seminar Press, New York. xiv + 279 pp.

Nietschmann, B. 1979. Caribbean Edge. The Coming of Modern Times to Isolated People and Wildlife. Bobbs-Merrill, Co., Inc., Indianapolis. xv + 280 pp.

Noble, G.K. 1918. The amphibians collected by the American Museum Expedition to Nicaragua in 1916. Bull. Amer. Mus. Nat. Hist. 38(10): 311–347.

Offen, K.H. 1999. The Miskitu Kingdom: Landscape and emergence of a Miskitu ethnic identity, Northeastern Nicaragua and Honduras, 1600–1800. Ph.D. Dissertation Univ. Texas, Austin. vxiii + 496 pp.

Olien, M.D. 1983. The Miskito kings and the line of succession. Jour. Anthropological Research 39(2):198–241.

Oliver, J.A. 1942. A check list of the snakes of the genus *Leptophis*, with descriptions of new forms. Occas. Pap. Mus. Zool., Univ. Michigan 462:1–19.

Ortega, M. 1991. Nicaraguan repatriation to Mosquitia. Center for Immigration Policy and Refugee Assistance, Georgetown Univ. Washington, D.C. v + 72 pp.

O'Shea, M.T. 1986a. Operation Raleigh Herpetological Survey of the Rio Paulaya and Laguna Bacalar regions northeastern Honduras, Central America. April-June 1985. Unpubl. Rep. iv + 78 pp.

O'Shea, M.T. 1986b. Geographic distribution. *Nothopsis rugosus*. Herpetol. Rev. 17(1):27.

Parsons, J.J. 1955. The Miskito pine savanna of Nicaragua and Honduras. Ann. Assoc. Amer. Geogr. 45:36–63.

Pellegrino, K.C.M., M.T. Rodrigues, Y. Yonenaga-Yassuda, and J.W. Sites, Jr. 2001. A molecular perspective on the evolution of microteiid lizards (Squamata, Gymnophthalmidae), and a new classification of the family. Biol. Jour. Linnean Soc. 74:315–338.

Peters, J.A. 1964. Dictionary of Herpetology. A Brief and Meaningful Definition of Words and Terms used in Herpetology. Hafner Publ. Co., New York. vii + 392 pp.

Peters, W. 1859. Über die von Hrn. Dr. Hoffmann in Costa Rica gesammelten und an das Königl. zoologische Museum gesandten Schlangen. Monatsber. Königl. Preuss. Akad. Wissensch. Berlin 1859:275–278.

Peters, W. 1861. Über neue Schlangen des Königl. zoologischen Museums: *Typhlops striolatus*, *Geophidium dubium*, *Streptophorus* (*Ninia*) *maculatus*, *Elaps hippocrepis*. Monatsber. Königl. Preuss. Akad. Wissensch. Berlin 1861:922–925.

Peters, W. 1863a. Über einige neue Arten der Sauria-Gattung *Anolis*. Monatsber. Königl. Preuss. Akad. Wissensch. Berlin 1863:135–149.

Peters, W. 1863b. Fernere Mittheilungen über neue Batrachier. Monatsber. Königl. Preuss. Akad. Wissensch. Berlin 1863:445–470.

Peters, W. 1863c. Über einige neue oder weniger bekannte Schlangenarten des zoologischen Museums zu Berlin. Monatsber. Königl. Preuss. Akad. Wissensch. Berlin 1863:272–289.

Peters, W. 1868. Über eine neue Nagergattung, *Chiropodomys penicillatus*, so wie über einige neue oder weniger bekannte Amphibien und Fische. Monatsber. Königl. Preuss. Akad. Wissensch. Berlin 1868:448–460.

Peters, W. 1873. Über eine neue Schildkrötenart, *Cinosternon Effeldtii* und einige andere neue oder weniger bekannte Amphibien. Monatsber. Königl. Preuss. Akad. Wissensch. Berlin 1873:603–618.

Peters, W. 1874. Über neue Amphibien (*Gymnopis, Siphonops, Polypedates, Rhacophorus, Hyla, Cyclodus, Euprepes, Clemmys*). Monatsber. Königl. Preuss. Akad. Wissensch. Berlin 1874:616–624.

Pough, F.H., R.M. Andrews, J.E. Cadle, M.L. Crump, A.H. Savitzky, and K.D. Wells. 2003. Herpetology. Third edition. Pearson Prentice Hall, Upper Saddle River, New Jersey. ix + 726 pp.

Powell, R., J.T. Collins, and E.D. Hooper, Jr. 1998. A Key to the Amphibians & Reptiles of the Continental United States and Canada. Univ. Kansas Press, Lawrence. 131 pp.

Raven, P.H., and L.R. Berg. 2001. Environment. Third edition. Harcourt College Publishers, Fort Worth, Texas. xxx + 612 pp.

Reeder, T.W., C.J. Cole, and H.C. Dessauer. 2002. Phylogenetic relationships of whiptail lizards of the genus *Cnemidophorus* (Squamata: Teiidae): A test of monophyly, reevaluation of karyotypic evolution, and review of hybrid origins. Amer. Mus. Novitates 3365:1–61.

Roberts, O.W. 1827. Narrative of Voyages and Excursions on the East Coast and in the Interior of Central America. Constable's Miscellany of Original and Selected Publications in the Various Departments of Literature, Science, and the Arts. Vol. XVII. Constable and Co., Edinburgh. xiii + 295 pp.

Russel, G. 1984. Indians caught in the middle. A jungle war flourishes over the right to land and autonomy. Time 124 (Aug. 20, 1984):40–41.

Russell, A.P., and A.M. Bauer. 2002. *Thecadactylus, T. rapicauda*. Cat. Amer. Amphib. Reptiles 7 53.1–753.16.

Samson J.R. 1993. Pech of Honduras, p. 233. *In* M.S. Miller (ed.). State of the Peoples: A Global Human Rights Report on Societies in Danger. Beacon Press, Boston. x + 262 pp.

Sanders, O. 1973. A new leopard frog (*Rana berlandieri brownorum*) from southern Mexico. Jour. Herpetol. 7(1):87–92.

Savage, J.M. 1987. Systematics and distribution of the Mexican and Central American rainfrogs of the *Eleutherodactylus gollmeri* group (Amphibia: Leptodactylidae). Fieldiana: Zool., New Series 33:i–iv, 1–57.

Savage, J.M. 1997. A new species of rainfrog of the *Eleutherodactylus diastema* group from the Alta Talamanca region of Costa Rica. Amphibia-Reptilia 18(3):241–247.

Savage, J.M. 2002. The Amphibians and Reptiles of Costa Rica. A Herpetofauna between Two Continents, between Two Seas. Univ. Chicago Press, Chicago, Illinois. xx + 934 pp.

Savage, J.M., J.R. McCranie, and M. Espinal. 1996. A new species of *Eleutherodactylus* from Honduras related to *Eleutherodactylus bransfordii* (Anura: Leptodactylidae). Proc. Biol. Soc. Washington 109(2):366–372.

Savage, J.M., and C.W. Myers. 2002. Frogs of the *Eleutherodactylus biporcatus* group (Leptodactylidae) of Central America and northern South America, including rediscovered, resurrected, and new taxa. Amer. Mus. Novitates 3357:1–48.

Savage, J.M., and J.B. Slowinski. 1996. Evolution of coloration, urotomy and coral snake mimicry in the snake genus *Scaphiodontophis* (Serpentes: Colubridae). Biol. Jour. Linnean Soc. 57: 129–194.

Schlegel, H. 1837. Essai sur la Physionomie des Serpens. Part 2. M.H. Schonekat, Amsterdam. 606 + xv pp.

Schmidt, K.P. 1936. Notes on Central American and Mexican coral snakes. Zool. Ser., Field Mus. Nat. Hist. 20:205–216.

Schmidt, O. 1857. Diagnosen neuer Frösche des zoologischen Cabinets zu Krakau. Sitzungsber. Mathemat. Naturwissensch. Akad. Wissensch. 24(1):10–15.

Schortman, E. and P. Urban. 2001. Southeast Mesoamerica, pp. 675–684. *In* S.T. Evans and D.L. Webster (eds.). Archaeology in Ancient Mexico and Central America: An Encyclopedia. Garland Publishers, New York. xliii + 948 pp.

Schulte, J.A., II, J.P. Valladares, and A. Larson. 2003. Phylogenetic relationships within Iguanidae inferred using molecular and morphological data and a phylogenetic taxonomy of iguanian lizards. Herpetologica 59(3):399–419.

Seidel, M.E. 2002. Taxonomic observations on extant species and subspecies of slider turtles, genus *Trachemys*. Jour. Herpetol. 36(2): 285–292.

Sletto, B. 1999. Getting it on the map. Wildlife Conserv. 102(6):24–29.

Smith, E.N., and M. Acevedo. 1997. The northernmost distribution of *Corallus annulatus* (Boidae), with comments on its natural history. Southwest. Nat. 42(3):347–349.

Smith, H.M. 1939. The Mexican and Central American lizards of the genus *Sceloporus*. Zool. Ser. Field Mus. Nat. Hist. 26:1–397.

Smith, H.M. 1940. Descriptions of new lizards and snakes from Mexico and Guatemala. Proc. Biol. Soc. Washington 53:55–64.

Smith, H.M. 1941. A new name for the Mexican snakes of the genus *Dendrophidion*. Proc. Biol. Soc. Washington 54:73–76.

Smutko, G. 1988. La Mosquitia: historia y cultura de la Costa Atlantica. Editorial La Ocarina, Managua. iv + 179 pp.

Stafford, P.J. 2002. Record of the colubrid snake *Dendrophidion nuchale* (Peters) from Nicaragua. Southwest. Nat. 47(4):615–616.

Stafford, P.J., and J.R. Meyer. "2000" (1999). A Guide to the Reptiles of Belize. Nat. Hist. Mus. London. xix + 356 pp.

Steindachner, F. 1864. Batrachologische Mittheilungen. Verhandl. Zool.-Bot. Gesellsch. Wien 14:239–288.

Stejneger, L. 1909. Description of a new snake from Panama. Proc. U.S. Natl. Mus. 36:457–458.

Stone, D. 1948. The basic cultures of Central America, pp. 169–193. *In* J. Steward (ed.). Handbook of South American Indians. Vol. 4. The Circum-Caribbean Tribes. Smithsonian Institution, Bureau of American Ethnology Bull. 143. United States Government Printing Office, Washington, D.C. 609 pp.

Suazo, S. 2002. Garüdia Lamina Lila Hererun Garinagu. Diccionario Escolar Garifuna. Ed. Guaymuras, Tegucigalpa, Honduras. 145 pp.

Taylor, E.H. 1949. Costa Rican frogs of the genera *Centrolene* and *Centrolenella*. Univ. Kansas Sci. Bull. 33(4):257–270.

Taylor, E.H. 1951. A brief review of the snakes of Costa Rica. Univ. Kansas Sci. Bull. 34:3–188.

Taylor, E.H. 1952. The salamanders and caecilians of Costa Rica. Univ. Kansas Sci. Bull. 34(12):695–791.

Taylor, E.H. 1954. Further studies on the serpents of Costa Rica. Univ. Kansas Sci. Bull. 36: 673–801.

Taylor, E.H. 1955. Additions to the known herpetological fauna of Costa Rica with comments on other species. No. II. Univ. Kansas Sci. Bull. 37:499–575.

Tompson, D.A. 2001. Frontiers of identity: The Atlantic Coast and the formation of Honduras and Nicaragua, 1786–1894. Ph.D. Dissertation. University of Florida. ix + 255 pp.

Townsend, J.H., H.C. Aldrich, L.D. Wilson, and J.R. McCranie. 2005. First report of sporangia of a myxomycete (*Physarum pusillum*) on the body of a living animal, the lizard *Corytophanes cristatus*. Mycologia. 97(2):346–348.

Vandelli, D. 1761. Epistola de Holothurio, et Testudine coriacea ad celeberrimum Carolum Linnaeum. Equitem Naturae Curiosum Dioscoridem II. Conzatti, Patavii. 12 pp.

Wagler, J. 1824. Serpentum Brasiliensium Species Novae ou Histoire Naturelle des Espècies Nouvelles de Serpens, Recueillies et Observées Pendant le Voyage dans l'Intérieur du Brésil dans les Années 1817, 1818, 1819, 1820, Exécuté par Orde de sa Majesté le Roi de Baviére. Franc. Seraph. Hübschmanni. Monachii. viii + 74 pp.

Wake, D.B., T.J. Papenfuss, and J.F. Lynch. 1992. Distribution of salamanders along elevational transects in Mexico and Guatemala, pp. 303–319. *In* S.P. Darwin and A.L. Welden (eds.). Biogeography of Mesoamerica. Proceedings of a Symposium. Mérida, Yucatán, Mexico. October 26–30, 1984. Tulane Stud. Zool. Bot., Sup. Publ. 1:1–342.

Wied-Neuwied, M. 1824. Verzeichnis der Amphibien, welche im zwehten Bande der Naturgeschichte Brasiliens vom Prinz Max von Neuwied werden berchrieben werden. Isis von Oken 6:cols. 661–674.

Wiegmann, A.F.A. 1828. Behträge zur Amphibienkunde. Isis von Oken 21(III–IV):cols. 364–383.

Wiegmann, A.F.A. 1833. Herpetologische Beyträge. I. Ueber die mexicanischen Kröten nebst Bemerkungen über ihnen verwandte Arten anderer Weltgegenden. Isis von Oken 26(7):cols. 651–662.

Wiegmann, A.F.A. 1834. Herpetologia Mexicana, seu descriptio Amphibiorum Novae Hispaniae, quae Itineribus comitis de Sack, Ferdinandi Deppe et Chr. Guil. Schiede in Museum Zoologicum Berolinense Pervenerunt. Pars Prima, Saurorum Species Amplectens. Adiecto systematis Saurorum prodromo, additisque multis in hunc Amphibiorum Ordinem observationibus. Sumptibus C.G. Lüderitz, Berolini. vi + 54 pp.

Wilber, S. 1996. The Honduran Mosquitia. A Pre-Investment Analysis for the Parks in Peril Program. The Nature Conserv., Arlington, Virginia. vii + 95 pp.

Wilson, L.D., and J.R. McCranie. 2002. Update on the list of reptiles known from Honduras. Herpetol. Rev. 33(2):90–94.

Wilson, L.D., and J.R. McCranie. 2003. Herpetofaunal indicator species as measures of environmental stability in Honduras. Caribbean Jour. Sci. 39(1):50–67.

Wilson, L.D., and J.R. McCranie. 2004. The conservation status of the herpetofauna of Honduras. Amphibian and Reptile Conservation 3(1):6–33.

Wilson, L.D., J.R. McCranie, and M.R. Espinal. 2001. The ecogeography of the Honduran herpetofauna and the design of biotic reserves, pp. 109–158. *In* J.D. Johnson, R.G. Webb, and O.A. Flores-Villela (eds.). Mesoamerican herpetology: Systematics, Zoogeography, and Conservation. Centennial Mus., Univ. Texas El Paso, Spec. Publ. 1:i–iv, 1–200.

Wilson, L.D., J.R. McCranie, S. Gotte, and J.H. Townsend. 2003. Distributional comments on some members of the herpetofauna of the Mosquitia, Honduras. Herpetol. Bull. 84:15–19.

Wilson, L.D., and J.R. Meyer. 1985. The Snakes of Honduras. 2nd Edition. Milwaukee Publ. Mus., Milwaukee, Wisconsin. x + 150 pp.

Wüster, W., J.L. Yrausquin, and A. Mijares-Urrutia. 2001. A new species of indigo snake from north-western Venezuela (Serpentes: Colubridae: *Drymarchon*). Herpetol. Jour. 11(4):157–165.

Yuscarán, G. 1990. Conociendo a la Gente Garifuna (The Garifuna Story). Nuevo Sol Publicaciones, Tegucigalpa. 71 pp.

Zaher, H. 1996. A new genus and species of pseudoboine snake, with a revision of the genus *Clelia* (Serpentes, Xenodontinae). Boll. Mus. Reg. Sci. Nat., Torino 14(2):289–337.

Zamora Villalobos, N. 2000. Arboles de la Mosquitia Hondureña. Descripción de 150 especies. CATIE, Serie Técnica, Manual Técnico 43, Turrialba, Costa Rica. xxx + 335 pp.

Zepeda, C. 1999. Tawahka Asangni Biosphere Reserve approved. Mesoamericana 4(4): 101–102.

Zhao, E.-M., and K. Adler. 1993. Herpetology of China. Soc. Study Amphib. Reptiles, Contrib. Herpetol., Ithaca, New York. 10:1–522.

# Index to Scientific Names

Page numbers in bold refer to the species account. Citations in light face represent entries in other test; when a number is followed by the letters F, P, or T, those letters refer to figures, photographs, or entries in a table, respectively. Only scientific names of amphibians and reptiles are listed alphabetically both by generic and specific names.


*Acoelorraphe wrightii* 7, 10
*acutus, Crocodylus* 33, **93–94**, 94P, 196T, 205T, 208, 215T, 225–226, 230, 234T, 242
*Adelphicos quadrivirgatum* 47, **140–141**, 141P, 144–145, 152, 154–155, 164–165, 173, 179–180, 183–184, 198T, 206T, 208, 219T, 224, 226, 229, 237T
*aeneus, Oxybelis* 49, 149, 156–159, 162, **166–167**, 166P, 167–168, 200T, 207T, 221T, 225–226, 229, 238T
*Agalychnis* 72, 203
*Agalychnis calcarifer* 29, **64**, 64P, 65–66, 194T, 202T, 204T, 212T, 224, 226, 229, 232T, 249
*Agalychnis callidryas* 29, 64, **64–65**, 65P, 66, 68, 194T, 202T, 204T, 209, 212T, 224, 226, 229, 232T, 249
*Agalychnis moreletii* 212T
*Agalychnis saltator* 18, 29, 64–65, **65–66**, 66P, 68, 194T, 202T, 204T, 212T, 224, 227, 229, 232T, 249
*Agouti paca* 13, 243
*ahaetulla, Leptophis* 49, 155, **159–160**, 159P, 161, 167–168, 199T, 207T, 220T, 225–226, 229, 238T, 249
*Ajaia ajaja* 240
*albogularis, Gonatodes* 37, **108–109**, 108P, 110, 196T, 205T, 216T, 225–226, 230, 235T
*albomaculata, Cochranella* 32, 58, **59**, 59P, 194T, 202T, 204T, 212T, 224, 226, 229, 232T, 248
*alleni, Micrurus* 18, 45, 169–171, 174, **186–187**, 186P, 187, 201T, 206T, 222T, 224, 227, 230, 239T
*Alligator sinensis* 92
*Alouatta palliata* 243
*Ameiva* 38F, 203
*Ameiva festiva* 38, 38F, **131–132**, 132P, 133–134, 143, 198T, 206T, 208, 218T, 224, 227, 229, 236T
*Ameiva undulata* 38, 38F, 132, **132–133**, 133P, 134, 198T, 206T, 218T, 224, 226, 229, 236T
*annulata, Leptodeira* 50, **157–158**, 157P, 158–159, 199T, 206T, 220T, 225–226, 229, 238T
*annulata, Rhinoclemmys* 36, 36F, 101, **102**, 102P, 103–105, 196T, 206T, 216T, 225–226, 230, 234T
*annulatus, Corallus* 45, 108, 139, **139–140**, 139P, 166, 198T, 207T, 209, 219T, 224, 227, 229, 237T, 249
*annulatus, Scaphiodontophis* 47–49, 153, 156, 169–171, 174, **174–175**, 174P, 186–187, 200T, 206T, 221T, 225–226, 230, 239T
*annulatus, Sibon* 19, 47, 149, 156, **175–176**, 175P, 176–178, 183, 200T, 207T, 222T, 224, 227, 230, 239T
*Anolis humilis* 125
*Anomalepis mexicanus* 19, 44, 44F, **136–137**, 136P, 138, 198T, 205T, 218T, 224, 227, 229, 236T
*Anotheca* 27F
*Anotheca spinosa* 18, 27, **66–67**, 66P, 72, 194T, 202T, 204T, 212T, 224, 226, 230, 232T, 249
*Ara ambigua* 242–243
*Ara macao* 242–243
*Ardea alba* 241
*areolata, Rhinoclemmys* 37, 101–102, **102–103**, 103P, 104–105, 196T, 205T, 216T, 224, 226, 230, 235T
*Aristida* sp. 7
*asper, Bothrops* 2, 21, 44, 185, 188, **189–190**, 189P, 191–192, 201T, 206T, 209, 223T, 225–226, 230, 240T
*Aspidoscelis* 203
*Aspidoscelis deppii* 39, 39F, 133, **133–134**, 133P, 134, 198T, 206T, 218T, 224, 226, 229, 236T
*Astrocaryum alatum* 9
*Ateles geoffroyi* 243
*Atelophryniscus chrysophorus* 211T
*Atropoides mexicanus* 223T
*aurilegulus, Craugastor* 213T
*aurula, Omoadiphas* 221T
*Avicennia germinans* 9

*Bactris gasipaes* 9
*barbouri, Nototriton* 211T
*Basiliscus* 112, 204, 254

*Basiliscus plumifrons* 42, 42F, **112**, 112P, 113, 128, 196T, 206T, 208, 216T, 224, 227, 230, 235T
*Basiliscus vittatus* 42, 42F, 112, **113**, 113P, 128, 197T, 207T, 216T, 225–226, 229, 235T
*baudinii, Smilisca* 30, 72, **74–75**, 74P, 76–77, 160, 195T, 202T, 204T, 209, 213T, 225–226, 229, 233T, 249
*berlandieri, Rana* 89
*bicolor, Dipsas* 45, **148–149**, 148P, 153, 155–156, 169–171, 174, 176–178, 183, 199T, 207T, 219T, 225, 227, 229, 237T
*biporcatus, Craugastor* 81
*biporcatus, Eleutherodactylus* 81
*biporcatus, Norops* 43, **118–119**, 119P, 119, 121–122, 126, 197T, 207T, 209, 217T, 225–226, 230, 235T, 249
*bipunctatus, Coniophanes* 49, **143–144**, 143P, 145–146, 179, 198T, 205T, 219T, 225–226, 229, 237T, 245
*biscutatus, Trimorphodon* 48, 50, 250
*Boa constrictor* 2, 45, 108, **138–139**, 139P, 140, 166, 198T, 207T, 219T, 224, 226, 229, 237T
*Bolitoglossa* 203
*Bolitoglossa conanti* 211T
*Bolitoglossa dofleini* 211T
*Bolitoglossa dunni* 211T
*Bolitoglossa mexicana* 23, **51–52**, 51P, 52, 193T, 202T, 211T, 224, 226, 229, 232T, 248
*Bolitoglossa porrasorum* 211T
*Bolitoglossa rufescens* 211T
*Bolitoglossa striatula* 23, 52–53, **52–53**, 52P, 193T, 202T, 209, 211T, 224, 227, 230, 232T, 248
*Bothriechis marchi* 223T
*Bothriechis schlegelii* 44, **188–189**, 188P, 189, 191–192, 201T, 207T, 209, 223T, 225, 227, 230, 240T
*Bothriechis thalassinus* 223T
*Bothriopsis* 188
*Bothrops asper* 2, 21, 44, 185, 188, **189–190**, 189P, 191–192, 201T, 206T, 209, 223T, 225–226, 230, 240T
*boulengeri, Scinax* 19, 27, **72–73**, 73P, 74, 194T, 202T, 204T, 209, 213T, 224, 226, 229, 233T
*bovallii, Rhinobothryum* 49, 149, 153, 156, 169–171, **173–174**, 173P, 183, 186–187, 200T, 207T, 221T, 224, 227, 230, 239T, 245, 249
*bransforsdii, Craugastor* 240
*brevirostris, Oxybelis* 48, 149, 156, 160–162, 167, **167–168**, 167P, 168, 200T, 207T, 221T, 224, 227, 230, 238T
*bromeliacia, Hyla* 212T
*bromeliacia, Smilisca* 240
*Brosimum allicastrum* 8
*Brosimum guianense* 8
*Brosimum lactescens* 8
*brownorum, Rana* 25, 25F, **89–90**, 89P, 90–91, 195T, 202T, 204T, 215T, 225–226, 229, 234T, 249
*Bufo* 203
*Bufo* sp. 23F
Bufo campbelli *211T*
*Bufo coccifer* 24, **54–55**, 54P, 57, 181, 193T, 202T, 204T, 211T, 224, 226, 229, 232T, 249
*Bufo haematiticus* 24, 54, **55–56**, 55P, 56–57, 193T, 202T, 204T, 211T, 224, 226, 229, 232T
Bufo leucomyos *211T*
*Bufo marinus* 2, 24, 54–55, **56**, 56P, 57, 185, 193T, 202T, 204T, 208, 211T, 224, 226, 229, 232T, 249
*Bufo valliceps* 24, 54–55, **56–58**, 57P, 193T, 202T, 204T, 208, 211T, 224, 226, 229, 232T, 249
*Bulbostylis paradoxa* 7
*Bursera simarubra* 8
*Byrsonima crassifolia* 6

*Caiman crocodilus* 33, **92–93**, 93P, 94, 196T, 205T, 215T, 225–226, 230, 234T, 242
*calcarifer, Agalychnis* 29, **64**, 64P, 65–66, 194T, 202T, 204T, 212T, 224, 226, 229, 232T, 249
*callidryas, Agalychnis* 29, 64, **64–65**, 65P, 66, 68, 194T, 202T, 204T, 209, 212T, 224, 226, 229, 232T, 249
*Calophyllum brasiliense* 8
*Calophyllum* cf. *chiapense* 242
*Caluptrogyne sarapiquensis* 242
*campbelli, Bufo* 211T
*capito, Norops* 43, 119, **119–120**, 119P, 120, 122–123, 126, 197T, 207T, 209, 217T, 225, 227, 230, 235T
*Carapa guianensis* 8
*cardiacalyptum, Hyalinobatrachium* 18, 32, **61–62**, 61P, 62–63, 194T, 202T, 204T, 212T, 224, 227, 230, 232T, 249
*Caretta* 34F
*Caretta caretta* 34, **95–96**, 95P, 96–97, 100, 196T, 205T, 215T, 227–228, 234T, 242
*caretta, Caretta* 34, **95–96**, 95P, 96–97, 100, 196T, 205T, 215T, 227–228, 234T, 242
*Castilla elastica* 8, 12
*Cebus capuchinus* 243
*Cedrela odorata* 8, 242
*Ceiba pentandra* 8, 242
*cenchoa, Imantodes* 46, 149, **155–156**, 155P, 157–159, 176–178, 199T, 207T, 220T, 225–226, 229, 238T, 249
*Centrolene* 59, 62
*Centrolene prosoblepon* 32, 32F, **58–59**, 58P, 193T, 202T, 204T, 209, 212T, 224, 226, 229, 232T, 248

*Centrolenella* 59
*cerasinus, Eleutherodactylus* 19, 27, 79, 83, **83–84**, 84P, 85, 195T, 202T, 214T, 224, 227, 230, 234T, 249
*Cerrophidion godmani* 223T
*chac, Craugastor* 213T
*Chamaedora* sp. 9
*charadra, Craugastor* 213T
*Chelonia* 34F
*Chelonia mydas* 12, 34, 95, **96–97**, 96P, 97, 100, 196T, 205T, 215T, 227–228, 234T, 242
*Chelydra serpentina* 12, 34, 35F, **98–99**, 98P, 101–107, 196T, 205T, 215T, 225–226, 230, 234T
*cherriei, Sphenomorphus* 39, 39F, 129, **130**, 130P, 198T, 205T, 208, 218T, 224, 226, 229, 236T
*Chironius grandisquamis* 45, 88, **141–142**, 141P, 143, 157–159, 162, 172, 179, 198T, 207T, 208, 219T, 225, 227, 229, 237T, 249
*chloroticus, Drymobius* 219T
*chrysophorus, Atelophryniscus* 211T
*chrysopleura, Plectrohyla* 213T
*chrysozetetes, Craugastor* 213T
*Clelia clelia* 48, **142–143**, 142–143P, 162, 172, 198T, 206T, 219T, 225, 227, 229, 237T
*clelia, Clelia* 48, **142–143**, 142–143P, 162, 172, 198T, 206T, 219T, 225, 227, 229, 237T
*Clethra macrophylla* 7
*Cnemidophorus* 38F, 203, 257
*Cnemidophorus lemniscatus* 39, 39F, 133–134, **134–135**, 134P, 198T, 206T, 218T, 224, 227, 229, 236T, 255
*coccifer, Bufo* 24, **54–55**, 54P, 57, 181, 193T, 202T, 204T, 211T, 224, 226, 229, 232T, 249
*Cochranella* 62
*Cochranella albomaculata* 33, 58, **59**, 59P, 194T, 202T, 204T, 212T, 224, 226, 229, 232T, 248
*Cochranella granulosa* 33, 58–59, **60**, 62, 194T, 202T, 204T, 212T, 224, 227, 229, 232T, 249
*Cochranella spinosa* 19, 32, 32F, 58–59, **60–61**, 60P, 194T, 202T, 204T, 212T, 224, 226, 229, 232T, 249
*Cocoloba* sp. 115
*Cocoloba uvifera* 10
*Cocos nucifera* 10, 12
*coffeus, Craugastor* 213T
*Coleonyx mitratus* 216T
*conanti, Bolitoglossa* 211T
*concolor, Hydromorphus* 46, 143, 152, 154, **154–155**, 154P, 182, 199T, 205T, 220T, 225, 227, 229, 237T
*Coniophanes* 141, 173, 180–181, 183–184, 204
*Coniophanes bipunctatus* 49, **143–144**, 143P, 145–146, 179, 198T, 205T, 219T, 225–226, 229, 237T, 245
*Coniophanes fissidens* 49, 144, **144–145**, 144P, 146, 180, 198T, 205T, 219T, 225–226, 229, 237T
*Coniophanes imperialis* 49, 144–145, **145–146**, 145P, 146, 180, 198T, 205T, 219T, 224, 226, 229, 237T
*Conocarpus erectus* 9
*Conophis* 203
*Conophis lineatus* 49, 144–146, **146–147**, 146P, 180, 198T, 206T, 219T, 225–226, 229, 237T
*constrictor, Boa* 2, 45, 108, **138–139**, 139P, 140, 166, 198T, 207T, 219T, 224, 226, 229, 237T
*continentalis, Ungaliophis* 219T
*corais, Drymarchon* 150
*Corallus* 45F
*Corallus annulatus* 45, 108, 139, **139–140**, 139P, 166, 198T, 207T, 209, 219T, 224, 227, 229, 237T, 249
*Cordia alliodora* 8
*coriacea, Dermochelys* 3, 95–98, **99–100**, 99P, 196T, 205T, 215T, 227–228, 234T, 242
*Corytophanes cristatus* 42, 42F, **113–114**, 114P, 163, 197T, 207T, 209, 216T, 225–226, 230, 235T
*Corytophanes hernandesii* 216T
*costaricensis, Typhlops* 44, 44F, 137, **137–138**, 137P, 198T, 205T, 218T, 224, 227, 229, 236T
*Craugastor* 28F, 54, 77–78, 80–82, 84–86
*Craugastor* sp. (*alfredi* group) 214T
*Craugastor aurilegulus* 213T
*Craugastor biporcatus* 81
*Craugastor bransfordii* 240
*Craugastor chac* 213T
*Craugastor charadra* 213T
*Craugastor chrysozetetes* 213T
*Craugastor coffeus* 213T
*Craugastor epochthidius* 18, 28, **77–78**, 77P, 78, 83, 195T, 202T, 210, 213T, 224, 227, 230, 233T
*Craugastor fecundus* 214T
*Craugastor fitzingeri* 18, 28, **78–79**, 78P, 83, 195T, 202T, 208, 214T, 224, 226, 229, 233T
*Craugastor gollmeri* 240
*Craugastor laevissimus* 214T
*Craugastor laticeps* 214T
*Craugastor lauraster* 28, 79, **79–80**, 79P, 83, 195T, 202T, 208, 214T, 225, 227, 230, 233T
*Craugastor megacephalus* 27, 79, **80–81**, 80P, 83, 195T, 202T, 203, 214T, 224, 226, 230, 233T
*Craugastor merendonensis* 214T
*Craugastor milesi* 214T
*Craugastor mimus* 28, 79, **81–82**, 81P, 82–83, 195T, 202T, 208, 214T, 224, 227, 229, 233T
*Craugastor noblei* 28, 79, 81, **82**, 82P, 83, 195T, 202T, 208, 214T, 225, 227, 229, 233T
*Craugastor olanchano* 214T

*Craugastor omoaensis* 214T
*Craugastor pechorum* 18, 29, 79, **83**, 83P, 195T, 202T, 210, 214T, 224, 227, 230, 233T
*Craugastor rostralis* 214T
*Craugastor stadelmani* 214T
*Crax rubra* 13, 242–243
*cristatus, Corytophanes* 42, 42F, **113–114**, 114P, 163, 197T, 207T, 209, 216T, 225–226, 230, 235T
*crocodilus, Caiman* 33, **92–93**, 93P, 94, 196T, 205T, 215T, 225–226, 230, 234T, 242
*Crocodylus* 94
*Crocodylus acutus* 33, **93–94**, 94P, 196T, 205T, 208, 215T, 225–226, 230, 234T, 242
*Crotalus simus* 223T
*crybetes, Hyalinobatrachium* 212T
*Cryptotriton nasalis* 211T
*Ctenosaura similis* 40, 40F, **115**, 115P, 197T, 206T, 217T, 225, 227, 230, 235T
*Cupania glabra* 8
*cupreus, Norops* 121
*cupreus dariense, Norops* 121
*Curatella americana* 6
*cyclocauda, Oedipina* 23, 52, **53**, 53P, 193T, 202T, 203, 211T, 224, 227, 229, 232T
*Cyclopes didactylus* 242

*dariense, Norops* 43, **120–121**, 120P, 122, 126, 189, 197T, 207T, 209, 217T, 225, 227, 229, 235T
*Dasyprocta punctata* 243
*Dasypus novemcinctus* 13
*decipiens, Urotheca* 19, 48, 141, 144–146, 152, 154, 164–165, 173, 180–181, **183–184**, 183P, 184, 201T, 205T, 222T, 224, 227, 230, 239T
*decorata, Rhadinaea* 19, 48, 141, 144–146, 154, 165, **172–173**, 173P, 180, 183–184, 200T, 205T, 221T, 225–226, 230, 239T
*degenhardtii, Stenorrhina* 222T
*dekayi, Storeria* 222T
*Dendrophidion* 203
*Dendrophidion nuchale* 48–49, 219T, 250
*Dendrophidion percarinatum* 49, **147**, 147P, 148, 150–151, 163, 198T, 206T, 219T, 225, 227, 229, 237T
*Dendrophidion vinitor* 19, 48, 147, **147–148**, 148P, 150–151, 163, 199T, 206T, 208, 219T, 225–226, 230, 237T
*deppii, Aspidoscelis* 39, 39F, 133, **133–134**, 133P, 134, 198T, 206T, 218T, 224, 226, 229, 236T
*depressirostris, Leptophis* 48–49, 250
*Dermochelys* 33F
*Dermochelys coriacea* 33, 95–98, **99–100**, 99P, 196T, 205T, 215T, 227–228, 234T, 242
*Dermophis mexicanus* 211T
*diademata, Ninia* 221T
*diastema, Eleutherodactylus* 19, 27, 79, 83, **84–85**, 84P, 86, 195T, 202T, 209, 214T, 224, 226, 230, 234T, 249
*diastema, Micrurus* 222T
*Didymopanax mortoni* 242
*dimidiatus, Sibon* 222T
*Dipsas bicolor* 45, **148–149**, 148P, 153, 155–156, 169–171, 174, 176–178, 183, 199T, 207T, 219T, 225, 227, 229, 237T
*dofleini, Bolitoglossa* 211T
*dorsalis, Mastigodryas* 220T
*dorsalis, Rhinophrynus* 24, 24F, 215T, 250
*Dryadophis* 164
*Drymarchon* 203
*Drymarchon corais* 150
*Drymarchon melanurus* 48, 143, **149–150**, 149P, 151, 162–163, 172, 199T, 206T, 219T, 225–226, 229, 237T
*Drymobius* 203
*Drymobius chloroticus* 219T
*Drymobius margaritiferus* 49, 150, **150–151**, 150P, 151, 163, 199T, 206T, 219T, 225–226, 229, 237T
*Drymobius melanotropis* 47, 49, 150, **151–152**, 151P, 160–163, 167–168, 199T, 206T, 210, 219T, 225, 227, 230, 237T
*Duellmanohyla salvavida* 212T
*Duellmanohyla soralia* 212T
*dunni, Bolitoglossa* 211T
*dunni, Sphaerodactylus* 216T

*ebraccata, Hyla* 31, **67–68**, 67P, 68–69, 194T, 202T, 204T, 209, 212T, 225–226, 229, 233T
*elapoides, Pliocercus* 48, 153, 156, 169, **169–170**, 170P, 171, 174, 186–188, 200T, 206T, 210, 221T, 224, 226, 230, 238T
*elegans, Gastrophryne* 215T
*Eleutherodactylus* 54, 77, 84, 203
*Eleutherodactylus biporcatus* 81
*Eleutherodactylus cerasinus* 19, 27, 79, 83, **83–84**, 84P, 85, 195T, 202T, 214T, 224, 227, 230, 234T, 249
*Eleutherodactylus diastema* 19, 27, 79, 83, **84–85**, 84P, 86, 195T, 202T, 209, 214T, 224, 226, 230, 234T, 249
*Eleutherodactylus ridens* 27, 79, 83–84, **85–86**, 85P, 195T, 202T, 209, 214T, 225–226, 230, 234T, 249
*Enuliophis sclateri* 19, 47, 141, **152**, 152P, 154–155, 164–165, 180, 199T, 206T, 208, 220T, 224, 227, 229, 237T
*Enulius flavitorques* 220T

*epochthidius, Craugastor* 18, 28, **77–78**, 77P, 78, 83, 195T, 202T, 210, 213T, 224, 227, 230, 233T
*Eretmochelys* 34F
*Eretmochelys imbricata* 12, 34, 95–96, **97–98**, 97P, 100, 196T, 205T, 215T, 227–228, 234T, 242
*Ermia* 188
*Erythrolamprus* 203
*Erythrolamprus mimus* 47, **152–153**, 153P, 156, 169–171, 174, 183, 186–187, 199T, 206T, 220T, 225, 227, 229, 237T
*espinali, Ninia* 221T
*Eumeces sumichrasti* 218T
*euryzonus, Pliocercus* 19, 48, 153, 156, 169–170, **170–171**, 171P, 174, 186–187, 200T, 206T, 208, 221T, 224, 227, 230, 238T, 250

*fecundus, Craugastor* 214T
*Felis concolor* 242
*Felis pardalis* 242–243
*festiva, Ameiva* 38, 38F, **131–132**, 132P, 133–134, 143, 198T, 206T, 208, 218T, 224, 227, 229, 236T
*Ficimia publia* 220T
*Ficus* spp. 242
*Ficus insipida* 242
*Ficus werckleana* 8
*fissidens, Coniophanes* 49, 144, **144–145**, 144P, 146, 180, 198T, 205T, 219T, 225–226, 229, 237T
*fitzingeri, Craugastor* 18, 28, **78–79**, 78P, 83, 195T, 202T, 208, 214T, 224, 226, 229, 233T
*flavimaculatum, Lepidophyma* 37, 131, **135–136**, 135P, 198T, 205T, 218T, 224, 226, 229, 236T
*flavirufa, Pseudelaphe* 221T
*flavitorques, Enulius* 220T
*fleischmanni, Hyalinobatrachium* 32, **62–63**, 62P, 194T, 202T, 204T, 212T, 224, 226, 229, 232T, 249
*fragilis, Leptodactylus* 26, **86–87**, 86P, 87–88, 161, 195T, 202T, 204T, 208, 215T, 225–226, 229, 234T, 249
*frenatus, Hemidactylus* 37, 109, **109–110**, 109P, 110–111, 193, 201, 205T, 216T, 227, 229, 235T
*fulgidus, Oxybelis* 49, 149, 156, 160–162, 167, **168**, 168P, 200T, 207T, 221T, 225–226, 230, 238T, 249
*funerea, Rhinoclemmys* 13, 36, 36F, 101–103, **103–104**, 104P, 196T, 205T, 208, 216T, 224, 227, 230, 235T

*Gastrophryne elegans* 215T
*Geophis hoffmanni* 47, 141, 152, **153–154**, 153P, 155, 164–165, 180, 199T, 206T, 220T, 225, 227, 229, 237T
*godmani, Cerrophidion* 223T
*gollmeri, Craugastor* 240
*Gonatodes* 37F, 108
*Gonatodes albogularis* 37, **108–109**, 108P, 110, 196T, 205T, 216T, 225–226, 230, 235T
*grandisquamis, Chironius* 45, 88, **141–142**, 141P, 143, 157–159, 162, 172, 179, 198T, 207T, 208, 219T, 225, 227, 229, 237T, 249
*granulosa, Cochranella* 33, 58–59, **60**, 60P, 62, 194T, 202T, 204T, 212T, 224, 227, 229, 232T, 249
*guatemalensis, Plectrohyla* 213T
*guentheri, Urotheca* 18, 48, 141, 144–146, 152, 154, 164–165, 180–181, 184, **184–185**, 184P, 201T, 205T, 222T, 224, 227, 230, 239T
*gutturosus, Polychrus* 41, 119, **128–129**, 128P, 197T, 207T, 218T, 225, 227, 229, 236T, 249
*Gymnophthalmus* 203
*Gymnophthalmus speciosus* 37, 37F, **131**, 131P, 135, 198T, 205T, 218T, 224, 227, 229, 236T
*Gymnopis multiplicata* **50–51**, 50P, 193T, 202T, 203, 208, 211T, 224, 227, 229, 232T

*haematiticus, Bufo* 24, 54, **55–56**, 55P, 56–57, 193T, 202T, 204T, 211T, 224, 226, 229, 232T
*Harpia harpyja* 242
*Harpyhalietus* 242
*Hemidactylus* 37F
*Hemidactylus frenatus* 37, 109, **109–110**, 109P, 110–111, 193, 201, 205T, 216T, 227, 229, 235T
*Hemidactylus mabouia* 216T
*hernandesii, Corytophanes* 216T
*hoffmanni, Geophis* 47, 141, 152, **153–154**, 153P, 155, 164–165, 180, 199T, 206T, 220T, 225, 227, 229, 237T
*humilis, Anolis* 125
*humilis, Norops* 125
*Hyalinobatrachium* 58–59
*Hyalinobatrachium cardiacalyptum* 18, 32, **61–62**, 61P, 62–63, 194T, 202T, 204T, 212T, 224, 227, 230, 232T, 249
*Hyalinobatrachium crybetes* 212T
*Hyalinobatrachium fleischmanni* 32, **62–63**, 62P, 194T, 202T, 204T, 212T, 224, 226, 229, 232T, 249
*Hyalinobatrachium pulveratum* 18, 32, 60–62, **63**, 63P, 194T, 202T, 204T, 212T, 224, 227, 229, 232T, 249
*Hydromorphus concolor* 46, 143, 152, 154, **154–155**, 154P, 182, 199T, 205T, 220T, 225, 227, 229, 237T
*Hyeronima alchorneoides* 8
*Hyla* 68, 72, 77, 203
*Hyla bromeliacia* 212T
*Hyla ebraccata* 31, **67–68**, 67P, 68–69, 194T, 202T, 204T, 209, 212T, 225–226, 229, 233T

*Hyla loquax* 31, 67, **68**, 68P, 75, 194T, 202T, 204T, 209, 212T, 225–226, 229, 233T, 249
*Hyla microcephala* 31, 67–68, **68–69**, 69P, 74–75, 194T, 202T, 204T, 209, 212T, 225–226, 229, 233T, 249
*Hyla miliaria* 19, 29, **69–70**, 70P, 77, 194T, 202T, 203, 213T, 224, 227, 230, 233T, 249
*Hyla picta* 31, 67–69, **70–71**, 70P, 194T, 202T, 204T, 213T, 224, 226, 229, 233T
*hypomykter, Ptychohyla* 31, **72**, 72P, 77, 194T, 202T, 203, 204T, 210, 213T, 225, 227, 229, 233T
*Hypopachus variolosus* 215T

*Iguana iguana* 41, 41F, 112–113, **115–116**, 116P, 128, 197T, 207T, 208, 217T, 225–226, 230, 235T, 249
*iguana, Iguana* 41, 41F, 112–113, **115–116**, 116P, 128, 197T, 207T, 208, 217T, 225–226, 230, 235T, 249
*Imantodes cenchoa* 46, 149, **155–156**, 155P, 157–159, 176–178, 199T, 207T, 220T, 225–226, 229, 238T, 249
*Imantodes inornatus* 46, 220T, 250
*imbricata, Eretmochelys* 12, 34, 95–96, **97–98**, 97P, 100, 196T, 205T, 215T, 227–228, 234T, 242
*imperialis, Coniophanes* 49, 144–145, **145–146**, 145P, 146, 180, 198T, 205T, 219T, 224, 226, 229, 237T
*incertus, Sphenomorphus* 218T
*inornatus, Imantodes* 46, 220T, 250

*Jabiru mycteria* 241
*Joturus picardi* 242

*kinkelini, Rhadinaea* 221T
*Kinosternon leucostomum* 12, 34, 35F, 101–105, **105–106**, 106P, 107, 196T, 205T, 208, 216T, 225–226, 229, 235T
*Kinosternon scorpioides* 12, 35, 101–106, **107–108**, 107P, 196T, 205T, 216T, 225–226, 229, 235T

*labialis, Leptodactylus* 87
*Laemanctus longipes* 216T
*laevissimus, Craugastor* 214T
*laeviventris, Norops* 217T
*Laguncularia racemose* 9
*Lampropeltis* 203
*Lampropeltis triangulum* 48, 153, **156–157**, 156P, 170–171, 174, 183, 186–187, 199T, 206T, 220T, 225–226, 229, 238T
*laticeps, Craugastor* 214T
*lauraster, Craugastor* 28, 79, **79–80**, 79P, 83, 195T, 202T, 208, 214T, 225, 227, 230, 233T
*lemniscatus, Cnemidophorus* 39, 39F, 133–134, **134–135**, 134P, 198T, 206T, 218T, 224, 227, 229, 236T, 255
*lemurinus, Norops* 43, 121, **121–122**, 121P, 126, 197T, 207T, 217T, 225–226, 229, 236T
*Lepidophyma* 203
*Lepidophyma flavimaculatum* 37, 131, **135–136**, 135P, 198T, 205T, 218T, 224, 226, 229, 236T
*Lepidophyma mayae* 218T
*Leptocoryphium* sp. 7
*Leptodactylus* 26F, 89–92, 203, 252, 259
*Leptodactylus fragilis* 26, **86–87**, 86P, 87–88, 161, 195T, 202T, 204T, 208, 215T, 225–226, 229, 234T, 249
*Leptodactylus labialis* 87
*Leptodactylus melanolomus* 2, 26, 86, **87**, 87P, 88, 195T, 202T, 204T, 215T, 225–226, 229, 234T, 245, 249
*Leptodactylus pentadactylus* 26, 86–87, **87–88**, 88P, 195T, 202T, 203, 204T, 208, 215T, 225–226, 230, 234T
*Leptodeira annulata* 50, **157–158**, 157P, 158, 199T, 206T, 220T, 225–226, 229, 238T
*Leptodeira nigrofasciata* 48, 50, 157, **158**, 158P, 159, 185, 199T, 206T, 220T, 225–226, 229, 238T, 245
*Leptodeira septentrionalis* 50, 149, 155, 157–158, **158–159**, 159P, 176–178, 199T, 207T, 209, 220T, 225–226, 229, 238T
*Leptodrymus pulcherrimus* 220T
*Leptophis* 204
*Leptophis ahaetulla* 49, 155, **159–160**, 159P, 161, 167–168, 199T, 207T, 220T, 225–226, 229, 238T, 249
*Leptophis depressirostris* 48–49, 250
*Leptophis mexicanus* 49, 155, 160, **160–161**, 160P, 161, 167–168, 181, 199T, 207T, 220T, 225–226, 229, 238T
*Leptophis nebulosus* 49, 155, 160–161, **161–162**, 161P, 167–168, 181, 199T, 207T, 220T, 224, 227, 230, 238T
*leucomyos, Bufo* 211T
*leucostomum, Kinosternon* 12, 34, 35F, 101–105, **105–106**, 106P, 107, 196T, 205T, 208, 216T, 225–226, 229, 235T
*limifrons, Norops* 43, 120–121, **122–123**, 122P, 124, 126, 197T, 207T, 217T, 224, 227, 230, 236T
*lineatus, Conophis* 49, 144–146, **146–147**, 146P, 180, 198T, 206T, 219T, 225–226, 229, 237T
*lintoni, Tantillita* 47, 141, 152, 154–155, 164–165, 180, **180–181**, 180P, 201T, 205T, 208, 222T, 225–226, 230, 239T

*lionotus, Norops* 18, 43, 120–122, 123–124, 123P, 126, 197T, 205T, 217T, 224, 227, 230, 236T
*longifrenis, Sibon* 18, 47, 149, 156, 175, **176–177**, 176P, 177–178, 200T, 207T, 210, 222T, 224, 227, 230, 239T
*longipes, Laemanctus* 216T
*loquax, Hyla* 31, 67, **68**, 68P, 75, 194T, 202T, 204T, 209, 212T, 225–226, 229, 233T, 249
*loveridgei, Norops* 217T
*Luehea seemanii* 242
*Luehea speciosa* 8

*mabouia, Hemidactylus* 216T
*Mabuya* 203
*Mabuya unimarginata* 39, 39F, **129–130**, 129P, 130, 197T, 205T, 218T, 224, 226, 229, 236T
*maculata, Ninia* 18, 47, 141, 152, 154–155, **164**, 164P, 165, 180, 200T, 200T, 205T, 210, 221T, 224, 227, 229, 238T
*maculata, Rana* 26, 89, **90**, 90P, 91, 195T, 202T, 204T, 215T, 225, 227, 229, 234T, 249
*malachiticus, Sceloporus* 41, **117**, 117P, 118, 197T, 207T, 210, 217T, 225, 227, 229, 235T
*Manikara chicle* 8
*marchi, Bothriechis* 223T
*margaritiferus, Drymobius* 49, 150, **150–151**, 150P, 151, 163, 199T, 206T, 219T, 225–226, 229, 237T
*marinus, Bufo* 2, 24, 54–55, **56**, 56P, 57, 185, 193T, 202T, 204T, 208, 211T, 224, 226, 229, 232T, 249
*Masticophis* 203
*Masticophis mentovarius* 49, 143, 147–148, 150–151, **162–163**, 162P, 163, 172, 199T, 206T, 220T, 225–226, 229, 238T
*Mastigodryas* 203
*Mastigodryas dorsalis* 220T
*Mastigodryas melanolomus* 49, 143, 147–148, 150–151, 162, **163–164**, 163P, 172, 199T, 206T, 208, 220T, 225–226, 229, 238T
*matudai, Plectrohyla* 213T
*mayae, Lepidophyma* 218T
*Mazama americana* 243
*megacephalus, Craugastor* 27, 79, **80–81**, 80P, 83, 195T, 202T, 203, 214T, 224, 226, 230, 233T
*melanolomus, Mastigodryas* 49, 143, 147–148, 150–151, 162, **163–164**, 163P, 172, 199T, 206T, 208, 220T, 225–226, 229, 238T
*melanonotus, Leptodactylus* 2, 26, 86, **87**, 87P, 88, 195T, 202T, 204T, 215T, 225–226, 229, 234T, 245, 249
*melanotropis, Drymobius* 47, 49, 150, **151–152**, 151P, 160–163, 167–168, 199T, 206T, 210, 219T, 225, 227, 230, 237T
*melanurus, Drymarchon* 48, 143, **149–150**, 149P, 151, 162–163, 172, 199T, 206T, 219T, 225–226, 229, 237T
*Meleagris gallopavo* 242
*mentovarius, Masticophis* 49, 143, 147–148, 150–151, **162–163**, 162P, 163, 172, 199T, 206T, 220T, 225–226, 229, 238T
*merendonensis, Craugastor* 214T
*mexicana, Bolitoglossa* 23, **51–52**, 51P, 53, 193T, 202T, 211T, 224, 226, 229, 232T, 248
*mexicanus, Anomalepis* 19, 44, 44F, **136–137**, 136P, 138, 198T, 205T, 218T, 224, 227, 229, 236T
*mexicanus, Atropoides* 223T
*mexicanus, Dermophis* 211T
*mexicanus, Leptophis* 49, 155, 160, **160–161**, 160P, 161, 167–168, 181, 199T, 207T, 220T, 225–226, 229, 238T
*Miconia* 7
*microcephala, Hyla* 31, 67–68, **68–69**, 69P, 74–75, 194T, 202T, 204T, 209, 212T, 225–226, 229, 233T, 249
*Micrurus* 153, 157, 183
*Micrurus alleni* 18, 45, 169–171, 174, **186–187**, 186P, 187, 201T, 206T, 222T, 224, 227, 230, 239T
*Micrurus diastema* 222T
*Micrurus mipartitus* 171
*Micrurus multifasciatus* 44, 171, 250
*Micrurus nigrocinctus* 45, 169–171, 174, 186, **187–188**, 187P, 201T, 206T, 208, 223T, 225, 227, 229, 239T
*milesi, Craugastor* 214T
*miliaria, Hyla* 19, 29, **69–70**, 70P, 77, 194T, 202T, 203, 213T, 224, 227, 230, 233T, 249
*millepunctatus, Sphaerodactylus* 37, 109, **110–111**, 110P, 196T, 205T, 208, 216T, 225, 227, 229, 235T
*mimus, Craugastor* 28, 79, **81–82**, 81P, 82–83, 195T, 202T, 208, 214T, 224, 227, 229, 233T
*mimus, Erythrolamprus* 47, **152–153**, 153P, 156, 169–171, 174, 183, 186–187, 199T, 206T, 220T, 225, 227, 229, 237T
*mipartitus, Micrurus* 171
*mitratus, Coleonyx* 216T
*moreletii, Agalychnis* 212T
*Morphnus* 242
*multifasciatus, Micrurus* 44, 171, 250
*multiplicata, Gymnopis* **50–51**, 50P, 193T, 202T, 203, 208, 211T, 224, 227, 229, 232T
*Mycteria Americana* 240
*mydas, Chelonia* 12, 34, 95, **96–97**, 96P, 97, 100, 196T, 205T, 215T, 227–228, 234T, 242
*Myrmecophaga tridactyla* 242

*nasalis, Cryptotriton* 211T
*nasutum, Porthidium* 44, 45F, 185, 188–189, **190–191**, 190–191P, 192, 201T, 206T, 208, 223T, 225, 227, 230, 240T
*nebulatus, Sibon* 47, 149, 156, 175–176, **177**, 177P, 178, 200T, 207T, 209, 222T, 225–226, 229, 239T
*nebulosus, Leptophis* 49, 155, 160–161, **161–162**, 161P, 167–168, 175, 181, 199T, 207T, 220T, 224, 230, 238T
*Nectandra membranacea* 8
*nigrocinctus, Micrurus* 45, 169–171, 174, 186, **187–188**, 187P, 201T, 206T, 208, 223T, 225, 227, 229, 239T
*nigrofasciata, Leptodeira* 48, 50, 157, **158**, 158P, 159, 185, 199T, 206T, 220T, 225–226, 229, 238T, 245
*nigroluteus, Tretanorhinus* 49, 155, **181–182**, 182P, 201T, 205T, 208, 222T, 225–226, 229, 239T
*Ninia* 204
*Ninia diademata* 221T
*Ninia espinali* 221T
*Ninia maculata* 18, 47, 141, 152, 154–155, **164**, 164P, 165, 180, 200T, 205T, 210, 221T, 224, 227, 229, 238T
*Ninia sebae* 47, 141, 143, 152–156, 164, **164–165**, 165P, 169–171, 174–175, 180, 186–187, 200T, 206T, 208, 221T, 225–226, 229, 238T, 249
*noblei, Craugastor* 28, 79, 81, **82**, 82P, 83, 195T, 202T, 208, 214T, 225, 227, 229, 233T
*Norops* 128, 203–204
*Norops* sp. 240
*Norops biporcatus* 43, **118–119**, 119P, 119, 121–122, 126, 197T, 207T, 209, 217T, 225–226, 230, 235T, 249
*Norops capito* 43, 119, **119–120**, 119P, 120, 122–123, 126, 197T, 207T, 209, 217T, 225, 227, 230, 235T
*Norops cupreus* 121
*Norops cupreus dariense* 121
*Norops dariense* 43, **120–121**, 120P, 122, 126, 189, 197T, 207T, 209, 217T, 225, 227, 229, 235T
*Norops humilis* 125
*Norops laeviventris* 217T
*Norops lemurinus* 43, 121, **121–122**, 121P, 126, 197T, 207T, 217T, 225–226, 229, 236T
*Norops limifrons* 43, 120–121, **122–123**, 122P, 124, 126, 197T, 207T, 217T, 224, 227, 230, 236T
*Norops lionotus* 18, 43, 120–122, **123–124**, 123P, 126, 197T, 205T, 217T, 224, 227, 230, 236T
*Norops loveridgei* 217T
*Norops ocelloscapularis* 217T
*Norops oxylophus* 124
*Norops pentaprion* 43, 120, 122, **124**, 124P, 197T, 207T, 209, 217T, 225, 227, 230, 236T, 249
*Norops pijolensis* 217T
*Norops quaggulus* 43, 120–121, **124–125**, 125P, 126–127, 197T, 206T, 217T, 224, 227, 230, 236T
*Norops rodriguezii* 217T
*Norops sagrei* 217T
*Norops sericeus* 43, 121–122, **125–126**, 125P, 197T, 207T, 217T, 225–226, 229, 236T
*Norops tropidonotus* 42F, 43, 120–121, 125–126, **126–127**, 126P, 127, 197T, 206T, 218T, 225–226, 229, 236T, 249
*Norops uniformis* 218T
*Norops wampuensis* 18, 43, 120–121, 125–127, **127–128**, 127P, 197T, 207T, 218T, 224, 227, 230, 236T
*Norops yoroensis* 218T
*Norops zeus* 218T
*Nothopsis rugosus* 45, 142, **165–166**, 165P, 179, 200T, 206T, 221T, 224, 227, 230, 238T
*Nototriton barbouri* 211T
*nuchale, Dendrophidion* 48–49, 219T, 250

*ocelloscapularis, Norops* 217T
*Odocoileus virginianus* 13, 243
*Oedipina cyclocauda* 23, 52, **53**, 53P, 193T, 202T, 203, 211T, 224, 227, 229, 232T
*olanchano, Craugastor* 214T
*Omoadiphas aurula* 221T
*omoaensis, Craugastor* 214T
*ophryomegas, Porthidium* 44, 45F, 185, 188–189, 191, **191–192**, 191P, 201T, 206T, 223T, 225, 227, 229, 240T
*Oxybelis* 204
*Oxybelis aeneus* 49, 149, 156–159, 162, **166–167**, 166P, 167–168, 200T, 207T, 221T, 225–226, 229, 238T
*Oxybelis brevirostris* 48, 149, 156, 160–162, 167, **167–168**, 167P, 168, 200T, 207T, 221T, 224, 227, 230, 238T
*Oxybelis fulgidus* 49, 149, 156, 160–162, 167, **168**, 168P, 200T, 207T, 221T, 225–226, 230, 238T, 249
*oxylophus, Norops* 124
*Oxyrhopus petola* 48, 130, 143, 153, 156, **168–169**, 169P, 170–171, 174–175, 186–187, 200T, 206T, 208, 221T, 225–226, 230, 238T

*Panthera onca* 228, 242–244
*Paspalum* sp. 7
*Paspalum pulchellum* 10
*pechorum, Craugastor* 18, 29, 79, **83**, 83P, 195T, 202T, 210, 214T, 224, 227, 230, 233T
*Penelope purpurascens* 13

*pentadactylus, Leptodactylus* 26, 86, **87–88**, 88P, 195T, 202T, 203, 204T, 208, 215T, 225–226, 230, 234T
*pentaprion, Norops* 43, 120, 122, **124**, 124P, 197T, 207T, 209, 217T, 225, 227, 230, 236T, 249
*percarinatum, Dendrophidion* 49, **147**, 147P, 148, 150–151, 163, 198T, 206T, 219T, 225, 227, 229, 237T
*petola, Oxyrhopus* 48, 130, 143, 153, 156, **168–169**, 169P, 170–171, 174–175, 186–187, 200T, 206T, 208, 221T, 225–226, 230, 238T
*phaeota, Smilisca* 30, 72, 75, **75–76**, 76P, 77, 195T, 202T, 204T, 209, 213T, 225–226, 229, 233T
*Phrynohyas* 203
*Phrynohyas venulosa* 29, 70, **71–72**, 71P, 72, 194T, 202T, 204T, 213T, 225–226, 229, 233T, 249
*Physalaemus pustulosus* 23, 215T, 250
*Physarum pusillum* 114
*picta, Hyla* 31, 67–69, **70–71**, 71P, 194T, 202T, 204T, 213T, 224, 226, 229, 233T
*pijolensis, Norops* 217T
*Pinus caribaea* 6, 10, 12, 16
*pipiens, Rana* 89
*Plectrohyla chrysopleura* 213T
*Plectrohyla guatemalensis* 213T
*Plectrohyla matudai* 213T
*Pliocercus* 183
*Pliocercus elapoides* 48, 153, 156, 169, **169–170**, 170P, 171, 174, 186–188, 200T, 206T, 210, 221T, 224, 226, 230, 238T
*Pliocercus euryzonus* 48, 153, 156, 169–170, **170–171**, 171P, 172, 186–187, 200T, 206T, 208, 221T, 224, 227, 230, 238T, 250
*plumifrons, Basiliscus* 42, 42F, **112**, 112P, 113, 128, 196T, 206T, 208, 216T, 224, 227, 230, 235T
*poecilonotus, Pseustes* 48, 157–159, 162, **171–172**, 172P, 200T, 207T, 208, 221T, 225–226, 230, 239T, 249
*Polychrus* 118
*Polychrus gutturosus* 41, 119, **128–129**, 128P, 197T, 207T, 218T, 225, 227, 229, 236T, 249
*porrasorum, Bolitoglossa* 211T
*Porthidium nasutum* 44, 45F, 185, 188–189, **190–191**, 190–191P, 192, 201T, 206T, 208, 223T, 225, 227, 230, 240T
*Porthidium ophryomegas* 44, 45F, 185, 188–189, 191, **191–192**, 191P, 201T, 206T, 223T, 225, 227, 229, 240T
*Pouteria campechiana* 9
*prosoblepon, Centrolene* 32, 32F, **58–59**, 58P, 193T, 202T, 204T, 209, 212T, 224, 226, 229, 232T, 248
*Protobothrops* 188
*proximus, Thamnophis* 48, 55, 146, **181**, 181P, 201T, 205T, 222T, 225–226, 229, 239T
*Pseudelaphe flavirufa* 221T
*Pseustes poecilonotus* 48, 157–159, 162, **171–172**, 172P, 200T, 207T, 208, 221T, 225–226, 230, 239T, 249
*Ptychohyla* 203
*Ptychohyla hypomykter* 31, **72**, 72P, 77, 194T, 202T, 203, 204T, 210, 213T, 225, 227, 229, 233T
*Ptychohyla spinipollex* 213T
*publia, Ficimia* 220T
*pulcherrima, Rhinoclemmys* 36F, 37, 101–104, **104–105**, 104P, 196T, 205T, 216T, 225–226, 229, 235T
*pulcherrimus, Leptodrymus* 220T
*pullatus, Spilotes* 45, 142, 172, **178–179**, 178P, 200T, 207T, 222T, 225–226, 229, 239T, 249
*pulveratum, Hyalinobatrachium* 18, 32, 60–62, **63**, 63P, 194T, 202T, 204T, 212T, 224, 227, 229, 232T, 249
*pustulosus, Physalaemus* 23, 215T, 250

*quadrivirgatum, Adelphicos* 47, **140–141**, 141P, 144–145, 152, 154–155, 164–165, 173, 179–180, 183–184, 198T, 206T, 208, 219T, 224, 226, 229, 237T
*quaggulus, Norops* 43, 120–121, **124–125**, 125P, 126–127, 197T, 206T, 217T, 224, 227, 230, 236T
*Quararibea* sp. 242
*Quercus oleoides* 6

*rabdocephalus, Xenodon* 21, 48, 157–159, **185**, 185P, 201T, 206T, 222T, 225–226, 230, 239T
*Rana* 25F, 86–88, 92, 203
*Rana berlandieri* 89
*Rana brownorum* 25, 25F, **89–90**, 89P, 90–91, 195T, 202T, 204T, 215T, 225–226, 229, 234T, 249
*Rana maculata* 26, 89, **90**, 90P, 91, 195T, 202T, 204T, 215T, 225, 227, 229, 234T, 249
*Rana pipiens* 89
*Rana vaillanti* 25F, 26, 89–90, **90–91**, 91P, 195T, 202T, 204T, 208, 215T, 225–226, 229, 234T
*Rana warszewitschii* 25, 89–91, **91–92**, 92P, 196T, 202T, 204T, 208, 215T, 224, 227, 230, 234T
*rapicauda, Thecadactylus* 37, 109–110, **111**, 111P, 196T, 207T, 216T, 225–226, 230, 235T
*Rhadinaea* 165, 204
*Rhadinaea decorata* 19, 48, 141, 144–146, 154, 165, **172–173**, 173P, 180, 183–184, 200T, 205T, 221T, 225–226, 230, 239T
*Rhadinaea kinkelini* 221T
*Rhinobothryum bovallii* 49, 149, 153, 156, 169–171, **173–174**, 173P, 183, 186–187, 200T, 207T, 221T, 224, 227, 230, 239T, 245, 249

*Rhinoclemmys* 36F, 101
*Rhinoclemmys annulata* 36, 36F, 101, **102**, 102P, 103–105, 196T, 206T, 216T, 225–226, 230, 234T
*Rhinoclemmys areolata* 37, 101–102, **102–103**, 103P, 104–105, 196T, 205T, 216T, 224, 226, 230, 235T
*Rhinoclemmys funerea* 13, 36, 36F, 101–103, **103–104**, 104P, 196T, 205T, 208, 216T, 224, 227, 230, 235T
*Rhinoclemmys pulcherrima* 36F, 37, 101–104, **104–105**, 104P, 196T, 205T, 216T, 225–226, 229, 235T
*Rhinophrynus dorsalis* 24, 24F, 215T, 250
*Rhizophora mangle* 9
*Rhynchospora* spp. 10
*ridens, Eleutherodactylus* 27, 79, 83–84, **85–86**, 85P, 195T, 202T, 209, 214T, 225–226, 230, 234T, 249
*rodriguezii, Norops* 217T
*rostralis, Craugastor* 214T
*rufescens, Bolitoglossa* 211T
*rugosus, Nothopsis* 45, 142, **165–166**, 165P, 179, 200T, 206T, 221T, 224, 227, 230, 238T

*sagrei, Norops* 217T
*saltator, Agalychnis* 18, 29, 64–65, **65–66**, 66P, 68, 194T, 202T, 204T, 212T, 224, 227, 229, 232T, 249
*salvavida, Duellmanohyla* 212T
*Sapota zapodilla* 12
*sartorii, Tropidodipsas* 47, 149, 153, 157, 170–171, 174, 176, **182–183**, 182P, 186–187, 201T, 206T, 222T, 224, 226, 230, 239T
*Scaphiodontophis* 175
*Scaphiodontophis annulatus* 47–49, 153, 156, 169–171, 174, **174–175**, 174P, 186–187, 200T, 206T, 221T, 225–226, 230, 239T
*Sceloporus* 203–204
*Sceloporus malachiticus* 41, **117**, 117P, 118, 197T, 207T, 210, 217T, 225, 227, 229, 235T
*Sceloporus variabilis* 41, 41F, 117, **117–118**, 117P, 197T, 206T, 217T, 225–226, 229, 235T
*schistosa, Tantilla* 222T
*schlegelii, Bothriechis* 44, **188–189**, 188P, 189, 191–192, 201T, 201T, 207T, 209, 223T, 225, 227, 230, 240T
*Scinax* 72, 77, 203
*Scinax boulengeri* 19, 27, **72–73**, 73P, 74, 194T, 202T, 204T, 209, 213T, 224, 226, 229, 233T
*Scinax staufferi* 27, 69, 73, **73–74**, 73P, 75, 194T, 202T, 204T, 209, 213T, 225–226, 229, 233T, 249
*sclateri, Enuliophis* 19, 47, 141, **152**, 152P, 154–155, 164–165, 180, 199T, 206T, 208, 220T, 224, 227, 229, 237T
*scorpioides, Kinosternon* 12, 35, 101–106, **107–108**, 107P, 196T, 205T, 216T, 225–226, 229, 235T
*scripta, Trachemys* 100–101
*sebae, Ninia* 47, 141, 143, 152–156, 164, **164–165**, 165P, 169–171, 174–175, 180, 186–187, 200T, 206T, 208, 221T, 225–226, 229, 238T, 249
*Senticolis triaspis* 221T
*septentrionalis, Leptodeira* 50, 149, 155, 157–158, **158–159**, 159P, 176–178, 199T, 207T, 209, 220T, 225–226, 229, 238T
*sericeus, Norops* 43, 121–122, **125–126**, 125P, 197T, 207T, 217T, 225–226, 229, 236T
*serpentina, Chelydra* 12, 34, 35F, **98–99**, 98P, 101–107, 196T, 205T, 215T, 225–226, 230, 234T
*Sibon* 19
*Sibon* sp. 47, 149, 156, 176–177, **177–178**, 178P, 183, 200T, 207T, 222T, 224, 227, 230, 239T
*Sibon annulatus* 19, 47, 149, 156, **175–176**, 175P, 176–178, 183, 200T, 207T, 222T, 224, 227, 230, 239T
*Sibon dimidiatus* 222T
*Sibon longifrenis* 18, 47, 149, 156, 175, **176–177**, 176P, 177–178, 200T, 207T, 210, 222T, 224, 227, 230, 239T
*Sibon nebulatus* 47, 149, 156, 175–176, **177**, 177P, 178, 200T, 207T, 209, 222T, 225–226, 229, 239T
*similis, Ctenosaura* 40, 40F, **115**, 115P, 197T, 206T, 217T, 225, 227, 230, 235T
*simus, Crotalus* 223T
*sinensis, Alligator* 92
*Smilisca* 70, 203
*Smilisca baudinii* 30, 72, **74–75**, 74P, 76–77, 160, 195T, 202T, 204T, 209, 213T, 225–226, 229, 233T, 249
*Smilisca bromeliacia* 240
*Smilisca phaeota* 30, 72, **75–76**, 76P, 77, 195T, 202T, 204T, 209, 213T, 225–226, 229, 233T
*Smilisca sordida* 30, 72, 75–76, **76–77**, 76P, 195T, 202T, 203, 204T, 213T, 224, 227, 229, 233T
*soralia, Duellmanohyla* 212T
*sordida, Smilisca* 30, 72, 75–76, **76–77**, 76P, 195T, 202T, 203, 204T, 213T, 224, 227, 229, 233T
*speciosus, Gymnophthalmus* 37, 37F, **131**, 131P, 135, 198T, 205T, 218T, 224, 227, 229, 236T
*Sphaerodactylus* 37F, 108, 203
*Sphaerodactylus dunni* 216T
*Sphaerodactylus millepunctatus* 37, 109, **110–111**, 110P, 196T, 205T, 208, 216T, 225, 227, 229, 235T
*Sphenomorphus* 203
*Sphenomorphus cherriei* 39, 39F, 129, **130**, 130P, 198T, 205T, 208, 218T, 224, 226, 229, 236T
*Sphenomorphus incertus* 218T
*Spilotes pullatus* 45, 142, 172, **178–179**, 178P, 200T, 207T, 222T, 225–226, 229, 239T, 249

*spinipollex, Ptychohyla* 213T
*spinosa, Anotheca* 18, 27, **66–67**, 66P, 72, 194T, 202T, 204T, 212T, 224, 226, 230, 232T, 249
*spinosa, Cochranella* 19, 32, 32F, 58–59, **60–61**, 60P, 194T, 202T, 204T, 212T, 224, 226, 229, 232T, 249
*Spizaetus* 242
*Spizastur* 242
*Spondius radlkoferi* 9
*Spondius mombin* 242
*stadelmani, Craugastor* 214T
*stadelmani, Typhlops* 219T
*staufferi, Scinax* 27, 69, 73, **73–74**, 73P, 75, 194T, 202T, 204T, 209, 213T, 225–226, 229, 233T, 249
*Staurotypus triporcatus* 216T
*Stenorrhina degenhardtii* 222T
*Storeria dekayi* 222T
*striatula, Bolitoglossa* 23, 52–53, **52–53**, 52P, 193T, 202T, 209, 211T, 224, 227, 230, 232T, 248
*sumichrasti, Eumeces* 218T
*Swietenia macrophylla* 9, 12
*Symphonia globulifera* 9

*Tabebuia rosea* 9
*taeniata, Tantilla* 47, 141, 144–146, 152, 154, 164–165, 173, **179–180**, 179P, 180–181, 184, 200T, 205T, 222T, 225, 227, 230, 239T
*Tantilla* 204
*Tantilla schistosa* 222T
*Tantilla taeniata* 47, 141, 144–146, 152, 154, 164–165, 173, **179–180**, 179P, 180–181, 184, 200T, 205T, 222T, 225, 227, 230, 239T
*Tantillita* 204
*Tantillita lintoni* 47, 141, 152, 154–155, 164–165, 180, **180–181**, 180P, 201T, 205T, 208, 222T, 225–226, 230, 239T
*Tapirus bairdii* 242–244
*Tayassu pecari* 99, 242–244
*Tayassu tajacu* 242–244
*Tetragastris panamensis* 9
*Thalassia testudinum* 97
*thalassinus, Bothriechis* 223T
*Thamnophis proximus* 48, 55, 146, **181**, 181P, 201T, 205T, 222T, 225–226, 229, 239T
*Thecadactylus* 37F
*Thecadactylus rapicauda* 37, 109–110, **111**, 111P, 196T, 207T, 216T, 225–226, 230, 235T
*Tinamus major* 13, 172, 243
*Tonina fluviatilis* 10
*Trachemys scripta* 100–101
*Trachemys venusta* 12–13, 33F, 36, 35–36F, **100–101**, 100P, 102–105, 107, 196T, 205T, 208, 215T, 225–226, 230, 234T
*Trachypogon* sp. 7
*Tretanorhinus nigroluteus* 49, 155, **181–182**, 182P, 201T, 205T, 208, 222T, 225–226, 229, 239T
*triangulum, Lampropeltis* 48, 153, **156–157**, 156P, 170–171, 174, 183, 186–187, 199T, 206T, 220T, 225–226, 229, 238T
*triaspis, Senticolis* 221T
*Trichechus manatus* 242
*Trichilia pallida* 9
*Trimorphodon biscutatus* 48, 50, 250
*triporcatus, Staurotypus* 216T
*Tropidodipsas sartorii* 47, 149, 153, 157, 170–171, 174, 176, **182–183**, 182P, 186–187, 201T, 206T, 222T, 224, 226, 230, 239T
*tropidonotus, Norops* 42F, 43, 120–121, 125–126, **126–127**, 126P, 127, 197T, 206T, 218T, 225–226, 229, 236T, 249
*Typhlops costaricensis* 44, 44F, 137, **137–138**, 137P, 198T, 205T, 218T, 224, 227, 229, 236T
*Typhlops stadelmani* 219T

*undulata, Ameiva* 38, 38F, 132, **132–133**, 133P, 134, 198T, 206T, 218T, 224, 226, 229, 236T
*Ungaliophis continentalis* 219T
*uniformis, Norops* 218T
*unimarginata, Mabuya* 39, 39F, **129–130**, 129P, 130, 197T, 205T, 218T, 224, 226, 229, 236T
*Urotheca* 173, 204
*Urotheca decipiens* 19, 48, 141, 144–146, 152, 154, 164–165, 173, 180–181, **183–184**, 183P, 184, 201T, 205T, 222T, 224, 227, 230, 239T
*Urotheca guentheri* 18, 48, 141, 144–146, 152, 154, 164–165, 180–181, 184, **184–185**, 184P, 201T, 205T, 222T, 224, 227, 230, 239T
*Utricularia sublata* 10

*vaillanti, Rana* 25F, 26, 89–90, **90–91**, 91P, 195T, 202T, 204T, 208, 215T, 225–226, 229, 234T
*valliceps, Bufo* 24, 54–55, **56–58**, 57P, 193T, 202T, 204T, 208, 211T, 224, 226, 229, 232T, 249
*variabilis, Sceloporus* 41, 41F, 117, **117–118**, 117P, 197T, 206T, 217T, 225–226, 229, 235T
*variolosus, Hypopachus* 215T
*venulosa, Phrynohyas* 29, 70, **71–72**, 71P, 72, 194T, 202T, 204T, 213T, 225–226, 229, 233T, 249
*venusta, Trachemys* 12–13, 33F, 36, 35–36F, **100–101**, 100P, 102–105, 107, 196T, 205T, 208, 215T, 225–226, 230, 234T
*vinitor, Dendrophidion* 19, 48, 147, **147–148**, 148P, 150–151, 163, 199T, 206T, 208, 219T, 225–226, 230, 237T
*Virola* sp. 242

*Virola koschnyi* 9, 67
*vittatus, Basiliscus* 42, 42F, 112, **113**, 113P, 128, 197T, 207T, 216T, 225–226, 229, 235T
*Vochysia ferruginea* 9

*wampuensis, Norops* 18, 43, 120–121, 125–127, **127–128**, 127P, 197T, 207T, 218T, 224, 227, 230, 236T
*warszewitschii, Rana* 25, 89–91, **91–92**, 92P, 196T, 202T, 204T, 208, 215T, 224, 227, 230, 234T

*Xenodon* 203
*Xenodon rabdocephalus* 21, 48, 157–159, **185**, 185P, 201T, 206T, 222T, 225–226, 230, 239T

*yoroensis, Norops* 218T

*Zanthoxylum ekmanii* 9
*zeus, Norops* 218T